AVIAN ECOLOGY AND CONSERVATION:

A Pennsylvania Focus with National Implications

Shyamal K. Majumdar
Terry L. Master
Margaret C. Brittingham
Robert M. Ross
Robert S. Mulvihill
Jane E. Huffman

EDITORS

BOOK PUBLICATIONS
of The Pennsylvania Academy of Science

1. Avian Ecology and Conservation: A Pennsylvania Focus with National Implications, 2010. ISBN: 0-945809-20-4.
2. Wildlife Diseases: Landscape Epidemiology, Spatial Distribution and Utilization of Remote Sensing Technology, 2005. ISBN: 0-945809-19-0.
3. Renewable Energy: Trends and Prospects, 2002. ISBN: 0-945809-17-4.
4. Science, Technology and National Security, 2002. ISBN: 0-945809-18-2.
5. Ethics in Academia, 2000. ISBN: 0-945809-16-6.
6. The Ecology of Wetlands and Associated Systems, 1998. ISBN: 0-945809-14-X.
7. The Era of Materials, 1998. ISBN: 0-945809-15-8.
8. Forests—A Global Perspective, 1996. ISBN: 0-945809-13-1.
9. Environmental Contaminants, Ecosystems and Human Health, 1995. ISBN: 0-945809-12-3.
10. Medicine and Health Care Into the 21st Century, 1995. ISBN: 0-945809-11-5.
11. The Oceans: Physical-Chemical Dynamics and Human Impact, 1994. ISBN: 0-945809-10-7.
12. Biological Diversity: Problems and Challenges, 1994. ISBN: 0-945809-09-3.
13. Conservation and Resource Management, 1993. ISBN: 0-945809-08-5.
14. Global Climate Change: Implications, Challenges and Mitigation Measures, 1992. ISBN: 0-945809-07-7.
15. Natural and Technological Disasters: Causes, Effects and Preventive Measures, 1992. ISBN: 0-945809-06-9.
16. Air Pollution: Environmental Issues and Health Effects, 1991. ISBN: 0-945809-05-0.
17. Science Education in the United States: Issues, Crises, and Priorities, 1991. ISBN: 0-945809-04-2.
18. Environmental Radon: Occurrence, Control and Health Hazards, 1990. ISBN: 0-945809-03-4.
19. Water Resources in Pennsylvania: Availability, Quality and Management, 1990. ISBN: 0-945809-02-6.
20. Wetlands Ecology and Conservation: Emphasis in Pennsylvania, 1989. ISBN: 0-945809-01-8.
21. Management of Hazardous Materials and Wastes: Treatment, Minimization and Environmental Impacts, 1989. ISBN: 0-9606670-9-1.
22. Ecology and Restoration of The Delaware River Basin, 1988. ISBN: 0-9606670-8-3.
23. Contaminant Problems and Management of Living Chesapeake Bay Resources, 1987. ISBN: 0-9606670-7-5.
24. Environmental Consequences of Energy Production: Problems and Prospects, 1987. ISBN: 0-9606670-6-7.
25. Endangered and Threatened Species Programs in Pennsylvania and Other States: Causes, Issues and Management, 1986. ISBN: 0-9606670-5-9.
26. Management of Radioactive Materials and Wastes: Issues and Progress, 1985. ISBN: 0-9606670-4-0.
27. Solid and Liquid Wastes: Management, Methods and Socioeconomic Considerations, 1984. ISBN: 0-9606670-3-2.
28. Hazardous and Toxic Wastes: Technology, Management and Health Effects, 1984. ISBN: 0-9606670-2-4.
29. Pennsylvania Coal: Resources, Technology and Utilization, 1983. ISBN: 0-9606670-1-6.
30. Energy, Environment, and the Economy, 1981. ISBN: 0-9606670-0-8.

Books Published by The Pennsylvania Academy of Science
Editor: Shyamal K. Majumdar • Professor Emeritus of Biology
Lafayette College, Easton, Pennsylvania 18042

Avian Ecology and Conservation:
A Pennsylvania Focus with National Implications

EDITED BY

SHYAMAL K. MAJUMDAR, Ph.D.
Kreider Professor Emeritus of Biology
Lafayette College
Easton, PA 18042

TERRY L. MASTER, Ph.D.
Professor of Biology
East Stroudsburg University of Pennsylvania
East Stroudsburg, PA 18301

MARGARET C. BRITTINGHAM, Ph.D.
Professor of Wildlife Resources
Penn State University
University Park, PA 16802

ROBERT M. ROSS, Ph.D.
Research Ecologist
Northern Appalachian Research Laboratory
United States Geological Survey (retired)
Wellsboro, PA 16901

ROBERT S. MULVIHILL, M.S.
Field Ornithologist
Carnegie Museum of Natural History, Powdermill Avian Research Center
Rector, PA 15677

JANE E. HUFFMAN, Ph.D.
Professor of Microbiology
East Stroudsburg University of Pennsylvania
East Stroudsburg, PA 18301

Founded on April 18, 1924

A Publication of
The Pennsylvania Academy of Science

Library of Congress Cataloging in Publication Data

Bibliography
Index
Majumdar, Shyamal K. 1938-, ed.

Library of Congress Control No. 2009934729

ISBN-0-945809-20-4

A Publication of
The Pennsylvania Academy of Science, Easton, PA 18042

Printed in the United States of America by

Sheridan Printing Company, Inc.
Alpha, NJ 08865

Avian Ecology and Conservation: A Pennsylvania Focus with National Implications

PREFACE

Within Pennsylvania, most people are probably unaware of the important bird conservation research and monitoring activities that have been conducted in the state, as well as of the wider significance of this body of work at regional and national levels. The book, *Avian Ecology and Conservation*, brings together in one volume a comprehensive overview of Pennsylvania's avian communities, current and emerging conservation issues, and the specific contributions Pennsylvania biologists, avian ecologists, and conservationists have made to the science of ornithology. Readers will find a historical overview of Pennsylvania ornithology, a synthesis of avian habitat associations and ecological studies, and overviews of conservation issues impacting birds, both here and around the world, during breeding, non-breeding, and migratory periods. A final section looks to the future with emerging issues we must be prepared to address. The wide array of topics, many pertinent and applicable beyond Pennsylvania's border, will be of interest to a diverse audience.

In addition to an introductory section, which offers the historical overview of Pennsylvania ornithology, the book contains 27 chapters with contributions from over 50 selected experts from Pennsylvania and other states. The volume is divided into four major sections: I. Breeding Birds of Pennsylvania and their Habitats, II. Migration and Wintering Ecology, III. Conservation Issues and Challenges, and IV. Emerging Issues and Their Impacts on Birds. Each section begins with an overview providing a summary of the chapters included within the section. Various habitat types, conservation challenges and management issues of Pennsylvania breeding birds are presented in section one. Topics on migration routes and wintering ecology of raptors and other land bird species, as well as tracking methodologies, such as satellite telemetry, genetic markers, and stable isotope technology, can be found in section two. Chapters in section three cover conservation issues facing birds in Pennsylvania and the northeast and offer management solutions for maintaining healthy and functional ecosystems for birds. Chapters on such diverse topics as global climate change, wind power mortality, West Nile Virus, avian influenza, and impact of environmental contaminants on avian populations are included in section four.

Through the publication of this book, the Pennsylvania Academy of Science strives to summarize and publicize recent research-based progress and emerging challenges concerning bird conservation in Pennsylvania. We believe that this book will be of interest and use to a diverse audience, including professional biologists, college students, natural resource managers, and conservationists; in fact, to anyone who has more than a passing interest in birds.

The editors are indebted to the authors for contributing their expertise to this volume. In addition, the editors express their gratitude for the support they received from their respective organizations: The Pennsylvania Academy of Science, Lafayette College, East Stroudsburg University, The Pennsylvania State University, United States Geological Survey, and Carnegie Museum of Natural History.

Shyamal K. Majumdar
Terry L. Master
Margaret C. Brittingham
Robert M. Ross
Robert S. Mulvihill
Jane E. Huffman

Editors

Acknowledgment

The publication of this book was aided
by contributions from the Pennsylvania Academy of Science,
E. Willard and Ruby S. Miller
book endowment publication fund, the
Charles B. Reif
book publication fund, and
Pennsylvania Game Commission,
Harrisburg, PA.

Professor Majumdar thanks
Nafis Hasan, Brook Estifanos, Ioana Marin, Pooja Shah and Ryan Shroff
for proofreading and indexing the galley pages of the book.

Avian Ecology and Conservation:
A Pennsylvania Focus with National Implications

Table of Contents

Avian Ecology and Conservation: A Pennsylvania Focus with National Implications

Avian Ecology and Conservation: A Pennsylvania Focus with National Implications. Edited by S. K. Majumdar, T. L. Master, M. C. Brittingham, R. M. Ross, R. S. Mulvihill and J. E. Huffman. © 2010. The Pennsylvania Academy of Science.

FOREWORD

Michael DiBerardinis
Former Secretary
PADCNR
Harrisburg, PA

A new publication from the Pennsylvania Academy of Sciences is always a welcome contribution to our collective understanding of the natural environment. A publication summarizing the research of leading ornithologists across Pennsylvania is both a professional and a personal pleasure for me. As secretary of the Department of Conservation and Natural Resources, birding is one of those wonderful convergences where my work and hobbies intersect.

I am, for want of a better term, a "casual" birder. I don't have a life list, and I don't drop everything to race out of my corner office to catch a glimpse of a rare avian visitor to the Commonwealth. I am an avid amateur birder, however, and try to build in every opportunity I can when traveling the Commonwealth on work-related business to do a bit of birding, especially in the spring and fall months. If it means getting up a little earlier, or doing some late-night research to find the best birding spot within a 20-mile radius of a meeting site, it's always worth the effort.

Birding for me is much more than just looking for rare birds. It's an opportunity to get outside, an increasingly difficult thing for so many citizens across our state. It's a rare chance to focus on the natural world, to block out manmade concerns, and to experience the immediate environment in a unique and transcendental way.

As a resident of an urban environment, Philadelphia, it continues to amaze me what a rich birding life there is in the midst of the Commonwealth's largest city. I recently had four large oak trees, huge spreading oaks, right outside my house that afforded a prime view of migratory birds passing through downtown Philadelphia; wood thrushes, common yellowthroats, broad-winged hawks, sharpies, Carolina wrens, at least four different warbler species. My neighbors may have been suspicious as I peered out of an upstairs window with binoculars, but what a spectacle to see outside! Today I don't have to venture far from my home to find birding hotspots in Tinicum marsh, Fairmount Park, or along the Delaware River. Observing in detail the comings and goings of another species, another world, can bring welcome solitude and a feeling of connectedness at the same time.

It is fitting that DCNR salutes the publication of this important volume on conservation issues and Pennsylvania's avian species. Many of the editors and authors of this work are current or former recipients of DCNR's Wild Resource Conservation Program grants that have supported work like osprey reintroduction, the ecology and behavior of specific species such as Willow Flycatcher, Ovenbird and Golden-winged Warbler, colonial water bird nesting ecology, evaluation and restoration of habitats including barrens, grasslands and wetlands, use of bioindicator species like the Louisiana Waterthrush, the 2nd Pennsylvania Breeding Bird Atlas and new research into areas such as potential wind power impacts on birds including Golden Eagles. DCNR is also working with multiple partners across the Commonwealth to protect important bird areas through acquisition of lands and easements, reforestation efforts like TreeVitalize, and large landscape-level initiatives to protect mosaics of natural lands and working lands to conserve important habitat and migratory corridors.

So, congratulations to the editors and the authors. I'll hope to see you out on the birding trails.

Michael DiBerardinis
Former Secretary
Pennsylvania Department of Conservation and Natural Resources

Avian Ecology and Conservation: A Pennsylvania Focus with National Implications. Edited by S. K. Majumdar, T. L. Master, M. C. Brittingham, R. M. Ross, R. S. Mulvihill and J. E. Huffman. © 2010. The Pennsylvania Academy of Science.

Message

Carl Roe
Executive Director
Pennsylvania Game Commission
Harrisburg, PA

As the state agency responsible for the wild birds and mammals in this Commonwealth, the Pennsylvania Game Commission's earliest actions addressed restoring, protecting, managing and promoting both game and non-game wildlife. This commitment continues to this day in the form of research, education, tangible action and conservation planning. Whether distributing bluebird boxes, training teachers to meet endangered species education requirements, purchasing property for rare species, or monitoring the eagle recovery, avian ecology is our daily mission.

Millions of Pennsylvania residents identify themselves as wildlife-watchers, many of whom feed or watch birds in their own yards. Couple this with the wealth of knowledge gained about birds from a century of research, some chronicled in this important book, it's easy to understand why birds have been and remain a focal point for conservation action. This effort has been further aided by this timely book. Long-term population trends are known for most state breeding bird populations; current distributions and population estimates have been generated by the breeding bird atlas; habitat requirements are known with some precision for most species. We actively participate in regional management initiatives that prioritize habitat management, build systems that help prioritize action, and coordinate multi-state recovery efforts. Couple this vast knowledge with their broad public constituency, birds become a touch-stone for conservation as a whole. The Game Commission plays central roles in all of these activities here in this state, and at times at the national, even international level.

On the 1.4 million acres comprising the agency's State Game Lands system, conservation of all wildlife is our express goal, and renewed planning efforts are setting objectives for specific species for discrete parcels. Pennsylvania's Wildlife Action Plan provides the most comprehensive wildlife conservation document ever produced in this state, the depths of which continue to unfold as new challenges face wildlife species. Conservation and studies in avian ecology are articulated in the Game Commission's mission "to manage all birds, mammals and their habitats for present and future generations." The 21st century provides unparalleled opportunities.

The conservation of birds and mammals has focused historically on game and endangered and threatened species, with legislated definitions and recovery as the goal. While state-listed species remain important, conservation is much more efficient and effective when actions are taken while a species is still common. Endangered species prevention, therefore, is one of our important goals, and is reflected in much of the effort described herein.

Future challenges and emerging issues necessitate forward-thinking approaches that integrate bird conservation into forest management, mine reclamation, and address broad global issues. This engages avian conservation for species living out their role in a particular ecosystem, and ensures no species is left behind or its importance minimized. We can do more. We must do more.

The state Constitution identifies public natural resources as the common property of all the people and charges the Commonwealth with the responsibility to conserve and maintain its natural resources for the benefit of all citizens. The Pennsylvania Game Commission is statutorily mandated within this Commonwealth to manage and protect wild birds and mammals. Its mission statement explicitly states that responsibility: to manage all birds, mammals and their habitats for present and future generations. Bird conservation has always been and will continue to be an important part of this agency's wildlife management programs.

Carl Roe
Executive Director
Pennsylvania Game Commission

Avian Ecology and Conservation: A Pennsylvania Focus with National Implications. Edited by S. K. Majumdar, T. L. Master, M. C. Brittingham, R. M. Ross, R. S. Mulvihill and J. E. Huffman. © 2010. The Pennsylvania Academy of Science.

INTRODUCTION

Historical Overview of Pennsylvania Ornithology

Scott Weidensaul
778 Schwartz Valley Rd.
Schuylkill Haven, PA 17972
sweidnsl@infionline.net

Pennsylvania was the cradle of American ornithology, even before Alexander Wilson—fresh off the boat in 1794 and walking to Philadelphia—shot a red-headed woodpecker and fell in love with the commonwealth's brilliant, colorful, and then still-mysterious birds. From William Penn marveling at its immense flocks of passenger pigeons, to the legions of high-tech modern atlasers documenting its breeding species at a level that would have stunned Wilson, Pennsylvania has long been the leader in both professional and avocational ornithology.

COLONIAL AND EARLY PERIODS

For the earliest views of Pennsylvania's birds, we are dependent on non-scientists—and men who often had a financial angle to boot, trying to sell the lure of the New World to potential investors and colonists back home. William Penn (1644–1718) may have been the most trustworthy of the lot, but even he was given to exaggeration, as a letter from 1683 makes clear:

"Of fowl of the land there is the turkey, (forty and fifty pounds weight) which is very great, pheasants, heath-birds, pigeons, and partridges in abundance. Of the water, the swan, goose, (white and gray;) brands, ducks, teal, also the snipe and curloe, and that in great numbers, but the duck and teal excel, nor so good have I ever eaten in other countries." (Janney 1852)

The "pheasant" to which Penn referred was most likely the ruffed grouse (*Bonasa umbellus*), and the "heath-birds" were undoubtedly heath hens, the now-extinct eastern race of the greater prairie-chicken (*Tympanchus cupido cupido*), which apparently ranged from the Poconos south and west to what are now Schuylkill, Union and Clinton counties, Lancaster and the extreme southeast of the state, where Penn would have encountered them (McWilliams and Brauning 2000).

The pigeons, of course, were passenger pigeons (*Ecopistes migratorius*), about whose abundance (and importance to the early European settlers) Penn wrote, "the wild pigeons came in such numbers, that the air was sometimes darkened by their flight; and flying low, those that had no other means to take them, sometimes supplied themselves by throwing at them as they flew, and salting up what they could not eat, they served them for bread and meat in one."

The earliest authors to treat the birdlife of the New World in a systematic way, men like John Lawson (1674?–1711) and Mark Catesby (1683–1749), never made it as far north as Pennsylvania, but instead focused on the Southeast. However, Pehr (often rendered Peter) Kalm (1716–79), a Finnish-born botanist and pupil of Linnaeus's, passed through New Jersey and Pennsylvania in 1749, during a tour of the colonies that took him on to New York and into Canada. His account, *Travels into North America* (1771), ranges from observations on soil types, farming practices and politics to descriptions of the flora and fauna of the region, including many birds.

Sailing up the Delaware, Kalm wrote that the "The *Whip-poor-will*, or *Goatsucker*, was likewise heard every where," though he noted that the sun "seems to stop their mouths, or dazzle their eyes, so as to make them sit still." He trapped northern cardinals, noting that "some of them, especially old ones…would die of grief on being put into cages." Of "partridges," as he called northern bobwhite (*Colinus virginianus*), Kalm wrote: "These birds are numerous…On going but a little way, you meet great coveys of them…They are always in lesser or greater coveys, do not fly very much, but run in the fields, and keep under the bushes and near the inclosures [sic], where they seek their food."

Although Kalm wasn't above passing on inaccurate hearsay, like the old canard about snakes "charming" birds in order to catch them, he was an astute scientist, and his account included snippets of sound natural history from experienced American observers like John Bartram.

Like Kalm, Bartram (1699–1777) was primarily a botanist, and although he was self-taught, this Philadelphia farmer established a global reputation, and appointment as royal botanist for the colonies by King George III. But it was William, Bartram's seventh child of 11, who was the first Pennsylvania scientist to pay close attention to the commonwealth's birdlife, as well as the first American-born naturalist to undertake an extensive natural exploration of his own country.

William Bartram (1739–1823) was not initially marked for greatness, however; as much as he loved tramping the woods with his father, he balked at several attempts John made to set him up in a trade. What business ventures he did undertake—an Indian trading post with an uncle, farming on a Florida plantation, and others—failed miserably. Not until the younger Bartram was in his thirties did he make a stab at a career in natural history, his great love. With financial support from backers in England, he set out on a five-year collecting expedition through the Southeast that resulted in a classic work, *Travels Through North and South Carolina, Georgia, East and West Florida* (1791).

Although this book focused primarily on the Southeast, it included a catalog of eastern North American birds, a number of which Bartram first described, along with "observations concerning their migration, or annual passages from North to South, and back again," largely based on Bartram's experiences in Pennsylvania.

In addition to providing the first systematic list of Pennsylvania birds, Bartram made some shrewd observations about migration. "In the spring of the year the small birds of passage appear very suddenly in Pennsylvania," he wrote, "which is not a little surprising, and no less pleasing: at once the woods, the groves, and meads, are filled with their melody, as if they dropped down from the skies. The reason or probable cause is their setting off with high and fair winds from the southward; for a strong south and south-west wind about the beginning of April never fails bringing millions of these welcome visitors."

WILSON AND AUDUBON

His *Travels* made Bartram a scientific celebrity, and many luminaries visited Bartram's Garden, the family's old estate near Philadelphia where William lived out the rest of his life. Not all were great men, however; in 1803, a simply dressed young man with a Scottish brogue introduced himself as the new school teacher in town—Alexander Wilson, a one-time weaver, failed poet and convicted blackmailer. Wilson (1766–1813), who had arrived in the United States nine years earlier and fallen instantly in love with American birds, found in Bartram a willing teacher of both ornithology and drawing, skills Wilson applied to creating his landmark *American Ornithology* (1808–14).

It is difficult to overstate the mammoth achievement embodied in this nine-volume work. Wilson was starting from zero when he undertook it; more than a year after stating his intention to create the first, comprehensive scientific treatment of American birds, he was sending his ornithological drawings to Bartram asking for identifications, "as, except three or four, I do not know them." (Cantwell 1961)

But he was a fast learner, and a man of remarkable energy. Besides collecting and drawing each specimen, Wilson learned to engrave the copper plates from which his book's illustrations were made, and many of the prints he also had to hand-tint himself, being unable to afford professional colorists. He traveled thousands of miles by foot, horse and boat between New England, the Mississippi and the Gulf Coast, collecting birds and selling subscriptions to his book.

Wilson catalogued more than three-quarters of the birds of eastern North America, including more than two dozen new species, describing their habits, ranges and plumages. To the roughly 140 species of Pennsylvania birds recorded by Bartram, he added another 51, and his text is rich in details on their life histories. Perhaps most remarkably, he conducted the first breeding bird census, sampling the habitats at Bartram's Garden to calculate the population of Pennsylvania's migrant and breeding birds, estimating the former at 100 million, with about 400 breeding pairs per square mile (Burtt and Peterson 1995, Cantwell 1961).

Wilson literally worked himself into an early grave, dying in 1813 at age 47, leaving the final two volumes of his *Ornithology* unfinished. But on one of his last expeditions, down the Ohio and Mississippi in 1810, Wilson had encountered a ne'er-do-well shopkeeper in Louisville, Kentucky who, doubtless inspired by Wilson's great project, decided to do much the same thing. The man was John James Audubon, another ornithologist whose passion took root in Pennsylvania—although the burgeoning ornithological community in Philadelphia, faithful to Wilson's memory, did everything they could to ensure that Audubon would fail.

Born illegitimately in Haiti to a chambermaid and a French naval captain, Audubon (1785–1851) was taken to France as a child, then sent to America in 1803 at age 18 to manage his father's estate of Mill Grove, on Perkiomen Creek near Valley Forge. Ignoring his business responsibilities—a recurrent theme in his early life—Audubon spent much of his time chasing birds for sport and to feed his growing interest in painting. It was while at Mill Grove that he struck upon a new method of wiring freshly-killed birds into lifelike poses, then transferring the drawing life-size to watercolor paper, with spectacular results (Ford 1988).

By the time he met Wilson in 1810, Audubon had married and entered into the mercantile business with a fellow French emigrant in Kentucky. Not long after, he began the pursuit that

Figure 1: Wilson's *American Ornithology* was the first comprehensive, scientific overview of the birds of the New World. (Academy of Natural Sciences, Ewell Sale Stewart Library)

would occupy most of the rest of his life, his four-volume *Birds of America* and the accompanying text, *Ornithological Biography*. Yet Audubon returned repeatedly to Pennsylvania over the years, not only to the halls of science in Philadelphia, where he was frequently snubbed, but travels of his own, like his six-week sojourn in 1829 into the old-growth forests of the upper Lehigh River, which resulted in some 95 bird and 60 egg paintings.

PHILADELPHIA: CENTER OF ORNITHOLOGY

By the late 18th and early 19th centuries, Philadelphia was recognized as the center of American science. The American Philosophical Society was founded there in 1743, and the Peale Museum, where Wilson later studied specimens, in 1786. The leading natural science institution in the new republic, however, was the Academy of Natural Sciences of Philadelphia (ANSP), founded in 1812, and which became the cradle of academic ornithology in America; a year later, when Wilson died, Academy vice-president George Ord (1781–1866) took over the task of completing the final two volumes of Wilson's *American Ornithology* (and devoting much of his spare time to thwarting Audubon's ambitions). Charles Lucien Bonaparte (1803–1857), nephew to Napoleon Bonaparte, spent five years at the Academy, where he completed a four-volume extension of Wilson's work (1825–33).

The Quaker tradition in Philadelphia produced a large crop of important ornithologists in the first decades of the 19th century, among them Thomas Say (1787–1834), who accompanied the Long Expedition across the southern Plains in 1819; John Townsend (1809–1851), who with botanist Thomas Nuttall crossed the Rockies to the Pacific, and then to Hawaii, in the early 1830s; and John Cassin (1813–1869). Artist/naturalist Titian Ramsay Peale (1799–1885), who joined Say exploring Florida, also went on the Long Expedition, producing some of the first images of western birds like lark sparrow (*Chondestes grammacus*).

During the pre-Civil War era, the ANSP expanded rapidly under the direction of president Thomas B. Wilson (1807–1865) and Cassin, the brilliant but irascible curator of birds. Wilson acquired more than 23,000 bird specimens from around the world during his tenure, including 1,500 Australian bird skins from John Gould, many of them type specimens. Cassin oversaw the rapidly growing collections at the ANSP for 35 years, although always in an honorary capacity; he was a successful businessman, and although Cassin hungered for an official curatorship, the institution was content to let him volunteer his considerable talents. His passion for ornithology eventually killed him; like Townsend, Cassin apparently died of arsenic poisoning, the toxin used to preserve specimens absorbing through his skin—and leaving a finch, auklet, sparrow and kingbird named in his honor (Gill 1995).

(Although Gill described Cassin as "an unhappy, bitter man" with an undisguised contempt for field collectors, he did have one saving social grace—his mentoring of Chester County native Graceanna Lewis [1821–1912], who in 1868 published the first volume of an expected 10-volume series, *The Natural History of Birds*. Another naturalist from the Quaker tradition, Lewis would likely have been the first female ornithologist of any stature, but she was unfortunately shut out of academia following Cassin's death, and spent the remainder of her long life as a writer and illustrator of nature articles for general audiences [Bonta 1995].)

Few Pennsylvanians have made a greater contribution to ornithology—or to science in general—than Spencer Fullerton Baird (1823–1887). Born in Reading and raised in Carlisle, he was a prodigy, graduating from Dickinson at age 17, already an accomplished collector. With his older brother William, he discovered the yellow-bellied (*Empidonax flaviventris*) and least flycatchers (*E. minimus*) (Baird and Baird 1843) and struck up a long-lasting friendship with Audubon, who in a gesture of extraordinary generosity, later gave the young man most of his bird collection, including many type specimens.

Baird founded the National Museum of Natural History at the Smithsonian, using two railway cars of his own material to jump-start the collections, and later rose to be the second Secretary of the Smithsonian. He was instrumental in seeding the West with collectors, many of them members of the U.S. Army Medical Corps—men already trained in science and protected, in hostile country, by armed troops.

Fingerhood (1992) has outlined the growing number of county bird lists in Pennsylvania, starting with Baird's 1845 efforts in Cumberland County, and including Crawford (1850), Delaware (1862), Chester (1863), Lancaster (1869), Bucks (1876), Westmoreland (1883) and Montgomery (1888) counties. Turnbull (1869) produced *The Birds of East Pennsylvania and New Jersey*, the first regional bird list, followed in 1876–77 by Gentry's two-volume *Life Histories of the Birds of Eastern Pennsylvania*.

RISE OF THE PROFESSIONALS

The late 19th century was a time of dramatic change in ornithology, with the professionalization of what had been a largely amateur-driven science. The American Ornithologists' Union (AOU) was founded in 1883, with Baird among the 23 original members (Palmer 1933), and the Wilson Ornithological Society came into existence in 1888. At the ANSP, Witmer Stone (1866–1939) began his 50-year tenure with the ornithology department, restoring the Academy's central role in ornithology after a long slide following Cassin's death (Gill 1995). He was also instrumental in forming the Delaware Valley Ornithological Club in 1890, second only to Massachusetts's Nuttall Club (1873) as the oldest such organization in the country.

Among the most notable Pennsylvania ornithologists of the late 19th century was Benjamin H. Warren, on the staff of the State Board of Agriculture. His 1888 book *Report on the Birds of Pennsylvania* was the first comprehensive, statewide account of the commonwealth's avifauna. The book, provided free to schools and agricultural societies, proved so popular that the initial printing of 6,000 copies had to be quickly supplemented with another 19,000 of a revised and enlarged edition (Chapman 1889).

Warren's work carried an odd and striking subtitle: "With Special Reference to the Food-Habits, based on over Four Thousand Stomach Examinations." For example, Warren's assistant, Walter Barrows, spent 26 pages in the book dissecting—literally—the food habits of American crows (*Corvus branchyrhynchos*), gently making the case for this much-maligned bird before throwing up his hands: "In concluding this imperfect summary of the insectivorous habits of the Common Crow it must be conceded that the showing is not very favorable for the bird."

This was the era of "economic ornithology," in which researchers sought to distinguish "beneficial" from "destructive" birds based on what they ate—injurious insects and weed seeds, in the case of the former, versus gamebirds or poultry in the case of most raptors, which were considered a bane by even most ornithologists and conservationists. "The Sharp-shinned and Cooper's Hawks, both bird-killers...are to be rated as our most objectionable birds of prey" (Sutton 1928).

Consequently, when word began to circulate in 1931 of a massive annual slaughter of migrating raptors along the Kittatinny Ridge, the result was almost universal apathy, even from organizations like the AOU and National Audubon Society pledged to bird protection. The only effective action came from New York social crusader Rosalie Edge (1877–1962), whose Emergency Conservation Committee purchased the mountaintop in Schuylkill and Berks counties in 1934, creating Hawk Mountain Sanctuary, the world's first refuge for birds of prey. Autumn counts begun by curator Maurice Broun (1906–1979), and now constituting a 75-year data set, revolutionized the understanding of diurnal raptor migration, and first documented the presence of a significant eastern population of golden eagles (*Aquila chrysaetos*) (Broun 1948). The privately owned sanctuary, which includes the Acopian Center for Conservation Learning, has today become one of the global leaders in raptor research, conservation and education.

The ornithology programs at both the Academy of Natural Sciences and the Carnegie Museum of Natural History in Pittsburgh grew dramatically in the first half of the 20th century, the latter under the leadership of W.E. Clyde Todd (1874–1969), one of the most productive ornithologists ever to work in the state. Serving as Carnegie's curator of ornithology from 1912 until his retirement in 1946, Todd continued for nearly a decade

Figure 2:   Maurice Broun (left) and Roger Tory Peterson confer on North Lookout at Hawk Mountain Sanctuary in this undated photograph. (Hawk Mountain Sanctuary Archives)

thereafter to travel into the Canadian Far North, an area of lifelong interest and almost two dozen expeditions (Parkes 1995).

Todd is best remembered, however, as the author of the landmark *The Birds of Western Pennsylvania* (1940), which grew out of surveys he started in the 1890s. In 1919 Todd hired an assistant curator, George Miksch Sutton (1898–1982), helping to launch the young man on what would become a nationally important career in ornithology. Even after leaving Carnegie in 1924 for the post of ornithologist with the Pennsylvania Game Commission, Sutton maintained a longstanding relationship with the museum and with Todd, including painting the 22 plates for his western Pennsylvania book (Parkes, 1995; Jackson 2007).

Two ANSP scientists are best remembered today for their contributions to Latin American and Caribbean ornithology. Rodolphe Meyer de Schauensee (1901–1984), the Italian-born son of Swiss nobility, "laid the foundations for modern study of the complicated avifauna of South America, much as Wilson had done in his time for North America" (Gill 1995). James Bond (1900–1989), Philadelphia-born but educated in England, did much the same for the birdlife of the West Indies—and it was from Bond's field guide to the Caribbean birds that novelist Ian Fleming, vacationing in Jamaica, took the name for his fictional secret agent (Gill 1995).

In more recent years, Kenneth C. Parkes (1922–2007) helmed the Carnegie ornithology department for more than 30 years, retiring in 1996—and leaving as a permanent legacy the familiar Humphrey-Parkes framework of bird molt. (Humphrey and Parkes 1959). At the ANSP, Frank B. Gill (1941–) and later South American bird specialist Robert S. Ridgely (1946–) directed the ornithology department. During Gill's tenure, the Academy created its VIREO (Visual Resources for Ornithology) bird image collection, now the world's largest, containing more than 140,000 images representing more than 6,900 species; the ANSP also sponsored (with the AOU and Cornell Lab of Ornithology) the milestone *Birds of North America* project, which completed publication in 2002, and is now being updated online.

Although in the early 20th century the collections of the Academy of Natural Sciences and Carnegie ranked among the three or four most important nationally, they have been somewhat eclipsed today. But they remain among the top ten in the nation, and are vital and growing resources for scientists. The ANSP maintains a collection of almost 200,000 skins representing more than 7,000 species, along with 15,000 tissue samples and specimens dating back to Wilson, Audubon and Gould. The collection includes about 1,500 type specimens and 2,500 skins of extinct or endangered species (N. Rice, ANSP, pers. comm.).

The Carnegie collection includes more than 154,000 skins of 5,700 species, including more than 550 holotypes from 27 countries, and about 180 extinct birds, as well as a skeletal collection of 16,000 specimens, and 10,000 sets of eggs (S. Rogers, Carnegie Museum of Natural History, pers. comm.). Both the ANSP and Carnegie collections have a global scope; the Academy's particular strength is South America, while Carnegie holds one of the largest eastern Arctic collections in the world, thanks to Todd's long work there.

Carnegie also maintains the Powdermill Nature Reserve in Westmoreland County. Since the inception of its fulltime banding program in 1961, Powdermill has ringed more than 400,000 birds of 150 species, collecting information from more than 100,000 recaptures and generating a database of more than half a million records. Not only is Powdermill by far the most important such research program in the state, it is one of the longest-running professional landbird banding programs in North America (R. Mulvihill, Powdermill Avian Research Center, pers. comm.).

Perhaps the most remarkable Pennsylvania ornithologist of the 20th century—and among the most remarkable of any century—did not come up through the usual academic or institutional ranks. Theodore A. Parker III (1953–1993) was born in Lancaster and was a teenage birding whiz, starting a record-breaking Big Year in 1971 while still in high school, and later dropping out of college to lead field trips, and to join Louisiana State University expeditions to South America. Parker had an extraordinary auditory gift; he was said to be able to identify, by sound alone, several thousand species of birds, and among his many achievements were 15,000 recordings of more than 1,600 species of birds, archived in the Macaulay Library of Natural Sounds at Cornell. Tragically, Ted Parker was killed in a small-plane crash in Ecuador in 1993, along with colleagues conducting a biological survey (Stap 1990, Bates and Schulenberg 1997).

"One can only speculate what Ted would have accomplished if he had lived. It is certain that his role in the conservation of tropical biotas would have continued to accelerate, and his storehouse of knowledge would have come to fruition through his publications and collaboration with others" (Robbins, Graves and Remsen 1997). A number of recently discovered Neotropical birds are named in Parker's honor, including a pygmy-owl, antwren, antbird, tyrannulet and tapaculo (Davis and O'Neill 1986, Robbins and Howell 1995, Graves 1997, Fitzpatrick and Stotz 1997, Krabbe and Schulenberg 1997, Remsen 1997).

ORNITHOLOGY SINCE THE ATLAS

As Fingerhood (1992) has noted, the presence of two strong ornithological institutions, in a state split by the Appalachian Mountains into two distinct regions, conspired against a unified, statewide approach to ornithology. (One of the few major figures in 20th century ornithology not working in either Philadelphia or Pittsburgh was Earl Poole [1892–1972], director of the Reading Public Museum in Berks County and, like Sutton, an artist of uncommon talent.)

The east-west split finally changed in the 1980s with one of the most ambitious undertakings in the history of Pennsylvania bird study—the commonwealth's first Breeding Bird Atlas (1983–89). Directed by Frank Gill and coordinated initially by Edward Fingerhood and, for the final six years, by Daniel W. Brauning, the atlas mobilized more than 2,000 volunteers to census 5,000 atlas blocks covering every one of the commonwealth's more than 47,000 square miles, a task that required 83,000 hours of field time. The result, published in 1992, was the most intensive survey ever of the state's birdlife, documenting in unprecedented detail the ranges of 230 species (Brauning 1992).

The atlas also crystallized the need for a more systematic, statewide approach to ornithology and bird conservation. In 1986, the Ornithological Technical Committee of the Pennsylvania Biological Survey was formed, and under its auspices, the Pennsylvania Ornithological Records Committee began operation two years later. In 1990, the Pennsylvania Society for Ornithology (PSO) was founded, at last giving the commonwealth an ornithological organization with statewide breadth. A small state birding listserve, PABIRDS, which began in late 1997, moved the following year to an Audubon server and began rapid growth; it currently has almost 1,100 members, most in the commonwealth but some as far-flung as Poland and the Federated States of Micronesia (Santasania 2007).

The result has been a large and rapidly expanding pool of enthusiastic, experienced bird-ers eager to participate in a variety of science-directed projects. Usually referred to as "cit-izen-science," they range from long-established projects like the Audubon Christmas Bird Count and federal Breeding Bird Survey to new efforts like Cornell's Birds in Forested Landscapes, Project FeederWatch and Golden-winged Warbler Atlas, or ongoing breeding-season monitoring of the more than 80 Important Bird Areas across the state designated by Audubon Pennsylvania.

The capstone, however, has been the second Pennsylvania Breeding Bird Atlas, which concludes its fifth season of fieldwork in 2008, overseen by Brauning and coordinated by Robert Mulvihill of Powdermill Nature Reserve. As Mulvihill more fully explains else-where in this volume, the differences between the original and second atlases—in the use of digital technology, the quantity and level of detail represented by the data—are extra-ordinary, and mark yet another exciting chapter in the ongoing development of ornitholo-gy in Pennsylvania.

REFERENCES

Academy of Natural Sciences of Philadelphia. History of ornithology at ANSP. http://www.ansp.org/research/biodiv/ornithology/history.php

_____. Ornithology collections. http://www.ansp.org/research/biodiv/ornithology/collections.php

Audubon, M., editor. 1897. *Audubon and His Journals.* Volume 2. Scribners' Sons. New York, pp. 554.

Baird, W. M. and S. F. Baird. 1843. Description of two species, supposed to be new, of the genus *Tyrannula Swainson,* found in Cumberland County, Pennsylvania. *Proc. Ac. Nat. Sci. Phila.* 1: 283–85.

Bartram, W. 1791. *Travels Through North & South Carolina, Georgia, East & West Florida.* James & Johnson. Philadelphia, PA, pp. 522.

Bates, J. M. and T. S. Schulenberg. 1997. In memoriam: Theodore A. Parker III 1953–1993. *Auk* 114: 110.

Brauning, D. W., ed. 1992. *Atlas of Breeding Birds in Pennsylvania.* University of Pittsburgh Press. Pittsburgh, PA, pp. 484.

Broun, Maurice. 1948. *Hawks Aloft.* Kutztown Publishing Co. Kutztown, PA, pp. 222.

Burtt, E. H. and A. P. Peterson. 1995. Alexander Wilson and the Founding of North American Ornithology. Pp. 359–386 in: W. E. Davis Jr. and J. A. Jackson (Eds.). *Contributions to the History of North American Ornithology.* Nuttall Ornithological Club. Cambridge, MA, pp. 501.

Cantwell, R. 1961. *Alexander Wilson: Naturalist and Pioneer.* Lippincott. Philadelphia and New York, pp. 319.

Carnegie Museum of Natural History. 2nd Pennsylvania Breeding Bird Atlas. http://www.carnegiemnh.org/atlas/home.htm.

_____. Section of birds. http://www.carnegiemnh.org/birds/index.html

Chapman, F.M. 1889. Notes and news (Warren's "Birds of Pennsylvania"). *Auk* 6: 283.

Davis, T. J. and J. P. O'Neill. 1986. A new species of antwren (Formicariidae: *Herpsilochmus*) from Perus, with comments on the systematics of the other members of the genus. *Wilson Bull.* 98: 337–352.

Fingerhood, E. D. 1992. History of Pennsylvania ornithology. Pp. 35–39 in: D. W. Brauning, editor. *Atlas of Breeding Birds in Pennsylvania.* University of Pittsburgh Press. Pittsburgh, PA, pp. 484.

Fitzpatrick, J. W. and D. F. Stotz. 1997. A new species of tyrannulet (*Phylloscartes*) from the Andean foothills of Peru and Bolivia, Pp. 37–44 in: Remsen, J. V. Jr. 1997. Studies in Neotropical ornithology honoring Ted Parker. *Ornithological Monographs* No. 48. American Ornithologists' Union. Washington, D.C.

Ford, A. 1988. *John James Audubon.* Abbeville Press. New York, pp. 528.

Gentry, T. G. 1876. *Life Histories of the Birds of Eastern Pennsylvania.* Volume 1. Published pri-vately. Philadelphia, pp. 399.

_____. 1877. *Life Histories of the Birds of Eastern Pennsylvania.* Volume 2. The Naturalist's Agency. Salem, MA, pp. 336.

Gill, F. 1995. Philadelphia: 180 years of ornithology at the Academy of Natural Sciences. Pp. 1–27 in: W. E. Davis Jr. and J. A. Jackson (Eds.). *Contributions to the History of North American Ornithology.* Nuttall Ornithological Club. Cambridge, MA, pp. 501.

Graves, G. R. 1997. Colorimetric and morphometric gradients in Colombian populations of dusky antbirds (*Cercomacra tyrannina*), with a description of a new species, *Cercomacra parkeri*, Pp. 21–35 in: Remsen, J. V. Jr. 1997. Studies in Neotropical orrnithology honoring Ted Parker. *Ornithological Monographs* No. 48. American Ornithologists' Union. Washington, D.C.

Humphrey, P. S. and K. C. Parkes. 1959. An approach to the study of molts and plumages. *Auk* 76: 1–31.

Jackson, J. 2007. *George Miksch Sutton.* University of Oklahoma Press. Norman, OK, pp. 239.

Kalm, P. 1771. *Travels into North America.* Volume 2. J. R. Forster, Ed. London, pp. 352.

Krabbe, N. and T. S. Schulenberg. 1997. Species limits and natural history of *Scytalopus* tapaculos (Rhinocryptidae), with descriptions of the Ecuadorian taxa, including three new species, Pp. 47–88 in: Remsen, J. V. Jr. 1997. Studies in Neotropical orrnithology honoring Ted Parker. *Ornithological Monographs* No. 48. American Ornithologists' Union. Washington, D.C.

McWilliams, G. M. and D. W. Brauning. 2000. *The Birds of Pennsylvania.* Cornell University Press. Ithaca, NY, pp. 479.

Palmer, T. S. 1933. A brief history of the American Ornithologists' Union. Pp. 7–27 in: C. M. Chapman and T. S. Palmer, editors. *Fifty Years' Progress of American Ornithology, 1883–1933.* AOU. Lancaster, PA, pp. 249.

Parkes, K. C. 1995. Ornithology at Carnegie Museum of Natural History. Pp. 163–181 in: W. E. Davis Jr. and J. A. Jackson, editors. *Contributions to the History of North American Ornithology.* Nuttall Ornithological Club. Cambridge, MA, pp. 501.

Penn, William, 1683, Pp. 235–41 in: Janney, S., editor. 1852. *The Life of William Penn with Selections from His Correspondence and Autobiography.* 2nd ed. Lippincot, Grambo & Co. Philadelphia.

Remsen, J. V. Jr. 1997. Studies in Neotropical orrnithology honoring Ted Parker. *Ornithological Monographs* No. 48. American Ornithologists' Union. Washington, D.C., pp. 932.

Robbins, M. B., G. R. Graves and J. V. Remsen Jr. 1997: In Memoriam: Theodore A. Parker III 1953–1993, Pp. 1–6 in: Remsen, J. V. Jr. 1997. Studies in Neotropical orrnithology honoring Ted Parker. *Ornithological Monographs* No. 48. American Ornithologists' Union. Washington, D.C.

Robbins, M. B. and S. N. G. Howell. 1995 A new species of pygmy-owl (Strigidae: *Glaucidium*) from the eastern Andes. *Wilson Bull.* 107: 1–6.

Santasania, C. 2007. An update on the PABIRDS listserv. *PSO Pileated* 18: 4–6.

Stap, D. 1990. *A Parrot Without a Name.* Knopf. New York, pp. 239.

Sutton, G. M. 1928. *An Introduction to the Birds of Pennsylvania.* J. Horace McFarland Co. Harrisburg, PA, pp. 169.

Todd, W. E. C. 1940. *The Birds of Western Pennsylvania.* University of Pittsburgh Press. Pittsburgh, PA, pp. 710.

Turnbull, W. P. 1869. *The Birds of East Pennsylvania and New Jersey.* Grambo & Co. Philadelphia, pp. 50.

Warren, B. H. 1890. *Report on the Birds of Pennsylvania.* Second edition. State Printing Office. Harrisburg, PA, pp. 432.

Avian Ecology and Conservation: A Pennsylvania Focus with National Implications. Edited by S. K. Majumdar, T. L. Master, M. C. Brittingham, R. M. Ross, R. S. Mulvihill and J. E. Huffman. © 2010. The Pennsylvania Academy of Science.

SECTION I

Breeding Birds Of Pennsylvania And Their Habitats

Section Overview

Terry L. Master

Department of Biological Sciences, East Stroudsburg University of Pennsylvania,
200 Prospect St., East Stroudsburg, PA 18301-2999
terry.master@po-box.esu.edu

Pennsylvania contains a wealth of habitat types ranging from the Lake Erie Plain in the northwestern corner of the state to the tidal marshes of the Delaware River in the extreme southeast in Philadelphia. In between these two extremes lies the habitat that Pennsylvania is perhaps best known for: its extensive deciduous and mixed forest, as well as a variety of successional habitats; both human-caused, in the case of the reclaimed strip mine grasslands, agricultural landscapes and regenerating old fields, and intrinsically successional wetlands and boreal bogs. Modest elevational differences enhance the variety and extent of these interior habitats.

Scott Stoleson and Jeff Larkin begin their chapter on forested habitats by describing the extent of forest cover in Pennsylvania. Forests cover 60% of the state, with some counties having nearly 100% forest cover, and Pennsylvania leads the nation in hardwood growing stock volume. The two major forest types, Oak-Hickory and Northern hardwoods, in conjunction with scattered stands of conifers, support characteristic avian communities reflecting a mixture of birds with both southern and northern affinities, many of which are forest interior species. The scarlet tanager, featured on the cover of this book, is perhaps *the* flagship forest interior species in Pennsylvania which supports 15% of the total population on only 4.5% of the breeding range. Avian community structure and population trends are subsequently discussed in the context of conservation challenges and management issues faced by the state's forest birds.

Seed dispersal by birds is an important component of the life history of many trees and thus necessary to maintain healthy forests. This is especially true with various species of oaks which are a major component of one of the two primary forest types in Pennsylvania as mentioned above. Michael Steele, Nathanael Lichti and Robert Swihart specifically use oak seed dispersal with respect to blue jays as an example of seed dispersal by birds in their chapter on avian mediated seed dispersal. Prefacing this example are sections on the importance of seed dispersal from plant and disperser perspectives, a discussion of its importance to plant recruitment and demography and the role that seed dispersers play in the spread of invasive species.

Interspersed within Pennsylvania's largely forested landscape are wetlands and riparian corridors. Douglas Gross and Catherine Haffner mention that 729,535 acres of Pennsylvania are covered by wetlands that are located disproportionately in the northeastern and northwestern portions of the state. The relatively small area occupied by wetlands belies the fact that 55% of the state's species of special concern and 79% of the endangered species depend on them to some extent. In addition to providing habitat for threatened and endangered species, a wide variety of other species depend on wetlands for a portion of their life cycle and as important migratory stopover habitats.

Two chapters, to varying extent, discuss riparian habitats and the birds found there. Douglas Gross and Catherine Haffner discuss riverine habitats in the context of being one of the many types of wetland found within the state. Pennsylvania is second only to Alaska in the density of rivers and streams within its borders. Some of the state's rarest wading birds and their nesting colonies are found on Pennsylvania's major river, the Susquehanna. Terry Master presents a broader view of riparian habitat emphasizing avian community structure and how it changes along the continuum from headwater stream to large river and from shoreline to surrounding upland.

Also interspersed within the state's extensive forest cover are open and successional habitats, many of whose flagship species are among the fastest declining of all birds in Pennsylvania and the United States. Glenn Stauffer, Matthew Marshall, Duane Diefenbach and Daniel Brauning discuss the somewhat improbable importance of Pennsylvania's extensive reclaimed strip mines to grassland bird species, especially the Henslow's sparrow. Michael Carey uses his long-term study of field sparrows in northeastern Pennsylvania to illustrate characteristics of the avian communities of early successional habitats.

Although focused on Pennsylvania, much of the information presented in these chapters has application far beyond the borders of the state. This is especially true of the conservation challenges and management issues highlighted for each habitat type and its associated avian community.

Avian Ecology and Conservation: A Pennsylvania Focus with National Implications. Edited by S. K. Majumdar, T. L. Master, M. C. Brittingham, R. M. Ross, R. S. Mulvihill and J. E. Huffman. © 2010. The Pennsylvania Academy of Science.

Chapter 1

Breeding Birds of Pennsylvania: Forest Communities

Scott H. Stoleson[1] and Jeffery L. Larkin[2]
[1]U.S. Forest Service, Northern Research Station, Irvine, PA 16329
[2]Indiana University of Pennsylvania, Department of Biology, Indiana, PA 15705
stoleson@fs.fed.us / larkin@iup.edu

FOREST HABITATS IN PENNSYLVANIA

Pennsylvania is a forested state—the very name means "Penn's woods". Despite being the sixth most populous state in the country, forests are the dominant land-cover type in Pennsylvania. Today approximately 60% of the commonwealth is forested, and Pennsylvania leads the nation in hardwood growing stock volume (Widmann 1995).

Forests are not uniformly distributed across the state, however. The most extensive and contiguous forests occur across the Allegheny High Plateau in the north central part of the state. For example, in this region Cameron and Forest Counties have > 93% forest cover (Widmann 1995). The Pocono Highlands and upland portions of the Ridge and Valley physiographic regions also retain heavy forest cover. In contrast, forests in the heavily urbanized southeast, the southern Pittsburgh Plateau, and the Great Lakes floodplain regions are sparse and, where they occur, highly fragmented. Across the state, most (79%) forested land is privately owned, the majority as small (< 50 acres) tracts by over half a million non-industrial owners (USDA 2004). Public forestlands (state forests and state game lands, and Allegheny National Forest) are disproportionately concentrated in the Allegheny High Plateau region, where they comprise 41% of the landscape.

Almost all of Pennsylvania's forests are classified as deciduous hardwoods or hardwoods mixed with conifers. Two major biomes intergrade here: the central hardwoods or oak-hickory type (47% of forested land), and the northern hardwoods type (38%) (Fike 1999). In addition to oaks (*Quercus* spp.) and hickories (*Carya* spp.), oak-hickory forests typically include tuliptree (*Liriodendron tulipifera*), blackgum (*Nyssa sylvatica*), and red maple (*Acer rubrum*). Northern hardwoods are dominated by American beech (*Fagus grandifolia*), sugar maple (*Acer saccharum*), black and yellow birches (*Betula lenta* and *B. alleghaniensis*), and eastern hemlock (*Tsuga canadensis*). Much of the High Plateau supports Allegheny hardwoods, an anthropogenic subtype resulting from the combination of large-scale clearcutting and rapid increase in deer numbers a century ago, and is dominated by black cherry (*Prunus serotina*) and red maple (Marquis 1975). Conifer-dominated forests are sparse in the state. These include a few high-elevation areas in the Poconos with spruce-fir association (*Picea rubra* and *Abies balsamea*), several remnant old growth stands of hemlock, white pine (*Pinus strobus*), and beech such as at Cook Forest State Park, and plantations of red pine (*Pinus resinosa*) or spruce (*Picea* spp.). Pennsylvania's forests support a high diversity of trees—over 100 species—yet just four account for 40% of tree stems statewide: red maple, black birch, black cherry, and American beech (USDA 2004).

Historical Trends

When the first European colonists arrived in what is now Pennsylvania, they encountered a landscape that was almost completely forested. Much of the original forests on the cooler, more mesic uplands were old growth beech-hemlock, while chestnut-oak dominated warmer and more xeric areas (Whitney 1990). William Penn prophetically recommended that "care be taken to leave one acre of trees for every five acres cleared." In fact, progressive clearing for agriculture and timber production through the 1700s and 1800s did reduce forest cover to about 20% by 1900 (USDA 2004). The subsequent regrowth of forests, coupled with the succession of abandoned farmland, has produced a gradual increase in forested land across the state (Askins 2000). The percentage of land in forest has stabilized at about 60% since the 1960s (McWilliams et al. 2004). Because of this history, much of the state's forests consist of relatively even-aged second-growth stands between 90 and 120 years old.

Concurrent with the extensive regrowth since 1900, many other factors have shaped the Pennsylvania forests we see today. One is the introduction of exotic pests and pathogens. The inadvertent spread of chestnut blight (*Cryphonectria parasitica*) and Dutch elm disease (*Ophiostoma* spp.) all but eliminated these once dominant trees. Additional diseases and insect pests are currently impacting American beech, butternut (*Juglans cinerea*), eastern hemlock, and ashes (*Fraxinus* spp.). This topic is explored further in Chapter 17. Changes in natural successional patterns due to fire suppression, reduction of beaver populations, and deer overabundance have altered forest structure and composition as well (Naiman, Johnston et al. 1988; Abrams and Ruffner 1995; Lorimer 2001; Horsley, Stout et al. 2003). Recent state-wide surveys indicate inadequate advance regeneration to be a statewide problem, particularly where alternate browse is unavailable (McWilliams et al. 2004). Suppression of wildfires has produced an increase in mesophytic species, particularly red maple and birches, in oak-hickory forests statewide, causing a marked loss in habitat value for bird communities. A study conducted in Centre County demonstrated that oak-dominated forests had greater diversity and abundance of birds in most seasons than otherwise similar maple-dominated forests (Rodewald and Abrams 2002).

The approximately 60% of Pennsylvania that currently is forested comprises almost 17 million acres (USDA 2004). Because our mature forests are dominated by even-aged trees > 80 yrs old, many of them are considered sufficiently mature to be harvested. The timber industry is now a $5 billion industry in Pennsylvania, and the value of its timber resources has helped to keep land in forest. However, most of the state's timbered lands are privately owned, and so are not subject to the regulations that promote and enforce sustainable management on public lands. Landowners often unwittingly allow their timber to be harvested in unsustainable ways—essentially "mining" the resource—and, by doing so, reducing the vigor, stocking, and species diversity of the forest. How this might affect the long-term habitat value of privately owned forests for Pennsylvania's birdlife remains unclear.

FOREST BIRD COMMUNITIES IN PENNSYLVANIA

Pennsylvania's extensive forests support a great abundance and diversity of forest birds, including many forest interior specialists that are of continental conservation concern (Rich et al. 2004). For some of these species, Pennsylvania is home to a disproportionately large fraction of the global breeding population. For example, population estimates based on BBS data suggest that about 15% of all scarlet tanagers (*Piranga olivacea*) breed within the state, despite the fact that Pennsylvania comprises only 4.5% of the total breeding range; similar statistics for wood thrush and Louisiana waterthrush are 8% (population) and < 5% (range in PA) (Table 1; data taken from Partners in Flight [PIF] estimated population database; Blancher et al. 2007). Additional species of conservation concern have a high proportion of their total population breeding within PA, albeit not out of proportion to their distribution (e.g., cerulean warbler *Dendroica cerulea*). For both groups of birds, Pennsylvania has a high stewardship responsibility according to Partners in Flight (Table 1; Rosenberg 2004).

In general, patterns of avian diversity (i.e., forest bird community structure) reflect the diversity of forest types and forest structure found across the state. The oak-hickory vs. northern hardwoods dichotomy represents one of the major forest habitat gradients in Pennsylvania. It approximates a south to north gradient, but it is also influenced by eleva-

Table 1. Birds of mature forest and forest edge for which a disproportionate fraction (% total population within PA >10% greater than % total range within PA) or a high portion (>4%) of their North American population breeds within Pennsylvania. Calculated from population and range size estimates in Partners in Flight population estimates database (Blancher et al. 2007).

Species	Estimated population within PA	% of N. American population within PA	% of N. American range within PA
Sharp-shinned hawk *Accipiter striatus*	14,000	2.33	1.12
Cooper's hawk *Accipiter cooperii*	12,000	2.40	1.44
Black-billed cuckoo *Coccyzus erythrophthalmus*	45,000	4.09	2.38
Ruby-throated hummingbird *Archilochus colubris*	240,000	3.43	2.39
Downy woodpecker *Picoides pubescens*	340,000	2.62	0.92
Northern flicker *Colaptes auratus*	150,000	1.00	0.84
Eastern wood-pewee *Contopus virens*	210,000	3.50	2.88
Acadian flycatcher *Empidonax virescens*	200,000	4.26	4.77
Red-eyed vireo *Vireo olivaceus*	3,600,000	2.57	1.35
Black-capped chickadee *Poecile atricapillus*	840,000	2.47	1.34
White-breasted nuthatch *Sitta carolinensis*	270,000	2.97	1.50
Wood thrush *Hylocichla mustelina*	1,100,000	7.86	3.37
Cedar waxwing *Bombycilla cedrorum*	530,000	3.53	1.58
Cerulean warbler *Dendroica cerulea*	50,000	8.93	9.52
American redstart *Setophaga ruticilla*	550,000	2.20	1.77
Worm-eating warbler *Helmitheros vermivorus*	50,000	7.14	6.70
Ovenbird *Seiurus aurocapillus*	610,000	2.54	2.26
Louisiana waterthrush *Seiurus motacilla*	20,000	7.69	4.87
Scarlet tanager *Piranga olivacea*	320,000	14.55	4.52
Baltimore oriole *Icterus galbula*	230,000	3.83	2.50

tion, aspect, and land use history. Our northern forests support a distinct suite of birds whose ranges lie primarily north of Pennsylvania. These birds tend to be common and widespread in the northern tier of counties and southward at higher elevations (> 500 m) in the mountains, but they are sparse or absent from lower elevations in the southern half of the state. Certain northern birds have particularly strong ties to conifers and are rarely found away from them. They reside in native white pine and hemlock (or spruce in the Poconos), but also are found in the numerous plantations of red pine and spruce across the state. Such birds include red-breasted nuthatch (*Sitta canadensis*), yellow-bellied fly-catcher (*Empidonax flaviventris*), golden-crowned kinglet (*Regulus satrapa*), Swainson's thrush (*Catharus ustulatus*), magnolia and yellow-rumped warblers (*Dendroica magnolia*, *D. coronata*), and purple finch (*Carpodacus purpureus*).

On the High Plateau, however, many northern birds are abundant in hardwood stands as well, even those dominated by oak. These include yellow-bellied sapsucker (*Sphyrapicus varius*), least flycatcher (*Empidonax minimus*), blue-headed vireo (*Vireo solitarius*), her-mit thrush (*Catharus guttatus*), black-throated green warbler (*Dendroica virens*), black-burnian warbler (*D. fusca*), Canada warbler (*Wilsonia canadensis*), dark-eyed junco (*Junco hyemalis*) and winter wren (*Troglodytes troglodytes*). Birds of more southern affini-ties that approach or reach the northern limits of their distribution within the state, occupy oak-hickory or bottomland riparian forests almost exclusively. They tend to be most abun-dant and widespread at lower elevations in the southeastern and southwestern parts of the state. Most are local, sparse or absent from the extensive forests of the Allegheny High Plateau, which has implications for their populations (see below). This suite includes red-bellied woodpecker (*Melanerpes carolinus*), Acadian flycatcher, (*Empidonax virescens*) Carolina chickadee (*Poecile carolinensis*), cerulean warbler, worm-eating warbler (*Helmitheros vermivorus*) and Kentucky warbler (*Oporornis formosus*), as well as spe-cialists of early-successional forests such as white-eyed vireo (*Vireo griseus*), prairie war-bler (*Dendroica discolor*), and yellow-breasted chat (*Icteria virens*). Many of these south-erners have been expanding their ranges northward since the early part of the 20th Centu-ry, and now can be found at least occasionally beyond the New York state line.

Many forest birds actually eschew deep, closed-canopy forest interiors, preferring instead more open woodlands, riparian forests with edges, gaps, and even suburban wood-lots or orchards. Such birds include yellow-billed cuckoo (*Coccyzus americanus*), eastern wood-pewee (*Contopus virens*), great crested flycatcher (*Myiarchus crinitus*), rose-breast-ed grosbeak (*Pheucticus ludovicianus*), and Baltimore oriole (*Icterus galbula*). In contrast, the closed canopies of extensive mature forests are the preferred haunts of blue-headed vireos, blackburnian warblers, black-throated green warblers, ovenbirds (*Seiurus auro-capillus*) and others. An associated gradient in understory density affects which forest birds are found in that stratum: for example, open forest floors associated with closed canopy forests are preferred by ovenbirds and hermit thrushes, while dense brushy under-stories associated with forest gaps and edges provide habitat for hooded warblers (*Wilso-nia citrina*), American redstart (*Setophaga ruticilla*) and veery (*Catharus fuscescens*).

Naturally, avian community composition changes over time with successional changes in forests following fires, wind damage, timbering, and clearing. When regenerating stands reach 12–20 years old, avian communities experience almost complete species turnover from early successional specialists (see Carey, chapter 5) to true forest birds (Hagan et al.

1997, Keller et al. 2002). As stands mature, the bird species that breed in them will gradually shift over time, those that prefer younger stands, such as American redstarts (Hunt
1998) dropping out over time while others colonize that specialize on mature stands, such
as brown creeper (*Certhia americana*) and cerulean warbler (Haney and Schaadt 1996,
Holmes and Sherry 2001).

Forest Area

Many forest birds respond to forest patch size and are considered to be area-sensitive. Fragmentation effects are discussed in depth in Brittingham, Chapter 15. Briefly, the density of
many of the most common forest species, such as red-eyed vireo (*Vireo olivaceus*), scarlet
tanager, wood thrush (*Hylocichla mustelina*), and ovenbird increase with patch size (Wilcove
1985, Askins 2000). Those breeding in forest interiors experience higher nest success than
those near edges, primarily because there tends to be a greater abundance of cowbirds
(*Molothrus ater*) and nest predators along edges (Brittingham and Temple 1983, Hoover and
Brittingham 1993, Robinson et al. 1995, Porneluzi and Faaborg 1999, Askins 2000).

Pennsylvania's forests all are fragmented to varying degrees by roads, utility rights-of-
way, agriculture, and urban sprawl, producing forest patches in a broad range of sizes. The
largest, most extensive tracts of contiguous forest are found primarily on the Allegheny
High Plateau, where public forests are concentrated. In contrast, forests become increasingly fragmented, and average patch size becomes smaller, towards the heavily populated
southwestern and southeastern corners of the state. As a consequence, much of the large,
high-quality forest tracts in the state are northern hardwoods and mixed woods, while the
most heavily fragmented forests tend to be oak-hickory. This dichotomy in habitat quality
between forest types has implications for the conservation of Pennsylvania's forest birds.

POPULATION TRENDS

Data acquired from two sources can be used to draw general inferences regarding population trends of birds that breed in Pennsylvania forests: the North American Breeding
Bird Survey and the Pennsylvania Breeding Bird Atlas. The North American Breeding
Bird Survey (BBS), initiated in 1966, is a standardized road-based point count survey run
annually along > 4000 routes distributed across the U.S. and southern Canada. BBS methods are potentially biased as they do not survey habitats away from roads and, therefore,
may fail to accurately measure populations of species that have a comparatively low tolerance of roads or edges (Bystrak 1981). Additionally, since no habitat data are collected
by the BBS, no direct inferences can be made regarding the long-term occurrence patterns
of species with respect to changes in habitat conditions. Nonetheless, interpreted with caution, BBS data do provide useful information regarding overall long-term trends in abundance, and they figure prominently in the establishment of management priorities, such as
Partners in Flight prioritization scheme (Rich et al. 2004).

Breeding bird atlases are comprehensive surveys usually conducted over five or more
consecutive years and repeated at long intervals (usually every 20–25 years). The Pennsylvania Breeding Bird Atlas determines presence-absence of species in 4,937 blocks, each
block equal to 1/6th of a standard USGS 7.5-minute series topographic map. Importantly,
because they are not strictly road-based, atlases have the potential to assess populations of
species poorly sampled by the BBS methods (Robbins et al. 1989). Data for 1st Pennsyl-

vania Breeding Bird Atlas was collected from 1983–1989 (Brauning 1992); data collection for the second began in 2004 and continued through 2008. The consistency in sampling unit and coverage between the 1st and 2nd Pennsylvania Breeding Bird Atlases provides an opportunity to examine patterns of species occupancy and spatial distribution across the span of approximately 20 years. Comparing range changes with various spatial datasets (e.g., land cover and habitat) may reveal or suggest causal relationships between landscape-scale factors and observed shifts in bird distributions.

Despite the considerable concern expressed in both the scientific and popular literature over declines in forest bird populations, the current situation is anything but clear-cut in Pennsylvania. Analyses of > 40 years of BBS data indicate that not all forest species are decreasing; indeed, many are increasing. Contrasting trends can be found even among closely related species, presumably because of subtle differences in their ecological requirements (e.g. hermit vs. wood thrush, cerulean vs. black-throated green warblers; Sauer et al. 2008). Many species show no significant trend.

Generally, populations of those forest birds associated with northern hardwoods tend to be stable or increasing within the state, while those found mostly in the more fragmented oak-hickory forests tend to be decreasing. We tested this tendency statistically by contrasting population trend directions within the state between birds of northern and southern affinities using the Fisher Exact Test, for the subset of forest birds considered to be species of concern in the state's Wildlife Action Plan (PAGC-PFBC 2004; see Table 2 for

Table 2. Population trends within Pennsylvania of forest birds designated as priority species in the state Wildlife Action Plan (PAGC-PFBC 2005) in relation to biogeographic affinities, based on BBS survey results from 1966–2007 (Sauer et al. 2008).

Species	Affinity[1]	Annual % change in PA	P
Red-shouldered hawk *Buteo lineatus*	S	–6.1	0.06
Whip-poor-will *Caprimulgus vociferus*	S	–5.7	0.24
Acadian flycatcher *Empidonax virescens*	S	–0.4	0.28
Cerulean warbler *Dendroica cerulea*	S	–2.9	0.03
Worm-eating warbler *Helmitheros vermivorus*	S	–2.4	0.09
Louisiana waterthrush *Seiurus motacilla*	S	0.1	0.93
Kentucky warbler *Oporornis formosus*	S	–3.2	0.05
Sharp-shinned hawk *Accipiter striatus*	N	8.4	0.14
Black-billed cuckoo *Coccyzus erythrophthalmus*	N	–2.6	0.01
Blue-headed vireo *Vireo solitarius*	N	4.3	<0.01
Winter wren *Troglodytes troglodytes*	N	3.8	0.09
Swainson's thrush *Catharus ustulatus*	N	1.1	0.55
Black-throated blue warbler *Dendroica caerulescens*	N	3.4	0.02
Black-throated green warbler *Dendroica virens*	N	2.0	0.03
Blackburnian warbler *Dendroica fusca*	N	1.4	0.22
Canada warbler *Wilsonia canadensis*	N	1.4	0.40
Broad-winged hawk *Buteo platypterus*	G	–0.2	0.92
Yellow-throated vireo *Vireo flavifrons*	G	0.3	0.61
Wood thrush *Hylocichla mustelina*	G	–2.3	<0.00
Scarlet tanager *Piranga olivaceus*	G	–0.5	0.24

[1]S = birds of mostly southern affinities; N = birds of mostly northern affinities; G = birds of general or broad distribution across eastern North America.

trends, species and affinities). A significantly larger proportion of southern birds (66%) are decreasing than northern species (11%) (Fisher Exact Test $P = 0.009$).

Of course, state-or region-wide trends can sometimes mask local trends. For example, the most recent trend estimates for the magnolia warbler (*Dendroica magnolia*) indicate a significant annual increase of 4.8% from 1966 to 2006 within Pennsylvania ($P < 0.001$; Sauer et al. 2008). However, populations just within the Ridge and Valley portion of the state have actually declined at 3% annually ($P = 0.008$, Sauer et al. 2008). In contrast, although cerulean warblers in Pennsylvania as a whole have declined by 2.8% annually in the same period (Sauer et al. 2008), that trend is primarily driven by losses in the increasingly fragmented southwestern corner, the stronghold for the species in the state (McWilliams and Brauning 2000). In recent years ceruleans have expanded northward and westward at least locally across the state (Sauer et al. 2008). These contrasts suggest that to be most effective, management actions should be developed that can address local conditions and problems, even if overall Pennsylvania conservation priorities are based on information about broader state or regional status.

CONSERVATION AND MANAGEMENT ISSUES

Many factors threaten the ecological integrity of Pennsylvania's forests, including non-sustainable timber harvesting, natural resource extraction, wind energy development, invasive forest pest species, acid deposition, and over-browsing by white-tailed deer. These factors ultimately can impact forest bird communities through habitat loss, degradation and fragmentation. While the direct effects of habitat loss on biodiversity are rather apparent and quantifiable, the effects of forest fragmentation are more indirect and not as easily discerned. Fragmentation threatens biodiversity by increasing extinction risk via isolation, reduction of genetic variability, modification of microhabitat features and increased risk of predation, nest parasitism, and establishment of invasive species (Brittingham and Temple 1986, Yahner et al. 1989, Opdam 1991, Saunders et al. 1991, Lockwood et al. 2007). Forest fragmentation effects on songbirds of eastern North America have been well documented (Parker et al. 2005)

The potential for large-scale habitat loss and fragmentation through widespread timber harvesting is of particular concern for avian communities inhabiting Pennsylvania forests. Due to maturation of largely even-aged stands, much of the 16.6 million acres of forest in the Commonwealth currently contains large, merchantable trees. The potential for widespread, unchecked timber harvest on a scale not unlike that of a century ago is magnified by the fact that almost 70% of Pennsylvania's forests are privately owned. This means that the collective stewardship decisions of many private landowners will have a significant influence on the future fate of forest habitats and their associated bird communities in Pennsylvania.

As energy demands increase, forest loss and fragmentation resulting from resource extraction activities (i.e., oil, gas, and coal) and wind energy development will likely also increase. Pennsylvania is one of the leading coal producing states due to an estimated bituminous coal reserve that totals 23 billion tons (US DOI Office of Surface Mining 2004). While most coal is now extracted by underground mining, surface mining methods are also utilized; in 2006, surface mines in Pennsylvania produced approximately 10.6 million tons of bituminous coal. Frequently, following extraction of timber and coal resources, structurally and botanically diverse forests are reclaimed to grasslands dominated by exotic grasses and forbs (Larkin et al. 2008). Further, these sites often persist in a state of arrested succession due to poor growing conditions, i.e., resulting from topsoil removal and surface compaction (Graves 1999).

Approximately, 34,000 acres were disturbed by surfaces mining in Pennsylvania between 2004 and 2007 (R. Agnew, PA Department of Environmental Protection). Moreover, since 1998 nearly 55,000 acres were reclaimed and approved for Stage II bond release (R. Agnew, PA Department of Environmental Protection). While mature forest dependant songbirds are negatively impacted by the conversion of forest habitat to reclaimed mineland, species that require earlier successional stages of forest regeneration appear to benefit. For example, golden-winged warbler (*Vermivora chrysoptera*), a shrubland nesting species of conservation concern, breeds on reclaimed surface mines in several Appalachian states (Patton et al. 2004, J. Larkin pers. obs.).

Increased energy demand is also creating a boom in oil and gas development in Pennsylvania. Pennsylvania's oil and gas fields are largely concentrated to the area west and north of the Allegheny Front (Pennsylvania Department of Environmental Protection 2007). This region of the state is also where some of the Commonwealth's most extensive forests are located. There are currently about 40,000 active gas wells in Pennsylvania (Swistock 2008). In 2007 alone, more than 4,000 oil and gas wells were drilled in Pennsylvania (www.dep.state.pa.us/dep/deputate/minres/oilgas/RIG07.htm). While the footprint of a single well site is generally small (< 6 acres) relative to a surface mine, the potential for cumulative negative impacts to forest biodiversity clearly is considerable. This is particularly true in forested areas where multiple well sites are constructed, where the extent of fragmentation that occurs from construction of well sites and their associated road and pipeline infrastructure can be tremendous (Swistock 2008). In areas of Warren and McKean counties, new well sites are often installed in grids at the maximum legal density of < 300 meters apart (S.H. Stoleson, pers. obs.). Nonetheless, the extent to which oil and gas development impacts avian communities in Pennsylvania's forests remains unknown. Due to recent discoveries of new gas reserves and advances in extraction technologies, the number of gas wells is expected to increase considerably over the next decade (Swistock 2008). Clearly, research that examines the effects of gas and oil development on Pennsylvania's wildlife should be a research priority.

Because of its potential to provide clean renewable energy, compared to the burning of fossil fuels, wind energy is the fastest growing energy sector in the United States (McLeish 2002, Reynolds 2006). According to the American Wind Energy Association, a total of 177 wind turbines have been installed across Pennsylvania (www.awea.org). These turbines are distributed among ten wind farms having from two to 43 turbines each. Additionally, there are 60 turbines under construction at two new wind farms (www.awea.org) and more wind turbines are planned for construction. Although wind power is a clean method of energy generation, the potential for avian mortalities via collisions with turbine blades has been recognized for decades (Schmidt et al. 2003). While mortalities resulting from birds (especially raptors) colliding with turbines is a conservation concern in some western states (Schmidt et al 2003), research and monitoring to date indicate that such mortalities may be much less common in eastern states. Bat mortality, however, has emerged as a major concern with regard to wind energy development in the mid-Appalachians. However, as with oil and gas development, the greatest threats to avian communities in Pennsylvania from wind energy development will be habitat loss and fragmentation of some of the state's last remaining large tracts of unbroken forests. For example, a 40-turbine wind farm located along the Allegheny Ridge in Cambria and Blair counties was placed on one of the few remaining forested ridges that connect the forests in northern Pennsylvania with those in southern portions of the state and West Virginia. In order to ensure that continued growth of the wind industry in Pennsylvania has minimal negative impacts on avian communities, monitoring protocols (including short-term mortality studies and long-term productivity and survivorship studies) should be developed that help track avian community response to disturbances associated with wind development.

Last but not least, overabundant white-tailed deer populations throughout portions of Pennsylvania also pose a threat to forest songbird communities. Ungulates, such as white-tailed deer (*Odocoileus virginianus*), serve many ecological roles that include influencing the rates of successional processes and the creation of spatial heterogeneity (Hobbs 1996). Ungulates have direct and indirect effects on a variety of fundamental ecosystem processes such as succession, nutrient cycling, fire regimes, and primary production (McNaughton 1992, Pastor et al. 2006, Hobbs 1996, Frank 1998). Effects of deer herbivory and trampling on plant species composition and structure have been well documented (Harper 1969, Pastor and Naiman 1992, Fleischner 1994, Augustine and McNaughton 1998, Dieni et al. 2000).

Forested areas with high white-tailed deer densities are often characterized by having minimal regeneration and a lack of diverse forest structure (Healy 1987, Tilghman 1989, Alverson and Waller 1997). Such modifications to forest structure can impact bird species through changes in food supply, loss of nest-sites, increased vulnerability to nest predation, or loss of roosting cover (Gill and Fuller 2007). Ultimately, the effects of over-browsing by white-tailed deer can result in the local extinction of animals and plant species and shifts in the species composition of a community (deCalesta 1994, Tilghman 1989, McCullough 1997, McShea and Rappole 1997). In Virginia, white-tailed deer browsing impacted the abundance and diversity of forest birds by reducing structural complexity (McShea and Rappole 2000).

In an enclosure experiment, species richness and abundance of mid-canopy nesting songbirds declined at moderate to high deer densities in northwestern Pennsylvania (> 7.9 deer/km^2; deCalesta 1994). A study in Massachusetts concluded that densities between 10–17 deer/km^2, deer prevented forest regeneration, with the result that oak stands were converted to open, park-like systems with poorly developed understory and midstory layers (Healy 1997). Anderson and Katz (1993) suggested that forests subjected to prolonged, high levels of browsing may require 70 years after alleviation of browsing pressure to recover a size class distribution of shade-tolerant, browse-sensitive tree species characteristic of eastern forests.

While the negative impacts of high deer densities on forest songbirds has been very well demonstrated (deCalesta 1994, McShea and Rappole 2000), deer may also play an important role in the maintenance of structurally heterogeneous forests that meet the habitat needs of a greater number of forest bird species. In fact, forests with low deer densities may be similar to those with high deer densities in that they fail to meet the structural requirements of a more diverse avian community. When deer herds are maintained below carrying capacity, herbivory may be beneficial to forested ecosystems (Starkey and Happe

1995). Herbivory by cervids increased plant species diversity in an old-growth forest, thereby increasing available niches for birds (Starkey and Happe 1995). It is important that future studies attempt to quantify the effects of deer herbivory on forest structure and regeneration relative to other system drivers (i.e., climate change, acid deposition, and invasive species), and to determine the range of deer densities beneficial for, or at least not detrimental to, Pennsylvania's forest bird communities.

FUTURE PROSPECTS FOR PENN'S WOODS AND ITS FOREST BIRDS

Conservation efforts must consider future as well as current issues affecting Pennsylvania's forests and their associated bird communities: these will include population growth and associated urban sprawl, and global climate change. As in much of the Northeast, Pennsylvania has experienced considerable urban sprawl in recent decades, and that pattern is projected to continue. Based on current patterns and rates of population expansion, Pennsylvania is predicted to lose 6,348 km^2, or 8.8%, of its forest lands to urban growth by 2050 (Nowak and Walton 2005). However, most of that growth is expected to radiate out from existing urban centers; the Allegheny High Plateau will probably remain rural and heavily forested, so its value as a refugium for forest bird populations will likely increase.

Current population levels and trends may be overwhelmed in the foreseeable future by large-scale environmental phenomena, especially global climate change. While there is disagreement as to the time frame and severity of climatic changes expected and their resulting effects on biodiversity, most experts agree that significant changes will occur in the next century in the distribution of species in temperate zones. Most climate change models predict a northward shift of forest types, such that little or no northern hardwoods will remain within Pennsylvania as they are replaced by oak-hickory and oak-pine over the next centuries (Hansen et al. 2001, McKenney et al. 2007).

The effects of such large-scale shifts in forest communities in Pennsylvania are likely to have concomitant effects on the state's breeding bird communities. Ornithologists have already detected northward shifts in the breeding distributions of migratory birds by about 2.35 km/yr (Hitch and Leberg 2007), as well as earlier arrival times and later departure times from breeding areas (Butler 2003, Jonzén et al. 2006). Various experts have predicted a decoupling of migration arrival times and the phenology of ripening fruits and prey insect emergences, with potentially very negative effects on bird survival and reproduction (Strode 2003, Both et al. 2006, but see Marra et al. 2005).

Matthews et al. (2004) predicted shifts in the potential ranges of birds based on current vegetation and environmental correlates of their current ranges, assuming shifts in those factors under a range of climate change scenarios. Ironically, some of the species of highest conservation concern within the state currently (those of southern and oak affinities) are predicted to increase in both range and abundance. In contrast, many of those currently doing very well within the Commonwealth may decline or disappear; these are primarily northern and montane species. For example, hermit thrushes are currently widespread in the northern and mountainous parts of the state with populations growing at approximately 3.2% annually (P < 0.01; McWilliams and Brauning 2000, Sauer et al. 2008). Yet the models by Matthews et al. (2004) suggest that the species will all but disappear from the state by the end of the 21st Century. Conversely, the Kentucky warbler now occurs primarily in remaining forests in the Southwest and Piedmont regions of the state, and, although it has spread northward locally in recent years, statewide populations have declined at 3.0% annually based on BBS surveys (McWilliams and Brauning 2000, Sauer et al 2008). Climate change models predict Kentucky warblers will spread across the entire state and increase in abundance (Matthews et al. 2004). These models, however, do not take into account the predicted loss and fragmentation of forests due to urban sprawl. Thus, the short-term and long-term prospects for individual species within Pennsylvania will often vary depending on the interplay of many factors. Clearly, forest bird conservation in Pennsylvania will present many challenges and opportunities for students and researchers, natural resource managers and agencies, and private businesses and landowners moving forward into the 21st Century.

Literature Cited

Abrams, M. D., and C. M. Ruffner. 1995. Physiographic analysis of witness-tree distribution (1765–1798) and present forest cover through north central Pennsylvania. Canadian Journal of Forestry Research 25:659–668.

Alverson, W. S. and D. M. Waller. 1997. Deer populations and the widespread failure of hemlock regeneration in northern forests. Pages 280–297 in McShea,W.J., H.B. Underwood, and J. H. Rappole (eds.). The science of overabundance. Smithsonian Institution Press, Washington, D.C., USA.

Anderson, R. C. and A.J. Katz. 1993. Recovery of browse-sensitive tree species following release from white-tailed deer *Odocoileus virginianus* Zimmerman browsing pressure. Biological Conservation 63:203–208.

Askins, R. A. 2000. Restoring North America's birds: Lessons from landscape ecology. Yale University Press, New Haven, Connecticut, USA.

Augustine, D. J., and S. J. McNaughton. 1998. Ungulate effects on the functional species composition of plant communities: herbivore selectivity and plant tolerance. Journal of Wildlife Management 62:1165–1183.

Blancher, P. J., K. V. Rosenberg, A. O. Panjabi, B. Altman, J. Bart, C. J. Beardmore, G. S. Butcher, D. Demarest, R. Dettmers, E. H. Dunn, W. Easton, W. C. Hunter, E. E. Iñigo-Elias, D. N. Pashley, C. J. Ralph, T. D. Rich, C. M. Rustay, J. M. Ruth, and T. C. Will. 2007. Guide to the Partners in Flight population estimates database. Version: North American Landbird Conservation Plan 2004. Partners in Flight Technical Series No 5.

Both, C., S. Bouwhuis, C. M. Lessells, and M. E. Visser. 2006. Climate change and population declines in a long-distance migratory bird. Nature 44:81–83.

Brauning, D. W. (ed.) 1992. Atlas of breeding birds in Pennsylvania. University of Pittsburgh Press, Pittsburgh, Pennsylvania, USA.

Brittingham, M. C., and S. A. Temple. 1983. Have cowbirds caused forest songbirds to decline? BioScience 33:31–35.

Butler, C. J. 2003. The disproportionate effect of global warming on the arrival dates of short-distance migratory birds in North America. Ibis 145:484–495

Bystrak, D. 1981. The North American Breeding Bird Survey. Studies in Avian Biology 6:34–41.

deCalesta, D. S. 1994. Effect of white-tailed deer on songbirds within managed forests in Pennsylvania. Journal of Wildlife Management 58:711–718.

Dieni, J. S., B. L. Smith, R. L. Rogers, and S. H. Anderson. 2000. Effects of ungulate browsing on aspen regeneration in northwestern Wyoming. Intermountain Journal of Science 6:49–55.

Fike, J. 1999. Terrestrial and palustrine plant communities of Pennsylvania. Bureau of Forestry, PA. Dept. of Conservation and Natural Resources, Harrisburg, PA; The Nature Conservancy, Middletown, PA; and Western Pennsylvania Conservancy, Pittsburgh, Pennsylvania, USA.

Fleischner, T. L. 1994. Ecological costs of livestock grazing in western North America. Conservation Biology 8:629–644.

Frank, D. A. 1998. Ungulate regulation of ecosystem processes in Yellowstone National Park: direct and feedback effects. Wildlife Society Bulletin 26:410–418.

Gill, R. M. A., and R. J. Fuller. 2007. The effects of deer browsing on woodland structure and songbirds in lowland Britain. Ibis 149:119–127.

Graves, D. 1999. Low mine soil compaction research. Pages 125–127 in Vories, K. C. and D. Throgmorton, eds., Enhancement of reforestation at surface coal mines: Technical interactive forum. U.S. Department of Interior, Office of Surface Mining, Alton, IL and Coal Research Center, Southern Illinois University, Carbondale, Illinois, USA.

Hagan, J. M., P. S. McKinley, A. L. Meehan, and S. L. Grove. 1997. Diversity and abundance of landbirds in a northeastern industrial forest. Journal of Wildlife Management 61:718–735.

Haney, J. C., and C. P. Schaadt. 1996. Functional roles of eastern old growth in promoting forest bird diversity. Pages 76–88 in M. B. Davis, ed. Eastern old-growth forests: Prospects for rediscovery and recovery. Island Press, Washington D.C., USA.

Hansen, A. J., R. P. Neilson, V. H. Dale, C. H. Flather, L. R. Iverson, D. J. Currie, S. Shafer, R. Cooke, and P. J. Bartlein. 2001. Global change in forests: Responses of species, communities, and biomes. BioScience 51:765–779.

Harper, J. L. 1969. The role of predation in vegetational diversity. Pages 46–62 in Diversity and stability in ecological systems. Brookhaven National Laboratory, Upton, New York, USA.

Healy, W. M. 1987. Influence of deer on the structure and composition of oak forests in central Massachusetts. Pages 249–266 in McShea,W. J., H. B. Underwood, and J. H. Rappole, eds. The science of overabundance. Smithsonian Institution Press, Washington, D.C., USA.

Hitch, A. T., and P. L. Leberg. 2007. Breeding distributions of North American bird species moving north as a result of climate change. Conservation Biology 21:534–539.

Hobbs, N. T. 1996. Modification of ecosystems by ungulates. Journal of Wildlife Management 60:695–713.

Holmes, R. T., and T. W. Sherry. 2001. Thirty-year bird population trends in an unfragmented temperate deciduous forest: importance of habitat change. Auk 118:589–609.

Hoover, J. P., and M. C. Brittingham. 1993. Regional variation in cowbird parasitism of Wood Thrushes. Wilson Bulletin 105:228–238.

Horsley, S. B., S. L. Stout, and D. S. deCalesta. 2003. White-tailed deer impact on the vegetation dynamics of a northern hardwood forest. Ecological Applications 13:98–118.

Hunt, P. D. 1998. Evidence from a landscape population model of the importance of early successional habitat to the American Redstart. Conservation Biology 12:1377–1389.

Jonzén, N, A. Lindén, T. Ergon, E. Knudsen, J. O. Vik, D. Rubolini, D. Piacentini, C. Brinch, F. Spina, L. Karlsson, M. Stervander, A. Andersson, J. Waldenström, A. Lehikoinen, E. Edvardsen, R. Solvang, N. C. Stenseth. 2006. Rapid advance of spring arrival dates in long-distance migratory birds. Science 312:1959–1961.

Keller, J. K., M. E. Richmond, and C. R. Smith. 2002. An explanation of patterns of breeding bird species richness and density following clearcutting in northeastern USA forests. Forest Ecology and Management 174:541–564.

Larkin, J. L., D. M. Maehr, J. J. Krupa, J. J. Cox, K. Alexy, D. W. Unger, and C. Barton. 2008. Small mammal response to vegetation and spoil conditions on a reclaimed surface mine in eastern Kentucky. Southeastern Naturalist, *in press.*

Lockwood, J. L., M. F. Hoopes, and M. P. Marchetti. 2007. Invasion ecology. Blackwell Publishing, Oxford, UK.

Lorimer, C. G. 2001. Historical and ecological roles of disturbance in eastern North American forests: 9,000 years of change. Wildlife Society Bulletin 29:425–439.

Marquis, D. A. 1975. The Allegheny hardwood forests of Pennsylvania. General Technical Report NE-15. U.S.D.A. Forest Service, Northeastern Forest Experiment Station. Upper Darby, Pennsylvania, USA.

Marra, P. P., C. M. Francis, R. S. Mulvihill and F. R. Moore. 2005. The influence of climate on the timing and rate of spring bird migration. Oecologia 142:307–315.

Matthews, S., R. O'Connor, L. R. Iverson, A. M. Prasad. 2004. Atlas of climate change effects in 150 bird species of the Eastern United States. General Technical Report NE-318. U.S.D.A. Forest Service, Northeastern Research Station. Newtown Square, Pennsylvania, USA.

McCullough, D. R. 1997. Irruptive behavior in ungulates. Pages 69–98 in McShea,W. J., H. B. Underwood, and J. H. Rappole, (eds.). The science of overabundance. Smithsonian Institution Press, Washington, D.C.

McKenny, D. W., J. H. Pedlar, K. Lawrence, K. Campbell, and M. F. Hutchinson. 2007. Potential impacts of climate change on the distribution of North American trees. BioScience 57:939–948.

McLeish, T. 2002. Wind power. Natural New England. 11:60–65.

McNaughton, S. J. 1992. The propogation of disturbance in savannas through food webs. Journal of Vegetation Science 3:301–314.

McShea, W. J. and J. H. Rappole. 1997. Herbivores and the ecology of forest understory birds. Pages 298–310 in McShea,W. J., H. B. Underwood, and J. H. Rappole, eds., The science of overabundance. Smithsonian Institution Press, Washington, D.C., USA.

McShea, W. J. and J. H. Rappole. 2000. Managing the abundance and diversity of breeding bird populations through manipulation of deer population. Conservation Biology 14:1161–1170.

McWilliams, G. M., and D. W. Brauning. 2000. The birds of Pennsylvania. Cornell University Press, Ithaca, New York, USA.

McWilliams, W. H., C. A. Alerich, D. A. Devlin, A. J. Lister, T. W. Lister, S. L. Sterner, and J. A. Westfall. 2004. Annual inventory report for Pennsylvania's forests: results from the first three years. U.S.D.A. Forest Service, Northeastern Research Station, Newtown Square, Pennsylvania, USA.

Naiman, R. J., C. A. Johnston, and J. C. Kelley. 1988. Alteration of North American streams by beaver. BioScience 38:753–762.

Nowak, D. J. and J. T. Walton. 2005. Projected urban growth (2000–2050) and its estimated impact on the US forest resource. Journal of Forestry 103:383–389.

Opdam, P. 1991. Metapopulation theory and habitat fragmentation: a review of holarctic breeding bird studies. Landscape Ecology 5:93–106.

PAGC-PFBC (Pennsylvania Game Commission and Pennsylvania Fish and Boat Commission). 2005. Pennsylvania comprehensive wildlife conservation strategy. Harrisburg, Pennsylvania, USA.

Parker, T. H., B. M. Stansberry, C. D. Becker, and P. S. Gipson. 2005. Edge and area effects on the occurrence of migrant forest songbirds. Conservation Biology 19:1157–1167

Pastor, J., Y. Cohen, and N. T. Hobbs. 2006. The role of large herbivores in ecosystem nutrient cycles. Pages 289–325 in K. Danell, R. Bergstroim, P. Duncan, and J. Pastor, eds. Large herbivore ecology, ecosystem dynamics, and conservation. Cambridge University Press, Cambridge, UK.

Pastor, J. and R. J. Naiman. 1992. Selective foraging and ecosystem processes in boreal forests. American Naturalist 139:690–705.

Patton L. L., S. Vorsek and J. L. Larkin. 2004. Golden-winged warbler on surface mines in Kentucky. Kentucky Warbler 80:73–75.

Pennsylvania Department of Environmental Protection. 2007. Oil and gas well drilling in Pennsylvania. Commonwealth of Pennsylvania, Department of Environmental Protection, Harrisburg, Pennsylvania, USA.

Porneluzi, P. A., and J. Faaborg. 1999. Season-long fecundity, survival, and viability of Ovenbirds in fragmented and unfragmented landscapes. Conservation Biology 13:1151–1161.

Reynolds, D. S. 2006. Monitoring the potential impact of a wind development site on bats in the Northeast. Journal of Wildlife Management 70:1219–1227.

Rich, T. D., C. J. Beardmore, H. Berlanga, P. J. Blancher, M. S. W. Bradstreet, G. S. Butcher, D. W. Demarest, E. H. Dunn, W. C. Hunter, E. E. Iñigo-Elias, J. A. Kennedy, A. M. Martell, A. O. Panjabi, D. N. Pashley, K. V. Rosenberg, C. M. Rustay, J. S. Wendt, and T. C. Will. 2004. Partners in Flight North American landbird conservation plan. Cornell Laboratory of Ornithology, Ithaca, NY.

Robbins, C. S, S. Droege, and J. R. Sauer. 1989. Monitoring bird populations with Breeding Bird Survey and atlas data. Annales Zoologici Fennici 26:297–304.

Robinson, S. K., F. R. Thompson III, T. M. Donovan, D. R. Whitehead, and J. Faaborg. 1995. Regional forest fragmentation and the nesting success of migratory birds. Science 267:1987–1990.

Rodewald, A. D., and M. D. Abrams. 2002. Floristics and avian community structure: implications for regional changes in eastern forest composition. Forest Science 48:267–272.

4

7

Rosenberg, K.V., 2004. Partners in Flight continental priorities and objectives defined at the state and bird conservation region levels: Pennsylvania. Cornell Laboratory of Ornithology, Ithaca, New York, USA.

Sauer, J. R., J. E. Hines, and J. Fallon. 2008. The North American Breeding Bird Survey, Results and Analysis 1966–2007. Version 5.15.2008. USGS Patuxent Wildlife Research Center, Laurel, MD.

Saunders, D. A., R. J. Hobbs, and C. R. Margules. 1991. Biological consequences of ecosystem fragmentation: a review. Conservation Biology 5:18–32.

Schmidt, E. A., A. J. Paggio, and C. E. Block. 2003. National Wind Technology Center site environmental assessment: bird and bat use and fatalities. Final Report NREL/SR-500-32981. National Renewable Energy Laboratory, Golden, Colorado, USA.

Starkey, E.E. and P.J. Happe. 1995. Ecological relationships between cervid herbivory and understory vegetation in old-growth Sitka Spruce-Western Hemlock forests in Olympic National Park: final report. U.S. National Park Service, Pacific Northwest Region.

Strode, P. K. 2003. Implications of climate change for North American wood warblers (Parulidae). Global Change Biology 9:1137–1144.

Swistock, B. 2008. Gas well drilling and your private water supply. Pennsylvania State University, College of Agriculture, Cooperative Extension. State College, Pennsylvania, USA.

Tilghman, N. G. 1989. Impacts of white-tailed deer on forest regeneration in northwestern Pennsylvania. Journal of Wildlife Management 53:524–532.

USDA 2004. The state of the forest: a snapshot of Pennsylvania's updated forest inventory 2004. United States Forest Service, Northeastern Area State and Private Forestry. NA-FR-03-04.

United State Department of Interior, Office of Surface Mining. 2004. Annual evaluation report for the regulatory and abandoned mine land reclamation programs. Office of Surface Mining Reclamation and Enforcement, Washington, D.C, USA.

Whitney, G. G. 1990. The history and status of the hemlock-hardwood forests of the Allegheny Plateau. The Journal of Ecology 78:443–458.

Widmann, R. H. 1995. Forest resources of Pennsylvania. Resource Bulletin NE-131. U.S. Forest Service, Northeastern Forest Experiment Station. Radnor, Pennsylvania, USA.

Wilcove, D. S. 1985. Nest predation in forest tracts and the decline of migratory songbirds. Ecology 66:1211–1214.

Yahner, J., T.E. Morrell, S.J. Rachael. 1989. Effects of edge contrast on depredation of artificial avian nests. Journal of Wildlife Management 53: 1135–1138.

Avian Ecology and Conservation: A Pennsylvania Focus with National Implications. Edited by S. K. Majumdar, T. L. Master, M. C. Brittingham, R. M. Ross, R. S. Mulvihill and J. E. Huffman. © 2010. The Pennsylvania Academy of Science.

Chapter 2

Avian-Mediated Seed Dispersal: An Overview and Synthesis with an Emphasis on Temperate Forests of Central and Eastern U.S.

Michael A. Steele[1], Nathanael Lichti[2], and Robert K. Swihart[2]
[1]Department of Biology, Wilkes University, Wilkes-Barre PA 18766
[2]Department of Forestry and Natural Resources, Purdue University, West Lafayette, IN 47907-2033
msteele@wilkes.edu

INTRODUCTION

Animal-mediated seed dispersal is a critical component of the life history of many plants (van der Pilj 1972) and has become a focal subject in ecology due to its far-reaching implications for plant demography, genetics, community ecology, and conservation (Howe 1989, Herrera et al. 1994, Schupp and Fuentes 1995, Terborgh et al. 2008). Yet, despite tremendous research in this area over the past two decades (see Dennis et al. 2007), the study of seed dispersal still lacks a succinct and unifying theoretical framework. As Schupp (2007) aptly noted, any previous semblance of such a framework was lost with the realization that most seed dispersal systems represent highly diffuse mutualisms that are non-equilibrial in nature.

Regardless of the direction of any theoretical developments, birds will always lie near the center of any discussion of seed dispersal, as avian seed dispersers contribute disproportionately to the process of seed deposition and seedling establishment in many systems. In this review, we summarize the importance of avian dispersal of seed and emphasize the contributions that studies of seed dispersal by birds have made in addressing key theoretical questions. We focus primarily on examples and studies from temperate forests, especially those in the eastern and central United States. Our specific objectives are to: (1) review the primary mechanisms by which birds disperse seeds and impact plant reproduction and demography; (2) highlight the importance of avian-mediated dispersal with regard to both current questions and new directions in the study of seed dispersal; (3) briefly evaluate the relative importance and relevance of seed dispersal by birds to central questions in conservation biology; and (4) provide a more detailed account of one dispersal system in eastern deciduous forests (the Blue Jay [*Cyanocitta cristata*]-*Quercus* system), which illustrates the complexity and potential importance of these interactions.

MECHANISMS OF SEED DISPERSAL BY BIRDS

Dispersal of seeds away from parent plants is critical because it allows escape from density-dependent predation, competition, and/or inbreeding close to the parent (Janzen 1970, Connell 1971). To be successful, dispersal must also result in the movement of seeds to sites that are suitable for germination, establishment, and recruitment (Schupp 1995, Schupp and Fuentes 1995, Terborgh et al. 2002); and, even after recruitment dispersal continues to influence plant demography, and genetics (Howe 1989). Plants disperse via a limited number of mechanisms: wind (anemochory), water, (hydrochory), gravity (barochory), self dispersal by creeping or by means of ballistic structures (autochory) and movement by animals (zoochory; van der Pijl 1972). Zoochory is the most common strategy among flowering plants and can be subdivided into several more specific categories. With regard to avian dispersal, the two most common subcategories include the passive movement of seeds within the gut of frugivorous animals (endozoochory) and the deliberate transport of seeds to new locations by food-caching granivores (synzoochory).

Zoochory results from the activity of just a few major groups of animals, primarily vertebrates and ants. In many ecosystems, birds appear to be the most important dispersal agents in terms of their ecological prevalence, their taxonomic dominance among potential dispersal agents, and the taxonomic dominance of plants on which they feed (Snow 1981, Jordano 2000, Stiles 2000). Birds are estimated to account for dispersal of 30–40 % of woody species in temperate zones and 90% or more in many tropical forests (Herrera 2002, Terborgh et al. 2002). It should be noted, however, that their dominance as dispersal agents may have been somewhat exaggerated by historical biases in research interests. Birds and the plants on which they feed also tend to be conspicuous, so birds have received more attention than other potential dispersal agents in the scientific literature. The influence of birds on herbaceous plants is less well established.

Regardless of the degree to which scientific attention has neglected other potential seed dispersers, birds unquestionably play a major role in seed dispersal. Worldwide, an estimated 17 families of birds (16%) can be considered strictly frugivorous, whereas 21 families (19%) exhibit a diet that is comprised predominately of fruit, and another 23 families (21%) exhibit mixed diets in which fruits comprise about half the diet (Snow 1981, Jordano 2000). Many others are primarily granivorous, often acting as seed predators but frequently moving or storing seeds. These factors, coupled with the high energy demands and overall vagility of birds, make them ideal agents of seed dispersal.

To further estimate the importance of avian-mediated dispersal in the Eastern U.S, we systematically reviewed the Birds of North America accounts (Cornell Ornithological Laboratory) of all breeding birds in Pennsylvania, summarized the evidence for dispersal by each species, and ranked each species from 1–5 with respect to their importance as seed dispersers (1 = highest). We estimated that 43.7% (83) of all species, representing 57.1% (24) of bird families found in the state, contribute to seed dispersal at some level. Among these 83 species, 39 (representing 15 families, 11 of which are passerines) were ranked 1 in their importance as dispersal agents.

Although frugivory and seed dispersal by birds are common in temperate North American forests (Willson 1986), neither plants nor birds seem to show the close association that would support a case for strong mutualism. Indeed several studies have concluded that the relationship between the seed-dispersing birds and plants is considered rather diffuse

(Wheelwright and Orians 1982, Herrera 1984a, b, Malmborg and Willson, 1988). For instance, a three-year study on interactions between 11 species of frugivorous birds and eight bird-dispersed plants showed no consistent correlations between fruit/seed size and gape size, body size or diversity of frugivores (Malmborg and Willson 1988).

Birds disperse seeds as a side effect of their foraging activities. Consequently, the mechanisms of seed dispersal and the strategies used by plants to obtain dispersal services depend largely on the dietary tendencies of the birds involved. Avian seed dispersers can be broadly categorized as frugivores, which can disperse seeds through passive endozoochory and by dropping seeds (possibly with pieces of fruit still attached), or as granivores. The latter act mainly as seed predators but can occasionally disperse seeds that pass through the digestive tract intact, or, more commonly, through synzoochory. The diffuse nature of the plant-disperser mutualism is further emphasized by the fact that many (probably most) bird species are neither strict frugivores nor granivores, but change dietary strategies depending on the season and the plant species on which they are feeding. Hence it is often difficult to categorize avian species by their impact on plant dispersal; nevertheless, some patterns have been identified. Among the 11 species studied by Malmborg and Willson (1988), for example, two distinct foraging guilds were recognized: subcanopy and understory foragers. These two guilds were distinguished by differences in body size, the frequency of regurgitation of seeds, the frequency with which they foraged on clumped fruits, and the speed at which they moved away from seed/fruit sources.

In both frugivory and granivory, plants attract potential dispersers with an offering of food—either fleshy fruit or the endosperm or cotyledon of the seeds themselves. Frugivorous birds are attracted to plants based on conspicuousness of potential food items (Schmidt et al. 2004), and dietary preferences are influenced by sugar, lipid, protein, and anthocyanin content of fruits (Lepczyk et al. 2000, Bosque and Calchi 2003, Schaefer et al. 2003, 2008, Tsujita et al. 2008). Granivorous birds select seeds on the basis of size and chemical composition (Ramos 1996, Valera et al. 2005, Carillo et al. 2007). For both frugivores and granivores, selection varies within the context of other available food items and temporal dynamics of physiological requirements (Lepczyk et al. 2000, Moore and Swihart 2006).

The overall efficacy of dispersal by birds is influenced by several additional factors. The number of seeds taken per foraging bout, the preferences of the bird species for a particular fruit/seed type given the types available at a given locality, and the relative abundance of the birds in relation to fruit abundance all affect the rate at which seeds leave the parent plant. The latter measures depend on both the population density of birds and the abundance of different fruit/seed types. All of these factors can be influenced by a range of other variables, thus illustrating the difficulty in assessing the significance of a single dispersal agent (Malmborg and Willson 1988). The rate of seed uptake also is influenced by the birds' general habitat preferences. For instance, some frugivorous birds forage selectively in tree fall gaps (9 of 11 species; Malmborg and Willson 1988), and fruit-removal by birds is higher in gaps than in interior forests (Thompson and Willson 1979). Hence bird-dispersed plants found in tree fall gaps may have a dispersal advantage, at least in terms of the number of seeds harvested (Malmborg and Willson 1988). However, the outcome of such higher removal rates is subsequently dependent on patterns of seed deposition. Murray (1988), for example, showed that shade-intolerant shrubs in a cloud forest in

Costa Rica was dispersal limited because their seeds were not dispersed to light gaps by their primary avian dispersal agents.

Once a seed has been harvested from the parent plant (either by itself or as part of a fruit), the bird can affect it in at least two ways: (1) the bird transports the seed and deposits it in an (often non-random) location away from the parent plant, and (2) the bird may alter the seed's physical state in some way (e.g. scarification of the seed coat). Dispersal often involves the consumption of the seed and fruit pulp and subsequent regurgitation or defecation of seeds at some other location. Because of the generally rapid departure of frugivorous birds from foraging sites (Hoppes 1985 cited by Malmborg and Willson 1988), the probability of seed movement and dispersal is high. For the 11 species of dispersers observed by Malmborg and Willson (1988), the probability of leaving the feeding site immediately following removal of a fruit/seed averaged 81% (46–100% per species) compared with 32% following insect-feeding bouts by the same species. Seed-caching granivores deliberately transport seeds to new locations, where they are stored. Often, these new locations lie some distance from the parent plant, since the same factors that increase mortality under the parent (e.g., attraction of seed predators) also increase the risk of cache pilferage.

Other factors that affect deposition patterns include landscape structure and habitat features, which influence the bird's movement and selection of perching, roosting, or caching locations. Such factors can direct the flow of seeds non-randomly across a landscape (Hutchinson and Vankat 1998, Gomez 2003, Levey et al. 2005, see further details below). Even after seeds are deposited or stored intact, their fates may be further altered by movement of other dispersal agents such as ants or rodents, a process known as secondary dispersal. Although documented in a few systems (Vander Wall and Longland 2005), the importance of secondary movement of seeds following deposition or hoarding by birds has received little attention.

In addition to determining the seed's initial deposition site, birds may also alter the seed physically or chemically. This is most obvious when the endosperm and/or cotyledon is consumed, in which case the seed is usually destroyed. However, the potential for birds to influence germination and establishment of seeds by partial consumption of fruits has not been fully explored. The Blue Jay, Common Grackle (*Quiscalus quiscula*, Steele et al. 1993), and Tufted Titmouse (*Parus bicolor*, N. Lichti, personal observation), for example, consume the basal portion of acorns of red oak species in response to chemical gradients in the cotyledon. The birds then discard the apical half of the nut, containing the embryo, which under some conditions can successfully germinate and establish (Steele et al. 1993).

When birds ingest the entire seed, the outcome is often an increase in the frequency and rate of seed germination as a result of either (1) chemical or mechanical scarification of the seed coat, (2) the removal of pulp that can interfere with germination, or (3) the deposition of fecal matter near the seed, which can aid in both germination and seedling establishment (Traveset et al 2001, Traveset and Verdu 2002, Traveset et al. 2007). Although several groups of vertebrate frugivores (primarily bats, birds, non-volant mammals, and reptiles) are known to disperse seeds endozoochorously, birds appear to have the greatest effect on germination. A recent meta-analysis of 351 experiments (from 83 studies) on the effects of gut passage on germination, of which >50% were from studies on birds, revealed that birds had the most significant effect (Traveset and Verdu 2002). For all frugivore groups combined there was a much higher effect of gut passage on tree seeds than seeds of shrubs or herbs.

CONTRIBUTIONS OF AVIAN STUDIES TO THEORETICAL DEVELOPMENTS IN SEED DISPERSAL

Although the last two decades has seen a steady flow of research on seed dispersal, difficulties in answering several central questions has led to rather slow development on the theoretical front (Wang and Smith 2002). With exception of higher density dependent mortality near parental seed sources (Wills et al. 1997, Harms et al. 2000, Howe and Miriti 2000, Wang and Smith 2002), most of the predictions following from the original Janzen-Connell model are still untested. We still do not have a strong grasp of how dispersal contributes to plant demography (Godinez-Alvarez and Jordano 2007), the relative significance of long-distance dispersal events (Clark et al. 1998a, Wang and Smith 2002), or the effect that dispersal has on recruitment limitation (Clark et al. 1998b, Hubbell et al. 1999). Increasingly, though, numerous studies, many of them involving avian-dispersal systems, are directed at these critical questions. The following highlights these contributions.

Effects of Seed Dispersal on Plant Recruitment and Demography

Although it is assumed that seed dispersal impacts plant demography, few studies have linked various life stages between dispersal and recruitment (Wang and Smith 2000). Regardless, recruitment limitation is considered a common phenomenon for many plants in both natural and human-impacted systems (Muller-Landau et al. 2002). Yet few studies have followed seeds through dispersal and subsequent stages of recruitment to determine how various factors influence this process (i.e., dispersal, germination, seedling establishment and sapling growth; but see Herrera et al. 1994, Clark et al. 1998a, Wenny 2000). Studies in which a cohort of seeds is followed through the entire seed dispersal cycle are rare (Wenny 2000) because of the many factors (e.g., seed predation, endaphic factors, seedling competition, herbivory) that influence the stages between dispersal, germination, establishment and recruitment (Schupp and Fuentes 1995, Hubbell et al. 1999, Nathan and Muller-Landau 2000).

Rey and Alacantara (2000) followed patterns of recruitment through sapling establishment of an avian-dispersed shrub and found that sites best suited for germination of seeds were unfavorable for developing seedlings. This resulted in a very different spatial pattern of dispersed seeds from that of recruited saplings. In this system, 35% of the seeds were dispersed, 27% of these developed into seedlings, but only 9% of the seedlings survived to the sapling stage. Among the saplings, 63% survived for two years. Identifying such bottlenecks in the cycle may be what is needed to link dispersal with demography. In other systems seedling establishment is the limiting factor (Clark et al 1998a). Many birds, especially those that disperse endozoochorous seeds, may deposit seeds in sites unsuitable for germination or establishment, and thus uncouple the various recruitment stages (Jordano and Herrera 1995, Schupp 1995, Schupp and Fuentes 1995). Other bird species may deposit seeds in target sites that are highly suitable for germination and establishment, a process known as directed dispersal (Wenny and Levey 1998). Clearly, more studies are needed to link avian movement of seeds to plant recruitment and demography, especially in temperate regions where such studies are under-represented.

Long Distance Dispersal

An increasing number of studies now conclude that the link between dispersal and establishment is disproportionate due to rare, long-distance dispersal events (Nathan 2006). Such long distance dispersal events can be viewed in two ways: (1) dispersal events that occur on the leading edge of a population and contribute to population expansion or migration (Clark 1998, Clark et al. 1998b), or (2) dispersal events that occur in the typical tail of a dispersal kernel as predicted by Janzen and Connell. In either case, such events are rarely documented by direct empirical studies that involve following seed fates. However, retrospective genetic studies that match seeds or seedlings with parental sources have been able to verify the importance of long-distance events (see review by Steele et al. 2007). Modeling approaches also have been successful in documenting the link between avian frugivore behavior and long-distance dispersal (Clark 1998, Powell and Zimmermann 2004, Levey et al. 2005). Such an approach, for example, was critical for resolving the long-standing Reid's Paradox, which characterizes the inconsistency between estimates of dispersal rates of many plant species and the observed rates of northward migration of these species at the close of the Pleistocene (see Clark 1998, Clark et al. 1998b). This apparent disagreement between theory and observation was rectified with models that either assume a higher frequency of rare dispersal events in the tail of the dispersal kernel (Clark 1998), or a corrective factor based on the density and spread of scatter hoards (Powell and Zimmermann 2004). This latter approach, for example, was used to specifically verify the movement of oaks (*Quercus*) by Blue Jays as well as stone pines (genus *Pinus* subsection *cembrae*) by Eurasian Nutcrackers (*Nucifraga caryocatactes*).

Recently, Levey et al. (2008) showed that the small-scale movements of Eastern Bluebirds (*Sialia sialis*) could be modeled to predict movement at greater spatial scales and to estimate the frequency of dispersal over longer distances. They found that patches with corridors or extensions encourage edge-following behavior across landscapes and in the process facilitated long-distance dispersal. Although the shape of dispersal kernels varied between homogeneous and heterogeneous landscapes, long-distance dispersal events (those >150 m) occurred >50% of the time (Levey et al. 2008).

Context and Neighborhood Effects

Seed removal by birds is heavily influenced by the spatio-temporal variation in the availability of fruits (Carlo 2005, Carlo and Morales 2008) and the composition of fruit neighborhoods (Manasse and Howe 1983, Sargent 1990, Carlo 2005). Likewise, deposition of fruits is often directed towards certain habitats or fruiting sites (Wenny and Levey 1998, Jordano and Schupp 2000, Schupp 2007) which also can vary over space and time (Kwit et al. 2004, Carlo et al. 2007). Together these processes in turn can result in "local hotspots of initial recruitment" (Hampe et al. 2008) which clarifies the necessity for understanding these complex interactions.

In one of the first studies to definitively demonstrate context-dependent dispersal, Carlo (2005) showed experimentally how the presence of an alternative fruit source influenced dispersal of a single plant species. In mixed neighborhoods, as compared with monospecific stands, there was no difference in the number of seeds dispersed, but there was a greater number of dispersal (deposition) events. Carlo (2005) concluded that these findings were most likely due to the increase in frugivore numbers as well as the increase in agonistic interactions in these mixed stands. (Carlo 2005). More recently, Carlo and Morales (2008) showed that as fruiting plants became more aggregated, the variability in removal rates increased and dispersal distances decreased. They found that the spatial pattern of fruiting interacted with bird foraging patterns both empirically and in spatially explicit simulations. Thus it appears that facilitation and competition between fruiting species can greatly influence dispersal patterns and that studies on single species may often be misleading.

CONSERVATION ISSUES AND SEED DISPERSAL BY BIRDS

Dispersal of Invasive Species

Avian dispersal agents can contribute significantly to the spread of invasive species, yet the finer details of this relationship are largely unexplored (see White and Stiles 1992, Hutchinson and Vankat 1998, Renne and Gauthreaux 2000, Renne et al. 2002, Bartuszevige and Gorchov 2006 for examples from North America). Dispersal of invasive plants by birds appears to follow one of three patterns. Established mutualisms can be expanded when a novel food source becomes available and incorporated into the diet of a native bird species, when a non-native bird species is reunited with an invasive species from its native range, or when a completely new mutualism results between an invasive plant and native bird species (Richardson et al. 2000).

White and Stiles (1992) compared the role of birds in dispersal of native vs. non-native species in central New Jersey. They observed that 33% of the 45 bird-dispersed species were non-native plants. Between 0.4–14% of the fruit biomass dispersed by birds (as determined by seed traps and fecal droppings) was from introduced species. Relative use of fruit and seeds of non-native species increased through the fall and peaked at approximately 50% of the fruit biomass in winter. White and Stiles (1992) suggested that this more intensive use of non-native species is a relatively recent phenomenon in the eastern U.S. Thus, while it often is assumed that considerable evolutionary time is necessary for the development of a strong interdependence between native fauna and non-native plants, there does appear to be significant potential for rapid ecological fitting between non-native plants and dispersal agents (White and Stiles 1992, Richardson et al. 2000).

The Chinese tallow tree (*Sapium sebiferum*), a common invasive species of the southeastern coastal plain of the U. S., is consumed and potentially dispersed by at least 14 species of birds, three of which (Northern Flicker [*Colaptes auratus*], American Robin [*Turdos migratorius*], and Boat-tailed Grackle [*Quiscalus major*]) appear to have the greatest potential for dispersing this species (Renne and Gauthreaux 2000). Avian seed consumers were collectively responsible for removing 40% of the seed crop in a single fruiting season which led Renne and Gauthreaux (2000) to conclude that the high lipid and protein levels of tallow seeds may give it a dispersal advantage over the seeds of many native species that fruit at the same time as the tallow.

Similar studies on the invasions of an invasive shrub (*Lonicera maackii*) show that this common ornamental is dispersed (by defecation) by five avian species (Hermit Thrush (*Catharus guttatus*), American Robin, Northern Mockingbird (*Mimus polyglottis*), European Starling (*Sturnus vulgaris*) and Cedar Waxwing (*Bombycilla cedrorum*) during winter months in eastern deciduous forests (Bartuszevige and Gorchov 2006). Dispersal of this invasive shrub was influenced by gut retention time and viability following defecation, both of which were highest for American Robins.

Gosper et al. (2005) advocate a functional approach to evaluate how avian traits (e.g., fruit handling techniques, gut-passage, social behavior, and movement patterns), fruit and seed traits (e.g., morphology, nutritional quality and phenology), and landscape features (fruit neighborhoods, habitat loss, fragmentation) all interact to influence dispersal of invasive species by birds. This review (Gosper et al. 2005) clearly reinforces the need to understand the link between seed characteristics, disperser, and plant demography, especially when evaluating the impact of avian fauna on non-native species. Gosper et al. (2005) further cite four approaches for reducing the probability of non-native plant invasion by means of manipulating seed dispersal by birds: (1) reducing fruit and seed production, (2) artificially directing dispersal (see also Wenny and Levey 1998) away from sites suitable for establishment and recruitment and towards sites where recruitment can be managed (e.g., manipulating perches to reduce/increase seed deposition), (3) identifying core and satellite sources of invasive species and manipulating access by dispersal agents (e.g., with dispersal barriers), and (4) providing alternative seed and fruit sources for dispersers.

Human Disturbance And Seed Dispersal

Animal-mediated seed dispersal, especially that involving mammals and birds, is often the mode of dispersal most susceptible to human disturbance, but is also the mode that frequently offers the fastest opportunity for disturbance recovery. In the tropics, the process of seed dispersal is greatly disrupted by poaching of frugivores for meat. Terborgh et al. (2008), for example, found that in tropical forests of South America where large birds and mammals were removed due to hunting, tree species composition shifted to species that depended on abiotic modes of dispersal or those involving small vertebrates (see also Pizo 2007, Wright 2007).

In an old-regrowth forest matrix in Pennsylvania and Delaware, the species diversity of understory flora declined in disturbed successional forests with distance from old-growth stands, and was shown to be limited by opportunity for dispersal rather than the suitability of establishment. And, among different modes of seed dispersal, those involving ingestion of seeds contributed to the fastest migration of understory species (Matlack 1994).

Landscape Structure and Seed Dispersal

Most studies on seed dispersal have been conducted on smaller spatial scales (Cain et al. 2000) and thus fail to consider the influence of landscape structure on the process (but see Gomez 2003, Tewksbury et al. 2002, McEuen and Curran 2004, Levey et al. 2005). It is well known that forest fragmentation and habitat loss alter the composition of avian communities (Acevedo and Restrepo 2008), avian movement (Castellon and Sieving 2005), and even patterns of fruit consumption by birds (Restrepo et al. 1999, Galetti et al. 2003). However, the effects of landscape features on seed deposition and dispersal have received limited attention.

Gomez (2003) provided strong evidence that landscape complexity can directly determine the shape of a seed shadow. Studying dispersal of acorns of holm oak (*Quercus ilex*) by European Jays (*Garrulus glandarius*), in a patchy environment in Spain, he showed that the jay's preference to cache under pines resulted in a distinctly bimodal dispersal shadow. The first mode resulted from dispersal within the source oak stand and reflected a classic dispersal kernel; the number of caches declined with increasing distance. The second mode (~200m), larger and more normally distributed than the first, corresponded to nearby pine-dominated stands where the risk of cache pilferage was reduced.

Landscape corridors and forest edges also influence movement of seeds, as observed by Basrtuszevige and Gorchov (2006) and demonstrated experimentally by Tewksbury et al. (2002) for a bird-dispersed holly. Most recently, Levey et al. (2005), directly tested the effects of landscape structure on avian-mediated dispersal. They used experimentally modified landscapes to test two alternative hypotheses regarding the effects of landscape corridors on dispersal (dispersal connectivity vs. drift fence hypotheses) of wax myrtle (*Myrica cerifera*) by Eastern Bluebirds. They parameterized a simulation model based on small-scale movements of the birds and then modeled the bird movement in their experimentally fragmented landscape. They tested the effects of three experimental habitat patches: square patches connected by corridors, rectangular patches, and square patches containing non-connecting corridors (wings). The simulation model successfully predicted observed patterns of seed rain (resulting from bird defecation) in habitats connected by corridors, thus supporting the corridor hypothesis. Levey et al. (2005) concluded that the corridor effect they observed was due to the edge-following behavior of the birds rather than any specific attributes of the corridor (e.g., composition, width).

Finally it is noteworthy that fragmented landscapes may favor dispersal of invasive plants. Edge habitats are often preferred by foraging birds (Malmborg and Willson 1988, Galetti et al. 2003) and often sustain the highest deposition of invasive species (With 2002, Gosper et al. 2005)

AVIAN-MEDIATED DISPERSAL OF *QUERCUS*

The subset of avian dispersal agents that disperse nuts, seeds, and fruit by means of scatter hoarding is relatively small in number. Included here are the corvids, especially the Jays, and a few other granivorous birds. However, while scatter-hoarding birds may be under-represented taxonomically, compared to those species that disperse seeds by other means, a few avian scatter hoarders may contribute disproportionately to plant dispersal in some systems. Nowhere perhaps is this more evident than for the dispersal of oaks by Jays.

The oaks (*Quercus*), represented by >500 species worldwide, are distributed throughout temperate (and even subtropical and some tropical) regions of the world. In the U.S., for example, oaks occur in 75% of the forest cover and are either dominant or co-dominant in many forests of the central, southeastern and eastern U.S (McWilliams et al. 2002). As for many angiosperms, dispersal away from parent trees is a critical stage in the life history of most oak species. And for the oaks this process is dependent primarily on the activity of scatter-hoarding rodents and birds (especially Jays). Rodents disperse acorns usually <150 m, often within forest patches (Steele and Smallwood 2002, Moore et al. 2007), whereas Jays move acorns ≥1 km (Darley-Hill and Johnson 1981, Johnson and Webb 1989, Kollman and Schill 1996), usually along or between the edges of forest stands (Johnson and Webb 1989, Kollman and Schill 1996, Monsandl and Kleinert 1998, and Gomez 2003). Jays are common throughout most oak forests and regularly consume, cache and, as a consequence, disperse acorns (the fruit of oak). Examples include the Scrub Jays (*Aphelocoma* spp., Degrange et al. 1989, Hubbard and McPherson 1997), the European Jay (Kollman and Schill 1996, Monsandl and Kleinert 1998, Pons and Pausas 2007a), and a few other species of corvids (*Corvus* spp. and *Pica pica*, Waite 1985). But perhaps the most well studied dispersal agent of oaks is the Blue Jay (Darley-Hill and Johnson 1981, Johnson and Webb 1989, Moore and Swihart 2006), common throughout the central and eastern half of North America. Although the activity and impact of Jays on oak dispersal is likely strong, much of the information to date is anecdotal and based on inferences from mostly descriptive investigations (Steele and Smallwood 2002, but see recent work by Gomez 2003, Pons and Pausas 2007a, b on European Jays and Moore and Swihart 2006 on Blue Jays).

Blue Jays harvest and cache thousands of acorns each season, sometimes removing more than half the acorn crops prior to seed fall (Darley-Hill and Johnson 1981), especially from smaller seeded oaks such as willow (*Q. phellos*) and pin oaks (*Q. palustris*). As an example, we continuously observed a flock of Blue Jays (7–12 birds) harvesting acorns from two mature pin oaks (M. A. Steele, Wilkes University, unpublished data). Over the course of three days, the birds made 1270 and 1959 visits to the two trees and dispersed an estimated 3175 and 4897 acorns, respectively (Fig 1). In most cases the Jays appeared to be carrying these acorns over 0.5 km. Similarly, individual Scrub Jays (DeGange et al. 1989) and European Jays (Bossema 1979) have been observed to cache 4000 and 8000 acorns per season, respectively.

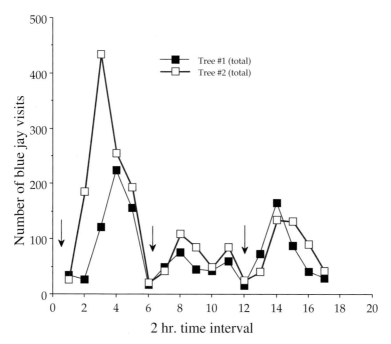

Figure 1: Number of visits by blue jays observed at two adjacent pin oak trees (Quercus palustris) over a three-day period in Northeastern Pennsylvania (October 1993). Arrows indicate the beginning of each day of observations. Although they occasionally consumed acorns, these birds (approximately 7-12 individuals) were harvesting and dispersing the acorns > 0.5 km from the site. Based on these and other observations, we estimate the birds were dispersing 2-3 pin oak acorns per visit. Results from unpublished data, M. A. Steele, Wilkes University.

The long distances that Jays have been observed to disperse acorns, along with their preferences for caching in opened, disturbed, or successional sites (Johnson and Webb 1989, see below), have distinguished them as the primary contributor to the rapid post-glacial migration of fagaceous species (e.g, *Quercus*) at the end of the late Quartenary in North America (Davis 1976, Delcourt and Delcourt 1987) and Europe (Bossema 1979, Le Corre et al. 1997, Monsandl and Kleinert 1998). Johnson et al. (1997) further predict that Jays will play a significant role in the regeneration of oaks in the face of growing forest fragmentation, habitat loss and climate change.

In addition to the sheer numbers of acorns and the distance they are moved by Jays, it appears that cache site selection by Jays in particular may enhance germination and estab-lishment, and thus even constitute a form of directed dispersal by Jays (Steele and Small-wood 2002). Blue Jays, like other Jays, tend to cache acorns in successional habitats, open grasslands and conifer stands (Steele and Smallwood 2002), where the probability of estab-lishment is high and the conditions for seedling growth are favorable (Johnson and Webb 1989). However, these cache sites are likely chosen because they offer a high return rate for the birds. Acorns may store best in these environments and may also be released from seed predation by granivorous rodents, which may be less numerous in these habitats. This pos-sibility, coupled with the growing evidence that Jays and other corvids possess keen spatial memory and are able to remember precise cache sites (see review by Brodin and Bolhuis 2008), suggests that oak dispersal and establishment as a result of the activity of scatter hoarding Jays may be more complicated than is typically assumed in the literature.

It is also widely assumed that the only mechanism by which Jays can disperse oaks is by caching acorns and subsequently failing to recover a portion of them. This assumption, however, ignores the potentially significant and largely unexplored possibility that Jays may disperse acorns short distances by dropping whole or partially-eaten, but viable, acorns of many species. Steele et al. (2007), for example, implicated the Blue Jay as a like-ly candidate of short-distance dispersal of some oaks (black [*Q. velutina*] and white oak [*Q. alba*]) after failing to match patterns of acorn dispersal by small mammals with pat-terns of seedling shadows (determined via paternity analyses). They argued that previous suggestions that Blue Jays only disperse small-seeded oaks (Scarlett and Smith, 1991) may be misleading. Recent acorn selection experiments, for example, show that Blue Jays often will consume larger-seeded species (white oak and red oak, *Q. rubra*) when other acorns are not available, and frequently will drop partially eaten acorns (Moore and Swihart 2006). Moreover, tannin gradients in acorns may encourage Jays and other seed consumers to consume only the basal portion of acorns and to discard the apical half, which contains the embryo and can still germinate and establish given the proper conditions (Steele et al. 1993). We suggest that the ability of Jays for carrying multiple small acorns in the crop may facilitate long-distance dispersal of these small-seeded species. In contrast, gape and crop size limitations require that Jays must carry larger acorns in the bill, which may pre-dispose these larger-seeded species to short-distance dispersal by means of partial con-sumption or dropping behavior. We also hypothesize that the ability of jays for multiple prey loading of smaller acorns (in the crop) may allow longer dispersal of these species because of the opportunity for carrying more acorn mass per dispersal event.

One final interaction that potentially influences oak dispersal involves the relationship between Jays and acorn-feeding insects, especially weevils (*Curculio* spp.). Like rodents

(Steele et al. 1996), Jays can detect infested acorns and often show a preference for non-infested acorns when caching (Fleck 1994, Dixon et al. 1997a). Such selective removal and hoarding of sound acorns may reduce cache losses to insect damage and enhance dispersal at least on those occasions when cached acorns are not recovered. Scrub Jays, for example, selectively disperse acorns from individual trees of Gambel oak (*Q. gambelii*) with lower levels of weevil infestation. However, weevil larvae also may serve as an important protein supplement for Jays (Johnson et al. 1993), which consistently lose weight when maintained on a diet of only acorns (Dixon et al. 1997b). Thus the selective consumption of infested acorns and weevils is likely for Jays, but has not been demonstrated as it has for rodents (Steele et al. 1996).

ACKNOWLEDGMENTS

We thank the organizers for the invitation to prepare this review and A. Pelak for reviewing earlier versions of the manuscript. Financial support for our research and the preparation of this review were provided by the National Science Foundation (DEB—0642434 and DEB—0642504), the Department of Biology, Wilkes University, and the Department of Forestry and Natural Resources, Purdue University.

LITERATURE CITED

Acevedo, M. A., and C. Restrepo. 2008. Land-cover and land-use change and its contribution to the large-scale organization of Puerto Rico's bird assemblages. Diversity and Distribution 14:114–122.

Bartuszevige, A. M., and D. L. Gorchov. 2006. Avian seed dispersal of an invasive shrub. Biological Invasions 8:1013–1022.

Bosque, C., and R. Calchi. 2003. Food choice by Blue-gray Tanagers in relation to protein content. Comparative Biochemistry and Physiology A—Molecular and Integrative Physiology 135:321–327.

Bossema, I. 1979. Jays and oaks: An eco-ethological study of a symbiosis. Behaviour 70:1–117.

Brodin, A., and J. L. Bolhuis. 2008. Memory and brain in food-storing birds: space oddities or adaptive specializations. Ethology 114:633–645.

Cain, M. L., B. G. Milligan, and A. E. Strand. 2000. Long-distance seed dispersal in plant populations. American Journal of Botany 87:1217–1227.

Carlo, T. A. 2005. Interspecific neighbors change seed dispersal pattern of an avian-dispersed plant. Ecology 88:2440–2449.

_____, and J. M. Morales. 2008. Inequalities in fruit removal and seed dispersal: consequences of bird behavior, neighborhood density and landscape aggregation. Journal of Ecology 96:609–618.

_____, J. E. Aukema, and J. M. Morales. 2007. Plant frugivore interactions as spatially explicit networks: Integrating frugivore foraging with fruiting plant spatial patterns. Pages 369–390 in A. J. Dennis, E. W. Schupp, R. J. Green, and D. A. Wescott, editors. Seed dispersal: Theory and its application in a changing world. CAB International, London, UK.

Carillo, C. M., E. Moreno, F. Valera, and A. Barbosa. 2007. Seed selection by the Trumpeter finch, *Bucanetes githagineus*. What currency does this arid-land species value. Annales Zoologica Fennici 44:377–386.

Castellon, T. D., and K. E. Sieving. 2005. An experimental test of matrix permeability and corridor use by an endemic understory bird. Conservation Biology 20:135–145.

Clark, J. S. 1998. Why trees migrate so fast: Confronting theory with dispersal biology and the paleorecord. The American Naturalist 152:204–224.

_____, E. Macklin, and L. Wood. 1998a. Stages and spatial scales of recruitment limitation in southern Appalachian forests. Ecological Monographs 68:213–235.

_____, C. Fastie, G. Hurtt, S. T. Jackson, C. Johnson, G. A. King, M. Lewis, J. Lynch, S Pacala, C. Prentice, E. W. Schupp, T. Webb III, and P. Wyckoff. 1998b. Reid's paradox of rapid plant migration: dispersal theory and interpretation of paleoecological records. BioScience 48:13–24.

Connell, J. H. 1971. On the role natural enemies in preventing competitive exclusion in some marine animals and in forest trees. Pages 298–312 in P. J. den Boer and G. R. Gradwell, editors. Dynamics of populations. Centre for Agricultural Publishing and Documentation (PUDOC), Wageningen, The Netherlands.

Darley-Hill, S., and W. C. Johnson. 1981. Acorn dispersal by the blue jay (*Cyanocitta cristata*). Oecologia 50:231–232.

Davis, M. B. 1976. Pleistocene biogeography of temperate deciduous forests. Geoscience and Man 13:13–26.

DeGange, A. R., J. W. Fitzpatrick, J. N. Layne, and G. E. Woolfenden 1989. Acorn harvesting by Florida scrub jays. Ecology 70:348–356.

Delcourt, P. A., and H. R. Delcourt. 1987. Long-term forest dynamics of the temperate zone. Ecological Studies 63, Springer, New York.

Dennis, A. J., E. W. Schupp, R. J. Green, and D. A. Wescott, editors. 2007. Seed dispersal: Theory and its application in a changing world. CAB International, London, UK.

Dixon, J. G., W. C. Johnson, and C. S. Adkinson. 1997a. Effects of caching on acorn tannin levels and blue jay dietary preferences. Condor 99:756–764.

_____. 1997b. Effects of weevil larvae on acorn use by blue jays. Oecologia 111:201–208.

Fleck, D. C. 1994. Chemical mediation of vertebrate-aided seed dispersal. Dissertation, University of Colorado, Boulder, Colorado, USA.

Galetti, M., C. P. Alves-Costa, and E. Cazetta. 2003. Effects of forest fragmentation, anthropogenic edges and fruit colour on the consumption of ornithocoric fruits. Biological Conservation 111:269–273.

Godinez-Alverez, H., and P. Jordano. 2007. An empirical approach to analyzing demographic consequences of seed dispersal by frugivores. Pages 391–406 in A. J. Dennis, E. W. Schupp, R. J. Green, and D. A. Wescott, editors. Seed dispersal: Theory and its application in a changing world. CAB International, London, UK.

Gomez, J. M. 2003. Spatial patterns of long-distance dispersal of *Quercus ilex* acorns by jays in a heterogenous landscape. Ecography 26:573–584.

Gosper, C. R., C. D. Stansbury, and G. Vivian-Smith. 2005. Seed dispersal of fleshy-fruited invasive plants by birds: contributing factors and management options. Diversity and Distribution 11:549–558.

Hampe, A., J. L. Garcia-Castano, E. W. Schupp, and P. Jordano. 2008. Spatio-temporal dynamics and local hotspots of initial recruitment in vertebrate-dispersed trees. Journal of Ecology 96:668–678.

Harms, K. E., S. J. Wright, O. Calderon, A. Hernandez, and E. A. Herre. 2000. Pervasive density-dependent recruitment enhances seedling diversity in a tropical forest. Nature 404:493–495.

Herrera, C. M. 1984a. Adaptation to frugivory of Mediterranean avian seed dispersers. Ecology 65: 609–617.

_____. 1984b. A study of avian frugivores, bird-dispersed plants, and their interactions in Mediterranean scrublands. Ecological Monographs 54:1–23.

_____. 2002. Seed dispersal by vertebrates. Pages 185–210 in C. M. Herrera and O. Pellmyr, editors. Plant–Animal interactions: An evolutionary approach. Blackwell Science, Oxford, UK.

_____, P. Jordano, L. Lopez-Soria, and J. A. Amat. 1994. Recruitment of a mast-fruiting, bird-dispersed tree: Bridging frugivore activity and seedling establishment. Ecological Monographs 64:315–344.

Howe, H.F. 1989. Scatter- and clump-dispersal and seedling demography: Hypotheses and implications. Oecologia 79:417–426.

_____, and M. N. Miriti. 2000. No question: Seed dispersal matters. Trends in Ecology and Evolution 15:434–436.

Hubbard, J. A., and G. R. McPherson. 1997. Acorn selection by Mexican jays: A test of a tri-trophic symbiotic relationship hypothesis. Oecologia 110:143–146.

Hubbell, S. P., R. B. Foster, S. T. O'Brien, K. E. Harms, R. Condit, B. Wechsler, S. J. Wright, and S. Loo de Lao. 1999. Light-gap disturbances, recruitment limitation, and tree diversity in a neotropical forest. Science 283:584–587.

Hutchinson, T. F., and J. L. Vankat. 1998. Landscape structure and spread of the exotic shrub *Lonicera maackii* (Amur honeysuckle) in southwestern Ohio forests. American Midland Naturalist 139:383–390.

Janzen, D. H. 1970. Herbivores and the number of tree species in tropical forests. American Naturalist 104:501–528.

Johnson, W. C., and C. S. Adkisson. 1986. Airlifting the oaks. Natural History 95(10):40–47.

_____, and T. Webb. 1989. The role of blue jays (*Cyanocitta cristata*) in the postglacial dispersal of Fagaceous trees in eastern North America. Journal of Biogeography 16:561–571.

_____, L. Thomas, and C. S. Adkisson. 1993. Dietary circumvention of acorn tannins by blue jays: Implications for oak demography. Oecologia 94:159–164.

_____, C. S. Adkisson, T. R. Crow, and D. M. Dixon. 1997. Nut caching by blue jays (*Cynaocitta cristata* L.): Implications for tree demography. American Midland Naturalist 138:357–370.

Jordano, P. 2000. Fruits and Frugivory. Pages 125–165 in M. Fenner, editor. Seeds: the ecology of regeneration in plant communities. CAB International Publishing, London, UK.

_____, and C. M. Herrera. 1995. Shuffling the offspring: uncoupling and spatial discordance of multiple stages in vertebrate seed dispersal. Ecoscience 2:230–237.

_____, and E. W. Schupp. 2000. Determinants of seed dispersal effectiveness: the quantity component in the *Prunus mahaleb*-frugivorus bird interaction. Ecological Monographs 70:591–615.

Kollmann, J., and H. P. Schill. 1996. Spatial patterns of dispersal, seed predation, and germination during colonization of abandoned grassland by *Quercus petrea* and *Corylus avellana*. Vegetatio 125:193–205.

Kwit, C., D. J. Levey, and C. H. Greenberg. 2004. Contagious seed dispersal beneath heterospecific fruiting trees and its consequences. Oikos 107:303–308.

Le Corre, V. N. Machon, R. Petit, and A. Kremer. 1997. Colonization with long-distance seed dispersal and genetic structure of maternally-inherited genes in forest trees: a simulation study. Genetic Research 69:117–125.

Lepczyk, C. A., K. G. Murray, K. Winnett-Murray, P. Bartell. E. Geyer, and T. Work. 2000. Seasonal fruit preferences for lipids and sugars by American robins. Auk 117:709–717.

Levey, D. J., B. M. Bolker, J. J. Tewsksbury, S. Sargent, and N. M. Haddad. 2005. Effects of landscape corridors on seed dispersal by birds. Science 309:146–148.

_____, J. J. Tewksbury, and B. M. Bolker. 2008. Modeling long-distance seed dispersal in heterogeneous landscapes. Journal of Ecology 96:599–608.

Malmborg, P. K., and M.F. Willson. 1988. Foraging ecology of avian frugivores and some consequences for seed dispersal in an Illinois woodlot. The Condor 90:173–186.

Manasse, R. S., and H. F. Howe. 1983. Competition for dispersal agents among tropical trees: influences of neighbors. Oecologia 59:185–190.

Matlack, G. R. 1994. Plant species migration in a mixed-history forest landscape in Eastern North America. Ecology 75:1491–1502.

McEuen, A., B., and L. M. Curran. 2004. Seed dispersal and recruitment limitation across spatial scales in temperate forest fragments. Ecology 85:507–518.

McWilliams, W. H., R. A. O'Brien, G. C. Reese, and K. L. Waddell. 2002. Distribution and abundance of oaks in North America. Pages 13–23 in W. J. McShea and W. M. Healy, editors. Oak forest ecosystems: Ecology and management for wildlife. Johns Hopkins University Press, Baltimore, Maryland, USA.

Monsandl, R. and A. Kleinert. 1998. Development of oaks (*Quercus petrea* (Matt.) Liebl.) emerged from bird-dispersed seeds under old-growth pine (*Pinus silvestris* L.) stands. Forest Ecology and Management 106:35–44.

Moore, J. E., and R.K. Swihart. 2006. Diet choice of captive blue jays: implications for tree dispersal. Condor 108:377–388.

_____, A. B. McEuen, R. K. Swihart, T. A. Contreras, and M. A. Steele. 2007. Determinants of seed removal distance by scatter-hoarding rodents in deciduous forests. Ecology 88:2529–2540.

Muller-Landau, H. C., S. J. Wright, O. Calderon, S. P. Hubbell, and R. B. Foster. 2002. Assessing recruitment limitation: Concepts, methods and a case study from tropical forests. Pages 35–53 in

D. J. Levey, W. R. Diva, and M. Galetti, editors. Seed dispersal and frugivory: Ecology, evolution and conservation. CAB International Publishing, London, UK.

Murray, K. G. 1988. Avian seed dispersal of three neotropical gap-dependent plants. Ecological Monographs 58:271–298.

Nathan, R. 2006. Long-distance dispersal of plants. Science 313(5788):786–788.

_____, and H. C. Muller-Landau. 2000. Spatial patterns of seed dispersal, their determinants and consequences for recruitment. Trends in Ecology and Evolution 15:278–283.

Pizo, M. A. 2007. Seed dispersal by birds in degraded areas of Brazil. Pages 615–627 in A. J. Dennis, E. W. Schupp, R. J. Green, and D. A. Wescott, editors. Seed dispersal: Theory and its application in a changing world. CAB International, London, UK.

Pons, J., and J. G. Pausas. 2007a. Acorn dispersal estimated by radiotracking. Oecologia 153:903–911.

_____. 2007b. Not only size matters: acorn selection by the European jay (*Garrulus glandarius*). Acta Oecologia 31:353–360.

Powell, J. A., and N. E. Zimmermann. 2004. Multiscale analysis of active seed dispersal contributes to resolving Reid's paradox. Ecology 85:490–506.

Ramos, J. A. 1996. The influence of size, shape, and phenolic content on the selection of winter foods by the Azores bullfinch (*Pyrrhula murina*). Journal of Zoology 238:415–433.

Renne, I. J., and S. A. Gauthreaux, Jr. 2000. Seed dispersal of the Chinese tallow tree (*Sapium sebiferum (L.) Roxb.*) by birds in coastal South Carolina. American Midland Naturalist 144:202–215.

_____, W. C. Barrow, L. A. J. Randall, and W. C. Bridges. 2002. Generalized avian dispersal syndrome contributes to Chinese tallow tree (*Sapium sebiferum*, Euphorbiaceae) invasiveness. Diversity and Distributions 8:285–295.

Richardson, D. M., P. Pysek, M. Rejmanek, M. G. Barbour, F. D. Panneta, and C. J. West. 2000. Naturalization and invasion of alien plants: concepts and definitions. Diversity and Distributions 6:93–107.

Sargent, S. 1990. Neighbourhood effects on fruit removal by birds: a field experiment with *Viburnum dentatum* (Caprifoliaceae). Ecology 71:1289–1298.

Scarlett, T.L., and Smith, K.G. 1991. Acorn preferences of urban blue jays (*Cyanocitta crsitata*) during fall and spring in northwestern Arkansas. Condor 93:438–442.

Schaefer, H. M., V. Schmidt, and F. Bairlein. 2003. Discrimination abilities for nutrients: which difference matters for choosy birds and why? Animal Behvaiour 65:531–541.

_____, K. McGraw, and C. Cantoni. 2008. Birds use fruit colour as honest signal of dietary antioxidant rewards. Functional Ecology 22:303–310.

Schmidt, V., H. M. Schaefer, and H. Winkler. 2004. Conspicuousness, not colour as foraging cue in plant–animal signaling. Oikos 106:551–557.

Schupp, E. W. 1995. Seed and seedling conflicts, habitat choice and patterns of plant recruitment. American Journal of Botany 82:399–409.

_____. 2007. The suitability of a site for seed dispersal is context dependent. Pages 445–462 in A. J. Dennis, E. W. Schupp, R. J. Green, and D. A. Wescott, editors. Seed dispersal: Theory and its application in a changing world. CAB International, London, UK.

_____, and M. Fuentes. 1995. Spatial patterns of seed dispersal and the unification of plant population ecology. Ecoscience 2267–275.

Snow, D. W. 1981. Tropical frugivorous birds and their food plants: a world survey. Biotropic 13:1–14.

Steele, M. A., and Smallwood, P. D. 2002. Acorn dispersal by birds and mammals. Pages 182–195 in W. J. McShea, W. M and Healy, editors. Oak forest ecosystems: Ecology and management for wildlife. Johns Hopkins University Press, Baltimore, Maryland, USA.

_____, L. Z. Hadj-Chikh, and J. Hazeltine. 1996. Caching and feeding behavior of gray squirrels: responses to weevil infested acorns. Journal of Mammalogy 77:305–314.

_____, T. Knowles, K. Bridle, and E. Simms. 1993. Tannins and partial consumption of acorns: implications for dispersal of oaks by seed predators. American Midland Naturalist 130:229–238.

_____, J. E. Carlson, P. D. Smallwood, A. B. McEuen. T. A. Contreras, and W. B. Terzaghi. 2007. Linking seed and seedling shadows: A case study in the oaks (*Quercus*). Pages 322–339 in A. J.

Dennis, E. W. Schupp, R. J. Green, and D. A. Wescott, editors. Seed dispersal: Theory and its application in a changing world. CAB International, London, UK.

Stiles, E. W. 2000. Animals as seed dispersers. Pages 111–124 in M. Fenner, editor. Seeds: the ecology of regeneration in plant communities. CAB International Publishing, London, UK.

Terborgh, J., N. Pitman, M. Silman, H. Schicter, and V. P. Nunez. 2002. Maintenance of tree species diversity in tropical forests. Pages 1–18 in D. J. Levey, W. R. Diva, and M. Galetti, editors. Seed dispersal and frugivory: Ecology, evolution and conservation. CAB International Publishing, London, UK.

_____, √G. Nuez-Iturri, N. C. A. Pitman, √F. H. Cornejo Valverde, P. Alvarez, V. Swamy, E. G. Pringle, and √C. E. T. Paine. 2008. Tree recruitment in an empty forest. Ecology 89:1757–1768.

√Tewksbury, J. J., D. J. Levey, N. M. Hadad, S. Sargent, L. Orrock, A. Weldon, B. J. Danielson, J. Brinkerhoff, E. I. Damschen, and P. Townsend. 2002. Corridors affect plant, animals, and their interactions in fragmented landscapes. Proceedings of the National Academy of Sciences of the United States of America 99:12923–12926.

Thompson, J. N., and M. F. Willson. 1979. Evolution of temperate fruit-bird interactions. Evolution 33:973–982.

Traveset, A., and M. Verdu. 2002. A meta-analysis of the effects of gut treatment on seed germination. Pages 339–350 in D. J. Levey, W. R. Diva, and M. Galetti, editors. Seed dispersal and frugivory: Ecology, evolution and conservation. CAB International Publishing, London, UK.

_____, N. Riera, and R. E. Mas. 2001. Passage through bird guts causes interspecific differences in seed germination characteristics. Functional Ecology 15:669–675

_____, A. W. Robertson, and J. Rodriguez-Perez. 2007. A review on the role of endozoochory in seed germination. Pages 78–103 in A. J. Dennis, E. W. Schupp, R. J. Green, and D. A. Wescott, editors. Seed dispersal: Theory and its application in a changing world. CAB International, London, UK.

Tsujita, K., S. Sakai, and K. Kikuzawa. 2008. Does individual variation in fruit profitability override color differences in avian choices of red or white Ilex serrata fruits? Ecological Research 23:445–450.

Valera, F., R. H. Wagner, M. Romero-Pujante, J. E. Gutierrez, and P. J. Rey. 2005. Dietary specialization on high protein seeds by adult and nestling sirens. Condor, 107:29–40.

van der Pilj, L. 1972. Principles of dispersal in higher plants. Springer Verlag, New York, USA.

Vander Wall, S. B, and W. S. Longland. 2005. Diplochory and the evolution of seed dispersal. Pages 297–314 in P.-M. Forget, J. E. Lambert, P. E. Hulme, and S. B. Vander Wall, editors. Seed fate: predation dispersal and seedling establishment. CAB International, London, UK.

Waite, R.K. 1985. Food caching and recovery by farmland corvids. Bird Study 32:45–49.

Wang, B. C., and T. B. Smith. 2002. Closing the seed dispersal loop. Trends in Ecology and Evolution 17:379–385.

Wenny, D. G. 2000. Seed dispersal, seed predation, and seedling recruitment of a Neotropical montane tree. Ecological Monographs 70:331–351.

_____, and D. J. Levey. 1998. Directed dispersal by bellbirds in a tropical cloud forest. Proceedings of the National Academy of Sciences USA 95:6204–6207.

Wheelwright, N. T., and G. H. Orians. 1982. Seed dispersal by animals: Contrasts with pollen, problems of terminology, and constraints on coevolution. American Naturalist 119:402.

White, D. W., and E. W. Stiles. 1992. Bird dispersal of fruit species introduced into eastern North America. Canadian Journal of Botany 70:1689–1696.

Wills, C., R. Condit, R. B. Foster, and S. P. Hubbell. 1997. Strong density- and diversity-related effects help maintain tree species diversity in a neotropical forest. Proceedings of the National Acdemy of Sciences USA 94:1252–1257.

Willson, M. F. 1986. Avian frugivory and seed dispersal in eastern North America. Pages 221–279 in R. F. Johnston, editor. Current Ornithology, Vol. 3, Plenum, New York, USA

With, D. W. 2002. The landscape ecology of invasive spread. Conservation Biology, 16:1192–1203.

Wright, S. J. 2007. Seed dispersal in anthropogenic landscapes. Pages 599–614 in A. J. Dennis, E. W. Schupp, R. J. Green, and D. A. Wescott, editors. Seed dispersal: Theory and its application in a changing world. CAB International, London, UK.

Avian Ecology and Conservation: A Pennsylvania Focus with National Implications. Edited by S. K. Majumdar, T. L. Master, M. C. Brittingham, R. M. Ross, R. S. Mulvihill and J. E. Huffman. © 2010. The Pennsylvania Academy of Science.

Chapter 3

Wetland Bird Communities: Boreal Bogs to Open Water

Douglas A. Gross and Catherine D. Haffner
Pennsylvania Game Commission
2001 Elmerton Avenue, Harrisburg, PA 17110-4250
Respective emails: dogross@state.pa.us and CDhaffner@yahoo.com

INTRODUCTION

I enter a swamp as a sacred place, — *a sanctum sanctorum.* — H. D. Thoreau

Wetlands serve a variety of functions in the landscape, including water storage, sediment and nutrient retention, groundwater recharge, and pollution abatement. They also provide crucial habitats for many animals, such as mussels, fish, turtles, snakes, frogs, salamanders, mammals, and birds. In Pennsylvania, many bird species depend upon or regularly use at least one of the various wetland types for their survival. Yet less than half of the state's wetlands existing prior to settlement remain today (Myers et al. 2000). This has significantly reduced avian species diversity not only in Pennsylvania but in the surrounding Mid-Atlantic states (Tiner 1987, Brauning 1992, Brauning et al. 1994, Gross 1998). Decrease in size and complexity of wetlands lead to a loss in basic resources that support bird populations, such as plant and arthropod abundance and diversity. The decline of Pennsylvania's wetland birds has therefore been a function of the decline in quantity and quality of the wetland ecosystems they inhabit (Goodrich et al. 2002).

The Importance of Wetlands

Wetlands are particularly critical for rare bird species in Pennsylvania. In 1990, an evaluation of wetlands across the state found that 79% of the species then listed as endangered or threatened and 55% of those listed as species of special concern were wetland obligates (endangered, threatened, and candidates) (Brooks and Croonquist 1990). Since then, the representation of wetland birds on the state list has only increased. For instance, the black-crowned night-heron (*Nyticorax nycticorax*), sora (*Porzana carolina*), common moorhen (*Gallinula chloropus*), yellow-bellied flycatcher (*Empidonax flaviventris*), and blackpoll warbler (*Dendroica striata*) have been added to the list of Species of Special Concern in recent years (Tables 2 and 3).

Wetlands also serve as critical stopover habitat for migrating birds, such as common tern (*Sterna hirundo*), solitary sandpiper (*Tringa solitaria*), and piping plover (*Charadrius melodus*). Many of these species are listed in the Pennsylvania Comprehensive Wildlife Action Plan (Pennsylvania Game Commission and Pennsylvania Fish and Boat Commission 2005) or as priority conservation species in the various continent-wide conservation plans such as the Partners in Flight (PIF) North American Conservation Landbird Conservation Plan (Rich et al. 2004), the United States Shorebird Conservation Plan (Brown et al. 2001), or the North American Waterfowl Plan (U.S. Department of the Interior and Environment Canada 1986).

Moreover, because many wetland birds are high in the food chain of their habitats, consuming a diversity of invertebrate and vertebrate prey, and are vulnerable to changes in vegetation brought on by perturbation and invasive species, they serve as "indicator species" for these habitats and barometers for ecosystem health. Inventory and monitoring of these species is therefore a particularly important challenge for the ornithological community (Brauning et al. 1994, Gross 1998, U.S. Fish and Wildlife Service 2002). Yet wetland birds are not monitored well by standard surveys such as the road-based Breeding Bird Survey, so basic population data including trends are lacking for these species. It is difficult to assess the consequences of environmental effects and human activity, including management actions, without a repeatable and unbiased monitoring program for ecosystems that support so many species of conservation concern.

WETLANDS OF PENNSYLVANIA

There are many ways to define and categorize wetland communities. But, for the purposes of this discussion, we will use the U.S. Fish and Wildlife Service definition (Cowardin et al. 1979): "Wetlands are lands transitional between terrestrial and aquatic systems where the water table is usually at or near the surface or the land is covered by shallow water. Wetlands must have one or more of the following three attributes: (1) at least periodically, the land supports predominantly hydrophytes; (2) the substrate is predominantly undrained hydric soil; and (3) the substrate is nonsoil and is saturated with water or covered by shallow water at some time during the growing season of each year." Deep water wetlands (lakes, ponds, and rivers) are referred to as 'lacustrine' and shallow water wetlands (swamps, marshes, bogs, and fens) are called 'palustrine'. Hydrophytes, or wetland plants, are well adapted to water-saturated anaerobic sediments (Tiner 1998) and are categorized as either *obligate* (found > 99% of time in wetlands), facultative wetland (67 – 99%), facultative (34 – 64%), or facultative upland (1 – 33%) (Reed 1988, Tiner 1993). Summaries of the various natural ecological communities found in wetlands can be found in *Terrestrial & Palustrine Plant Communities of Pennsylvania* (Fike 1999) and a summary of wetland habitat types can be found in Appendix 2 of the Comprehensive Wildlife Action Plan (Pennsylvania Game Commission and Pennsylvania Fish and Boat Commission 2005). It is important to be consistent when referencing wetland types because they can be described in a number of ways. Therefore, we have provided definitions of wetland types found in Pennsylvania and will refer to these throughout this chapter (Table 1).

Pennsylvania does not have many wetlands and these wetlands are not a major component of the landscape in most parts of the state. There is a total of 729,535 acres found in over 160,000 wetlands in the state (Tiner 1990). Of these areas, 146,816 acres (20.1%) are categorized as lacustrine and 410,009 acres (56.2%) are considered palustrine. There are 172,068 acres of river and stream habitat and only 643 acres of estuarine habitat remaining in the Delaware River watershed of southeastern Pennsylvania. Pennsylvania has only a few natural lakes and many human-made impoundments. Emergent (marshes and wet meadows) and shrub-scrub wetlands comprise 10 – 20% of wetland acres in the state.

Table 1. Definitions of Pennsylvania wetland types relevant to bird conservation (Cowardin et al. 1979, Tiner 1998).

Wetland type	Definition
Bog	Type of wetland forming on acidic peats (peatland), typically formed by the accumulation of peat moss (*Sphagum* spp.) in a nutrient poor environment and colonized by ericaceous shrubs like leatherleaf (*Chaemaedaphne calyculata*) or evergreen trees like black spruce (*Picea mariana*).
Fen	Type of wetland growing on variably mineral-rich peats, typically with significant ground-water inflow, and dominated by sedges and mineral-loving species; characteristic of boreal and glaciated regions.
Kettle pond or hole	Glacially formed pond or depression resulting from the melting of ice blocks left by the retreating glacier about 10,000 years ago.
Lacustrine	Wetlands and deepwater habitats with all the following characteristics: 1. situated in a topographic depression or a dammed river channel, 2. lacking trees, shrubs, persistent emergents, emergent mosses, or lichens with greater than 30% areal coverage; and 3. total area exceeds 8 ha (20 acres). May be tidal or non-tidal, but ocean-derived salinity always less than 0.5%. Lacustrine systems include permanently flooded lakes and reservoirs, including islands.
Marsh	Type of wetland dominated by emergent (herbaceous) plants growing in shallow water for all or most of the growing season, often characterized by one or a few species, particularly cattails (*Typha* spp.) and bulrushes (*Scirpus* spp.).
Meadow, wet	Type of wetland dominated by herbaceous plants growing in soils saturated at or near the surface for extended periods during growing season; may be inundated for brief periods.
Palustrine	All nontidal wetlands dominated by trees, shrubs, persistent emergents, emergent mosses or lichens, and all such wetlands that occur in tidal areas where salinity due to ocean-derived salts is below 0.5%. It also includes wetlands lacking such vegetation, but with all of the following characteristics: 1. area less than 8 ha (20 acres), 2. active wave-formed or bedrock shoreline features lacking; 3. water depth in the deepest part of basin less than 2 m at low water; and 4. salinity due to ocean-derived salts less than 0.5%. Palustrine systems include marsh, swamp, bog, fen.
Peatland	Area where peat dominates, including bogs and fens.
Seep	Point of groundwater discharge where the earth's surface is saturated but flowing water is not typically observed; discharge may be seasonal or permanent.
Scrub-shrub	Type of wetland that is dominated by woody vegetation less than 6 m (20 feet) tall; this can include true shrubs, small or stunted trees in any wetland regime. There are subcategories of this type, including broad-leafed deciduous, needle-leaved deciduous, broad-leafed evergreen, needle-leafed evergreen, or dead vegetation (from flooding, fire, or other causes).
Swamp	Type of wetland dominated by woody vegetation (trees or shrubs); in general usage, refers to any vegetated area that is wet for extended periods on a frequent, recurring basis. The subcategories are same as for scrub-shrub.
Vernal pool	Shallow, often seasonal pond (typically surrounded by upland woods).

The northwestern and northeastern parts of the state contain most of the wetlands (40%) remaining in Pennsylvania (Tiner 1990). Most counties have very few wetlands; Pike and Monroe counties are leaders among those with the highest proportion of wetland habitat. Lacustrine wetlands (ponds and lakes) are concentrated in the coastal zone of Lake Erie, but also scattered throughout the state. Thus, these areas are where most of the wetland-dependent birds are concentrated. There are pockets of wetlands in other parts of the state, even in the heavily-developed southeastern counties.

Headwater wetlands

A variety of wetlands emerge in the headwaters of streams, namely fens, bogs, marshes, scrub-shrub wetlands, swamps, and beaver-altered wetlands with some open water (Table 1). In many cases, headwater wetlands are a mixture of these categories. They provide diverse vegetative cover, edges between different habitats within the wetland, and contrast with the surrounding landscape, which is typically forested.

Peatlands (bogs and fens) can be poorly vegetated with low plant diversity or richly vegetated with a diversity of plant species and dense structure with a commensurately complex bird community. There is higher bird diversity in swamps than in more open fens where bird diversity can be fairly poor. Most conifer swamps are dominated by eastern hemlock (*Tsuga canadensis*) or red spruce (*Picea rubra*) with associated eastern white pine (*Pinus strobus*), American larch (*Larix laricina*), and most rarely, balsam fir (*Abies balsamea*). The native boreal conifer species (spruces, balsam fir, and American larch) are concentrated in the northern counties, especially the glaciated northeast (Rhoads and Klein 1993). The various types of Pennsylvania palustrine forests and woodlands are found in the glaciated northeast, the Pocono Plateau, Ridge and Valley, and the unglaciated Allegheny Plateau (Fike 1999). Some of the best examples of conifer swamps are Coalbed Swamp in the Dutch Mountain wetlands (Wyoming County) and Adam Swamp in the High Poconos (Monroe County). Hemlock swamps are more widely dispersed, including throughout much of the Ridge and Valley province.

It is often difficult to distinguish different wetland types and their bird constituents. Many bird species occur in a number of different kinds of wetlands and also use adjacent terrestrial ecosystems. For example, several common species in conifer swamps also nest and forage in nearby upland conifer forest. This surrounding forest may provide important post-breeding dispersal habitat for fledglings hatched in the wetland. Great blue herons (*Ardea herodias*) may forage in the wetland, but nest in trees on the slope nearby. Northern harriers (*Circus cyaneus*) will nest in a scrub or emergent wetland and forage in scrub barrens and grasslands. These various habitats sometimes interconnect like fingers, providing a matrix of nesting and foraging opportunities for birds.

Boreal conifer swamps are among the rarest ecosystems in the state with two Pennsylvania endangered species dependent on them. All blackpoll warblers and almost all yellow-bellied flycatchers breeding in the state have been found in boreal conifer forested wetlands (Gross 2003). Blackpoll warblers are confined to spruce-dominated conifer swamps in Wyoming County. Most yellow-bellied flycatchers have been found in spruce swamps, but some populations also have been found in swamps dominated by hemlocks. One of the most important variables in conifer swamps is the percentage canopy cover. Where there is a continuous canopy cover by spruce or hemlock, the understory can be sparse and depauperate. When there are gaps in the canopy, the swamp vegetation is much more diverse and complex with an increase in bird diversity. The presence of yellow-bellied flycatcher is associated with canopy gaps. Sections of wetlands that support nesting yellow-bellied flycatcher populations have >80% ground cover of moss, herbs, and ferns; cover averages 87% at 0.5 m (2 ft) but only 23% at 3.5 m (12 ft.) (Gross 2002). The dense, but patchy, shrub layer also attracts high densities of Canada warbler (*Wilsonia canadensis*), white-throated sparrow (*Zonotrichia albicollis*), common yellowthroat (*Geothlypis trichas*), and other forest and thicket species.

Table 2. Select characteristic bird species of headwater wetlands (mostly swamps, fens, bogs, and scrub-shrub wetlands), their status, limiting factors and conservation challenges. Note that any listed species also is a Wildlife Action Plan (WAP) priority species. Information gleaned from Birds of North America accounts (Poole, Ed. 2009, multiple authors) and Wildlife Action Plan species accounts (Pennsylvania Game Commission and Pennsylvania Fish and Boat Commission 2005).

Bird Species	State Status / Conservation Plan Listings	Habitat Specifications, Limiting Factors and Conservation Challenges
Acadian flycatcher *Empidonax virescens*	Secure; WAP Priority	Mature riparian forests, particularly where eastern hemlock is dominant. Threats include forest fragmentation and the pests and diseases of eastern hemlock.
Alder flycatcher *Empidonax alnorum*	Secure; WAP Priority	Generally more northerly and higher elevations than similar Willow Flycatcher. Shrubland and wetlands loss are limiting factors.
American woodcock *Scolopax minor*	Game species; WAP Priority	In addition to young forests and old fields, it inhabits bogs, fens, shrubby wetlands, boreal swamps, especially peatlands, and beaver-altered wetlands. Needs high shrub cover and good earthworm populations.
Blackburnian warbler *Dendroica fusca*	Secure; PIF and WAP Priorities	Tall conifers and sometimes deciduous trees. Loss of conifers, especially hemlocks from pests is primary threat.
Blackpoll warbler *Dendroica striata*	Endangered; WAP Priority	Very limited distribution in spruce-dominated boreal swamps and forests in NE counties. Hemlock loss is a threat.
Blue-headed vireo *Vireo solitarius*	Secure; WAP Priority	Riparian conifer forests and conifer wetlands. Hemlock loss from pests is threat.
Canada warbler *Wilsonia canadensis*	Secure: PIF and WAP Priority	Forest interior species found at higher elevations and where there is cool, moist, forest with with high foliage density in understory and shrub layer. Found in peatlands. Threatened by loss of shrub layer, simplification of vegetative structure, and forest fragmentation.
Magnolia warbler *Dendroica magnolia*	Secure	Dense lower and mid-canopy needle-leafed evergreen cover, especially young second-growth spruce and hemlock. Also found in mature forest. Conifer pests and diseasesr, especially to hemlocks, are a threat to habitat.
Nashville warbler *Vermivora ruficapilla*	Secure	Rare breeder in state. Moist early successional forest, peatland with spruce or larch and bordered with shrubs. Mixed second growth forest and wetland, including aspen, birch, alder.
Northern saw-whet owl *Aegolius acadicus*	Secure; extensive research in state	High foliage density and shrub layer; conifer cover. Needs trees for cavity nest.
Northern waterthrush *Seiurus noveboracensis*	Secure; WAP Priority	Boreal forested wetlands and pond edges with dense understory. Limited by the health and size of peatlands with shrub cover, forest fragmentation and simplification.
Olive-sided flycatcher *Contopus cooperi*	Extirpated; PIF Priority	Boreal conifer forests, burned over areas, forest and pond edges. Unknown causes for continental decline. Lack of fire, decline in conifer cover, wetland decline possible causes of decline in PA.

(continued)

Table 2. (Continued)

Bird Species	State Status / Conservation Plan Listings	Habitat Specifications, Limiting Factors and Conservation Challenges
Red-breasted nuthatch *Sitta canadensis*	Secure	Nests in conifer groves, both native and exotic, including forested wetlands. More likely found in higher elevations. Threatened by conifer forest health and size, hemlock loss from pests.
Red crossbill *Loxia curvirostra*	Candidate Undetermined; WAP Priority	Native conifer forests and swamps, including lower elevation riparian conifers and pine barrens. Size, health, diversity, and distribution of conifer forests and conifer swamps. Populations greatly fragmented. Species includes several "types" that function as biological species.
Swainson's thrush *Catharus ustulatus*	Candidate – Rare; WAP Priority	High elevation conifer forests and wetlands including riparian hemlock and spruce woods; seep areas. Threatened by conifer forest pests and fragmentation of habitat.
White-throated sparrow *Zonotrichia albicola*	Secure, but limited distribution	Shrub component in wetland; often found in peatlands.
Winter wren *Troglodytes troglodytes*	Secure; WAP Priority	Downed timber, forest diversity. Threatened by hemlock loss.
Yellow-bellied flycatcher *Empidonax flaviventris*	Endangered; WAP Priority	High elevation, cool conifer-dominated wetlands and forests, usually mossy. Threatened by loss of hemlock and sphagnum moss; forest fragmentation; very limited distribution in cool, shady peatlands with conifers.

Conifers are an important component of boreal wetlands. In addition to rare species, conifers host more common birds in high densities. Blackburnian warblers (*Dendroica fusca*), blue-headed vireos (*Vireo solitarius*), golden-crowned kinglets (*Regulus satrapa*), magnolia warblers (*Dendroica magnolia*), yellow-rumped warblers (*Dendroica coronata*) and purple finches (*Carpodacus pupureus*) are common residents. One bird particularly closely linked to conifers is the red crossbill (*Loxia curvirostra*). This enigmatic songbird forages almost exclusively on seeds of evergreen conifers. It once nested much more extensively in the state including in pine barrens and spruce swamps.

Declines in boreal conifer species have been noticed in the Appalachians for many years, but the scattered and isolated nature of this habitat has not lent itself well to analysis. The isolated islands of habitat are not sampled by standardized methods such as the roadside Breeding Bird Survey. Recently, declines in some ecological indicator species for mountain spruce-fir forests were detected. Using off-road point count data, King et al. (2008) found declines for yellow-bellied flycatcher, Bicknell's thrush (*Catharus bicknelli*), and magnolia warbler (*Dendroica magnolia*). Similar declines have been documented in the high elevation Appalachian conifer forests of West Virginia (Hall 1985).

Shrub-scrub wetlands are not very common in Pennsylvania except for the glaciated northeast. Alder flycatchers (*Empidonax alnorum*) are locally abundant in these wetlands. Other songbirds may have high densities in shrubby wetlands where insects are abundant and readily accessible. Such wetlands can have high densities of common yellowthroat,

Canada warbler, eastern towhee (*Pipilo erythrophthalmus*), and white-throated sparrow. White-throated sparrow reaches the southern limit of its breeding range in Pennsylvania (Falls and Kopachena 1994). Although generally associated on its wintering ground as a seed-eater, this husky sparrow is insectivorous when nesting in shrub-scrub wetlands.

Region-wide, forested wetland areas have declined greatly. Dahl and Zoltai (1997) estimated total forested wetland area in Pennsylvania has declined 67% from pre-settlement times, from 296,578 ha to 98,554 ha. This decline is even greater than the general wetland loss in the state (Tiner 1990). There are only 24,700 ha of northern forested wetlands remaining in the state. This loss has been widespread in the Great Lakes and New England region. These losses resulted from converting many wetlands to recreational lakes, peat mining, deforestation during the timbering era, and conversion of wetlands to agriculture and development. The effect of this loss has created more isolation between wetland bird populations and decreased the opportunities for colonization of locations and gene flow typical of healthy populations. Many of the northern forested wetlands were not inventoried by an ornithologist before the wetland, and its bird community, was lost. Therefore, it is difficult to assess the severity of population declines of many boreal birds.

Emergent Marshes and Open Water

Many of the largest and most significant wetlands in Pennsylvania are emergent marshes. They represent 13% of Pennsylvania's wetlands (Pennsylvania Game Commission and Pennsylvania Fish and Boat Commission 2005) and are often dominated by common cattail (*Typha latifolia*) and hardstem bulrush (*Scirpus acutus*) as well as similar plants. Because they are typically found at the edges of open water or in a low lying depression in the landscape, emergent marshes are inundated entirely or partially throughout the year. Thus, these ecosystems are highly productive and support an intricate food web from aquatic decomposers to terrestrial predators.

The list of bird species that use marshes for breeding or stopover migration habitat is quite long, so we have provided an abbreviated list of the most characteristic bird species (Table 3). Certain habitat characteristics unite several of the wetland nesting birds of Pennsylvania. Several rails and herons require a combination of open water and emergent, obligate wetland vegetation, referred to as a "hemi-marsh" stage (*sensu* Weller and Spatcher 1965), which provides both foraging and nesting opportunities. The interstitial spaces between clumps of cattails and reeds are critical for their occupancy. Many of these wetland birds build nests on top of vegetation or a floating platform made of vegetation that depends on the relative stability of water depth. Most wetland birds forage on a variety of invertebrates and small vertebrates including insects, amphibians, and fishes. Therefore, their populations and nesting success depends on the health of the wetland community and the diversity of life in it.

Marshlands also provide critical stopover habitat for migrating birds. Sandpipers and plovers often stop in shallow waters and mudflats of marshes. Solitary sandpiper is a regular passage migrant and visitor to Pennsylvania's wetlands, especially shallow marshes, lake and pond shores, and beaver meadows. Although it does not have the reputation as a rare species, the solitary sandpiper is a "species of high concern" for its global population in the United States Shorebird Conservation Plan (Brown et al. 2001). It has one of the smallest populations of shorebirds in North America, is suspected to be declining, but is poorly studied wherever it is found (Brown et al. 2001).

Table 3. Select characteristic bird species of emergent marshes, their status, and their limiting factors and conservation challenges. All are breeding birds except where noted. Note that any listed species also is a Wildlife Action Plan (WAP) priority species. Information gleaned from Birds of North America accounts (Poole, Ed. 2009, multiple authors) and Wildlife Action Plan species accounts (Pennsylvania Game Commission and Pennsylvania Fish and Boat Commission 2005).

Bird Species	Status	Habitat Specialties, Limiting Factors and Threats
American bittern *Botaurus lentiginosus*	Endangered	High cover-water interspersion needed in shallow wetlands. Somewhat area sensitive; more common in larger wetlands (>10 hectares).
American black duck *Anas rubripes*	Game bird, Declining	Variety of wetlands and near ponds, usually away from agriculture. Threats are genetic swamping by closely related mallard (*A. platyrhynchos*) and reduction of habitat.
American coot *Fulica americanus*	Candidate – Rare	Matrix of dense emergent vegetation and fairly deep open water; highest densities in semi-permanent wetlands and where there is high degree of interstitial spaces. Likes open water more than moorhens. Quickly pioneers new habitats.
Bald eagle *Haliaeeatus leucocephalus*	Threatened	Extensive water with good fish populations; adequate nesting structure (usually a large tree) for large stick nest. Sensitive to nest disturbance.
Black rail *Laterallus jamaicensis*	Secure (but very rare)	Shallow water marshes and wet meadows. Edge of range in state; very rare in region, difficult to detect.
Black tern *Chlidonias nigra*	Endangered	Edge of range; needs balance of shallow open water and emergent vegetation (about 50 :50 ratio). Prefers large marshes and complexes (> 20 ha).
Common moorhen *Gallinula chloropus*	Candidate – At Risk	Combination of dense emergent vegetation and open water (about 50: 50 ratio); prefers water depth of 15 – 120 cm. Larger marshes used more often. Floating mats of vegetation used much.
Great blue heron *Ardea herodias*	Secure	Colonial with large stick nests in trees or snags, usually difficult-to-reach places like swamps, steep hillsides, islands near waterways with good fish populations.
Great egret *Ardea alba*	Endangered	Very limited and local in breeding range; colonial on islands or in wetlands. In PA, only nesting in urban areas. Forages in shallows where water willows dominate.
Green-winged teal *Anas crecca*	Candidate – At Risk	Edge of range. Often nests in brush thickets, woods, or wet meadow near marsh or pond.
Hooded merganser *Lophodytes cucullatus*	Game	Natural cavity or nest box for nesting; clear water with abundant fish, crayfish, and aquatic insects.
King rail *Rallus elegans*	Endangered	Edge of range. Identification confusion. Needs large, complex, high quality wetlands. May be area sensitive. Drying swales important during brooding.
Least bittern *Ixobrychus exilus*	Endangered	Dense, tall vegetation with clumps of woody vegetation near open water. Strong association with large wetlands (>10 ha) dominated by cattails with stable water regimes.
Marsh wren *Cistothorus palustris*	Candidate – Rare	Diversity of marshlands, but found more in bulrush (*Scirpus validus*) later in season. Tolerant of artificial or restored wetlands.
Northern harrier *Circus cyaneus*	Candidate – At Risk	Open and extensive wetlands, including wet pastures, meadows, adjacent upland fields.

(continued)

Table 3. (continued)

Bird Species	Status	Habitat Specialties, Limiting Factors and Threats
Northern shoveler *Anas clypeata*	Game, but rare	Rare and local breeding species at edge of range. Margins of open, shallow wetlands with open water / cover ratio of at least 50:50. Does well in managed wetlands.
Osprey *Pandion haliaetus*	Threatened	Found primarily near lakes, impoundments, and large streams. Needs nesting structures, adequate fish populations. Particularly susceptible to contaminants.
Pied-billed grebe *Podolymbus podiceps*	Candidate – Rare	Fairly open wetlands including ponds with combination of dense stands of emergent or aquatic vegetation and open water. Limited by wetland number, size, and quality.
Prothonotary warbler *Podilymbus podiceps*	Candidate – Rare	Standing or slow-moving water in wooded area. Nests in tree cavity or substitute in well-shaded area.
Ruddy duck *Oxyurus jamaicensis*	Candidate – Rare	Edge of range, generally found in prairie potholes. Wetlands or ponds with extensive emergent vegetation and open water.
Rusty blackbird *Euphagus carolinus*	Secure, but declining	Passage migrant and rare wintering species. Forages in shallow water (generally 10 cm or less) in wetlands, moist forests, and field edges for insects, fruits, acorns; roosts in trees.
Sedge wren *Cistothorus platensis*	Endangered	Edge of range. Tall sedges in wet meadows, marshes, wet pastures, hayfields, bogs. Nomadic and erratic breeder with extended nesting season.
Sora *Porzanoa Carolina*	Candidate – Rare	Relatively shallow open water with emergent vegetation. Greater interspersion of vegetation and water preferred.
Swamp sparrow *Melospiza georgiana*	Secure; indicator	Marshes, fens, bogs, shrub-scrub wetlands, pond edges. Not area sensitive.
Virginia rail *Rallus virginianus*	Secure but declining	Marshes with moderate cover to water ratio. Avoids dry habitats and wetlands without mudflats or pools.
Willow flycatcher *Empidonax traillii*	Secure; indicator WAP Priority	Shrubby, often wet, areas including wet thickets, wet meadows, shrubby riparian areas, wet pastures, and shrubby margins of marshes. Generally found at lower elevations than alder flycatcher.
Wilson's snipe *Gallinago delicata*	Candidate – At Risk	Alder and willow swamps, peatlands, sedge bogs, fens, wet meadows and pastures. Avoids marshes with tall vegetation.
Wood duck *Aix sponsa*	Game	Wooded swamps and other forested wetlands as well as riparian forests and flooded timber. Natural or man-made cavities near still water with plentiful invertebrates.

Songbirds also depend on emergent wetlands for stopover habitat. One of the emerging bird conservation priorities has been the rusty blackbird (*Euphagus carolinus*), a widespread nesting bird of the North American boreal forest and wetlands. The rusty blackbird now is considered a PIF Watch List species of Continental Importance for the United States and Canada (Rich et al. 2004). The decline of this species has been long-term and especially precipitous since 1960 when quantitative surveys have been more available for comparisons (Greenberg and Droege 1999). The PIF plan is for a population increase of 100%, but the size of the state's population in unknown (Rich et al. 2004, Rosenberg 2004). This is one of the continent's most poorly studied species because of its retiring nature and remote breeding habitat of bogs, muskegs, and forest swamps including beaver meadows (Avery 1995). In Pennsylvania, it is most frequently seen stopping in the wetlands of northwestern Pennsylvania especially Pymatuning Swamp where it has been noted for many decades (Todd 1940, McWilliams and Brauning 2000). Many rusty blackbirds also are observed at Conneaut Marsh and at impoundments and wetlands in many counties, including the suburbs. Declines have been steeper in the eastern part of its range so the scattered Pennsylvania wetlands in the Delaware and Susquehanna River drainages may be particularly critical stopover sites. Because this species forages in shallow water and consumes both soft and hard mast in migration, there is potential for finding management practices that benefit both this migrant songbird and some waterfowl species that use the same habitat.

Although wetland birds have many common threats, each of these species has its own set of limiting factors. As a group, wetland birds are considered secretive and elusive, and difficult to inventory, monitor and research. Moreover, their nests can be very difficult to find because they are well-hidden or difficult to access (Baicich and Harrison 1997). Standardized surveys using call-broadcasts of vocalizations have been devised and their use is increasing in the region (Conway 2004, Conway and Gibbs 2005). Using this standardized approach at a large emergent wetland in northwestern Pennsylvania, Pennsylvania Audubon documented the occurrence of king rail (*Rallus elegans*), a state endangered species (Van Fleet 2008).

Pennsylvania's open water habitats provide important stopover and wintering areas for many waterfowl species (Table 4). Several locations have been designated as Important Bird Areas for this reason. Middle Creek Wildlife Management Area is a particularly important waterfowl stopover location in addition to its popularity for public viewing of wildlife. Spring migration of waterfowl can be a spectacular event, especially in Southeastern Pennsylvania where thousands of snow geese (*Chen caerulescens*), Canada geese, (*Branta canadensis*), and tundra swan (*Cygnus columbianus*) stop off at lakes, reservoirs, and rivers. Numbers of snow goose have increased in recent years and large flocks of "tens of thousands of birds" stop off at and fly over Octororo Lake, Muddy Run, and Middle Creek (Morrin et al. 1991). In a single day, observers have experienced over 125,000 snow geese at Middle Creek (McWilliams and Brauning 2000).

Riverine Habitats

Pennsylvania is second only to Alaska for its density of rivers and streams. This abundance of flowing water provides unique habitats, such as river islands, for breeding and migrating birds. Forested islands can be important nesting habitat for some of our large, rare breeding birds of the state. The most important colony for two endangered wading bird species, great egret and black-crowned night-heron, is on Wade Island near Harrisburg. Romano et al. (2006) found great egrets traveled great distances from the colony, but most birds foraged on small fish, tadpoles (*Ranidae*), and crayfish (*Cambarinae*) near the island in water willow (*Justicia americana*), a dense, emergent aquatic plant. Egrets tend to be more successful when foraging in shallower water where they especially target rusty crayfish (*Cercopagis pengoi*), a non-native species. Egret decoys were deployed on a nearby island with the hope of attracting egrets to that island, thus spreading the population over a larger area. Thus far, egrets have not initiated nesting on the "model island" but often visit the island in large numbers (T. Master, personal communication).

Table 4. Locations in Pennsylvania important to the conservation of wetland birds as identified by the Pennsylvania Important Bird Areas project (Crossley 1999). Bird list was taken from a variety of sources including IBA surveys, Pennsylvania Birds county reports, Pennsylvania Society for Ornithology Special Areas Project, and Pennsylvania Game Commission surveys.

Location	Physiographic Region	Wetland Types +	Wetland and Open Water Species Supported
Presque Isle State Park	CL	DS, EW, OW	Breeding: American bittern, least bittern, black tern, pied-billed grebe, bald eagle, osprey, marsh wren, prothonotary warbler. Migration: waterfowl, shorebirds, rusty blackbird.
Roderick Wildlife Reserve (SGL 314)	CL	SS, OW	Breeding: American woodcock and many thicket species. Migrant and wintering waterfowl.
Pymatuning, Hartstown Complex, SGL 214	AP	DS, EW, SS, OW	Breeding: American bittern, least bittern, pied-billed grebe, king rail, sora, Virginia rail, American coot, common moorhen, Wilson's snipe, northern harrier, marsh wren, prothonotary warbler. Migration: common goldeneye, hooded merganser, tundra swan; shorebirds including solitary sandpiper; rusty blackbird.
Cussawago Bottom	AP	DS	Breeding: bald eagle, pied-billed grebe, green-winged teal, prothonotary warbler. Migration: waterfowl and rusty blackbird.
Erie National Wildlife Refuge	AP	DS, SS(?)	Breeding: pied-billed grebe, bald eagle, American coot, Wilson's snipe, sedge wren. Migration: rusty blackbird.
Conneaut (Geneva) Marsh, SGL 213	AP	DS, EW, SS, OW	Breeding: pied-billed grebe, American bittern, least bittern, bald eagle, black tern, Virginia rail, sora, common moorhen, and several species of waterfowl. Migration: waterfowl, shorebirds including solitary sandpiper, rusty blackbird.
Shenango Reservoir	AP	MF, OW	Migration: waterfowl, shorebirds.
Penny, Black, and Celery Swamp, SGL 284	AP	DS, EW, SS, OW	Breeding: American bittern, least bittern, pied-billed grebe, Virginia rail, king rail, sora, American coot, marsh wren, sandhill crane. Migration: waterfowl, rusty blackbird.
The Glades, SGL 95	AP	EW, OW	Breeding: Pied-billed grebe, bald eagle, Wilson's snipe, sandhill crane, Virginia rail, sora. Migration: waterfowl and rusty blackbird.
Moraine State Park	AP	EW, OW	Breeding: bald eagle, osprey, pied-billed grebe, Virginia rail, American coot, Wilson's snipe. Migration: waterfowl and other water birds including ruddy duck, lesser scaup, redhead, American coot.
Akeley Swamp, SGL 282	AP	DS, EW, OW	Breeding: American bittern, least bittern, pied-billed grebe, king rail, Virginia rail, sora, common moorhen, American coot, northern harrier, bald eagle. Migration: osprey, bald eagle, waterfowl, shorebirds, rusty blackbird.
Lake Somerset	AP	MF, OW	Migration: waterfowl including canvasback, long-tailed duck, lesser scaup: shorebirds.
Yellow Creek State Park	AP	OW	Migration: Canada goose, tundra swan, green-winged teal, mallard, ring-necked duck, lesser scaup, bufflehead, long-tailed duck, hooded and red-breasted mergansers, ruddy duck, American coot, rusty blackbird.

(continued)

Table 4. (continued)

Location	Physiographic Region	Wetland Types +	Wetland and Open Water Species Supported
Marsh Creek Wetlands, SGL 313	AP	DS, EW, OW	Breeding: great blue heron, osprey, American bittern, least bittern, pied-billed grebe, Virginia rail, sora, common moorhen, Wilson's snipe, green-winged teal, northern harrier. Migration: rusty blackbird.
Tamarack Swamp Natural Area	AP	CS	Breeding: American woodcock, alder flycatcher, northern waterthrush, Canada warbler. Formerly: olive-sided flycatcher.
Black Moshannon State Park	AP	CS, DS, SS, OW	Breeding: pied-billed grebe, American woodcock, alder flycatcher, blue-headed vireo, Blackburnian warbler, northern waterthrush, Canada warbler. Migration: waterfowl including Canada goose, tundra swan, wood duck, ring-necked duck, greater scaup, red-breasted merganser.
Sheets Island Archipelago	VR	MF, OW	Breeding: great egret, black-crowned night-heron. Migration: common loon, bufflehead, ring-billed and bonaparte's gulls; shorebirds. Winter: bald eagle.
Codorus State Park	VR	OW	Breeding: bald eagle. Migration: Canada goose, mallard, American black duck, redhead, bufflehead, horned grebe, American coot, ring-billed gull, Caspian tern.
Dutch Mountain Wetlands Complex, SGL 57	AP	CS, DS, SS, OW	Breeding: red-shouldered hawk, American woodcock, yellow-bellied flycatcher, olive-sided flycatcher (formerly), alder flycatcher, blue-headed vireo, magnolia warbler, Blackburnian warbler, blackpoll warbler, northern waterthrush, Canada warbler, red crossbill (occasional?).
Ricketts Glen State Park, Creveling Lake Area (SGL 13, 57)	AP	CS, DS, SS, OW	Breeding: green-winged teal, American bittern, northern harrier, yellow-bellied flycatcher (formerly, occasional?), olive-sided flycatcher (formerly), blue-headed vireo, Swainson's thrush, magnolia warbler, blackburnian warbler, northern waterthrush, Canada warbler. Migration: waterfowl, shorebirds.
Susquehanna Riverlands	VR	OW	Breeding: American black duck (formerly), alder flycatcher, willow flycatcher. Migration: Canada goose, mallard, American black duck, wood duck, ring-necked duck, common merganser, black tern, rusty blackbird.
Lake Ontelaunee	NE	OW	Migration: Canada goose, snow goose, wood duck, horned grebe, osprey.
Blue Marsh Lake	NE	OW	Migration: Canada goose, snow goose, redhead, ring-necked duck, bufflehead, common merganser.
Middle Creek Management Area	PI	DS, SS, EW, OW	Breeding: bald eagle. Migration: waterfowl including tundra swan, Canada goose, snow goose, mallard, redhead, common merganser.
Conejehola Flats	PI	MF, OW	Breeding: bald eagle, osprey, prothonotary warbler. Migration: tundra swan, Canada goose, snow goose, mallard, wood duck, common merganser. Shorebirds: including semipalmated sandpiper, spotted sandpiper, greater yellowlegs, lesser yellowlegs, least sandpiper, buff-breasted sandpiper. Forster's tern.
Conowingo Reservoir, Muddy Run	PI	MF, OW	Breeding: bald eagle, osprey. Migration: tundra swan, snow goose, American black duck.

(continued)

Table 4. (continued)

Location	Physiographic Region	Wetland Types +	Wetland and Open Water Species Supported
Octorora Reservoir	PI	OW	Breeding: bald eagle, prothonotary warbler. Migration: Canada goose, snow goose, common merganser.
Upper Delaware Scenic River	AP	OW	Breeding: bald eagle, osprey, cerulean warbler. Winter: bald eagle.
Shohola Wildlife Management Area, SGL 180	AP	EW, OW	Breeding: wood duck, American black duck, bald eagle, American woodcock, golden-winged warbler, Canada warbler. Migration: Canada goose, wood duck, American black duck, mallard, golden-winged warbler, rusty blackbird.
Promised Land State Park / Bruce Lake Natural Area	AP	OW	Breeding: bald eagle, American woodcock, blue-headed vireo, magnolia warbler, blackburnian warbler, northern waterthrush, Canada warbler. Migrants: waterfowl and shorebirds.
Pocono Lake Preserve	AP	CS, DS, SS, OW	Breeding : American woodcock, osprey, yellow-bellied flycatcher (formerly), alder flycatcher, olive-sided flycatcher (formerly), blue-headed vireo, magnolia warbler, blackburnian warbler, northern waterthrush, Canada warbler.
Long Pond Preserve	AP	OW	Breeding: American bittern, northern harrier, Alder flycatcher, olive-sided flycatcher, Canada warbler, golden-winged warbler, northern waterthrush, Canada warbler.
Quakertown Swamp, SGL 139	PI	DS, EW, SS	Breeding: American bittern, least bittern, Virginia rail, sora, marsh wren. Migration: shorebirds especially solitary sandpiper and rusty blackbird.
Peace Valley Park	PI	OW	Migration: Canada goose, mallard, wood duck, osprey, bald eagle.
Green Lane Reservoir	PI	OW	Breeding: bald eagle.
Glen Morgan Lake	PI	OW	Breeding: ruddy duck, pied-billed grebe, American coot.
Great Marsh	PI	EW, SS	Breeding: American bittern, least bittern, pied-billed grebe, Virginia rail, sora, American coot, marsh wren. Migration: rusty blackbird.
John Heinz NWR at Tinicum and Mud Island	AC	OW	Breeding: American Bittern, least bittern, Virginia rail, marsh wren. Migration: northern pintail, green-winged teal, semipalmated sandpiper, pectoral sandpiper, rusty blackbird.

Notes: Physiographic Regions: Central Lowlands (CL); Applachian Plateau Province (AP); Valley and Ridge Province (VR); Piedmont Province (PI); New England Province (NE); Atlantic Coastal Plain Province (AC).

+ Abbreviations for wetland types: DS: Deciduous swamp (deciduous forested wetland); EM: emergent marsh; EW: emergent wetland; MF: mud flats; NS: needle-leafed (coniferous) swamp; OW: open water; SS: scrub-shrub wetland

Night-herons are extremely rare in the state. The southeastern counties seem to be a stronghold for the Commonwealth's black-crowned night-heron population, so it is alarming that most of the larger, more established colonies are steadily declining in this region (Haffner et al. 2008). It is possible that in these larger colonies black-crowned night-herons are dispersing to form smaller colonies in surrounding areas due to loss of nest trees and human disturbance (Kim Van Fleet, personal communication). Yellow-crowned night-herons are very restricted in range and the rarest of the state's wading birds. Inexplicably, this species is fairly tolerant of some human activities and readily nests along wooded streams near humans, including backyards. The tendency of this species to nest in urban and suburban areas is not unique to Pennsylvania, but is characteristic of the Chesapeake Bay area including Virginia (Watts 1989). It is suspected these herons may benefit from human proximity by avoiding predation by large nocturnal predators such as great horned owls (*Bubo virginianus*).

Riverine wetlands, or floodplains, occur along riparian corridors of rivers and streams across the Commonwealth. The importance of this transition zone from aquatic to terrestrial systems is often not recognized. These areas are essential for maintaining hydrological connectivity between groundwater and surface water. This connection lessens the impact from floods, promotes groundwater recharge, and normalizes stream flow. Characteristic floodplain tree species, namely sycamore (*Platanus occidentalis*), red maple (*Acer rubrum*), silver maple (*Acer saccarinum*), American and red elm (*Ulmus spp.*), ashes (*Fraxinus spp.*), birches (*Betula spp.*) and willows (*Salix spp.*), provide foraging opportunities and nesting sites for numerous bird species including Baltimore oriole (*Icterus galbula*), bald eagle (*Haliaeetus leucocephalus*), and great blue heron. In fact, the largest great blue heron rookery in Pennsylvania (over 200 nests) thrives in towering sycamores within the floodplain of the Little Shenango River, Mercer County.

WETLAND CONSERVATION AND MANAGEMENT

Conservation

Many threats are commonly mentioned for most or all wetland types and, thus, wetland bird communities, including wetland loss (quantity and quality), pollution from sediments, pesticides and other contaminants, invasive species, lack of habitat complexity, and climate change (Schneider and Pence 1992, Chang 2004). Conserving the state's remaining wetlands is of greatest importance to support sustainable wetland bird communities. However, in addition to protecting the existing wetland, the surrounding landscape must also be protected. If the wetland is inadequately buffered by a zone of undisturbed vegetation, polluted run-off (sediment, nutrients, and chemicals) can reduce the quality of wildlife habitat. Maintaining a buffer also provides additional habitat for wetland birds. For example, American bitterns (*Botaurus lentiginosus*) and green-winged teals (*Anas crecca*) will nest in upland vegetation near the wetland if it is available (Gibbs et al. 1992, Johnson 1995).

Along with conservation, wetland restoration and creation can positively affect wetland bird communities. Most wetland birds do not require pristine conditions and adapt readily to changes. Emergent and shrub-scrub wetlands can be created by natural and man-made processes. Wetland birds can react quickly to these opportunities and will colonize new or altered wetlands opportunistically. For example, beavers (*Castor canadensis*) create wetland habitat by damming streams and thus flooding adjacent areas. Beaver ponds provide the open water and a prey-base for open-water wetland species such as pied-billed grebe (*Podilymbus podiceps*), American coot (*Fulica americana*), and common moorhen. Newly created, open water attracts pied-billed grebes fairly quickly. American coots will also pioneer new wetlands and ponds quickly and will respond to creation of new wetland habitat (Aliskauskas and Arnold 1994). This was observed when Pymatuning Lake was created (Grimm 1952). Coots tend to swim out into open areas more than the closely related common moorhen. Where there is extensive emergent vegetation, openings created by muskrats (*Ondatra zibethicus*) may be an important feature for grebes and other swimming waterbirds, helping to maintain the open aquatic habitat they prefer. If not already present, emergent vegetation and shrubs will colonize wet areas soon afterward especially if a history of wetland habitat provides a seed base.

Colonization of new wetlands by birds often follows a series of stages as vegetation responds to water levels. Species such as American woodcock (*Scolopax minor*) and Wilson's snipe (*Gallinago delicata*) can colonize open meadows and seasonally flooded areas while swamp sparrows (*Melospiza georgiana*) and alder flycatchers respond to new emergent vegetation and scrub-shrub habitat, respectively. Many species of scrub habitat are predisposed to colonize new habitats and even declining species, such as golden-winged warbler, will respond to new opportunities. Disturbance regimes may be required for the continued occupancy of wetlands and scrublands by golden-winged warblers and other early successional species (Hunter et al. 2001).

Management

Management and maintenance of constructed wetlands, particularly for moist-soil habitat, is an important consideration to ensure high biological diversity and abundance (Lane and Jensen 1999). Proper timing and control of water levels will create moist-soil or deep water habitats at times most advantageous to migrating and breeding waterfowl and marshbirds (Jacobs et al. 1992, Lane and Jensen 1999). Slow draw downs in April or May enable seed germination for aquatic plants and expose moist-soil habitats, rich in macroinvertebrates, tubers, and seeds, that offers prime foraging opportunities for shorebirds, waterfowl, wading birds, and upland wildlife (Jacobs et al. 1992, Lane and Jensen 1999). Moderate flooding in winter to early spring attracts migrating waterfowl and other waterbirds (Jacobs et al. 1992, Lane and Jensen 1999). By actively monitoring and adjusting water levels in constructed wetlands, it is possible to provide critical habitat for imperiled songbirds (e.g. marsh wren - *Cistothorus palustris*) and marshbirds (e. g. least bittern - *Ixobrychus exilis*) as well as wetland game species (e.g. ducks and geese).

Encroachment of non-native invasive species in wetlands (e.g. purple loosestrife (*Lythrum salicaria*), reed canarygrass (*Phalaris arundinacea*), common reed (*Phragmites australis*)) poses a significant threat to vegetation heterogeneity (Thompson et al. 1987) and, therefore, control methods should be identified in management plans. Federal and state agencies, such as the U.S. Department of Agriculture and Pennsylvania Department of Conservation and Natural Resources, offer resources and assistance to control non-native invasive species. Optimal suppression techniques vary with each invasive species and can include mechanical, chemical, and/or biological control methods. For example, Pennsylvania was one of the first states to release non-native beetles (*Galerucella* spp.) to control purple loosestrife, only after extensive studies demonstrated that the beetles targeted only the non-native loosestrife (Malecki et al. 1993, Hight et al. 1995, Blossey 2002). Efficacy of the beetle releases continues to be assessed; however several states have observed complete defoliation of purple loosestrife and a 95% reduction in biomass (Blossey 2002). Preventing the spread of purple loosestrife and other noxious wetland weeds is paramount to maintaining interstitial spaces between wetland vegetation that are used by imperiled marshbirds for protective cover and foraging.

THE FUTURE FOR WETLAND BIRDS

Restoring and sustaining viable populations of wetland birds will require restoring and sustaining the ecosystems upon which they depend. The rate of wetland loss has declined over the decades, although we continue to convert an estimated 75 wetland acres per year statewide to other uses, primarily developed lands (Pennsylvania Game Commission and Pennsylvania Fish and Boat Commission 2005). The outlook for the future is promising, however. Governmental incentive programs to restore and create wetlands (e.g. U.S. Department of Agriculture Natural Resources Conservation Service's Wildlife Habitat Incentives Program and Environmental Quality Incentives Program) coupled with environmental laws requiring no net loss of wetland habitat (e.g. Pennsylvania Department of Environmental Protection Chapter 105) have succeeded in regaining nearly 4,000 acres of wetlands across the state since 1990 (Pennsylvania Department of Environmental Protection 2000). Through partnerships, enhanced monitoring activities, and smart land use planning decisions, we can strive to protect Pennsylvania's most valuable wetlands and the unique assemblage of birds found within them for future generations to enjoy.

Acknowledgments

We thank D. Brauning, J. Haffner, and S. Rier for their useful comments on earlier drafts of this manuscript.

LITERATURE CITED

Aliskauskas, R. T. and T. W. Arnold. 1994. American Coot. Chapter 9, pages 126–143 In Migratory Shore and Upland Game Bird Management in North America. (T. C. Tacha and C. E. Braun, eds.) International Assoc. of Fish and Wildlife Agencies In Cooperation with Fish and Wildlife Service, U.S. Dept of Interior, Allen Press, Lawrence, KS.

Avery, M. L. 1995. Rusty Blackbird (*Euphagus carolinus*). In The Birds of North America, No. 200 (A. Poole and F. Gill, eds.). The Academy of Natural Sciences, Philadelphia, and The American Ornithologists' Union, Washington, D.C.

Blossey, B. 2002. In: Van Driesche, R., et al. Biological Control of Invasive Plants in the Eastern United States, USDA Forest Service Publication FHTET-2002-04, 413 p.

Brauning, D. W. Editor. 1992. Atlas of Breeding Birds in Pennsylvania. University of Pittsburgh Press, Pittsburgh, Pennsylvania.

Brauning, D. W., Brittingham, M. C., Gross, D. A., Leberman, R. C., Master, T. L. and R. S. Leberman. 1994. Pennsylvania Breeding Birds of Special Concern: Listing Rationale and Status Update. Journal of Pennsylvania Academy of Science 68: 3–28.

Brooks, R. P. and M. J. Croonquist. 1990. Wetland habitat, and trophic response guilds for wildlife species in Pennsylvania. J. of the Pennsylvania Acad. Of Science 64: 93–102.

Brown, S., Hickey, C., Harrington, B., and R. Gill, eds. 2001. United States shorebird conservation plan, 2nd Ed. Manomet Center for Conservation Sciences, Manomet, MA.

Chang, H. 2004. Water quality impacts of climate change and land use changes in southeastern Pennsylvania. The Professional Geographer 56: 240 – 257.

Conway, C. J. 2004. Standardized North American Marsh Bird Monitoring Protocols. Wildlife Research Report #2004-07. U.S. G. S. Wildlife Research Report #2004-07.

Conway, C. J. and J. P. Gibbs. 2005. Effectiveness of call-broadcast surveys for monitoring marsh birds. Auk 122: 26–35.

Cowardin, L. M., V. Carter, F. C. Golet, and E. T. LaRoe. 1979. Classification of wetlands and deep-water habitats of the United States. FWS/OBS – 79/31. Office of Biological Services, Fish and Wildlife Services, U. S. Department of the Interior, Washington, D.C.

Crossley, G. J. (compiler). 1999. A guide to critical bird habitat in Pennsylvania: Pennsylvania Important Bird Areas Program. Pennsylvania Audubon Society, Harrisburg, PA.

Dahl, T. E. and S. C. Zoltai. 1997. Forested northern wetlands of North America. Pp. 3–18 In Northern Forested Wetlands Ecology and Management (C. C. Trettin, M. F. Jurgensen, D. F. Grigal, M. R. Gale, and J. K. Jeglum, eds). CRC Press, Boca Roton, FL.

Falls, J. B. and J. G. Kopachena. 1994. White-throated Sparrow (*Zonotrichia albicollis*). In The Birds of North America, No. 126 (A. Poole and F. Gill, eds.). The Birds of North America, Inc., Philadelphia, PA.

Fike, J. 1999. Terrestrial and palustrine plant communities of Pennsylvania. Pennsylvania Department of Conservation and Natural Resources, Harrisburg; The Nature Conservancy, Middletown,and Western Pennsylvania Conservancy, Pittsburgh.

Goodrich, L.M.J., Brittingham, M.B., Bishop, J.A. and P. Barber. 2002. Wildlife habitat in Pennsylvania: Past, present and future. Report to State Agencies. Dept. Conservation and Natural Resources, Harrisburg, Pennsylvania.

Greenberg, R. and S. Droege. 1999. On the decline of the rusty blackbird and the use of ornithological literature to document long-term population trends. Conservation Biology 13: 553–559.

Grimm, W. C. 1952. Birds of the Pymatuning region. Pennsylvania Game Commission, Harrisburg, Pennsylvania.

Gross, D. A. 1998. Birds: review of status in Pennsylvania. Pages 137–170 In Inventory and monitoring of biotic resources in Pennsylvania [J. D. Hassinger, R. J. Hill, G. L. Storm, and R. H. Yahner, tech. Editors]. Pennsylvania Biological Survey.

_____. 2002. The status, distribution, and conservation of the yellow-bellied flycatcher. Final Report for WS #023 01 4150 01 for the Pennsylvania Game Commission, Harrisburg, Pennsylvania.

_____. 2003. Avian population and habitat assessment project: Pennsylvania important bird area #48 —- state game lands #57, Wyoming, Luzerne, and Sullivan counties. Ecology III, Inc., 804 Salem Boulevard, Berwick, Pennsylvania 18603.

Haffner, C. D., Gross, D. A. and D. Seifkin. 2008. Colonial nesting bird study. Annual job report number 70004 submitted to Pennsylvania Game Commission, Harrisburg, Pennsylvania.

Hall, G. A. 1985. A long-term bird population study in an Appalachian spruce forest. Wilson Bull. 96: 228–240.

Hight, S. D., Blossey, B., Laing, J. and R. DeClerck-Floate. 1995. Establishment of insect biological control agents from Europe against *Lythrum salicaria in North America*. Environmental Entomology 24: 967–977.

Hunter, W. C., Buehler, D. A., Canterbury, R. A. J., Confer, L. and P. B. Hamel. 2001. Conservation of disturbance-dependent birds in North America. Wildlife Society Bulletin 29: 440–455.

Jacobs, K. J., Diefenbach, D. R. and J. P. Dunn. 1992. Predictions of emergent vegetation establishment following drawdown in various state game lands. Final Project Report 06510, Job 51005. Pennsylania Game Commission, Harrisburg, USA.

Johnson, K. 1995. Green-winged Teal (*Anas crecca*). In The Birds of North America, No. 193. A. Poole and F. Gill, eds.). The Academy of Natural Sciences, Philadelphia, PA.

King, D. I., Lambert, J. D., Buoncaccorsi, J. P. and L. S. Prout. 2008. Avian population trends in the vulnerable montane forests of the Northern Appalachians, USA. Biodiversity and Conservation 17: 2691–2700.

Lane, J. J. and K. C. Jensen. 1999. Moist-soil impoundments for wetland wildlife. Technical Report EL-99-11, U.S. Army Engineer Research and Development Center, Vicksburg, Mississippi.

Malecki, R. A., Blossey, B., Hight, D., Schroeder, D., Kok, L. T. and J. R. Coulson, 1993. Biological control of purple loosestrife. BioScience 43: 680–686.

McWilliams, J., and D. Brauning. 2000. The Birds of Pennsylvania. Cornell University Press, Ithaca, New York, USA.

Morrin, H. B., ed. committee chairman. 1991. A guide to the birds of Lancaster County, Pennsylvania. Lancaster County Bird Club.

Myers, W.L., et al. 2000. Pennsylvania Gap Analysis Project: Leading landscapes for collaborative conservation. Final Report. U.S. Geol. Survey-Gap Analysis Program.

Pennsylvania Department of Environmental Protection. 2000. Wetland restoration summary 1990–1999. Unpublished report. Pennsylvania Department of Environmental Protection, Bureau of Water Quality Protection, Division of Waterways, Wetlands, and Erosion Control, Harrisburg, Pennsylvania.

Pennsylvania Game Commission and Pennsylvania Fish and Boat Commission. 2005. Pennsylvania Comprehensive Wildlife Conservation Strategy, Version 1.0. www.pgc.state.pa.us/pgc/lib/pgc/SWG/PAWAP.pdf

Poole, A. (Editor). 2009. The Birds of North America Online: http://bna.birds.cornell.edu/BNA. Cornell Laboratory of Ornithology, Ithaca, NY.

Reed, P. B. 1988. National list of plant species that occur in wetlands: 1988 national summary. U. S. Fish and Wildlife Service, Washington Biol. Rep. 88 (24).

Rhoads, A. F. and W. M. Klein, Jr. 1993. The vascular flora of Pennsylvania: annotated checklist and atlas. American Philosophical Society, Philadelphia, PA.

Rich, T. D., Beardmore, C. J., Berlanga, H., Blancher, P. J., Bradstreet, M. S. W., Butcher, G. S., Demarest, D. W., Dunn, E. H., Hunter, W. C., Inogo-Elias, E. E., Kennedy, J. A., Martell, A.M., Panjabi, A. O., Pashley, D.N., Rosenberg, K. V., Rustay, C. M., Wendt, J. S. and T. C. Will. 2004. Partners in Flight North American landbird conservation plan, Cornell Laboratory of Ornithology, Ithaca, NY.

Romano, B., Detwiler, D. and T. Master (East Stroudsburg University). 2006. Great egrets in the city: habitat selection and foraging behavior on the Susquehanna River in Harrisburg, PA. Poster at IV North American Ornithological Conference, Veracruz, Mexico, October 2006.

Rosenberg, K. P. 2004. Partners in Flight continental priorities and objectives defined at the state and bird conservation region levels: Pennsylvania. Cornell Laboratory of Ornithology, Ithaca, NY.

Schneider, K. J. and D. M. Pence (Editors). 1992. Migratory nongame birds of management concern in the northeast. U.S. Department of the Interior. Fish and Wildlife Service, Region 5. Newton Square, MA.

Thompson, D. Q., Stuckey, R. L. and E. B. Thompson. 1987. Spread, impact, and control of purple loosestrife. U.S. Fish Wildlife Service, Fish and Wildlife Restoration 2:1–55.

Tiner, R. W. 1987. Mid-Atlantic wetlands: a disappearing natural treasure. U.S. Fish and Wildlife Service, Fish and Wildlife Enhancement, National Wetlands Inventory Project. Newton Corner, Massachusetts.

_____. 1990. Pennsylvania's wetlands: Current status and recent trends. Pennsylvania Bureau of Water Resources Management. Harrisburg, Pennsylvania. USA.

_____. 1993. Using plants as indicators of wetland. Pages 240 – 253 In Wetland plants: diversity, function, and importance – a symposium. Proceedings of The Academy of Natural Sciences of Pennsylvania 144: 239–340.

_____. 1998. In search of swampland: a wetland sourcebook and field guide. Rutgers University Press, New Brunswick, New Jersey, and London.

Todd, W. E. C. 1940. Birds of western Pennsylvania. University of Pittsburgh Press, Pittsburgh, PA.

U.S. Department of the Interior and Environment Canada. 1986. North American waterfowl management plan. U.S. Department of the Interior, Washington, D.C., USA.

U.S. Fish and Wildlife Service. 2002. Birds of conservation concern, 2002. Division of Migratory Bird Management, Arlington, VA.

Van Fleet, K. 2008. Marsh bird monitoring conservation project, January 2006 through December 2007. A report submitted to Pennsylvania Game Commission, Wildlife Diversity Section, State Wildlife Grant center.

Watts, B. D. 1989. Nest-site characteristics of yellow-crowned night-herons in Virginia. Condor 91: 979–983.

Weller, M. W. and C. S. Spatcher. 1965. Role of habitat in the distribution and abundance of marsh-birds. Iowa State Univ., Agric. And Home Econ. Exp. Sta., Spec. Rep. 43, Ames, Iowa.

Avian Ecology and Conservation: A Pennsylvania Focus with National Implications. Edited by S. K. Majumdar, T. L. Master, M. C. Brittingham, R. M. Ross, R. S. Mulvihill and J. E. Huffman. © 2010. The Pennsylvania Academy of Science.

Chapter 4

Avian Community Characteristics and Riparian Habitats

Terry L. Master
Department of Biological Sciences, East Stroudsburg University of Pennsylvania
200 Prospect Street, East Stroudsburg, Pennsylvania 18301-2999
terry.master@po-box.esu.edu

INTRODUCTION

Definition

The word riparian is sometimes used synonymously with riverine, thus giving the impression that the term applies only to relatively large rivers. In fact, it can apply to a first order rivulet emanating at a seep in a hemlock ravine to the largest of meandering rivers. Technically, even the shorelines of ponds and lakes fall within the realm of riparian habitat although this chapter will focus more narrowly on streams and rivers. It is derived from the Latin, "riparious" meaning bank, as in stream bank, but also refers to land adjacent to any body of water. Some authorities exclude the aquatic component completely and apply the term only to surrounding land, others include both terrestrial and aquatic components (Karr and Schlosser 1978). Official definitions consequently abound but most consider riparian zones to be characterized by hydrophytic vegetation, degree of soil saturation, microclimate, geology, land-forms, natural disturbances and characteristic soils and vegetation types (Swanson et al. 1988, Brosofske 1996). A more detailed view defines riparian corridors as "encompassing the stream channel and that portion of the terrestrial landscape from the high water mark toward the uplands where vegetation may be influenced by elevated water tables or flooding and the ability of soils to hold water" (Naiman et al. 1993). The Eastern Region of the U.S. Forest Service concludes that riparian areas are "composed of aquatic ecosystems, riparian ecosystems and wetlands. They have three dimensions: longitudinal, extending up and down streams and along the shores; lateral to the estimated boundary of land with direct land-water interactions; and vertical from below the water table to above the canopy of mature trees" (Parrott et al. 1989). Whatever the definition, the following basic characteristics are commonly associated with riparian areas (Lock and Naiman 1998, Ilhardt et al. 2000):

1) water or a feature that contains or transports water for a portion of the year

2) ecotones between aquatic and terrestrial ecosystems

3) abiotic and biotic interactions that occur predictably in relation to stream order

4) highly variable widths or boundaries

5) characteristic disturbance regimes

Extent of Riparian Habitat

Nationally, the extent of riparian habitat is difficult to estimate due to differing definitions, as described above, and whether or not it is measured by stream length or acreage.
The National Resources Inventory and the U.S. Environmental Protection Agency (EPA),
both of which consider riparian habitat to extend 15.24 m (50 ft) from the edge of streams
and rivers, estimate there are 26 million ha (62 million acres) and 16 million ha (38 million
acres), respectively, of wetlands excluding Alaska (National Research Council – Riparian
Areas). Brinson et al. (1981) liberally estimates an upper limit of 50 million ha (121 million acres) based on lands within 100-year flood plains in the continental United States. The
EPA estimates 5,353,600 km (3,346,000 mi) of streams and rivers in the lower 48 states.

Pennsylvania contains approximately 132,800 km (83,000 mi) of streams and rivers with
riparian habitat covering 71,695 ha (172, 067 acres) (PA DCNR) These rivers and streams
are divided into seven drainage basins. The major basins are the Ohio, Allegheny, Susquehanna and Delaware drainages. Minor basins include the Potomac in south central Pennsylvania, the Genesee in the north central portion of the state and the Monongahela in the
southwest. Riparian acreage is greatest in Dauphin County along the Susquehanna River
(8322 ha -19,972 acres), Northumberland County where both branches of the Susquehanna
River meet (4808 ha - 11, 540 acres) and Allegheny County (3985 ha - 9,564 acres).

Biodiversity

There are a variety of ways that diversity can be measured, largely based on spatial scale
and whether the diversity being measured is within a habitat or that associated with the rate
of change of diversity among habitats. Alpha (within habitat), beta (rate of change among
habitats) and gamma (within a landscape scale or larger area) diversity are the diversity
terms most commonly used (Ward and Tockner 2001). In the western United States, alpha
diversity is especially high in riparian habitats relative to the number of potential species
(Knopf and Samson 1994). Beta diversity varies across a watershed where riparian avian
communities differ most from surrounding terrestrial communities at the highest and lowest elevations. The longitudinal riparian corridor facilitates movement, and thus mixing, of
species on a landscape or larger scale which increases gamma diversity.

The definitions given above imply that because terrestrial and aquatic species meet
along a riparian ecotone, diversity levels are raised above those of the surrounding external habitat. Indeed, diversity is perhaps the most frequently cited attribute of riparian systems and thus it will be used, along with distribution and abundance, throughout this chapter as a unifying theme to describe how riparian bird communities are affected by abiotic
and biotic interactions laterally across stream valleys, longitudinally from low to high
order streams and with regard to succession.

Context and Perspective

The importance of riparian habitat to avian biodiversity is also dependent upon the landscape context within which streams and rivers flow. The degree of difference in habitats
that meet along riparian features influences the level of biodiversity that riparian ecotones
support. In the east, habitats interfacing with forested riparian ecotones run the gamut from
agriculture and open habitats to shrub dominated and forested ones, the latter often con-

sisting of forest differing in composition from the riparian forest itself, especially at the highest and lowest watershed elevations. The likelihood of an open habitat interface with riparian forest increases as stream order increases.

The number of birds dependent upon riparian habitat is difficult to estimate because the degree of dependency varies considerably and is subject to individual interpretation. Table 1 lists 43 species of birds found in the eastern United States considered to have a reasonably strong preference for riparian habitat at some season of the year (DeGraff and Yamasaki 2000). This total represents 9.5% of the approximately 450 species inhabiting the eastern United States.

In contrast, riparian forests in the Great Plains and southwestern United States meet vastly different desert/grassland habitats creating a more definitive ecotone supporting a wider array and/or greater proportion of species than in the east (Szaro 1980, Tubbs 1980). Some riparian forests in the southwest support 50% of the bird species inhabiting the entire region (Johnson et al. 1977, Kreuper 1996). More than 60% of the non-game migratory bird species identified as conservation priorities by Partners In Flight, consisting of millions of individuals, regularly use western riparian areas for breeding, migration or wintering habitat (Kreuper 1993). In northern Colorado, 82% of all bird species utilize riparian vegetation (Knopf and Samson 1994). These western percentages may represent facultative, as well as obligate use of riparian areas but nevertheless the proportion of birds dependent on riparian habitat is much higher in the great plains and southwest where riparian ecotones are distinct and where such areas are often the only available source of water.

RIPARIAN STRUCTURE AND BIODIVERSITY

Riparian ecotones are characterized by lateral and longitudinal zonation, an elongated shape with a high edge-to-area ratio, sharp physical gradients (e.g., soil and air temperature, relative humidity, incident solar radiation and wind velocity) and characteristic vegetation patterns (e,g,, species composition, density, biomass, basal area and successional stage) (Naiman et al. 2005). These features are affected by types, frequency and severity of disturbances that typify the dynamic nature of riparian habitat and create successional habitats. These attributes conspire to create numerous microhabitats and are thus the underlying cause of high riparian biodiversity (Crow et al. 1994, Brosofske et al. 1997).

Lateral Zonation

Lateral zonation is most obviously manifested by well-defined valley and fluvian landforms (e.g., sloughs, oxbow lakes, depositional shelves, active channel bars, natural levees, swales, alluvial terraces, benches and steep banks), arranged from most to least hydric, based on increasing height above the wetted channel, decreasing flow duration and flooding frequency and characterized by distinctive vegetative communities based on the landforms and on soil structure and composition (Hupp and Osterkamp 1985, 1996; Brinson 1990; Rot et al. 2000). Even the narrow, steep valleys often associated with headwater streams support different vegetative types and structures along an elevational gradient (Nilsson 1992). Caterral et al. (2001) found that of the physical variables measured at a site in Australia, elevation played the major role in determining avian community characteristics.

Table 1. Pennsylvania bird species frequently associated with riparian habitats.

Species Common Name	Species Scientific Name	Seasonality	Riparian Habitat Preference*
Double-crested Cormorant	*Phalacrocorax auritus*	summer resident	Susquehanna River
Least Bittern	*Ixobrychus exilis*	summer resident	Delaware River
Yellow-crowned Night-Heron	*Nyctanassa violacea*	summer resident	Susquehanna River tributaries
Black-crowned Night-Heron	*Nycticorax nycticorax*	summer resident	Susquehanna River and tributaries
Great Blue Heron	*Ardea herodias*	permanent resident	rivers
Great Egret	*Ardea alba*	summer resident	Susquehanna River
Snowy Egret	*Egretta thula*	formerly summer resident	Susquehanna River
Cattle Egret	*Bulbucus ibis*	formerly summer resident	Susquehanna River
Glossy Ibis	*Plegadis falcinellus*	formerly summer resident	Susquehanna River
Common Goldeneye	*Bucephala clangula*	winter resident	rivers
Bufflehead	*Bucephala albeola*	winter resident	rivers
Common Merganser	*Mergus merganser*	permanent resident	rivers and smaller streams
Common Loon	*Gavia immer*	winter resident	rivers
Osprey	*Pandion haliaetus*	summer resident	rivers
Bald Eagle	*Haliaeetus leucocephala*	permanent resident	rivers
Red-shouldered Hawk	*Buteo lineatus*	summer resident	hemlock ravines, benches
Wislon's Snipe	*Gallinago delicata*	migrant, summer resident	streamside wetlands
American Woodcock	*Scolopax minor*	summer resident	streamside wetlands, thickets
Caspian Tern	*Hydroprogne caspia*	winter resident, migrant	rivers
Barred Owl	*Strix varia*	permanent resident	hemlock ravines, benches
Belted Kingfisher	*Ceryle alcyon*	permanent resident	streams, rivers
Acadian Flycatcher	*Empidonax virescens*	summer resident	hemlock ravines, benches, stream margins

(continued)

Earlier, serial stages of vascular plants and herbaceous vegetation are typically found adjacent to the wetted channel where there are relatively low nutrient levels, more intense light penetration and more frequent and severe disturbance (Fonda 1974, Higler 1993, Vada and Sanger 1997). At slightly higher elevations there is a larger proportion of woody, long-lived, shade tolerant and often water tolerant vascular plant species. In locations with well-defined elevational gradients, such as headwater streams, plant communities are more distinct compared with gradual elevational changes downstream that broaden lateral overlaps in vegetation communities. Vegetation patterns, including both species composition and structure, play a key role in the distribution of riparian birds.

In the Delaware Water Gap National Recreation Area (DEWA) in northeastern Pennsylvania and northwestern New Jersey, one of the most distinct, lateral riparian ecotones occurs on headwater streams between surrounding, upland deciduous forests, composed largely of oak (*Quercus* spp.), hickory (*Carya* spp.) and red maple (*Acer rubrum*) and eastern hemlock (*Tsuga canadensis*) stands found adjacent to, and extending narrowly along

Table 1. (continued)

Species Common Name	Species Scientific Name	Seasonality	Riparian Habitat Preference*
Eastern Phoebe	*Sayornis phoebe*	summer resident	streams
Blue-headed Vireo	*Vireo solitarius*	summer resident	hemlock ravines
Yellow-throated Vireo	*Vireo flavifrons*	summer resident	rivers lined with tall shade trees
Warbling Vireo	*Vireo gilvus*	summer resident	rivers lined with tall shade trees
Fish Crow	*Corvus ossifragus*	permanent resident	rivers
Bank Swallow	*Riapria riparia*	summer resident	rivers
Marsh Wren	*Cistothorus palustris*	summer resident	Delaware River
Winter Wren	*Troglodytes troglodytes*	summer resident	hemlock ravines, benches
Veery	*Catharus fuscescens*	summer resident	riparian margins
Prothonotary Warbler	*Protonotaria citrea*	summer resident	rivers
Northern Parula	*Parula americana*	summer resident	hemlock ravines, benches
Magnolia Warbler	*Dendroica magnolia*	summer resident	hemlock ravines, benches
Yellow-rumped Warbler	*Dendroica coronata*	summer resident	hemlock ravines, benches
Blackburnian Warbler	*Dendroica fusca*	summer resident	hemlock ravines, benches
Black-throated Green Warbler	*Dendroica virens*	summer resident	hemlock ravines, benches
Yellow-throated Warbler	*Dendroica dominica*	summer resident	rivers lined with tall shade trees
Cerulean Warbler	*Dendroica caerulea*	summer resident	rivers lined with tall shade trees
Kentucky Warbler	*Oporornis formosus*	summer resident	riparian margins
Canada Warbler	*Wilsonia canadensis*	summer resident	riparian margins
Louisiana Waterthrush	*Seiurus motacilla*	summer resident	streams
Orchard Oriole	*Icterus spurius*	summer resident	rivers lined with tall shade trees

* sources include Atlas of Breeding Birds in Pennsylvania (Brauning 1992), 2nd Pennsylvania Breeding Bird Atlas, Birds of Pennsylvania (McWilliams and Brauning 2000), Pennsylvania Wildlife Action Plan (2006), DeGraff and Yamasaki 2000, and personal observation.

stream benches and steep ravines. These stands host a characteristic, near-obligate, bird assemblage that includes barred owl (*Strix varia*), Acadian flycatcher (*Empidonax virens*), winter wren (*Troglodytes troglodytes*), blue-headed vireo (*Vireo solitarius*), black-throated green warbler (*Dendroica virens*), blackburnian warbler (*Dendroica fusca*) and Louisiana waterthrush (*Seiurus motacilla*) (Swartzentruber 2003, Ross et al. 2004, Allen et al. 2009), as well as species like the veery, (*Catharus virescens*) which are often more abundant than in the surrounding, more xeric upland deciduous forest (TM, personal observation). Ross et al. (2004) noted that species richness and pair density were higher on hemlock benches than in ravines underscoring the importance that physical attributes, such as valley shape and width, may have on avian community structure.

Diversity and Richness

As stated previously, bird species diversity and richness generally increase in riparian areas compared to surrounding uplands. In the lower Mississippi River valley, 100 species of birds are seasonally associated with bottomland riparian forests (Klimas et al. 1981).

Numerous other studies in riparian zones with ecotones between contrasting habitats have confirmed this general pattern in species richness (Smith 1977, Dickson 1978, Stauffer and Best 1980, Szaro 1980, Tubbs 1980).

However, species diversity may not be higher in situations where riparian habitat is similar to upland habitat or is not clearly distinct. Murray and Stauffer (1995) sampled measures of bird abundance and habitat characteristics along an elevational gradient from stream to upland in southwestern Virginia. Results indicated no significant riparian influence on total bird relative abundance or species richness. Only the Acadian flycatcher and Louisiana waterthrush showed a significant positive association with streams.

Sabo et al. (2005) analyzed species richness patterns described in numerous studies covering a wide range of taxa, including birds, and found that riparian zones did not harbor more species but rather provided habitat for a different subset of species than those typical of adjacent uplands. For example, the distinctiveness of bird species composition in riparian hemlock stands was highlighted above but Ross et al. (2004) noted that overall species richness was lower than in surrounding deciduous habitat. Thus, riparian zones did not influence localized alpha species richness but did significantly increase gamma or regional richness. In fact, inclusion of riparian habitats can easily increase regional diversity by > 50%. The influence of riparian zones on species richness may therefore depend somewhat on geographic scale.

Finch (1989) studied bird communities along a nearly 989 m (3,000 ft) elevational gradient in southeastern Wyoming extending from riparian lowlands to subalpine habitats. Community-habitat relationships, as well as bird abundance, diversity and richness, were viewed at two spatial scales, the entire elevational continuum and within three elevational zones separated by elevation-dependent physical and vegetational characteristics. She observed that species abundance, richness and the number of foraging guilds were all highest at the lowest elevational zone consisting primarily of cottonwood habitat. This pattern was attributed to the greater structural complexity of this habitat type compared to the conifer dominated subalpine habitats.

Master (1980) investigated bird species diversity, richness and abundance along a much more modest 366 m (1,200 ft) elevational gradient in DEWA on the west-facing slope of Kittatinny Ridge in New Jersey. Emlen (1977) transects established at four elevations were used to determine vegetative characteristics and avian territory density over a two year period. Species diversity was also highest at river level and declined linearly with elevation but not significantly. Richness, however, was significantly different (P<0.05) with a mean of 27 species detected per transect traverse on the lowest transect on Poxono Island in the Delaware River compared to 16 species on the highest transect paralleling the Appalachian Trail atop Kittatinny Ridge. Mean pair density was also significantly higher (P<0.005) at river level (42.09 prs/ha) compared to the ridge top (6.20 prs/ha). The Poxono Island transect contributed disproportionately to species richness with 13 species observed exclusively at river level, thus, this transect had the lowest similarity (Horn's Index) among transects (Horn 1966). Those species most frequently detected on Poxono Island were common yellowthroat (*Geothlypis trichas*), common grackle (*Quiscalus quiscula*), gray catbird (*Dumetella carolinensis*), Baltimore oriole (*Icterus galbula*) and song sparrow (*Melospiza melodia*) compared to ovenbird (*Seiurus aurocapillus*), black-and-white warbler (*Mniotilta varia*), blue jay (*Cyanocitta cristata*), great-crested flycatcher (*Myiarchus crinitus*) and eastern towhee (*Pipilo erythrophthalmus*) on the ridge top transect. Vegetative similarity indices between Poxono Island and the ridge top were also very low for overstory (9%) and understory (4%) trees and shrubs (Mueller-Dombois and Ellenberg 1974) underscoring the relationship between avian community characteristics and vegetative composition and structure.

Both diversity and richness were significantly positively correlated with plant species diversity, foliage volume and tree height. Foliage height diversity, a measure of foliage distribution (MacArthur 1966), was negatively correlated with diversity and richness because the understory foliage layer was largely missing on the island due to regular scouring by floods and ice floes. In spite of missing an entire foliage layer, richness was still highest on the island, probably due to the structurally complex, tall silver maples (*Acer sacchar inum*), as with the cottonwood habitat in Wyoming mentioned above, and the positive effect of the proximity of water (MacArthur 1966, Karr 1968, Carothers et al. 1974).

Longtitudinal Zonation

As with lateral zonation, longitudinal zonation is most fundamentally controlled by abiotic characteristics including variation in elevation, channel gradient, valley shape, geomorphic processes, sediment loads and substrate composition (Roe et al. 2000, Catteral et al. 2001). Spatially, many of these factors co-vary along the length of a stream controlling in large part, along with disturbance, vegetative communities and the distribution and abundance of riparian species. Biotic factors, such as competition, also play a role and are more important than in lateral zonation (Keddy 1989, Naiman and Rogers 1997). Fish and insect communities change as streams increase in size (Platts 1975, Minshall et al. 1983) as do forest characteristics (Swanson et al. 1982, Nilsson et al. 1989). Interestingly, there are few empirical studies of riparian characteristics from headwaters to broad floodplains and thus there is limited comprehensive data on qualitative and quantitative aspects of community level changes along the length of a riparian corridor.

Knopf (1985) and Finch (1986) noted changes in riparian breeding bird communities from headwaters to larger downstream rivers. Lock and Naiman (1998) compared vegetation composition and configuration and avian community structure between sets of low and high order streams on the Olympic Peninsula in Washington. Percent cover of deciduous vegetation was significantly higher on the larger rivers with coniferous vegetation cover inversely proportional to stream size. Deciduous vegetation was proportionately more common in the mid-story layer on all streams and rivers. Of 31 bird species detected, 58% were common to all sites, 29% occurred only on large rivers and 13% were found only on the smaller streams. The effect of river size was greater than the individual river effect on avian abundance in a two-factor, nested ANOVA random effects model.

In Pennsylvania, headwater streams typically begin as rivulets emanating from springs on steep banks or relatively flat benches and subsequently flow through steep-sided valleys, often cloaked in stands of Eastern Hemlock as discussed earlier (Figure 1). Such streams are shaded, narrow, relatively shallow, composed of relatively equal lengths of pools and riffles, possess a cobble substrate, receive most of their nutrient input from the surrounding terrestrial environment and are dominated faunally by macroinvertebrates and small fish species. Large, meandering rivers are basically opposite in their characteristics being largely un-shaded, wide, relatively deep, composed mostly of stretches of slack water, possessing a fine, silty substrate, receiving most of their nutrients from upstream and photosynthesis, are dominated by tall, deciduous shade trees including American sycamore (*Platanus occidentalis*) and Silver Maple (see Chapter 3 on "Wetland Bird Communities: Boreal Bogs to Open Water") and are characterized by larger fish species. Avian community characteristics also change. In-stream and riparian forest passerine species that feed largely on aquatic macroinvertebrate nymphs (Louisiana waterthrush) and/or adults (Acadian flycatcher and winter wren), dominate the headwaters while non-passerine, fish eating, diving and wading species, including belted kingfisher (*Ceryle alcyon*), double-crested cormorant (*Phalacrororax auritus*), great blue heron (*Ardea herodias*), black-crowned night-heron (*Nycticorax nycticorax*) and, rarely in Pennsylvania, yellow-crowned night-heron (*Nyc-*

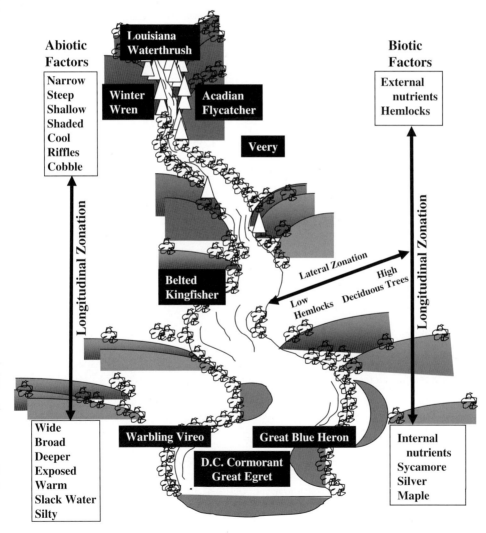

Figure 1: Biotic and abiotic characteristics of lateral and longitudinal zonation along a riparian corridor in Pennsylvania (T. Master).

tanassa violacea), characterize the larger rivers (Kelsey and West 1998). The lower Susque-hanna River, and Wade Island in particular, are representative of this environment in Penn-sylvania (see chapter 19 on "Colonially Nesting Waders"). A few passerine species, such as the warbling vireo (*Vireo gilvus*), are also characteristic of larger rivers in Pennsylvania.

Species Diversity and Richness

On a worldwide spatial scale, there are 60 species of specialist riverine birds totally dependent on streams and rivers for most of their food resources (Buckton and Ormerod 2002). Many factors contribute to observed distribution of species richness patterns including mean temperature, precipitation, primary productivity and geomorphological (surface) complexity. Regions with the highest surface complexity host the most obligate riverine species, including the eastern Himalayas where the ranges of 13 species overlap and the central Andes where six species are sympatric (Buckton and Ormerod 2002). Other high mountain areas, such as the Rocky Mountains, host only one or two species indicat-ing that the interplay of factors is most important, not simply vertical relief, in controlling richness patterns. More of these species (42%) occur on small streams compared to large meandering rivers (3%) and more occur where sediments are coarse (35%) rather than fine (13%). The River Continuum Concept (RCC) (Ward 1998) states that the reduced diversi-ty in headwaters (defined as very near stream sources at high elevations in this case) is the result of low nutrient availability and low thermal heterogeneity which synergize to limit richness despite a high degree of habitat complexity. Diversity in lower altitude, larger rivers is relatively low due to reduced habitat heterogeneity, high turbidity and low dis-solved oxygen levels despite high productivity. Conversely, in middle reaches at moderate elevation, where the most of these species overlap in the Himalayas and Andes, produc-tivity is sufficiently high, thermal regimes are varied enough and geomorphological com-plexity great enough to provide the most favorable conditions for riverine species (Buck-ton and Ormerod 2002).

Many studies at small scales indicate that high order streams may support more species in general than low order streams (Loch and Naiman 1998). A deciduous/coniferous ratio proved to be an accurate predictor of bird species richness in the Pacific Northwest where the D/C ratio was highest on large rivers where deciduous trees were more common than on headwater streams (Loch and Naiman 1998). This illustrates the interaction between stream size, vegetation characteristics and species richness.

No specific longitudinal studies of abundance, richness and diversity exist for Pennsyl-vania. The species list in Table I would indicate that richness is approximately equal for small streams vs. large rivers and somewhat reduced for species favoring the middle reach-es of streams, perhaps because the lateral ecotones are more distinct for headwaters and the largest rivers.

DISTURBANCE AND SUCCESSION

The patterns in avian community structure outlined above are subject to changes caused by disturbance regimes and succession—processes that are major attributes of riparian sys-tems. This is especially true for lateral zones nearest to the wetted channels of streams and rivers and for larger rivers where flood events last longer (also influenced by the size of the watershed) and depositional and erosional actions both create and destroy habitats, respectively (Allen 1965, Brinson 1990). Riparian areas undergo both primary and secondary succession initially involving colonization by grasses and forbs, followed by woody vines, shrubs and young trees (open canopy stage), successively larger trees (closed canopy stage) and finally old growth forest with a multi-layered closed canopy (Kelsey and West 1998). On islands within Pennsylvania's largest rivers, all of these stages of succession can be seen from the upstream end, subject to regular disturbance, (e.g., flooding and ice scouring in the spring) to the relatively undisturbed downstream end of the island where the final stages of succession remain relatively secure from all but the most severe events. Changes in vegetation structure and composition result in concomitant changes in the riparian avifauna. Understory seed-eaters and insectivores are characteristic of the earliest stages of succession followed by shrub and sapling species and finally canopy species (Kelsey and West 1998). In Pennsylvania, early successional species would be typified by the song sparrow, later shrub/sapling species would include the common yellowthroat and gray catbird while mature forest would provide habitat for great-crested flycatchers and warbling vireos.

CONSERVATION AND MANAGEMENT

There are a variety of reasons to protect riparian habitat ranging from flood control and maintenance of water quality (see Chapter 18 on "The Lousiana Waterthrush as an Indicator of Headwater Stream Quality in Pennsylvania") to the preservation of the high levels of biodiversity characteristic of this habitat. Perhaps the most current conservation issue in riparian habitat management is determining the most effective width necessary for the conservation of riparian function as well as for birds and other components of riparian biodiversity. Suggested riparian buffer width mandated by various regulatory and resource management agencies is generally oriented only towards maintaining water quality as opposed to concern over habitat value (Naiman et al. 2005). When habitat quality is of concern, it often emphasizes a particular species rather than maintaining overall biodiversity. The question of correct buffer width is therefore a difficult question to answer given differing species requirements which range from a few meters on either side of a stream for salamanders to a kilometer or more for nesting colonies of great blue herons (Brinson et al. 1981). A blanket approach covering all species would, in many instances, result in a buffer so wide as to be economically and spatially unfeasible from a management point of view. Thus, the appropriate buffer width should be determined by prioritizing the most important aspects of individual streams and tailoring the width to those specific characteristics.

LITERATURE CITED

Allen, J. R. L. 1965. A review of the origin and characteristics of recent alluvial sediments. Sedimentology 5: 89–191.

Allen, M. C., Sheehan, J. Jr., Master, T. L. and R. S. Mulvihill. 2009. Acadian flycatcher responses to hemlock woolly adelgid infestation in Appalachian riparian forests. The Auk. 125 (3):543–553.

Brauning, D. W. 1992. Atlas of breeding birds in Pennsylvania. University of Pittsburgh Press, Pittsburgh, PA. 484 pp.

Brinson, M. M., Swift, B. L., Plantico, R. C., and J. S. Barclay. 1981. Riparian ecosystems: their ecology and status. FWS/OBS-81/17, U. S. Fish and Wildlife Service, Biological Services Program, Kearneysville, WV.

_____. 1990. Riverine forests. Pages 87–141, in Forest Wetlands: Ecosystems of the World, D. W. Goodall (ed.). Elsevier, New York.

Brosofske, K. D. 1996. Effects of harvesting on microclimate from small streams to uplands in western Washington. Masters Thesis, Michigan Technological University. 72 pp.

Buckton, S. T. and S. J. Ormerod. 2002. Global patterns of diversity among the specialist birds of riverine landscapes. Freshwater Biology 47:695–709.

Carothers, S. W. and R. R. Johnson. 1974. Population structure and social organization of southwestern riparian birds. American Zoologist 14: 97–108.

Caterral, C. P., Piper, S. D., Bunn, S. E. and J. M Arthur. 2001. Flora and fauna assemblages vary with local topography in a subtropical eucalypt forest. Australian Ecology 26:56–69.

Crow, T. R., Haney, A. and D. M. Waller. 1994. Report on the scientific roundtable on biological diversity convened by the Chequamegon and Nicotel National Forests. Gen. Tech. Rep. NC-166. U.S. Dept. of Agriculture, Forest Service, North Central Forest Experiment Station, St. Paul, MN. 55 pp.

DeGraff, R. M. and M. Yamasaki. 2000. Bird and mammal habitat in riparian areas. Pages 139–156 in Riparian Management in Forests of the Continental Eastern United States, E.S. Verry, J. W. Hornbeck and C. A. Dolloff, Eds. Lewis Publishers, New York, NY.

Dickson, J. G. 1978. Forest bird communities of bottomland hardwoods. Pages 66–73, in Proceedings of Workshop on Management of Southern Forests for Nongame Birds, R. F. DeGraff, tech. coord. U. S. Forest Service Gen. Tech. Rep. SE-14.

Emlen, J. T. 1977. Estimating breeding season bird densities from transect counts. The Auk 94: 455–468.

Finch, D. M. 1986. Similarities in riparian bird communities among elevational zones in southeastern Wyoming. Pages 105–110 in Proceedings of Wyoming Water and Streamside Zone Conference: Wyoming's Water Doesn't Wait While We Debate. Wyoming Water Resources Center, Laramie, WY.

_____. 1989. Habitat use and overlap of riparian birds in three elevational zones. Stream Ecology 70: 866–880.

Fonda, R. W. 1974. Forest succession in relation to river terrace development in Olympic National Park. Ecology 55:927–942.

Higler, L. W. G. 1993. The riparian community of north-west European streams. Freshwater Biology 29:229–241.

Horn, H. S. 1966. Measurement of overlap in comparative ecological studies. American Naturalist 100: 419–424.

Hupp and W. R. Osterkamp. 1985. Bottomland vegetation distribution along Passage Creek, Virginia, in relation to fluvial landforms. Ecology 66: 670–681.

_____ and _____. 1996. Riparian vegetation and fluvial geomorphic processes. Geomorphology 14: 277–295.

Ilhardt, B. L., Verry, E. S. and B. J. Palik. 2000. Defining riparian areas. Pages 23–41, in Riparian Management in Forests, E. S. Verry, J. W. Hornbeck and C. A. Dolloff (eds.). Lewis Publishers, New York, NY.

Johnson, R. R., Haight, L. T. and J. M. Simpson. 1977. Endangered species vs. endangered habitats: A concept. Pages 68–74, in Importance, Preservation and Management of Riparian Habitat: A Symposium (proceedings), R. R. Johnson and D. A. Jones (tech. coord.). Gen. Tech. Rep. RM-43, USDA Forest Service, Rocky Mountain Forest and Range Experimental Station, Fort Collins, CO.

Karr, J. R. 1968. Habitat and avian diversity on strip-mined land in east central Illinois. Condor 70: 348–357.

_____, and I. J. Schlosser. 1978. Water resources and the land-water inferface. Science 201:209–234.

Keddy, P. A. 1989. Competition, population and community ecology. Chapman and Hall, New York, NY.

Kelsey, K. A. and S. D. West. 1998. Riparian wildlife. Pages 235–258 in R. J. Naiman and R. E. Bilby, Eds. River Ecology and Management: Lessons from the Pacific Coastal Ecoregion. Springer-Verlag, New York, NY.

Klimas, C. V., Martin, C. O. and J. W. Teaford. 1981. Impacts of flooding regime modification on wildlife habitats of bottomland hardwood forests in the lower Mississippi Valley. Technical Rep. E1-81-13, Amry Corps of Engineers Waterways Exp. Station, Vicksburg, MS.

Knopf, F L. 1985. Significance of riparian vegetation to breeding birds across an altitudinal cline. Pages 105–111 in USDA Forest Service Gen. Tech. Rep. RM-120. Rocky Mountain Forest and Range Experiment Station, Fort Collins, CO.

_____, and F. B. Samson. 1994. Scale perspectives in avian diversity in western riparian ecosystems. Conservation Biology 8: 669–676.

Kreuper, D. J. 1993. Effects of land use practices on Western riparian ecosystems. Pages 321–330, in Status and Management of Neotropical Migratory Birds, D. M. Finch and P. W. Stangel (eds.). Gen. Tech. Rep. RM 229, USDA Forest Service, Rocky Mountain Forest and Range Experiment Station, Fort Collins, CO.

_____. 1996. Effects of livestock management on Southwestern riparian ecosystems. Pages 281–301, in Desired Future Conditions for Southwestern Riparian Ecosystems: Bringing Interests and Concerns Together, D. W. Shaw and D. M. Finch (tech. cords.). Gen. Tech. Rep. RM-GTR-272, USDA Forest Service, Rocky Mountain Forest and Range Experiment Station, Fort Collins, CO.

Lock, P. A. and R. J. Naiman. 1998. Effects of stream size on bird community structure in coastal temperate forests of the Pacific Northwest. J. of Biogeography 25:773–782.

MacArthur, R. H., Recher, H. and M. Cody. 1966. On the relation between habitat selection and species diversity. American Naturalist 100: 319–325.

McWilliams, G. M. and D. W. Brauning. 2000. The birds of Pennsylvania. Comstock Publishing Associates, Cornell University, Ithaca, New York, 479 pp.

Master, T. L. 1980. An analysis of the relationship between bird species diversity and foliage configuration along an elevational gradient in the Delaware Water Gap National Recreation Area. Masters Thesis, East Stroudsburg University of Pennsylvania. 193 pp.

Minshall, G. W., Petersen, R. C., Cummins, K. W., Bott, T. L., Sedell, J. R., Cushing, E. E. amd R. L. Vanote. 1983. Interbiome comparison of stream ecosystem dynamics. Ecol, Monogr. 53:1–25.

Mueller-Dombois, D. and H. Ellenberg. 1974. Aims and methods of vegetation ecology. John Wiley and Sons, Inc. New York, NY. 547 pp.

Murray, N. L. and D. F. Stauffer. 1995. Nongame bird use of habitat in central Appalachian riparian forests. J. Wildlife Manage. 59: 78–88.

Naiman, R. J., Decamps, H, and M. Pollock. 1993. The role of riparian area corridors in maintaining regional diversity. Ecological Applications 3:209–212.

_____, and K. H. Rogers. 1997. Large animals and the maintenance of system-level characteristics in river corridors. Bioscience 47: 521–529.

_____, _____, and M. E. McClain. 2005. Riparia: ecology, conservation and management of streamside communities. Elsevier Press, New York, NY. 430 pp.

Nilsson, C., Grelsson, G., Johansson, M. and U. Sperens. 1989. Patterns of plant species richness along riverbanks. Ecology 70:77–84.

_____. 1992. Conservation management of riparian communities. Pages 352–372, in Ecological Principles of Nature Conservation, L. Hansson (ed.). Elesevier, Amsterdam.

Parrott, H. A., Marions, D. A. and R. D. Perkinson. 1989. A four-level hierarchy for organizing stream resources information. Pages 41–54, in Proceedings, Headwater Hydrology Symposium, American Water Resources Association, Missoula, MT.

Platts, W. S. 1975. Relationships among stream order, fish populations and aquatic geomorphology in an Idaho river drainage. Fisheries 4:5–9.

Ross, R. M., Redell, L. A, Bennett, R. M. and J. A. Young. 2004. Mesohabitat use of threatened hemlock forests by breeding birds of the Delaware River Basin in Northeastern United States. Natural Areas Journal 24: 307–315,

Rot, B. W., Naiman, R. J., and R. E. Bilby. 2000. Stream channel configuration, landform, and riparian forest structure in the Cascade Mountains, Washington. Canadian Journal of Fisheries and Aquatic Sciences 57:699–707.

Sabo, J. L., Sponseller, R., Dixon, M., Gade, K., Harms, T., Heffernan, J., Jani, A., Katz, G., Soykan, C, Watts, J. and J. Welter. 2005. Riparian zones increase regional species richness by harboring different, no more, species. Ecology 86: 56–62.

Smith, K. G. 1977. Distribution of summer birds along a forest moisture gradient in an Ozark watershed. Ecology 58: 810–819.

Stauffer, D. F. and L. B. Best. 1980. Habitat selection by birds of riparian communities: evaluating effects of habitat alterations. J. Wildl. Manage. 44: 1–15.

Swanson, F. J., Gregory, S. V., Sedell, J. R. and H. G. Campbell. 1982. Land-water interactions: the riparian zone. Pages 267–291 in Analysis of Coniferous Forest Ecosystems in the Western United States, R. L. Edmonds (ed.). Hutchinson Ross Publishing Co., Stroudsburg, PA.

_____, Kratz, T. K., Caine, N. and R. G. Woodamnsee. 1988. Landform effects on ecosystem patterns and processes. Bioscience 38:92–98.

_____, and J. F. Franklin. 1992. New forestry practices from ecosystem analysis of Pacific Northwest forests. Ecological Applications 2:262–274.

Swartzentruber, B. 2003. The effects of hemlock woolly adelgid (*Adelgaes tsugae*) on breeding populations of eastern hemlock (*Tsuga Canadensis*). Unpublished Masters Thesis, East Stroudsburg University of Pennsylvania. 66 pp.

Szaro, R. C. 1980. Factors influencing bird populations in southwestern riparian forests. Pages 403–418, in Proceedings of Workshop on Management of Western Forests and Grasslands for Nongame Birds, pp. 403–418. R. M. DeGraff and N. G. Tilghman, (eds.) Gen. Tech. Rep. INT-86, U. S. Department of Agriculture, Forest Service, Intermountain Forest and Range Experiment Station, Ogden, UT.

Tubbs, A. A. 1980. Riparian bird communities of the great plains. Pages 419–434, in Workshop Proceedings: Management of Western Forests and Grasslands for Non-game Birds, R. M. DeGraff and N. G. Tilghman, eds. Gen. Tech. Rep. INT-86, U. S. Department of Agriculture, Forest Service, Intermountain Forest and Range Experiment Station, Ogden, UT.

Vadas, R. L. and J. E. Sanger. 1997. Lateral zonation of trees along a small Ohio stream. Ohio Journal of Science 97:107–112.

Ward, J. V. 1998. Riverine landscapes: biodiversity patterns, disturbance regimes and aquatic conservation. Biological Conservation 83: 269–278.

_____, and K. Tochner. 2001. Biodiversity: towards a unifying theme for river ecology. Freshwater Biology 46:807–819.

Avian Ecology and Conservation: A Pennsylvania Focus with National Implications. Edited by S. K. Majumdar, T. L. Master, M. C. Brittingham, R. M. Ross, R. S. Mulvihill and J. E. Huffman. © 2010. The Pennsylvania Academy of Science.

Chapter 5

Early Successional and Shrubland Communities with Special Reference to Field Sparrow (*Spizella pusilla*) Breeding Biology

Michael Carey
Department of Biology
The University of Scranton
Scranton, PA 18510-4623
careym1@scranton.edu

DISTURBANCE HABITATS

Early successional and shrubland habitats can be more generally termed disturbance habitats (Brawn et al. 2001, Lorimer 2001) and many of the bird species breeding in such habitats are termed as disturbance-dependent species (Hunter et al. 2001). Ecological disturbance has been defined as "any relatively discrete event in time that disrupts ecosystem, community, or population structure and changes resources, substrate availability, or the physical environment" (Pickett and White 1985). Habitat disturbance can be natural (e.g. fire, blow-down) or anthropogenic (e.g. agriculture, logging). In addition, this definition of disturbance habitat can also be applied to reclaimed surface mine and grassland communities in Pennsylvania and the bird communities found there (See chapter on Strip Mines/Grassland Communities).

Compared to the efforts that have been applied to many other habitats, conservation and management of disturbed habitats have been largely neglected (Askins 1993). For example, Noss et al. (1995) make no mention of shrub-scrub or successional habitats in their extensive analysis of ecosystem loss and degradation. Askins (2001) went so far as to term these as "unpopular" habitats. Perhaps this lack of "popularity" was due to the inclusion of the word "disrupt" in the definition of disturbance above, making habitat disturbance seem synonymous with habitat destruction, and thus something to be avoided rather than conserved. However, in recent decades it has been recognized that natural or human mediated disturbance can actually be essential in maintaining biodiversity (Brawn et al. 2001).

Estimates of the extent of disturbance habitat in the eastern US vary widely. Historically, Lorimer (2001) and Lorimer and White (2003) found it difficult to estimate the amount of disturbance habitat pre-European settlement. It perhaps varied widely around a mean of 10–15% of the land area. With heavy logging and the spread of agriculture, such habitats may have increased to cover 55–60% of the land in the late 19th century. Trani et al. (2001)

reported that in 1989 seedling-sapling timberland in Pennsylvania covered 965,000 ha, 15% of total timberland area, with the area decreasing in extent for at least the previous three decades (similar declines are seen throughout the northeast and north central regions of the US). McWilliams et al. (2004) estimated that sapling timber acreage in Pennsylvania has decreased by 50% since 1950. Between 1978 and 2002 early successional acreage in Pennsylvania also declined by 50% and covered 11.8% of state acreage (Alerich 1993, McWilliams et al. 2004). These decreases will likely continue as fires are suppressed, as more former farmland succeeds to forest, and as human occupancy spreads. Thus, the current availability of disturbance habitat in Pennsylvania and throughout the eastern US may be at or below the pre-European settlement mean.

Perhaps the primary ecological factor to which disturbance-dependent species must adapt is the transitory nature of their breeding habitat. In Pennsylvania, disturbance habitats, if left unmanaged, will undergo ecological succession and return to a relatively stable forested state (Beckwith 1954, Horn 1974). The early communities in this succession (the subject of this chapter) are faced with particularly rapid changes. On my study site in northeastern Pennsylvania (see below), the habitat changed from open grassland to large shrub/young forest in a 20 yr span. Adaptation to these rapid changes is thought to select for disturbance-dependent species to be habitat generalists, breeding across a wide range of early successional stages, and also select for them to be able to readily disperse to new disturbance habitats as they become available (Orians 1969, Chase et al. 2005, but see below).

Conservation of disturbance habitat does more than help maintain diversity of disturbance-dependent species. There is a general trend toward decreasing net productivity with advancing successional age (Horn 1974). Thus the higher productivity in disturbance habitats can benefit species other than those classed as disturbance-dependent. For example, forest-breeding species often use these habitats as migratory stopover sites (Rodewald and Brittingham 2004). R. Smith (see Chapter on Stopover Ecology) has data suggesting that migrants stopping-over in successional habitats are in better condition than conspecifics stopping in more forested habitats. Forest-breeding species also use disturbance habitats during the post-breeding period, perhaps due to the higher food resources (particularly fruits) found in successional habitats in autumn (Vitz and Rodewald 2007).

THE DISTURBANCE-DEPENDENT BIRD COMMUNITY

In the northeastern US, Dettmers (2003) estimated that disturbance-dependent bird species made up ~15% of the overall avian diversity in the region. Many remain relatively common, although due to declining habitat, numbers are significantly declining for many (Hunter et al. 2001, Sauer et al. 2006, Butcher and Niven 2007). Whether current population sizes are less than pre-European settlement sizes is debatable, but management of these species is clearly a growing necessity.

Table 1 lists bird species found in the Pennsylvania Breeding Bird Atlas (Brauning 1992) that were classified by Hunter et al. (2001) as using large patches of disturbance habitat for breeding (Table 1 also includes the taxonomic names for all bird species mentioned below). A similar long list of species could be added to cover those breeding in more open grassy habitats (see chapter on Strip Mines/Grassland Communities) or in small open forest patches and edges (Hunter et al. 2001, see Chapter on Forest Fragmentation).

Table 1. Continental and Pennsylvania population trends (Sauer et al. 2006) for bird species breeding in Pennsylvania (Brauning 1992) that are associated primarily with large patches of early successional, shrub-scrub, or forest edge habitats (generally >3 yrs after disturbance). Species list adapted from Hunter et al. (2001).

Species	Continental BBS Trend[a]	Pennsylvania BBS Trend[a]
Ruffed grouse (*Bonasa umbellus*)	−2.23*	−5.59
Wild turkey (*Meleagris gallopavo*)	+13.83*	+6.07*
American woodcock (*Scolopax minor*)	+0.78	−7.29
Mourning dove (*Zenaida macroura*)	−0.16	+2.07*
Black-billed cuckoo (*Coccyzus erythropthalmus*)	−1.56*	−3.63*
Whip-poor-will (*Caprimulgus vociferous*)	−2.32*	−7.24
Alder flycatcher (*Empidonax alnorum*)	−0.05	−0.50
Willow flycatcher (*Empidonax trailli*)	−0.87*	+1.89*
Least flycatcher (*Empidonax minimus*)	−1.12*	−1.26*
Warbling vireo (*Vireo gilvus*)	+1.21*	+3.48*
Veery (*Catharus fuscescens*)	−1.38*	−0.45
Gray catbird (*Dumetella carolinensis*)	−0.12	+0.32
Brown thrasher (*Toxostoma rufum*)	−1.19*	−1.82*
Cedar waxwing (*Bombycilla cedrorum*)	+1.08*	+1.01
Blue-winged warbler (*Vermivora pinus*)	−0.61	+2.15*
Golden-winged warbler (*Vermivora chrysoptera*)	−2.28*	−8.75*
Nashville warbler (*Vermivora ruficapilla*)	+1.48*	−5.65
Yellow warbler (*Dendroica petechia*)	+0.41*	+0.53
Chestnut-sided warbler (*Dendroica pensylvanica*)	−0.55*	+1.66*
Prairie warbler (*Dendroica discolor*)	−2.02*	−2.92
Northern waterthrush (*Seiurus noveboracensis*)	−0.07	−7.24
Mourning warbler (*Oporornis philadelphia*)	−1.11*	+6.90
Common yellowthroat (*Geothlypis trichas*)	−0.33*	+0.48
Yellow-breasted chat (*Icteria virens*)	+0.01	−4.94*
Northern cardinal (*Cardinalis cardinalis*)	+0.13	+0.08
Blue grosbeak (*Guiraca caerulea*)	+0.99*	−21.95*
Indigo bunting (*Passerina cyanea*)	−0.58*	−0.52*
Eastern towhee (*Pipilo erythropthalmus*)	−1.75*	−2.51*
Clay-colored sparrow (*Spizella pallida*)	−1.18*	—
Field sparrow (*Spizella pusilla*)	−3.06*	−3.91*
Swamp sparrow (*Melospiza georgiana*)	+1.44*	+2.19
Song sparrow (*Melospiza melodia*)	−0.58*	−1.26*
American goldfinch (*Carduelis tristis*)	−0.04	−0.96*

[a]Breeding Bird Survey census trend 1966–2003. + = increasing; − = decreasing; # = % annual change; * = significant change (significance set at P < 0.1) (see Sauer et al. 2006 for methods).

Of the 33 species in Table 1, 23 (70%) show a continental trend toward decreasing numbers in Breeding Bird Survey (BBS) routes, 17 significantly so (Sauer et al. 2006). If confined specifically to Pennsylvania BBS data (Table 1), the trends are typically similar in direction (but see willow flycatcher, chestnut-sided warbler, and blue grosbeak) and often larger in magnitude (Sauer et al. 2006, Butcher and Niven 2007). Rather than being typical disturbance-dependent species, the minority of species in Table 1 that are continentally increasing are often: 1) actively managed (e.g. wild turkey), 2) species not exclusively associated with disturb-ance habitat (e.g. warbling vireo and swamp sparrow), or 3) species undergoing range expansion (e.g. blue grosbeak, but see Pennsylvania trend) (Hunter et al. 2001). Thus, although not typically classed as threatened or endangered, much of the disturbance-dependent bird community in the US and in Pennsylvania is of conservation concern.

Although the species in Table 1 are thought to be habitat generalists in successionally changing areas, each does have a relatively specific "optimal" breeding habitat within the successional stages. For example, field sparrows (see below) prefer open habitats with few scattered trees or shrubs (Carey et al. 1994); prairie warblers prefer later stages, e.g. open habitats with small trees and shrubs (Nolan 1978, Nolan et al. 1999); gray catbirds prefer even later stages, e.g. non-canopy habitats with dense shrub or vine cover (Lent 1990, Cimprich and Moore 1995). In community-wide assessments, while the species breeding in each habitat were similar, Bullock and Buehler (2006) found significant differences in capture rates of the species when comparing regenerating forests, utility rights-of-ways (ROW), and reclaimed surface mine land in Tennessee. In the northeastern US, Confer and Pascoe (2003) also found differences in capture rates between ROWs managed with herbicides relative to those managed by cutting. These capture rate differences probably reflect differences in structural habitat preferences in each disturbance-dependent species.

In longitudinal studies of bird communities in relation to ecological succession, disturbance-dependent species differ in the habitat ages and successional stages at which they first appear, reach peak densities, and disappear. Lanyon's (1981) study compiled complete counts of breeding pairs at a site on Long Island, NY, over a period of 45 years. In that study, focusing only on species included in Table 1, song sparrows and field sparrows settled within 2 years of cultivation and disappeared after 20 and 30 years respectively. Four other species (indigo bunting, common yellowthroat, gray catbird, and blue-winged warbler) settled 6–7 years following cultivation and remained through the study duration. Others, e.g. brown thrasher and eastern towhee, settled at even later field ages and remained throughout the study. Similar differential patterns among species are seen in the studies of Johnston and Odum (1956) in Georgia and Shugart and James (1973) in Arkansas, although in these two studies each species typically had a much more restricted range of breeding field ages than did those of Lanyon (1981). Since each disturbance-dependent species appears to have specific preferences in the successional sequence, management plans for such species should insure that all major successional stages are present in sufficient amounts at all times (Thompson and DeGraaf 2001). Perhaps a useful small-scale model of such management would be one using a rotating cutting plan similar to that seen in the Barrens Grouse Habitat Management Area of central Pennsylvania (Yahner 2003). The general outline for the conservation of successional habitats in the Pennsylvania Comprehensive Wildlife Conservation Strategy (Pennsylvania Game Commission and Pennsylvania Fish and Boat Commission 2005) does include conserving a mosaic of early successional habitats as a priority.

FIELD SPARROWS: A DISTURBANCE-DEPENDENT SPECIES

Since 1987, I have been studying the breeding biology of a population of field sparrows in northeastern Pennsylvania. Below I use them as an example of the responses of a disturbance-dependent species to 20 years of successional change in their habitat.

The Species

Field sparrows are monomorphic, build open nests, and are common in early successional habitats throughout the eastern US. In northeastern Pennsylvania, the species is a short distance migrant, with males arriving from the southern US in mid to late April; females ~1 May. Pairing in this socially monogamous species is rapid and nesting begins ~10 May. Only females build nests, and during nest-building and egg-laying periods they are typically followed closely by their social mates. May nests are built on or near the ground, usually at the base of woody vegetation. June/July nests are elevated (mean height = 43 cm), typically in dogwood (*Cornus* spp.), honeysuckle (*Lonicera* spp.), or rose (*Rosa* spp.). Only females incubate eggs and brood nestlings; feeding of nestlings and fledglings is shared roughly equally by the adult pair (Carey 1990). On average 40–50% of nests fledge young; the remainder are lost, primarily to predators. If nests survive depredation, double brooding is the rule. Over the course of this study, there has been virtually no brown-headed cowbird (*Molothrus ater*) parasitism (Burhans et al. 2001). Latest nests of the year are typically initiated prior to 15 July. Young fledged on the site rarely return as adults. For additional species information, see Walkinshaw (1978) and Carey et al. (1994).

Methods

Since 1987, specific methods and objectives have varied, but the general methods described below have remained constant. From early April to 1 August, I worked the site on virtually a daily basis. With few exceptions, all breeding adults were captured in mist nets, then measured and banded with a numbered U.S.G.S. aluminum band plus a unique combination of 2–3 color plastic bands on their legs. Individuals were sexed by the presence of a brood patch (female) or cloacal protuberance (male) and by differences in flattened wing length (Carey et al. 1994). Prior to banding individual males were also identified by variations in song structure. Surviving nestlings were weighed and banded with an aluminum band at 4–5 days of age.

Complete breeding histories for each individual adult on the site were compiled. During a single breeding season, data collected included settlement date, pairing date, dates of nesting activity, nest location, nest success, fledging (reproductive) success, seasonal fidelity to the breeding territory, and mate changes, if any. Between years, data were collected on return rates to the site, territory fidelity, mate fidelity, and lifetime reproductive success.

In addition to the above general methods, from 1990–2002, a 50 µl sample of blood was drawn from the brachial vein of adults and nestlings after banding and measuring. Following the methods of Westneat (1993), DNA extracted from the blood samples was used to make DNA fingerprints. Fingerprints of nestlings were compared to those of their putative parents and to other adult males to determine if any extra-pair fertilizations (EPF) were present and, if so, to determine the identity of the extra-pair male.

In 1998, I also collected 22 variables of vegetation diversity and structure in 25-m^2 plots centered on each field sparrow nest. The same assessment was done on 25-m^2 plots that were randomly distributed in each field age class. Comparing nest to random plots permitted me to differentiate between mean field characters and mean field sparrow nest site characters.

Study Site

The study site is 47.5 ha of adjacent old fields located 1.5 km east of La Plume, Benton Township, Lackawanna County, Pennsylvania (Fig. 1). In 2007, the fields could be classed into 5 age categories ranging from 7 to ~32 years since last human disturbance (descriptions in Fig. 1). Fields younger than ~10 years are characterized by a lush ground cover of grasses and other forbs, most commonly goldenrod (*Solidago* spp.). Scattered throughout are patches of small woody vegetation (usually <1.5 m high), most commonly dogwood, honeysuckle, rose, and Viburnum (*Viburnum* spp.). As the fields age, this woody vegetation becomes taller and more widespread. At >20 yrs the fields are primarily covered with dense thickets of woody vegetation, primarily still the same species as above, with only scattered small patches of open herbaceous vegetation.

Responses to Successional Changes

Population Size

Table 2 shows that field sparrows began colonizing the area 1 yr after human use ceased. Breeding territories increased in number, typically up to 8–12 yrs. On older fields territo-

Figure 1:   Aerial photograph of the field sparrow research site and field age classes (defined below). Photo taken in early spring 2002. Field age classes: A – Mowing ceased ~1975; 16.4 ha. Data collection started 1987; B – Mowing ceased 1987, partially resumed 1999 and completely mowed annually since 2003; 5.0 ha. Data collection started 1988; C – Mowing ceased ~1980; 12.4 ha. Data collection started 1990; D – Mowing ceased 1991; 1.6 ha. Data collection started 1992; E – Tomato cultivation ceased 2000; 12.1 ha. Data collection started 2001.

Table 2. Number of field sparrow territories (occupied continuously for >1 wk) on each of the field age classes according to age of field. Data include censuses from 1987 through 2007.

Field Age[a]	Field age class[b]				
	A	B	C	D	E
0	–	0	–	0	0
1	–	5	–	1	1
2	–	9	–	2	1
3	–	7	–	2	3
4	–	12	–	2	6
5	–	9	–	2	6
6	–	8	–	2	9
7	–	6	–	2	12
8	–	8	–	2	19
9	–	6	–	2	
10	–	6	15	1	
11	–	6	17	2	
12	12	mowing resumed	12	3	
13	12		9	2	
14	11		8	1	
15	9		9	1	
16	8		8	1	
17	8		6		
18	6		6		
19	6		4		
20	6		5		
21	4		7		
22	4		8		
23	4		8		
24	2		7		
25	1		5		
26	2		3		
27	3		3		
28	0				
29	1				
30	0				

[a]Years since last mowing or cultivation
[b]See Fig. 1 for field age descriptions

ries decreased in number, and use of the habitat ceased after ~30 yrs. When field age is >25 yrs, territories were typically held only short-term during the summer: either a male settled on a territory then left after failing to gain a mate or a nest failed and both pair members disappeared in midseason (Carey unpublished).

Territory Preference

Vegetation analysis indicated that fields 8–11 yrs old have general characters that most closely approach those of field sparrow nest sites (e.g. see Fig. 2). At that age, analysis showed that the fields were primarily open herbaceous habitats, with small trees and shrubs covering ~30% of the acreage. While mean tree height increased with field age, mean height around nest sites remained constant (Fig. 2). Similar constancy of nest site

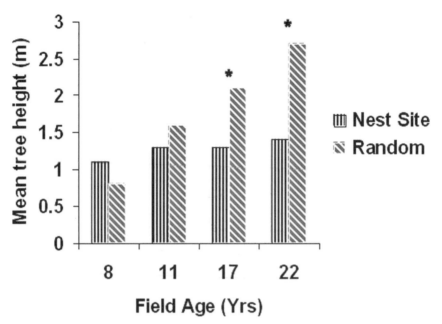

Figure 2:   Mean tree stem height in 25-m^2 plots centered on field sparrow nest sites compared to mean heights in randomly dispersed 25-m^2 plots in relation to field age. * = significant difference at $p < 0.05$ (ANOVA and Tukey's test).

preference is seen in most of the other vegetation variables (Carey unpublished). Not only do the nest site vegetation preferences remain constant across field ages, but virtually all breeding parameters that might indicate breeding habitat quality also remain invariant. Fig. 3, for example, shows that fledging success per female did not decrease with year ($r = -0.22$, $df = 19$, $P = 0.33$). Separate analyses for each field age class also showed no decline in fledging success with year (Carey unpublished). The only breeding parameter that significantly changed with field age was the proportion of EPF. Between 1990 and 2002, the correlation between population size decrease and decline in EPF rate was highly significant ($r = 0.77$, $df = 11$, $P = 0.002$, Carey, unpublished). However, this correlation may simply be due to the fewer opportunities for EPF in smaller populations with more widely dispersed territories. The relative constancy of nest site vegetation and of breeding parameters in a rapidly changing successional habitat indicates that field sparrows occupy territories only in the decreasing number of patches of relatively open, preferred habitat that remain over time. If such a result were true of other disturbance-dependent species, they may not be the broad habitat generalists that they are often hypothesized to be (Orians 1969, Chase et al. 2005).

Territory Fidelity and Dispersal

Dispersal ability may not be as high as hypothesized either. In field sparrows, regardless of male age, ~50% of males present at the end of a breeding season, returned in the following year, and with few exceptions, they returned to roughly the same breeding territory (Carey et al. 1994, unpublished). Given the high territory fidelity, it is likely that the

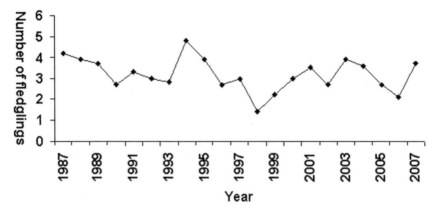

Figure 3:   Mean number of field sparrow fledglings produced per breeding female according to year (all field ages pooled).

50% return figure also represents annual male survivorship. As a result, the few males that bred for 6–8 years on the site were often defending territories that appeared to be no longer optimal. Anecdotal support for this tendency not to disperse as habitat changed was seen in a 6-year-old male holding territory in field age class B (Fig. 1) when the field began to be mowed again. The male returned for 2 additional summers and settled unmated on the edges of this now grassland habitat.

These results suggest that field sparrow dispersal is likely associated only with first year breeders (Carey unpublished). For example, the large increase in breeding population size in field age class E in 2007 (Table 2) was due to large numbers of males and females settling and nesting in midseason, well after migration and initial settlement were completed (Carey unpublished). None of these late settlers were previously banded, and, given the territory fidelity of older birds, all were likely in their first breeding year.

SUMMARY

Often neglected as a conservation priority in the past, disturbance habitats are rapidly declining throughout the eastern US. As a result, most disturbance-dependent bird species are also declining (Table 1). If field sparrow responses to the rapid successional changes in disturbance habitats (see above) are applicable to other disturbance-dependent species, then active conservation strategies that support a sufficient sample of all varieties of successional habitat types are a necessity if diversity is to be maintained.

ACKNOWLEDGEMENTS

Field sparrow studies were partially supported by grants from the University of Scranton Research Committee and by a Howard Hughes Medical Institute grant awarded to the University of Scranton Department of Biology that enabled funding for numerous undergraduate research assistants. Thanks are due to a large number of unfunded student assistants who also provided invaluable help. Special thanks are due to Anna Bushko and Joseph Thomas for allowing me over two decades of free use of their properties as my research site.

REFERENCES

Alerich, C. L. 1993. Forest statistics for Pennsylvania—1978 and 1989. Resource Bulletin NE-126. USDA Forest Service, Northeastern Forest Experiment Station, Radnor, Pennsylvania, USA.

Askins, R. A. 1993. Population trends in grassland, shrubland, and forest birds in eastern North America. Current Ornithology 11:1–34.

_____. 2001. Sustaining biological diversity in early successional communities: the challenge of managing unpopular habitats. Wildlife Society Bulletin 29:407–412.

Beckwith, S. L. 1954. Ecological succession on abandoned farm lands and its relationship to wildlife management. Ecological Monographs 24:349–376.

Brauning, D. W., editor. 1992. Atlas of breeding birds in Pennsylvania. University of Pittsburgh Press, Pittsburgh, Pennsylvania, USA.

Brawn, J. D., S. K. Robinson, and F. R. Thompson III. 2001. The role of disturbance in the ecology and conservation of birds. Annual Review of Ecology and Systematics 32:251–276.

Bullock, L. P. and D. A. Buehler. 2006. Avian use of early successional habitats: are regenerating forests, utility right-of-ways and reclaimed surface mines the same? Forest Ecology and Management 236:76–84.

Burhans, D. E., B. M. Strausberger, and M. D. Carey. 2001. Regional variation in response of field sparrows to the threat of brown-headed cowbird parasitism. Auk 118:776–780.

Butcher, G. S. and D. K. Niven. 2007. Combining data from the Christmas bird count and the breeding bird survey to determine the continental status and trends of North American birds. National Audubon Society report [Online] Available at http://stateofthebirds.audubon.org/cbid/content/Report.pdf.

Carey, M. 1990. Effects of brood size and nestling age on parental care by male field sparrows (Spizella pusilla). Auk 107:580–586.

Carey, M., D. E. Burhans, and D. A. Nelson. 1994. Field sparrow (Spizella pusilla) in A. Poole and F. Gill, editors. The Birds of North America, No. 103. The Academy of Natural Sciences, Philadelphia, Pennsylvania, USA and The American Ornithologists' Union, Washington, D. C., USA.

Chase, M. K., A. L. Holmes, T. Gardali, G. Ballard, G. R. Geupel, and N. Nur. 2005. Two decades of change in a coastal scrub community: songbird responses to plant succession. Pages 613–616 in USDA Forest Service General Technical Report PSW-GTR-191.

Cimprich, D. A. and F. R. Moore. 1995. Gray catbird (Dumatella carolinensis) in A. Poole and F. Gill, editors. The Birds of North America, No. 167. The Academy of Natural Sciences, Philadelphia, Pennsylvania, USA and The American Ornithologists' Union, Washington, D. C., USA.

Confer, J. L. and S. M. Pascoe. 2003. Avian communities on utility rights-of-ways and other managed shrublands in the northeastern United States. Forest Ecology and Management 185:193–205.

Dettmers, R. 2003. Status and conservation of shrubland birds in the northeastern US. Forest Ecology and Management 185:81–93.

Horn, H. S. 1974. The ecology of secondary succession. Annual Review of Ecology and Systematics 5:25–37.

Hunter, W. C., D. A. Buehler, R. A. Canterbury, J. L. Confer, and P. B. Hamel. 2001. Conservation of disturbance-dependent birds in eastern North America. Wildlife Society Bulletin 29:440–455.

Johnston, D. W. and E. P. Odum. 1956. Breeding bird populations in relation to plant succession on the Piedmont of Georgia. Ecology 37:50–62.

Lanyon, W. E. 1981. Breeding birds and old field succession on fallow Long Island farmland. Bulletin of the American Museum of Natural History 168:1–60.

Lent, R. A. 1990. Relationships among environmental factors, phenotypic characteristics, and fitness components in the gray catbird (Dumatella carolinensis). Dissertation, State University of New York at Stony Brook, Stony Brook, New York.

Lorimer, C. G. 2001. Historical and ecological roles of disturbance in eastern North American forests: 9,000 years of change. Wildlife Society Bulletin 29:425–439.

Lorimer, C. G., and A. S. White. 2003. Scale and frequency of natural disturbances in the northeastern US: implications for early successional forest habitats and regional age distributions. Forest Ecology and Management 185:41–64.

McWilliams, W. H., C. A. Alerich, D. A. Devlin, J. Lister, T. W. Lister, S. L. Sterner, and J. A. Westfall. 2004. Annual inventory report for Pennsylvania's forests: results from the first three years.

Resource Bulletin NE-159. USDA Forest Service, Northeastern Research Station, Newtown Square, Pennsylvania, USA.

Nolan, V. Jr. 1978. The ecology and behavior of the prairie warbler *Dendroica discolor*. Ornithological Monographs 26:1–595.

Nolan, V. Jr., E. D. Ketterson, and C. A. Buerkle. Prairie warbler (*Dendroica discolor*) in A. Poole and F. Gill, editors. The Birds of North America, No. 455. The Academy of Natural Sciences, Philadelphia, Pennsylvania, USA and The American Ornithologists' Union, Washington, D. C., USA.

Noss, R. F., E. T. LaRoe III, and J. M. Scott. 1995. Endangered ecosystems of the United States: a preliminary assessment of loss and degradation. National Biological Service Biological Report 28.

Orians, G. H. 1969. On the evolution of mating systems in birds and mammals. American Naturalist 103:589–603.

Pickett, S. T. A. and P. S. White, editors. 1985. The ecology of natural disturbance and patch dynamics. Academic Press, San Diego, California, USA.

Rodewald, P. G. and M. C. Brittingham. 2004. Stopover habitats of landbirds during fall: use of edge-dominated and early-successional forests. Auk 121:1040–1055.

Sauer, J. R., J. E. Hines, and J. Fallon. 2006. The North American breeding bird survey, results and analysis 1966–2006. Version 6.2.2006 US Geological Survey Patuxent Wildlife Research Center, Laurel, Maryland, USA.

Shugart, H. S. Jr. and D. James. 1973. Ecological succession of breeding bird populations in northwestern Arkansas. Auk 90:62–77.

The Pennsylvania Game Commission and Pennsylvania Fish and Boat Commission. 2005. Pennsylvania Wildlife Conservation Strategy. [Online] Available at http://www.pgc.state.pa.us/pgc/cwp/view.asp?a=496&q=162067

Thompson, F. R. III and R. M. DeGraaf. 2001. Conservation approaches for woody, early successional communities in the eastern United States. Wildlife Society Bulletin 29:483–494.

Trani, M. K., R. T. Brooks, T. L. Schmidt, V. A. Rudis, and C. M. Gabbard. 2001. Patterns and trends of early successional forests in the eastern United States. Wildlife Society Bulletin 29:413–424.

Vitz, A. C. and A. D. Rodewald. 2007. Vegetative and fruit resources as determinants of habitat use by mature-forest birds during the postbreeding period. Auk 124:494–507.

Walkinshaw, L. H. 1978. Life history of the eastern field sparrow in Calhoun County, Michigan. University Microfilm International, Ann Arbor, Michigan, USA.

Westneat, D. F. 1993. Polygyny and extra-pair fertilizations in eastern red-winged blackbirds (*Agelaius phoeniceus*). Behavioral Ecology 4:49–60.

Yahner, R. H. 2003. Responses of bird communities to early successional habitat in a managed landscape. Wilson Bulletin 115:292–298.

Avian Ecology and Conservation: A Pennsylvania Focus with National Implications. Edited by S. K. Majumdar, T. L. Master, M. C. Brittingham, R. M. Ross, R. S. Mulvihill and J. E. Huffman. © 2010. The Pennsylvania Academy of Science.

Chapter 6

Reclaimed Surface Mine Habitat and Grassland Bird Populations

Glenn E. Stauffer[1], Matthew R. Marshall[2],
Duane R. Diefenbach[3] and Daniel W. Brauning[4]
[1]School of Forest Resources, Pennsylvania State University, University Park, PA 16802
[2]National Park Service, University Park, PA 16802
[3]USGS, Pennsylvania Cooperative Fish and Wildlife Research Unit,
University Park, PA 16802
[4]Pennsylvania Game Commission, Harrisburg, PA 17110
matt_marshall@nps.gov

GRASSLANDS AND GRASSLAND BIRDS

The ornithological and birding community in Pennsylvania long has known that many bird species typically thought of as being grassland obligate (or at least associated with grasslands), occur on the large swaths of "grassland" habitat created through the coal surface-mining and reclamation process (Whitmore 1980, Whitmore and Hall 1978). Species include Henslow's (*Ammodramus henslowii*), grasshopper (*A. savannarum*), Savannah (*Passerculus sandwichensis*), and vesper (*Pooecetes gramineus*) sparrows; bobolinks (*Dolichonyx oryzivorus*), eastern meadowlarks (*Sturnella magna*), upland sandpipers (*Bartramia longicauda*), and short-eared owls (*Asio flammeus*) among others. The ornithological and birding community also knows that unfortunately many North American grassland bird species have experienced severe and consistent population declines during the past 30 years (Herkert 1995, Sauer et al. 2007). In fact, since 1966 the guild of grassland bird species had the lowest percentage of increasing species in the U.S. Breeding Bird Survey (Pardieck and Sauer 2000). Population declines are rooted in the near collapse of the native tallgrass prairie ecosystem and severe losses in most other native prairie systems (Samson and Knopf 1994, Warner 1994). Most states have lost 99 percent of their native tallgrass prairie, and grasslands top the list of critically endangered native ecosystems (Noss et al. 1995). However, intensive surface coal mining and subsequent reclamation in western Pennsylvania have created large tracts of grassland habitat during the past 30 to 40 years. In this chapter we hope to provide an overview of the research we and others have undertaken to try to assess how much of this habitat is available in Pennsylvania, how many individuals of a few key species are using it, and if these habitats are suitable for successful breeding and reproduction. We hope to demonstrate the importance of these human created and maintained habitats and Pennsylvania's role in the global conservation of grassland birds.

Historically, tall-grass prairie was an important breeding habitat for grassland birds, but >99% of tall-grass prairie habitat present in the mid-western United States at the time of European settlement has been developed or converted to agricultural uses (Samson and

Knopf 1994). Most tall-grass prairie and other natural grasslands were located in the mid-western United States, and there is limited historical information about the distribution of naturally occurring grasslands or grassland birds in the eastern United States including Pennsylvania. However, agriculture activity and intentional forest burning by Native Americans and the activities of beavers (*Castor canadensis*) are thought to have created sufficient open grassland habitat to support eastern populations of grassland birds (Askins 1999). Two additional lines of evidence support the notion that grasslands bird populations in the eastern United States occupied historical grasslands and do not merely represent eastward range expansions following the clearing of extensive portions of eastern forests. First, fossil evidence points to the existence of grassland species >10,000 years ago in Pennsylvania, and second, the distinctiveness of some eastern subspecies of grassland birds suggests that these populations existed in isolation for a long time (Askins 1999).

Despite losses of traditional grassland bird habitat, enactment of the Conservation Reserve Program (CRP) in 1986 and reclamation or abandonment of extensive bituminous coal surface mines during the latter half of the 20th century have created new habitat on a large scale in the eastern United States and Pennsylvania. Although the purpose of the CRP was to reduce soil erosion (Dunn et al. 1993), there is considerable evidence that CRP fields also provide benefits to various species of wildlife, especially grassland obligate birds (see chapter 16 on " The Status and Conservation of Farmland Birds in Pennsylvania").

Surface mine grasslands, although not as extensive as CRP habitat, represent a substantial alternative habitat to cropland and CRP habitat for grassland birds in the upper midwestern and eastern United States. Vegetation on these grasslands in Pennsylvania typically consists of hardy and largely exotic grasses, forbs, and some scattered woody shrubs and small trees (Piehler 1987, Brothers 1990, Mattice et al. 2005). For example, on our study sites (Mattice et al. 2005, Stauffer 2008) abundant forb species include goldenrods (*Solidago* sp.), bird's foot trefoil (*Lotus corniculata*), clovers (*Trifolium* sp.), and Queen Anne's lace (*Daucus carota*), and dominant grass species include orchard grass (*Dactylis glomerata*), timothy (*Phleum pretense*), smooth brome (*Bromus inermis*), and fescue (*Festuca* sp.). Because of differing phenologies and rapid growth of many of these herbaceous species, the structure of the herbaceous vegetation changes dramatically during the course of the nesting season. Woody species planted to reclaim mines included black locust (*Robinia pseudoacacia*), spruces (*Picea* sp.), and pines (*Pinus* sp.), but invasion by autumn olive (*Eleagnus umbellata*), multiflora rose (*Rosa multiflora*), honeysuckles (Lonicera sp.), and blackberries (*Rubus allegheniensis*) also are common. The oftentimes acidic, nutrient poor, and compacted soils of reclaimed sites discourage growth of woody vegetation (grasses and legumes tend to be the most successful and persistent vegetation types) (Vogel 1981, Brothers 1990), and provide little potential for agricultural or timber production. As a result, these often undisturbed fields have a slow rate of ecological plant succession and therefore require relatively little management to be maintained as grasslands (Bajema et al. 2001).

HOW MUCH SURFACE MINE GRASSLAND HABITAT EXISTS IN PENNSYLVANIA?

Surface mine grasslands exist in widely distributed fragments ranging in size from >1,000 hectares in a mostly agricultural matrix in Indiana (Bajema et al. 2001), Ohio (Ingold 2002), and Illinois (Brothers 1990), to ≤100 hectares in largely forested landscapes in West Virginia (Whitmore 1980), Maryland (Skipper 1998), Kentucky (Monroe and Ritchison 2005), and Pennsylvania (Piehler 1987), but we are not aware of any estimates of the total amount of suitable surface mine grassland over a large area. We approached this question for nine counties in western Pennsylvania during the summers of 2003 and 2004 and also used distance sampling methods (observers walking transects and recording bird detections; Buckland et al. 2001) to estimate abundance of Henslow's, Savannah, and grasshopper sparrows across the entire study area (Mattice et al. 2005). We conducted our study in Armstrong, Butler, Cambria, Clarion, Clearfield, Indiana, Jefferson, Somerset, and Venango counties, totaling 18,648 km², an area roughly equivalent to the state of New Jersey (Fig. 1). These counties overlay the main bituminous coal field in Pennsylvania (Cuff et al. 1989) where coal is removed primarily by surface mining. Less than 30 percent of available coal has been mined in the majority of these counties with ongoing and

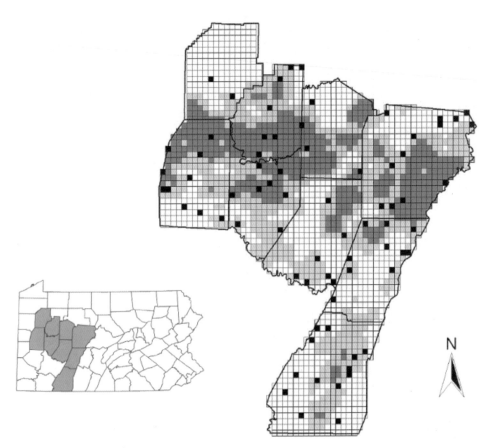

Figure 1:   The nine-county study area stratified by reclaimed surface mine area estimated to con-
            tain high (dark gray cells), medium (light gray cells), and low or no habitat (white cells)
            suitable for grassland birds and the location of these counties in Pennsylvania, 2001.
            Black cells indicate blocks surveyed for reclaimed surface mine area and abundance of
            grasshopper, Henslow's, and Savannah sparrows.

reclaimed sites creating a mosaic of farms, forest, active mine sites and reclaimed grass-lands across the study area landscape. We used a geographic information system (GIS) to overlay a grid, with 9-km^2 blocks, over the entire 9-county study area. We employed strat-ified random sampling using a GIS map of permitted and abandoned mine sites, combined with a vegetation cover classification map from the Pennsylvania Gap Analysis Project (PA GAP, Final Report, Pennsylvania State University and U.S. Geological Survey, June 2000), to create three strata of the area of reclaimed surface mine in each block (high, medium, low). We randomly selected blocks, by stratum, for sampling (habitat and spar-row abundance).

Within the 74 surveyed blocks, we mapped 108 reclaimed areas totaling 1,634 ha of suitable grassland songbird habitat. These patches of habitat ranged in size from 1 to 120 ha and averaged 15 ha. We estimated a total of 35,373 ha (95 percent CI = 26,758 – 46,870) of suitable reclaimed surface mine grassland habitat in the 9-county study area. Observers walked a total of 70.45 km of transects and recorded 325 grasshopper sparrow, 144 Henslow's sparrow, and 83 Savannah sparrow singing males within the 108 surveyed areas. We estimated the total population of singing males occupying the estimated 35,000 ha of suitable reclaimed surface mine habitat to be 1,921 Savannah sparrows (95 percent CI = 848 – 2,790), 9,650 grasshopper sparrows (95 percent CI = 4,390 – 13,614), and 4,884 Henslow's sparrows (95 percent CI = 2,128 – 8,460). From the estimates of total suitable reclaimed-mine grassland area and total populations, we calculated an average density of singing males of each species on suitable reclaimed surface mine habitat over the entire study area: 7 Savannah sparrow, 28 grasshopper sparrow, and 14 Henslow's sparrow singing males per 100 ha.

This >35,000 ha of potentially suitable habitat for grassland birds likely represents some of the most important breeding habitat in Pennsylvania for grassland-obligate sparrows (Mattice et al. 2005). Grasshopper, Henslow's, and Savannah sparrows occupy these sites in densities comparable to populations found in CRP fields and remnant tall-grass prairie. Data from the first Pennsylvania Breeding Bird Atlas (Reid 1992) indicated that Henslow's sparrows in Pennsylvania likely nest primarily on reclaimed surface mines. Preliminary data from the second Pennsylvania Breeding Bird Atlas (2nd PBBA, unpublished data, http://www.carnegiemnh.org/atlas/home.htm) indicate that the range of the Henslow's sparrow within Pennsylvania now is restricted almost exclusively to the region in western Pennsylvania with the most extensive concentration of reclaimed surface mines.

Pennsylvania's contribution to the global population of Henslow's sparrows is substantial, with approximately 5,000 singing males on reclaimed sites in our 9-county study area. Moreover, we believe we have underestimated abundance by as much as 2–5 times their actual abundance (Diefenbach et al. 2007). To place our estimate in context for conservation and management planning, we compared it to estimates for states reported in the 1996 Henslow's sparrow Federal status assessment (Pruitt 1996). Although these estimates were based on different methods, we found comparisons informative. Few states estimated popu-lations in excess of several hundred birds, and only Oklahoma, Missouri, and Kansas report-ed populations in excess of 1,000 birds in known colonies or projected to occur in the matrix of natural and agricultural grasslands. In comparison to our estimates for Pennsylvania, Mis-souri is the only state with a larger population of Henslow's sparrows (Pruitt 1996).

Since publication of the Henslow's sparrow status assessment (Pruitt 1996), many stud-ies, including ours (Mattice et al. 2005), have been initiated to evaluate the status of

Henslow's sparrow populations. In some instances, significant new populations were identified. Notably, many of these have been on reclaimed surface mines, including locations in Indiana (Bajema et al. 2001), Illinois, and Ohio (Ingold 2002). These surveys indicate larger populations than expected from the 1996 assessment, suggesting that much of the extant population occurs on reclaimed surface mines. Therefore, management of reclaimed strip mine areas as grasslands may help mitigate overall declines in global grassland songbird populations due to habitat loss and degradation, and Pennsylvania clearly has an opportunity to continue to provide crucial habitat.

GRASSLAND SONGBIRD NESTING ECOLOGY

While it was clear from our work and others that large numbers of grassland bird species were using reclaimed surface mines during the breeding season, it was unclear how successful they were at reproducing, and therefore, how valuable these habitats are to the long-term viability of the species. During the summers of 2003–2007 we looked at various aspects of the breeding ecology of the same three sparrow species we had sampled to estimate abundance. Our most intensive efforts took place in 2006–2007 (Stauffer 2008) and focused on finding and monitoring nests to estimate nest success. One goal of this study (Stauffer 2008) was to assess whether nesting success of grasshopper, Henslow's, and Savannah sparrows on reclaimed surface mine grasslands in Pennsylvania is adequate to maintain stable populations. In most passerine nesting studies, the most common cause of nest failure is predation (Martin 1992) although in some intensively managed grasslands mowing can also be an important source of nest failure (Kershner and Bollinger 1996). Predation rates can vary temporally and can be influenced by edge effects, fragmentation, parasitism, weather, and nest age. Rates of nest parasitism by brown-headed cowbirds (*Molothrus ater*) of grassland songbird nests tend to be low (Dixon 1978, Winter 1999, Peer et al. 2000, Winter et al. 2000, Ammer 2003, Winter et al. 2004, Renfrew et al. 2005), but several studies found that 50% of grassland bird nests contained cowbird eggs (Elliott 1978, Davis and Sealy 2000). Over a large geographical scale, the best overall predictor of parasitism levels seems to be regional cowbird density (Herkert et al. 2003). Because cowbird density in western Pennsylvania is relatively low (Sauer et al. 2007), we did not expect to find much parasitism of grassland sparrow nests.

To evaluate various aspects of the breeding success of these sparrow species, we chose four reclaimed surface mines for intensive study. The two sites in Clearfield County were reclaimed ≤10 years ago and located approximately 20 km apart in a largely forested and residential landscape. There was no active management of these sites, except that a portion of one site was hayed annually. The sites in Clarion County were about 1km apart on State Game Lands 330, known colloquially as the Piney Tract, in an approximately 1,000-ha complex of surface mines reclaimed prior to 1980. We systematically searched for nests of grasshopper, Henslow's, and Savannah sparrows during two nesting seasons (2006 – 2007) from approximately 14 May until 14 August. We monitored all located nests every 2 – 3 days until they either failed or fledged young.

Overall, we located 131 grasshopper sparrow nests, 34 Henslow's sparrow nests, and 35 Savannah sparrow nests. The earliest estimated nest initiation date was 12 May for grasshopper sparrows, 9 May for Henslow's sparrows, and 7 May for Savannah sparrows, and the latest known fledge date was 11 August for grasshopper sparrows, 22 July for

Henslow's sparrows, and 6 August for Savannah sparrows. Savannah sparrow nests had smaller clutch sizes, smaller brood sizes, and fledged fewer young than nests of grasshopper and Henslow's sparrows (Table 1). We did not document any instances of nest parasitism by cowbirds. Nest success varied across the study sites and by year and also was associated with several weather and nest-site vegetation measurements (Stauffer 2008). Overall, the estimated nest success (probability of a nest attempt fledging at least one young) was higher for grasshopper sparrows (0.42; 95% CI = 0.36 – 0.49) and Henslow's sparrows (0.369; 95% CI = 0.288 – 0.472) than it was for Savannah sparrows (0.158; 95% CI = 0.066 – 0.379). These estimates of grasshopper and Henslow's sparrow nesting success fall within the ranges reported in other studies, but success of Savannah sparrow nests was lower than often reported from other studies (Table 2). Nesting success of grassland sparrows varies widely in time and space, and it is not clear whether the low nesting success of Savannah sparrows in 2006 – 2007 compared to grasshopper and Henslow's sparrows represents a low point in naturally varying nesting success on reclaimed surface mines in Pennsylvania or whether reclaimed surface mines are unsuitable nesting habitat for Savannah sparrows. However, preliminary simulation analyses (Stauffer 2008) do suggest that this level of nest success is sufficient to sustain viable breeding populations for all three species when juvenile survival is assumed to be > 0.30 (and as low as 0.20 for grasshopper and Henslow's sparrows).

Similar to most other passerines (Martin 1992), the majority of nest failures were attributed to predation of the nest contents, but it is not clear who are the primary predators of grassland sparrow nests on reclaimed surface mines. Although we have not documented predation by specific predators, we have encountered a wide suite of potential predators including mammals (striped skunks [*Mephitis mephitis*], weasels [*Mustela* sp.], and white-tailed deer [*Odicoileus virginiana*]), birds (northern harrier [*Circus cyaneus*], red-tailed hawk [*Buteo jamaicensis*], American kestrel [*Falco sparverius*], common raven [*Corvus corax*], American crow [*Corvus brachyrynchos*], and blue jay [*Cyanocitta cristata*]), and snakes (black rat snake [*Elaphe obsoleta obsoleta*], black racer [*Coluber constrictor constrictor*], and eastern milk snake [*Lampropeltis triangulum triangulum*]). Video footage documented snakes as common predators of grassland birds in a grassland pasture in Wisconsin (Renfrew and Ribic 2003) and as the predominant nest predator in an old field in

Table 1. Clutch size, brood size, and average number of young fledged per successful nest of grasshopper (GRSP), Henslow's (HESP), and Savannah (SASP) sparrows on reclaimed surface mines in western Pennsylvania, USA, 2006 – 2007 where n = number of nests, = mean, and SD = standard deviation of the mean (from Stauffer 2008).

Species	Clutch size[a]			Brood size[b]			Number fledged[c]		
	n	$\bar{x}$	SD	n	$\bar{x}$	SD	n	$\bar{x}$	SD
GRSP	97	4.46	0.678	105	4.02	0.940	83	4.05	1.02
HESP	26	4.62	0.637	28	4.21	0.940	22	3.95	1.05
SAVS	28	3.71	1.18	25	3.48	1.00	13	3.54	0.519

[a] Clutch size was calculated only from nests that were monitored during egg stage.
[b] Brood size was calculated only from nests that were monitored during brooding stage and thus is conditional on nests surviving to egg stage.
[c] The number of fledged young per nest is calculated only from successful nests and thus is conditional on nest survival.

Table 2. Nesting success (%) of grasshopper (GRSP), Henslow's (HESP), and Savannah (SAVS) sparrows in various habitats (from Stauffer 2008).

Habitat	GRSP	Species HESP	SAVS	reference
Reclaimed mine	42.2	36.9	15.8	Stauffer (2008)
Reclaimed mine	7 – 47		22 – 39	Wray et al. (1982)
Reclaimed mine	43.4	33.3		Galligan et al. (2006)
Reclaimed mine	33			Ammer (2003)
Reclaimed mine	46			Ingold (2002)
Reclaimed mine		18.8 – 32.1		Monroe and Ritchison (2005)
CRP	14.5			McCoy et al. (1999)
CRP	30			Patterson and Best (1996)
CRP	11.9 – 28.5		1.9 – 15.5	Koford (1999)
WPA	10.6		22.0 – 24.9	Koford (1999)
Tallgrass prairie	22.0	39.5		Winter and Faaborg (1999)
Tallgrass prairie	17			Rohrbaugh et al. (1999)
Tallgrass prairie			31.4	Winter et al. (2004)
Maritime island			23	Dixon (1978)
Sandplain	42			Vickery et al. (1992)
Other		28.7		Robb et al. (1998)

Missouri (Thompson et al. 1999). Snakes also were directly observed eating grassland bird eggs on a reclaimed surface mine in Indiana (Galligan et al. 2006), and were believed to be responsible for most nest predation on a reclaimed surface mine in West Virginia (Wray et al. 1982). A better understanding of the predator community on reclaimed surface mines and of their responses to experimental management is needed to optimize surface mine grassland management for grassland sparrows.

MANAGEMENT OF SURFACE MINE GRASSLANDS

The Surface Mining Control and Reclamation Act of 1977 (P.L. 95-87) requires that mined sites be returned to a similar topographic contour and plant species composition that existed prior to removing coal. As a result, mining operators are required to plant trees as part of the reclamation process. While often difficult to accomplish due to the low soil organic matter, low fertility, and poor physicochemical and biological properties (Ussiri and Lal 2005), woody vegetation can and does become established, making these sites unsuitable for grassland birds. Moreover, many approved trees for planting are non-native to this region and planted in unnatural, single species stands. From the perspective of grassland birds, it should be noted that grasses remain the dominant vegetative cover on many reclaimed sites (Vogel 1981, Scott and Lima 2004) with some sites in Pennsylvania remaining suitable for grassland songbirds for >25 years (unpublished data). However, the practice of planting mostly non-native trees (while meeting the intent of the 1977 Reclamation Act) and the general, albeit slow, natural invasion of woody vegetation begs several questions. The first is a larger, policy and restoration question related to whether mining operators should be required to plant trees given what we now know about the value of these lands to grassland bird conservation. The second is a more practical management question regarding the removal of woody vegetation (regardless of origin) at sites and at times when it begins to make the site unsuitable for grassland birds. Management of woody vegetation could be adaptive and carried out in a replicated experimental framework, so that effects on nest survival and bird density can be identified reliably. We currently are pursuing this second question in an experimental context in collaboration with the Pennsylvania Game Commission.

Related management and ecological questions center around the topographic, vegetative, size, and landscape characteristics of an individual "patch" required for it to be of most value to grassland birds. In short, we recognize that not all reclaimed surface mines will be suitable for grassland birds with the size of the patch being an important determinant (grassland birds, like most birds, have minimum area requirements; Herkert 1994, Bollinger 1995, Johnson 2001). The answer to these questions will help inform decision makers when trying to decide whether or not to focus on grassland birds when restoring a mined site (that is, exceptions to the reforestation standard). It was in this context that we explored this issue (Diefenbach et al. *unpublished data*) using data on grasshopper, Henslow's and Savannah sparrow density on 236 reclaimed surface mine grassland "patches" ranging in size from 1 to 157 ha. Using patch size and a variety of landscape and vegetation measurements in the analysis, we concur with others (e.g., Scott et al. 2002, Roth et al. 2005) that a diversity of vegetation characteristics (e.g., litter depth, vegetation height, percent coverage of grass, etc.), at different spatial scales (Walk and Warner 2000), can provide habitats suitable for multiple species throughout the matrix of mine grasslands in western Pennsylvania. Also, grassland patches should be >50 ha for this region of Pennsylvania to address the area sensitivity exhibited by Henslow's sparrows, and probably larger for Savannah sparrows, although the recommended size could vary depending on other vegetation, physical and landscape factors (obstruction of the horizon, area of nonforest surrounding the reclaimed mine, etc.). Grasshopper sparrows had relatively high densities even on small reclaimed mine areas (<15 ha), but we suggest areas >50 ha be given the greatest priority when surface mines are considered for reclamation as grasslands or for habitat management activities (e.g., restoring or maintaining grassland habitat) to align with the area-sensitivity of the other two sparrow species. Our research demonstrated the size, spatial context, and slope that ideally provides habitat for grassland birds in order to obtain a higher ecological value than derives from routine reforestation.

CONCLUSIONS

Grassland sparrows and other important grassland species are common on many reclaimed surface mines in the Pennsylvania (Mattice et al. 2005, Diefenbach et al. 2007) and elsewhere (Bajema et al. 2001, Ingold 2002, Ammer 2003). Our results (Stauffer 2008) confirm that reclaimed surface mines are important nesting habitat for grassland sparrows where reproduction, especially of grasshopper and Henslow's sparrows, likely is adequate to maintain stable populations. Because grassland bird reproduction is often poor in agricultural grasslands (Rodenhouse and Best 1983, Bollinger et al. 1990), reclaimed surface mines can play a crucial role in the conservation of grassland songbirds, especially in states such as Pennsylvania that have little other suitable nesting habitat for many grassland songbird species. This especially is true for Henslow's sparrows which, in Pennsylvania, nest almost exclusively on reclaimed surface mines, and for which Pennsylvania may harbor a substantial portion of the global population (Mattice et al. 2005, Diefenbach et al. 2007). Pennsylvania has a high degree of responsibility for this species, and maintaining viable populations will require maintaining the nontraditional nesting habitat provided by reclaimed surface mine grasslands.

LITERATURE CITED

Ammer, F. K. 2003. Population level dynamics of grasshopper sparrow populations breeding on reclaimed surface mountaintop mines in West Virginia. Dissertation. West Virginia University, Morgantown, West Virginia, USA.

Askins, R. A. 1999. History of grassland birds in eastern North America. Studies in Avian Biology 19:60–71.

Bajema, R. A., DeVault, T.L.. Scott, P. E. and S. L. Lima. 2001. Reclaimed coal mine grasslands and their significance for Henslow's sparrows in the American Midwest. Auk 118:422–431.

Bollinger E. K. 1995. Successional changes and habitat selection in hayfield bird communities. Auk 112:720–730.

_____, Bollinger, P. B. and T. A. Gavin. 1990. Effects of hay-cropping on eastern populations of the bobolink. Wildlife Society Bulletin 18:142–150.

Brothers, T. S. 1990. Surface-mine grasslands. Geographical Review 80:209–225.

Buckland, S. T., Anderson, D.R., Burnham, K. P., Laake, J. L., Borchers, D. L. and L. Thomas. 2001. Introduction to Distance Sampling. Oxford University Press, New York, New York, USA.

Cuff, D. J., Young, W. J., Muller, E. K. Zelinsky, W. and R. F. Abler, editors. 1989. The Atlas of Pennsylvania. Philadelphia, PA: Temple University Press.

Davis, S. K., and S. G. Sealy. 2000. Cowbird parasitism and nest predation in fragmented grasslands in southwestern Manitoba. Pages 220–228 In J. N. Smith, T. L. Cook, S. I. Rothstein, S. K. Robinson, and S. G. Sealy, editors. Ecology and management of cowbirds and their hosts. University of Texas Press. Austin, Texas, USA.

Diefenbach, D. R., Marshall, M. R., Mattice, J. A. and D. W. Brauning. 2007. Incorporating availability for detection in estimates of bird abundance. Auk 124:96–106.

Dixon, C. L. 1978. Breeding biology of the Savannah Sparrow on Kent Island. Auk 95:235–246.

Dunn, C. P., Stearns, F., Guntenspergen, G. R. and D. M. Sharpe. 1993. Ecological benefits of the Conservation Reserve Program. Conservation Biology 7:132–139.

Elliott, P. F. 1978. Cowbird parasitism in Kansas tall grass prairie. Auk 95:161–167.

Galligan, E. W., DeVault, T. L. and S. L. Lima. 2006. Nesting success of grassland and savanna birds on reclaimed surface coal mines of the midwestern United States. Wilson Journal of Ornithology 118:537–546.

Herkert, J. R. 1995. Analysis of midwestern breeding bird population trends 1966–1993. American Midland Naturalist 134:41–50.

_____. 1994. The effects of habitat fragmentation on midwestern grassland bird communities. Ecological Applications 4:461–471.

_____, Reinking, D. L, Wiedenfeld, D. A., Winter, M., Zimmerman,J. L., Jensen, W.E., Finck, E., Koford, R. R., Wolfe, D. H., Sherrod, S. K., Jenkins, M. A., Faaborg, J. and S. K. Robinson. 2003. Effects of prairie fragmentation on the nest success of breeding birds in the midcontinental United States. Conservation Biology 17:587–594.

Ingold, D. J. 2002. Use of a reclaimed stripmine by grassland nesting birds in east-central Ohio. Ohio Journal of Science 102:56–62.

Johnson, D. H. 2001. Habitat fragmentation effects on birds in grasslands and wetlands: a critique of our knowledge. Great Plains Research 11:211–213.

Kershner, E. L., and E. K. Bollinger. 1996. Reproductive success of grassland birds at east-central Illinois airports. American Midland Naturalist 136:358–366.

Martin, T. E. 1992. Interaction of nest predation and food limitation in reproductive strategies. Current Ornithology 9:163–197.

Mattice, J. A., Brauning, D. W. and D. R. Diefenbach. 2005. Abundance of grassland songbirds on reclaimed surface mines in western Pennsylvania. Pages 504–510 in C. J. Ralph and T. D. Rich, editors. Bird Conservation Implementation and Integration in the Americas: Proceedings of the Third International Partners in Flight Conference. USDA Forest Service General Technical Report PSW-GTR191.

Monroe, M. S., and G. Ritchison. 2005. Breeding biology of Henslow's sparrows on reclaimed coal mine grasslands in Kentucky. Journal of Field Ornithology 76:143–149.

Noss, R. F., LaRoe, E. T. III, and J. M. Scott. 1995. Endangered ecosystems of the United States: A preliminary assessment of loss and degradation. Biological Report no. 28. Washington, DC: National Biological Service, U.S. Department of the Interior.

Pardieck, K. L., and J. R. Sauer. 2000. The 1995–1999 summary of the North America Breeding Bird Survey. Bird Populations 5: 30–48.

Peer, B. D., Robinson, S. K. and J. R. Herkert. 2000. Egg rejection by cowbird hosts in grasslands. Auk 117:892–901.

Piehler, K. G. 1987. Habitat relationships of three grassland sparrows on reclaimed surface mines in Pennsylvania. Thesis. West Virginia University, Morgantown, West Virginia, USA.

Pruitt, L. 1996. Henslow's Sparrow status assessment. Bloomington, IN: Bloomington Ecological Services Field Office, U.S. Fish and Wildlife Service.

Reid, W. 1992. Henslow's Sparrow (Ammodramus henslowii). Pages 386–387 in D. Brauning, editor. Atlas of Breeding Birds in Pennsylvania. University of Pittsburgh Press, Pittsburgh, Pennsylvania, USA.

Renfrew, R. B., Ribic, C. A. and J. L. Nack. 2005. Edge avoidance by nesting grassland birds: A futile strategy in a fragmented landscape. Auk 122:618–636.

_____, and _____. 2003. Grassland passerine nest predators near pasture edges identified on videotape. Auk 120:371–383.

Rodenhouse, N. L., and L. B. Best. 1983. Breeding ecology of vesper sparrows in corn and soybean fields. American Midland Naturalist 110:265–275.

Roth A.M., Sample, D. W., Ribic, C. A., Paine, L., Undersander,D. J. and G. A. Bartelt. 2005. Grassland bird response to harvesting switchgrass as a biomass energy crop. Biomass and Bioenergy 28:490–498.

Samson, F., and F. Knopf. 1994. Prairie conservation in North America. Bioscience 44:418–421.

Sauer, J. R., Hines, J. E. and J. Fallon. 2007. The North American Breeding Bird Survey, Results and Analysis 1966–2006. Version 10.13.2007. USGS Patuxent Wildlife Research Center, Laurel, Maryland, USA.

Scott, P. E. and S. L. Lima. 2004. Exotic grasslands on reclaimed midwestern coal mines: An ornithological perspective. Weed Technology 18:1518–1521 (Suppl. S).

_____, DeVault, T. L., Bajema, R. A. and S. L. Lima. 2002. Grassland vegetation and bird abundances on reclaimed midwestern coal mines. Wildlife Society Bulletin 30:1006–1014.

Skipper, C. S. 1998. Henslow's Sparrows return to previous nest site in western Maryland. North American Bird Bander 23:36–41.

Stauffer, G. E. 2008. Nesting ecology and site fidelity of grassland sparrows on reclaimed surface mines in Pennsylvania. Thesis, Pennsylvania State University, University Park, Pennsylvania, USA.

Thompson, F. R., Dijak, W. and D. E. Burhans. 1999. Video identification of predators at songbird nests in old fields. Auk 116:259–264.

Ussiri, D. A. N., and R. Lal. 2005. Carbon sequestration in reclaimed minesoils. Critical Reviews in Plant Sciences 24:151–165.

Vogel, W. G. 1981. A guide for revegetating coal minespoils in the eastern United States. Gen. Tech. Rep. NE-68. Broomall, PA: Northeast Forest Experimental Station, Forest Service, U. S. Department of Agriculture; 190 p.

Walk, J. W., and R. E. Warner. 2000. Grassland management for the conservation of songbirds in the Midwestern USA. Biological Conservation 94:165–172.

Warner, R. E. 1994. Agricultural land-use and grassland habitat in Illinois – future-shock for midwestern birds. Conservation Biology 8(1): 147–156.

Whitmore, R. C. 1980. Reclaimed surface mines as avian habitat islands in the Eastern forest. American Birds 34:13–14.

_____, and G. A. Hall. 1978. The response of passerine species to a new resource: Reclaimed surface mines in West Virginia. American Birds 32:6–9.

Winter, M. 1999. Nesting biology of Dickcissels and Henslow's sparrows in southwestern Missouri prairie fragments. Wilson Bulletin 111:515–526.

_____, Johnson, D. H. and J. Faaborg. 2000. Evidence for edge effects on multiple levels in tall-grass prairie. Condor 102:256–266.

_____, _____, Shaffer, J. A. and W. D. Svedarsky. 2004. Nesting biology of three grassland passerines in the northern tallgrass prairie. Wilson Bulletin 116:211–223.

Wray, T., II, Strait, K. A. and R. C. Whitmore. 1982. Reproductive success of grassland sparrows on a reclaimed surface mine in West Virginia. Auk 99:157–164.

Avian Ecology and Conservation: A Pennsylvania Focus with National Implications. Edited by S. K. Majumdar, T. L. Master, M. C. Brittingham, R. M. Ross, R. S. Mulvihill and J. E. Huffman. © 2010. The Pennsylvania Academy of Science.

SECTION II

Migration and Wintering Ecology
Section Overview

Paul Hess
Pennsylvania Ornithological Records Committee, 1412 Hawthorne St.,
Natrona Heights, PA 15065-1629
phess@salsgiver.com

Asked to associate Pennsylvania with one seminal aspect of research in avian migration, ornithologists may think of two iconic words: Hawk Mountain. The obvious reason is that Hawk Mountain Sanctuary has been a global leader in raptor research and conservation for more than 70 years. As important studies continue there, ornithologists elsewhere in Pennsylvania are making notable strides toward understanding migration and wintering ecology of raptors and other landbird species. Investigations described by this section's authors are relevant on both a continental and a worldwide scale.

Keith Bildstein's inspiring historical account of the hard work at Hawk Mountain is dramatic proof of the practical value of high-quality ornithological research. This history is embodied most famously, of course, in data that demonstrated shocking raptor declines associated with widespread use of DDT and other biocides. Raptor migration research in Pennsylvania is advancing exponentially at other locations as well, with data accumulating rapidly from at least 28 hawkwatch sites across the state.

Satellite telemetry has become a powerful tool for tracking the geographic origin, migration routes, and wintering grounds of individual raptors that pass through Pennsylvania. T. A. Miller, D. Brandes, M. J. Lanzone, D. Ombalski, C. Maisonneuve, and T. E. Katzner describe a tracking project that delineates precisely the migration paths of Golden Eagles along Appalachian ridges. This information is vital to minimize eagle mortality by identifying the least harmful sites for mountaintop wind turbines. Equally important, the project sheds light on locations where Golden Eagles are wintering—crucial knowledge for protecting these preferred sites.

Meanwhile, a pioneering "citizen science" project in Pennsylvania named the Winter Raptor Survey (WRS) is telling us about mid-winter distribution of vultures and open-country raptors. Gregory Grove explains how volunteer observers count raptors on standardized annual motor routes statewide, providing data to enable interpretation of distributional patterns, long-term trends, and associations between weather and numbers of birds. Efforts to begin similar surveys are under way in other states, and Grove is enthusiastic not only about the value of data collected but also about the extent of participation by volunteers.

Within a decade, Pennsylvania has risen to the top rank of research into the migration of a tiny raptor, the Saw-whet Owl. Scott Weidensaul reports history-making confirmation that Appalachian ridges are a major Saw-whet Owl flyway. In autumn 2007 alone, more than 1,500 of the owls were banded at 10 capture sites in Pennsylvania. The extensive banding study is adding new knowledge about Saw-whet migrants' seasonal phenology, rates of passage, annual fluctuations, sex and age ratios, and geographic origin.

The Christmas Bird Count (CBC), sponsored by the National Audubon Society for over a century, is the quintessential example of an immense database made possible by volunteer "citizen scientists." Countless CBC-based analyses have documented population trends, winter distribution, and periodic irruptions. Nick Bolgiano illustrates two phenomena by using Pennsylvania CBC data: 1) dramatic fluctuations in Carolina Wren populations in northern areas of the range, where numbers are affected powerfully by winter weather conditions; 2) a mysterious near-absence since the early 1980s of irruptions by chickadees and "winter finches," which traditionally had made periodic incursions southward. Bolgiano offers interesting speculations on possible causes of this remarkably sudden behavioral change.

The stopover ecology of songbird migrants is much less studied than breeding and wintering ecology, even though resting and refueling stops are critically important to birds' survival. Robert Smith and Margret Hatch note that investigations of stopover ecology are challenged by limitation to particular sites where birds stay only briefly and where results may not generalize to other migrants with different species-specific microhabitat and dietary requirements. Smith and Hatch are clarifying the picture in northeastern Pennsylvania. Their conclusions reinforce recent findings by Paul Rodewald and Margaret Brittingham in central Pennsylvania that highlight the importance of diverse, structurally complex, and early-successional plant communities as stopover sites suitable for a great variety of migrants. Smith and Hatch also explain how invasive exotic plants, overbrowsing by deer, and insect infestations threaten stopover habitat diversity. These studies point valuably toward conservation and management goals.

Underlying present and future research in Pennsylvania is the promise of new technologies for studying "migratory connectivity," a term referring to geographic patterns that connect breeding grounds, migration routes, and wintering grounds of individual birds and local populations throughout their annual cycle. Satellite telemetry is a key to this research, as exemplified by the Golden Eagle study. As lighter-weight and less-expensive telemetry units become available, a new vista will open for tracking small landbirds' annual movements. Two further technological advances are discussed by Shawn Rummell, Fred Brenner, and Christina Genarea, who explain how genetic markers and stable isotope technology can uncover birds' geographic origin and migratory connectivity. These two techniques' full potential has yet to be tapped by researchers in Pennsylvania, but it is only a matter of time until the methods significantly advance our knowledge of birds' migration and wintering ecology.

Avian Ecology and Conservation: A Pennsylvania Focus with National Implications. Edited by S. K. Majumdar, T. L. Master, M. C. Brittingham, R. M. Ross, R. S. Mulvihill and J. E. Huffman. © 2010. The Pennsylvania Academy of Science.

Chapter 7

Diurnal Raptor Migration

Keith L. Bildstein
Hawk Mountain Sanctuary,
Acopian Center for Conservation Learning,
410 Summer Valley Road, Orwigsburg, Pennsylvania, USA 17961
bildstein@hawkmtn.org

INTRODUCTION

Except for the remarkable observations of William Bartram in and around Philadelphia in 1802–1822 (Stone 1913), the migrations of diurnal raptors in Pennsylvania went largely unnoticed by ornithologists until the first few decades of the 20th Century (Bildstein 2006). Shortly thereafter migrating raptors were on the radar screens of both Pennsylvania's ornithologists and its hawk shooters (Sutton 1928a, Poole 1930), and at least one major migration corridor had been recognized (Sutton 1928a, Poole 1934). The founding of Hawk Mountain Sanctuary near Drehersville in Schuylkill County in 1934 as the world's first refuge for migrating birds of prey, and subsequent season-long, autumn counts of migrating raptors at that site (Broun 1935, 1939, 1949; Harwood 1973, Bildstein and Compton 2000) helped to make Pennsylvania a leader in the study of raptor migration for the remainder of the 20th Century. Declining counts of migrants in Pennsylvania during the DDT-Era of the 1940s–1970s—and increasing numbers since then—established Pennsylvania's raptor-migration watchsites as a useful monitoring scheme for populations of these important bio-indicators (Bednarz et al. 1990, Bildstein 1998). Today, 28 raptor-migration watchsites are at least intermittently active in Pennsylvania (Zalles and Bildstein 2000, Heintzelman 2004), where 20 species of North America's approximately 34 species of diurnal birds of prey are known to migrate at least occasionally (McWilliams and Brauning 2000). In addition to spectacular autumn flights of Broad-winged Hawks (*Buteo platypterus*), regionally significant outbound migrations of two species of New World Vultures, Ospreys (*Pandion haliaetus*) Bald Eagles (*Haliaeetus leucocephalus*), Northern Harriers (*Circus cyaneus*), three species of Accipiters, three additional species of Buteos, Golden Eagles (*Aquila chrysaetos*), and three species of falcons, including the Peregrine Falcon (*Falco peregrinus*), are currently monitored at migration watchsites in Pennsylvania (Zalles and Bildstein 2000, Bildstein et al. 2008). Although return migration also occurs in the state, spring migration appears to be less massive and, possibly, more broad-frontal than autumn migration (McCarty et al. 1999). Recently, studies involving both conventional and satellite tracking have added to our knowledge of raptor migration in the state.

A BRIEF HISTORY

William Bartram's records of bird migration in and around Philadelphia in 1802–1822 represent what are believed to be the oldest multi-year records of bird migration in North

America (Stone 1913). Included within them are some of earliest and best 19th Century records of raptor migration in Pennsylvania. Bartram listed spring arrival dates of between 2 and 29 April for Ospreys (*Pandion haliaetus*) in 7 years between 1802 and 1819, as well as autumn movements of "hawks and owls," and winter occurrences of both Bald Eagles (*Haliaeetus leucocephalus*) and American Kestrels (*Falco sparverius*) (Stone 1913).

Unfortunately, little ornithological knowledge regarding raptor migration was added over the remainder of the 19th Century. Two of the most authoritative works from the 1890s, B. H. Warren's *Birds of Pennsylvania* (Warren 1890) and W. Stone's *The birds of eastern Pennsylvania and New Jersey* (Stone 1894), for example, mention the migratory movements of raptors largely in passing

Warren (1890), who considered sightings of Black Vultures (*Coragyps atratus*), Swallow-tailed Kites (*Elanoides forficatus*), and Mississippi Kites (*Ictinia mississippiensis*) as representing "stragglers" from the South, only alluded to the seasonal movements of many common partial migrants (sensu Bildstein 2006), including Northern Harriers (*Circus cyaneus*), Sharp-shinned Hawks (*Accipiter striatus*), Cooper's Hawks (*A. cooperii*) and American Kestrels by noting their greater abundance during spring and autumn (Warren 1890). On the other hand, he did mention the Osprey's arrival in March and its departure in November, the Northern Goshawk (*A. gentilis*) as a scarce breeder and an irregular winter visitor, the Rough-legged Hawk (*Buteo lagopus*) as a "winter sojourner," and the Golden Eagle (*Aquila chrysaetos*) as "an occasional winter visitant" (Warren 1890). He also classified the Peregrine Falcon (*F. peregrinus*) as "a straggler in spring and fall" and "a rather rare and irregular winter visitor," much the same as the Merlin (*F. columbarius*) (Warren 1890). Warren also discussed the flocking behavior in Red-tailed Hawks (*B. jamaicensis*) during migration, but, curiously, not that of Broad-winged Hawks (*B. platypterus*) (cf. see Bildstein 1999). In fact, like many other ornithologists of his era, including regional luminaries such as the Academy of Natural Science of Philadelphia's Witmer Stone (Stone 1894), western Maryland's G. Eifrig (1904), and Delaware's Samuel N. Rhoads and C. J. Pennock (1905), Warren (1890) characterized the Broad-winged Hawk as a year-round "resident," completely overlooking its massive, albeit acute, movements across the state in September.

A "revolution" in field equipment in the 1890s that included the use of 7×–10× prismatic binoculars and the automobile, allowed birdwatchers to find and "see" high flying, soaring migrants such as Broad-winged Hawks (Bildstein 2006), and, as a result, by 1911 Berwyn's Franklin Lorenzo Burns was able to devote 16 pages of his 180-page monograph on this species to its large-scale migratory movements (Burns 1911). Seven years later, backed by additional field observations, Burns correctly classified the Broad-winged Hawk as a common "summer" resident in his *The ornithology of Chester County, Pennsylvania*, noting that he was doing so, given the lack of winter records, in spite of the species earlier classification as a year-round resident (Burns 1919).

Binocular-assisted observations of both high-flying and low-flying raptor migrants continued to increase in the 1920s and 1930s as did, unfortunately, the tendency to disparage the birds' predatory behavior, particularly when the prey in question was another bird or game animal (Bildstein 2008). State ornithologist George Miksch Sutton, in his highly regarded "Birds of Pennsylvania," for example, included "chicken hawk" as a second name for the Northern Harrier, as well as for all three species of *Accipiters,* and all four species of *Buteos* (Sutton 1928b). At the time, the three abundant falcons, still bore their official common names of Sparrow Hawk (American Kestrel), Pigeon Hawk (Merlin), and Duck Hawk (Peregrine Falcon). Sutton was particularly hard on *Accipiters*, beginning his descriptions of them with the following three statements: "The Sharp-shin is the enemy of all small birds," "The Sharp-shin and Cooper's Hawks, both bird killers, are fairly common and are to be rated as our most objectionable birds of prey," and "The Goshawk is our most savage destroyer of small game" (Sutton 1928b). He concluded his description of the Cooper's Hawk with the statement that "They [both the Sharp-shinned and Cooper's hawks] are not protected in Pennsylvania" (Sutton 1928b), left little doubt as to the intended take-home message: *Accipiters* killed other birds, small game, or both, and their numbers needed to be held in check. Somewhat similarly, Earl L. Poole, the curator of the Reading Public Museum writing in 1930, described both the Peregrine Falcon and Merlin as "in a sense parasitic" on waterbird migrants staging at the Maiden Creek Dam near Reading, Pennsylvania (Poole 1930). Unfortunately, Pennsylvania wildlife authorities and ornithologists were not alone during this era of beneficial versus harmful hawks (Bildstein 2006) and, indeed, as recently as 1935 no state was protecting its *Accipiters* even though many were protecting other species of birds of prey (May 1935).

Things took a decided turn for the worse in Pennsylvania in the late 1920s, largely due to two years of irruptive movements of Northern Goshawks during the autumns and winters of 1926–27 and 1927–28 (Bildstein and Compton 2000). Goshawks were not welcome in Pennsylvania, and rural inhabitants along the Kittatinny Ridge, or Blue Mountain, in Schuylkill and Berks counties, 120 km northwest of Philadelphia, reported the predatory "invasion" to a local game protector who relayed the message to George Miksch Sutton at the Game Commission. Both men subsequently visited the ridgetop 3 km above Drehersville, Pennsylvania, in mid October 1927, where an over-the-mountain road and a blueberry (*Vaccinium* spp.) and huckleberry (*Gaylussacia baccata*) bald had attracted a small army of shooters since the early 1920s. Three days later the game protector and several others returned to collect the carcasses of more that 150 birds of prey. No wonder the place was known locally as "hawk mountain" (Bildstein and Compton 2000).

Sutton summarized his observations in two papers published in *The Wilson Bulletin* several years thereafter (Sutton 1928a, 1931). The first paper had two diametrically opposing effects. One was the establishment of a $5 state bounty on Goshawks between November and May (Gerstell 1937). The second was to raise awareness in the ornithological and conservation communities about the slaughter of migrating raptors at Hawk Mountain (Bildstein and Compton 2000).

After reading Sutton's first paper, Earl Poole began visiting Hawk Mountain in 1929. Poole's 1934 accounts of the flight, which included a 2000-bird flight of Broad-winged Hawks on 22 September 1932, represent the first detailed description of raptor migration at the site (Poole 1934). Sutton's articles also brought Philadelphia raptor conservationists Henry H. Collins and Richard Pough to the site, and both expanded on Sutton's descriptions of the shooting there (Pough 1932, Collins 1933). Pough and Collins's publication of photographs depicting the shooting at Hawk Mountain led the Philadelphia Society for the Prevention of Cruelty to Animals to send a State Policemen to the site to curb the violence, and a slide-illustrated talk by Pough at a meeting of birders and conservationists in New York City in 1933 alerted Emergency Conservation Committee head, Rosalie Edge, to the problem.

Table 1. Some widely recognized raptor migration watchsites in Pennsylvania (after Zalles and Bildstein 2000, Heintzelman 2004).

Watchsite	Location
Allegheny Front	Allegheny Mountains, Bedford County, near Central City
Bake Oven Knob	Kittatinny Ridge, Lehigh County, near New Tripoli
Bear Rocks	Kittatinny Ridge, Lehigh County, near New Tripoli
Brady's Bend Hawk Watch	Bluff overlooking Allegheny River, Armstrong County, near East Brady
Chickies Rock	Cliff overlooking Susquehanna River, Lancaster County, near Marietta
College Hill Hawk Watch	College Hill, Northampton County, Easton
Council Cup Hawk Watch	Cliff overlooking north branch of the Susquehanna River, Luzerne County, near Wapwallopen
Hawk Mountain Sanctuary	Kittatinny Ridge, Schuylkill and Berks counties, near Drehersville
Jack's Mountain	Jack's Mountain, Mifflin County, near Belleville
Lehigh Furnace Gap	Kittatinny Ridge, Lehigh County, near Slatedale
Lehigh Gap	Kittatinny Ridge, Lehigh County, near Slatington
Little Gap	Kittatinny Ridge, Northhampton County, near Danielsville
Militia Hill Hawk Watch	Militia Hill, Montgomery County, near Fort Washington
Presque Isle State Park	Lake Erie shoreline, Erie County, Erie
Rocky Ridge County Park	Rocky Ridge, York County, near York
Rose Tree Park Hawk Watch	Eastern edge of the Piedmont Plateau, Delaware County, near Media
Route 183	Kittatinny Ridge, Schuylkill County, near Strausstown
Route 309	Kittatinny Ridge, Lehigh and Schuylkill counties, near New Tripoli
Second Mountain Hawk Watch	Second Mountain, Lebanon County, near Fort Indiantown Gap
State Hill Hawk Watch	State Hill, Berks County, near Reading
Sterrett's Gap	Kittatinny Ridge, Perry County, near Carlisle Springs
Stone Mountain	Stone Mountain, Huntingdon County, near Ennisville
Tuscarora Mountain	Tuscarora Mountain, Fulton County, near Chambersburg
Tussey Mountain Hawk Watch	Tussey Mountain, Centre County, near State College
Waggoner's Gap	Kittatinny Ridge, Cumberland County, near Carlisle
West Lake Middle School	Lake Erie shoreline, Erie County, Erie
White Deer Ridge Hawk Watch	North White Deer Ridge, Lycoming County, near South Williamsport
Wildcat Rocks	South Mountain, Cumberland County, near Newville

Edge asked the National Association of Audubon Societies to act to stop the slaughter and when they did not, she visited the site in the summer of 1934 and leased the 565 hectares that became the core of Hawk Mountain Sanctuary. Edge then hired a young New England birder, Maurice Broun, as "ornithologist in charge," and bought the property outright in 1935. The rest, as they say, is history (cf. Broun 1949, Harwood 1973, Bildstein and Compton 2000).

In its second year of operations, Hawk Mountain Sanctuary attracted 1,250 visitors and the stage was set for making the site a birding Mecca. Maurice Broun had initiated counts of migrants at the Sanctuary primarily to document the numbers of raptors that were being saved there (Broun 1935, Bildstein and Compton 2000), but it quickly became apparent to him that annual counts would allow Hawk Mountain to monitor the conservation status of the region's migrants, and by 1935 the migration count had become the Sanctuary's primary field effort. Early scientific contributions resulting from the count included (1) a flight of 39 Golden Eagles in 1934, establishing a new migration route for eastern populations of this species (Broun 1935), (2) an acute migration of thousands of Broad-winged Hawks, typically centered around the 16th and 17th of September (Broun 1949), and (3) confirmation of a strong association between enhanced raptor migration at the site and the passage of cold fronts (Broun 1951). All three of these contributions have been confirmed by later studies (Bednarz et al. 1990, Allen et al. 1995, 1996).

As news of the new sanctuary spread and as visits by conservationists, ornithologists, and hawk watchers accumulated, the sport of hawkwatching grew to the point that additional migration watchsites began to spring up, initially in the Northeast, and eventually throughout North America and the world (Zalles and Bildstein 2000, Heintzelman 1986, 2004). Today, at least 28 raptor-migration watchsites operate, regularly or intermittently within Pennsylvania (Table 2), and more than 380 operate globally (Zalles and Bildstein 2000).

Although counts at individual migration watchsites frequently vary among years as a result of annual differences in weather and other factors extrinsic to population change, evidence suggests that over the long-term, numbers of migrants reported at watchsites typically reflect the long term-status of source populations (Newton 1979, Bednarz et al. 1990, Bildstein 1998). Furthermore, there is a growing body of evidence that the appropriate analysis of counts from groups of watchsites can be used to monitor regional and even continental populations of migrants (Farmer et al. 2007, Bildstein et al. 2008).

Table 2. Species, type migrant, and occurrences of migrating raptors in Pennsylvania.

Species	Type migrant[a]	Seasonal occurrence
Turkey Vulture (*Cathartes aura*)	Partial migrant	Year-round
Black Vulture (*Coragyps atratus*)	Partial migrant	Year-round
Osprey (*Pandion haliaetus*)	Complete migrant	Rare in winter
Swallow-tailed Kite (*Elanoides forficatus*)	Partial migrant	Rare migrant
Mississippi Kite (*Ictinia mississippiensis*)	Complete migrant	Rare migrant
Bald Eagle (*Haliaeetus leucocephalus*)	Partial migrant	Year-round
Northern Harrier (*Circus cyaneus*)	Partial migrant	Year-round
Northern Goshawk (*Accipiter gentilis*)	Partial and sometimes irruptive migrant	Year-round
Sharp-shinned Hawk (*A. striatus*)	Partial migrant	Year-round
Cooper's Hawk (*A. cooperii*)	Partial migrant	Year-round
Broad-winged Hawk (*Buteo platypterus*)	Complete migrant	Rare in winter
Swainson's Hawk (*B. swainsoni*)	Complete migrant	Rare migrant
Red-tailed Hawk (*B. jamaicensis*)	Partial migrant	Year-round
Red-shouldered Hawk (*B. lineatus*)	Partial migrant	Year-round
Rough-legged Hawk (*B. lagopus*)	Complete migrant	Not in summer
Golden Eagle (*Aquila chrysaetos*)	Partial migrant	Extremely rare in summer
American Kestrel (*F. sparverius*)	Partial migrant	Year-round
Merlin (*F. columbarius*)	Partial migrant	Rare in summer
Gyrfalcon (*F. rusticolus*)	Partial migrant	Rare, not in summer
Peregrine Falcon (*Falco peregrinus*)	Partial migrant	Year-round

[a]Partial migrants are species in which fewer than 90% of all individuals migrate; complete migrants are species in which at least 90% of all individuals migrate; irruptive migrants are species in which the extent of migratory movements varies annually, typically due to among-year shifts in prey abundance.

MIGRATION GEOGRAPHY IN PENNSYLVANIA

Annual counts of migrants at Hawk Mountain Sanctuary, together with those at other sites along the Kittatinny Ridge, including Bake Oven Knob, Sterrett's Gap, and Waggoner's Gap (Table 2), have established the Kittatinny as the preeminent leading line (sensu Bildstein 2006) (see Brandes and Ombalski 2004 for a fluid-flow analogy of why this might be so) for raptors traveling within and across the state in autumn. Migrants also concentrate in other parts of the state, either in autumn, in spring, or at both times of the year. Additional significant areas include, but are not limited to, parts of the Valley-and-Ridge Physiographic Province to which the Kittatinny Ridge belongs northwest of the Kittatinny, South Mountain, directly southeast of the Kittatinny, the Delaware River and small mountains and hills directly west of it, the Alleghenies on the southeastern edge of the Allegheny Plateau, and the shoreline of Lake Erie in the northwestern-most Pennsylvania (Heintzelman 1986, Van Fleet 1997, Zalles and Bildstein 2000).

The extent to which the Kittatinny Ridge functions as a "leading" versus a "diversion" line for migrants in autumn has been of interest to raptor biologists for some time. (See Bildstein 2006 for an explanation of the difference in these terms). In 1940, Edward Snively Frey suggested a 30% overlap in migrants seen at Hawk Mountain Sanctuary and Sterrett's Gap, two watchsites approximately 110 km apart along the Kittatinny (Frey 1940), and, more recently, a series of publications comparing sightings of infrequently seen Bald Eagles and Golden Eagles at Bake Oven Knob and Hawk Mountain Sanctuary, two watchsites approximately 26 km apart on the Kittatinny, reached similar conclusions (Heintzelman 1982, Hawk et al. 2002, Teter et al. 2003). Most recently, conventional radio tracking of southbound Sharp-shinned and Cooper's hawks reveals a similar pattern of ridgeline use (L. J. Goodrich, pers. comm.). Thus, the Kittatinny hosts many more migrants than are counted at any one watchsite along it, with individual migrants joining and leaving the ridge line at various points over the course of the ridge's more than 300-km length. That said the Kittatinny does appear to continue to retain migrants crossing water gaps along it (cf. Klem et al. 1985), and a study of raptor movements across the Valley-and-Ridge Province suggests that southbound flights along the Kittatinny all-but equal the combined totals of several parallel ridges, including, among others, Jacks, Stone, and Bald Eagle, north and west of it, particularly early in the autumn (Van Fleet 1997).

Autumn trapping and banding efforts along the Kittatinny and at other migration concentration points elsewhere in Pennsylvania also have amassed useful information on the origins and destinations of Sharp-shinned Hawks passing through the state as well as on migration short stopping (Viverette et al. 1996). Unfortunately, this resource has yet to be used to any great extent.

Spring migration appears to be more broad-frontal than autumn migration in Pennsylvania (McCarty et al. 1999), and field evidence suggests, overall, that concentrated movements of raptors pass farther west in the state in spring than in autumn (cf. Kerlinger 1989, Brandes 1998, Zalles and Bildstein 2000). Much remains to be learned about spring migration in Pennsylvania, in part because fewer hawkwatchers are active at this time of year than in autumn (Bildstein et al. 2008).

Although migration watchsites and banding continue to provide useful information regarding migration geography, the relatively recent development of tracking raptors by satellite promises to increase our knowledge of the geography of raptor migration in Pennsylvania considerably. Tracking units placed on six Golden Eagles in the James Bay region of Canada in 1992 indicate at least some of the Golden Eagles seen at migration watch-sites in Pennsylvania breed in that region of Canada (Brodeur et al. 1996). And more recent satellite tracking by Todd Katzner and colleagues suggests that Golden Eagles from breeding areas throughout Quebec, migrate through or winter in central Pennsylvania (T. Katzner, pers. comm.). In addition, satellite tracking of 11 Turkey Vultures trapped and tagged in eastern Pennsylvania in 2004 and 2005 indicates that whereas some Turkey Vultures migrate as far as central Florida, others migrate only to Maryland and southern New Jersey, and others still remain within the state year-round (Hawk Mountain Sanctuary, unpubl. data). Although it is still a new technology, satellite tracking offers the ability to track individual migrants on a daily and even hourly basis. As miniaturization continues and as costs decline, this new technique is likely to become an increasingly important tool in understanding raptor migration in the state (Bildstein 2006).

CONSERVATION STATUS

Organized assessments of populations of migratory raptors in Pennsylvania in the 17th, 18th and 19th centuries are virtually non-existent, and much of what we know about pop-ulations of these birds comes in the form of species reports from the great naturalists of the era (Catesby 1731–1743, Wilson 1808–1814, and Audubon 1840), all of whom com-mented on these species only in general terms, and from the state bird books of Warren (1890), Sutton (1928b), etc., mentioned above. The first real indication of functionally sig-nificant populations of raptors in Pennsylvania comes in the 1880s when rural animosity against birds of prey resulted in the passage of a fifty-cent bounty on the "heads" of all birds of prey, including owls. The so-called "Scalp Act" or "Fool Hawk Law" of 1885—which opinion polls at the time indicated support from at least 90% of the general public—resulted in 180,000 "scalps" being sent to Harrisburg over the course of the next two years, setting the stage for a lengthy period of state-paid bounties on birds of prey that continued until the 1960s (Bildstein 2001). Although the act was rescinded in the late 1880s due to surging populations of small mammal and insect vermin, a drain on the state treasury, and a series of fraudulent claims (Bildstein 2006), bounties on raptors were reinstated in 1913. In 1921 the state paid a total of $128,269 in predator bounties, and its own employees killed at least 600 hawks and destroyed more than 40 nests (Kosack 1995). Most birds of prey were unprotected in the state until 1937, when, except for the three *Accipiters*, most species received legal protection (Kosack 1995). Unfortunately, protective measures remained spotty for several decades thereafter. It was not until 1972, when the federal gov-ernment amended the Migratory Bird Treaty Act of 1918 to include birds of prey, that all raptors, including owls, were legally protected in Pennsylvania (Bildstein 2006). (See Bildstein 2001 and 2008 for additional details on this era of raptor conservation in Penn-sylvania history.)

As the problem of human persecution began to wane in the middle of the 20th Century, a new threat began to take hold. The widespread misuse of organochlorine biocides dur-ing the DDT-Era of mid-20th Century North America forced many populations of Penn-sylvania's birds of prey even further downward (Hickey 1969), exacerbating the effects of residual shooting (Bildstein 2006, 2008). The best known of these new biocides, DDT (dichloro-diphenyl-trichloroethane), came into widespread use in the late 1940s and early

1950s. Initially heralded as "wonder chemicals" the second generation of "safer" pesticides proved to have the significant, if unintended effect of reducing reproductive success via eggshell thinning (Bildstein 2006). Although warnings about the new pesticides' effects on populations of birds date from the late 1940s, it was not until the publication of Rachel Carson's *Silent Spring* in the early 1960s (Carson 1962), that biologists recognized the potential magnitude of the problem. And, it was not until a group of raptor biologists met in Madison, Wisconsin in 1965 that the demise of eastern North American populations of Peregrine Falcons—a "poster child" for other species of birds of prey during the DDT-Era—became fully apparent to raptor conservationists (Hickey 1969). An analysis of the Hawk Mountain counts of 12 species of raptors between 1934 and 1966 presented at the meeting, demonstrated the widespread nature of the effect of organochlorine pesticides on birds of prey (Spofford 1969). In 1972 the federal government banned the widespread use of DDT and, subsequently, other organochlorine pesticides. Despite serious concerns regarding the organophosphates that were later used in insect control (cf. Bildstein 2006), an analysis of Hawk Mountain's then 53-year long migration data set in the late 1980s, confirmed a turnabout in most raptor population declines beginning in the early to mid 1970s (Bednarz et al. 1990, Bildstein 1998).

The most recent analysis of Hawk Mountain's long-term counts, together with those from six other migration watchsites in eastern Great Lakes and northeastern North America, including the Audubon's Hawk Watch at Waggoner's Gap, from 1974 through 2004, indicates increasing or stable regional trends for 7 of 16 species of birds of prey monitored at the two sites, decreases for 1 species (American Kestrel) and variable long-term trends for 8 others (Farmer et al. 2008). See Table 3 for details concerning trends from these two Pennsylvania watchsites.

DISCUSSION

As populations of migratory birds of prey continue to rebound from DDT-Era lows of the mid-20th Century, and as many species continue to adapt to human-dominated as well as more natural landscapes, increasingly, raptor conservationists will need to deal with public concerns about the apparent "overabundance" of raptors and their so-called increased impacts on other wildlife (cf. Bildstein 2001). In almost all instances, concerns such as these are best addressed proactively through conservation education at the state and local levels, and the Department of Conservation and Natural Resources as well as the Game Commission also have potentially large roles to play in this area.

Studies of raptor migration continue to thrive in Pennsylvania. The new technology of satellite tracking offers the promise of important new insights into the movements of many species of raptors within the state, and it, together with accumulating migration watchsite counts and banding returns, promises to help raptor migration scientists and conservationists better understand and protect this important conservation resource. Pennsylvania has a long history of leadership in this area, and recent and current actions by scientists and conservationists in the state (cf. Bildstein et al. 2008) suggest that this is likely to continue well into the future.

Although it is challenging to look too far into the future regarding raptor conservation in Pennsylvania, one area of recent and growing concern regarding Pennsylvania's migratory raptors is the potential threat of wind turbines. Wind power can affect raptors in at least

Table 3. Species trends at Hawk Mountain Sanctuary and Audubon's Hawk Watch at Waggoner's Gap, 1974–2004, summarized from Farmer et al. (2008) with additional comments by the author.

Species	Hawk Mountain	Waggoner's Gap	Comments
Black Vulture	Increasing[a]	Increasing	Due at least in part to range expansion to the North
Turkey Vulture	Increasing	Increasing	Due at least in part to range expansion to the North
Osprey	Increasing	Increasing	Increase has slowed or stabilized since the early 1990s
Bald Eagle	Increasing	Increasing	Uniform increase from the Pesticide Era lows of the 1950s–1970s
Northern Harrier	Decreasing[b]	Unclear[c]	Counts highly variable; trends vary over space and time
Sharp-Shinned Hawk	Decreasing	Unclear	Counts are more variable at Waggoner's Gap; decrease possibly due to short-stopping
Cooper's Hawk	Increasing	Increasing	Steady increase at both site
Northern Goshawk	Decreasing	Unclear	Irruptive migrant, highly variable counts at both sites
Red-shouldered Hawk	Unclear	Unclear	Hint of a decreasing trend at Hawk Mountain
Broad-winged Hawk	Decreasing	Unclear	Stable or possibly decreasing overall, but unclear
Red-tailed Hawk	Decreasing	Unclear	Decrease possibly due to short stopping
Rough-legged Hawk	Too few to analyze	Too few to analyze	
Golden Eagle	Increasing	Increasing	Steady increase at both sites
American Kestrel	Decreasing	Unclear	Strong recent decline at Hawk Mountain
Merlin	Increasing	Increasing	May be peaking at Hawk Mountain; steady increase at Waggoner's Gap
Peregrine Falcon	Increasing	Increasing	Appears to be stable since early 1990s

[a]Increasing: significant (P < 0.05) or marginally significant (P < 0.10) increase at the site.
[b]Decreasing: significant (P < 0.05) or marginally significant (P < 0.10) decrease at the site.
[c]Unclear: no significant trend at the site.

three ways: first via collisions with the turbines, themselves, second via habitat disturbance associated with turbine construction and maintenance, and third via avoidance of areas with wind turbines. A growing body of evidence suggests that new as well as old turbines can be problematic, and that improperly sited and inappropriately managed wind turbines can cause problems for migratory raptors (Percival 2005, Bildstein 2006, de Lucas et al. 2007). Historically, Pennsylvania's enthusiastic embrace of developing energy resources, most notably coal and nuclear power, produced numerous unintended consequences for state residents and natural resources. It would be unfortunate if the state's current embrace of wind power proceeded without careful and thoughtful consideration of the likelihood of similar unintended consequences associated with the widespread use of that technology.

Overall I remain guardedly optimistic about our ability to maintain the current functional populations of migratory raptors we now enjoy in Pennsylvania. As long as we continue to study and better understand the ecological requirements of these birds, and as long as we remain willing to learn from our past, we can expect to enjoy and benefit from this important wildlife resource for some time.

ACKNOWLEDGMENTS

I thank the many ornithologists, banders, and hawkwatchers who have contributed to our understanding of raptor migration in Pennsylvania. D. Brandes, C. Farmer, and L. Goodrich read and commented on earlier versions of the paper. The late Sarkis Acopian and Hawk Mountain Sanctuary Association provided me with the resources to complete this work. This is Hawk Mountain Sanctuary Contribution to conservation science number 172.

REFERENCES

Allen, P. E. , L. J. Goodrich, and K. L. Bildstein. 1995. Hawk Mountain's million-bird database. Birding 27:25–32.

Allen, P. E. , L. J. Goodrich, and K. L. Bildstein. 1996. Within- and among-year effects of cold fronts on migrating raptors at Hawk Mountain, Pennsylvania, 1934–1991. Auk 113:329–338.

Audubon, J. J. 1840. The birds of America. Vol. I. J. B. Chevalier, Philadelphia Pennsylvania.

Bednarz, J. C., D. Klem Jr., L. J. Goodrich, and S. E. Senner. 1990. Migration counts of raptors at Hawk Mountain, Pennsylvania, as indicators of population trends, 1934–1986. Auk 107:96–109.

Bildstein, K. L. 1998. Long-term counts of migrating raptors: a role for volunteers in wildlife research. Journal of Wildlife Management 62:535–445.

Bildstein, K. L. 1999. Racing with the sun: the forced migration of the Broad-winged Hawk. Pages 79–102 in K. P. Able, editor. Gatherings of angels: migrating birds and their ecology. Cornell University Press, Ithaca, New York, USA.

Bildstein, K. L. 2001. Raptors as vermin: a history of human attitudes towards Pennsylvania's birds of prey. Endangered Species Update 18:124–128.

Bildstein, K. L. 2006. Migrating raptors of the world: their ecology and conservation. Cornell University Press, Ithaca, New York, USA.

Bildstein, K. L. 2008. A brief history of raptor conservation in North America. In K. L. Bildstein, J. Smith, and E. Ruelas, editors. The State of North America's birds of prey. Series in Ornithology No. 3. Nuttall Ornithological Club, Cambridge, Massachusetts; and American Ornithologists'' Union, Washington, D.C.

Bildstein, K. L., and R. A. Compton. 2000. Mountaintop Science: the history of conservation ornithology at Hawk Mountain Sanctuary. Pages 153–181 in W. E. Davis, Jr. and J. A. Jackson, editors. Contributions to the History of North American Ornithology. Nuttall Ornithological Club, Cambridge, Massachusetts, USA.

Bildstein, K. L. J. Smith, and E. Ruelas. editors. 2008. The State of North America's birds of prey. Series in Ornithology No. 3. Nuttall Ornithological Club, Cambridge, Massachusetts; and American Ornithologists'' Union, Washington, D.C.

Brandes, D. 1998. Spring Golden Eagle Passage through the Northeast U. S.—evidence for a geographically concentrated flight? HMANA Migration Studies 23(2):38–42

Brandes, D., and D. W. Ombalski. 2004. Modeling raptor migration pathways using a fluid-flow analogy. J. Raptor Res. 38:195–207.

Brodeur, S., R. Decarie, D. Bird, and M. Fuller. 1996. Complete migration cycle of Golden Eagles breeding in northern Quebec. Condor 98:293–299.

Broun, M. 1935. The hawk migration during the fall of 1934, along the Kittatinny Ridge in Pennsylvania. Auk 52:233–248.

Broun, M. 1939. Fall migration of hawks at Hawk Mountain, Pennsylvania, 1934–1938. Auk 56:429–441.

Broun, M. 1949. Hawks Aloft: the Story of Hawk Mountain. Cornwall Press, Cornwall, New York, USA.

Broun, M. 1951. Hawks and weather. Atlantic Nat. 6:105–112.

Burns, F. L. 1911. A monograph of the Broad-winged Hawk (*Buteo platypterus*). Wilson Bulletin 23:141–320.

Burns, F. L. 1919. The ornithology of Chester County, Pennsylvania. Gorham Press, Boston, Massachusetts, USA.

Carson, R. 1962. Silent Spring. Houghton Mifflin, Boston, Massachusetts.

Catesby, M. 1731–1743. The natural history of Carolina, Florida, and the Bahama Islands. 2 vols. London, England.

Collins, H. H., Jr. 1933. Hawk slaughter at Drehersville. Ann. Rep. Hawk and Owl Soc. Bull. 3:10–18.

de Lucas, M., G. F. E. Janss, and M. Ferrer. Editors. 2007. Birds and wind farms: risk assessment and mitigation. Quercus, Madrid, Spain.

Eifrig, G. 1904. Birds of Allegany and Garret counties, Western Maryland. Auk 21:234–250.

Farmer, C. J., D. J. T. Hussell, and D. Mizrahi. 2007. Detecting population trends in migratory birds of prey. Auk 124:1047–1062.

Farmer, C. J., R. J. Bell, B. Drolet, E. Greenstone, L. Goodrich, D. Grove, D. J. T. Hussell, D. Mizrahi, F. Nicoletti, and J. Sodergren. 2008. Trends in autumn counts of migratory raptors in northeastern North America.

1974–2004. In K. L. Bildstein, J. Smith, and E. Ruelas, editors. The State of North America's birds of prey. Series in Ornithology No. 3. Nuttall Ornithological Club, Cambridge, Massachusetts; and American Ornithologists" Union, Washington, D.C.

Frey, E. S. 1940. Hawk notes from Sterrett's Gap, Pennsylvania. Auk 57:247–250.

Gerstell, R. 1937. The Pennsylvania bounty system. Research Bull. 1. The Pennsylvania Game Commission, Harrisburg, Pennsylvania.

Harwood, M. 1973. The View from Hawk Mountain. New York (NY): Scribner's. McCarty, K. M., M. Farhoud, J. Ottinger, L. G. Goodrich, and K. L. Bildstein. Spring migration at Hawk Mountain Sanctuary, 1969–1998. 1999. Pennsylvania Birds 3:11– 15.

Hawk, S., N. A. Chingiz kizi, J. Musina, and K. McCarty. 2002. Ridge adherence in Bald Eagles migrating along the Kittatinny Ridge between Bake Oven Knob and Hawk Mountain Sanctuary, Pennsylvania, autumn 1998–2001. American Hawkwatcher 28:11–17.

Heintzelman, D. S. 1982. Variation in utilization of the Kittatinny Ridge in eastern Pennsylvania in autumn by migrating Golden Eagles and Bald Eagles (1968–1981). American Hawkwatcher 3:1–4.

Heintzelman, D. S. 1986. The migrations of hawks. Indiana University Press, Bloomington, Indiana.

Heintzelman, D. S. 2004. Guide to hawk watching in North America. Globe Pequot Press, Guilford, Connecticut.

Hickey, J. J. ed. 1969. Peregrine Falcons: their biology and decline. University of Wisconsin Press, Madison, Wisconsin.

Kerlinger, P. 1989. Flight strategies of migrating hawks. University of Chicago Press, Chicago, Illinois.

Klem, D., Jr., B. Hillgass, D. A. Peters, J. A. Villa, and K. Kranick. 1985. Analysis of individual flight patterns of migrating raptors at a break in the Kittatinny Ridge: Lehigh Gap, Pennsylvania. Pages 1–12 in M. Harwood, editor. Proceedings of Hawk Migration Conference IV. Hawk Migration Association of North America, Lynchburg, Virginia.

Kosack, J. 1995. The Pennsylvania Game Commission: 100 years of wildlife conservation. Pennsylvania Game Commission, Harrisburg, Pennsylvania.

May, J. B. 1935. The hawks of North America. The National Association of Audubon Societies, New York City, New York.

McCarty, K. M., M. Farhoud, J. Ottinger, L. G. Goodrich, and K. L. Bildstein. 1999. Spring migration at Hawk Mountain Sanctuary, 1969–1998. Pennsylvania Birds 13:11–15.

McWilliams, G. M., and D. W. Brauning. 2000. The birds of Pennsylvania. Cornell University Press, Ithaca, New York.

Newton, I. 1979. Population ecology of raptors. Buteo Books, Vermillion, South Dakota.

Percival, S. 2005. Birds and windfarms: what are the real issues? British Birds 98:194–204.

Poole, E. L. 1930. The fall migration of waterbirds and others at Reading, Pa. Auk 47:427428.

Poole, E. L. 1934. The hawk migration along the Kittatinny Ridge in Pennsylvania. Auk 51:17–20.

Pough, R. H. 1932. Wholesale killing of hawks in Pennsylvania. Bird-Lore 34:429–430.

Rhoads, S. N., and C. J. Pennock. 1905. Birds of Delaware: a preliminary list. Auk 22:194–205.

Spofford, W. R. 1969. Hawk Mountain counts as indices in northeastern America. Pages 323–332 in J. J. Hickey, editor. Peregrine Falcons: their biology and decline. University of Wisconsin Press, Madison, Wisconsin.

Stone, W. 1913. Bird migration records of William Bartram, 1802–1822. Auk 30:325–358.

Stone, W. 1894. The birds of eastern Pennsylvania and New Jersey. Delaware Valley Ornithological Club, Philadelphia, Pennsylvania, USA.

Sutton, G. M. 1928a. Notes on a collection of hawks from Schuylkill County, Pennsylvania. Wilson Bull. 40:84–95.

Sutton, G. M. 1928b. An introduction to birds of Pennsylvania. J. Horace McFarland Company, Harrisburg, Pennsylvania.

Sutton, G. M. 1931. The status of the Goshawk in Pennsylvania. Wilson Bull. 43:108–113.

Teter, S., A. Khalilieh, E. Ashworth, S. Wamiti, and L. Bonner. 2003. Ridge adherence in Golden Eagles migrating along the Kittatinny Ridge between Bake Oven Knob and Hawk Mountain Sanctuary, Pennsylvania, autumn 2000–2002. American Hawkwatcher 29:9–14.

Van Fleet, P. K. 1997. The geographic distribution of diurnal raptors migrating through the Valley and Ridge Province of central Pennsylvania. Unpublished M.S. Thesis, Shippensburg University, Shippensburg, Pennsylvania.

Viverette, C. B., S. Struve, L. J. Goodrich, and K. L. Bildstein. 1996. Decreases in migrating Sharp-shinned Hawks (*Accipiter striatus*) at traditional raptor-migration watch sites in eastern North America. Auk 113:32–40.

Warren, B. H. 1890. Birds of Pennsylvania. Second edition. E. K. Meyers, State Printer, Harrisburg, Pennsylvania, USA.

Wilson, A. 1808–1814. American ornithology. 9 vols. Bradford and Inskeep, Philadelphia, Pennsylvania.

Zalles, J. I., and K. L. Bildstein. Editors. 2000. Raptor Watch: a Global Directory of Raptor Migration Sites. BirdLife International, Cambridge, England; Hawk Mountain Sanctuary, Kempton, Pennsylvania.

Avian Ecology and Conservation: A Pennsylvania Focus with National Implications. Edited by S. K. Majumdar, T. L. Master, M. C. Brittingham, R. M. Ross, R. S. Mulvihill and J. E. Huffman. © 2010. The Pennsylvania Academy of Science.

Chapter 8

Golden Eagle Migration and Winter Behavior in Pennsylvania

T.A. Miller[1], D. Brandes[2], M.J. Lanzone[1],
D. Ombalski[3], C. Maisonneuve[4], T.E. Katzner[5]
[1]Carnegie Museum of Natural History, Powdermill Nature Reserve,
1847 Route 381, Rector, PA 15677
[2]Dept of Civil & Environmental Engineering, Acopian Engineering Center,
Lafayette College, Easton, PA 18042
[3]Tussey Mountain Hawk Watch, Mulberry Street, Unionville, PA 16844
[4]Ministère des Ressources Naturelles et de la Faune,
92 2e rue Ouest, Rimouski, QC G5L 8B3, Canada
[5]Department of Conservation and Field Research, National Aviary,
700 Arch St., Allegheny Commons West, Pittsburgh, PA 15212
todd.katzner@aviary.org

INTRODUCTION

Golden eagles have long held a special place in Pennsylvania ornithological lore. Maurice Broun, in his 1935 article in "The Auk" reporting on his just completed first season of observations at Hawk Mountain, said "the occasional appearance of Golden Eagles among the lesser Falconiformes proved to be the most interesting feature of the season, and a revelation to the many persons who were fortunate enough to see some of these magnificent birds." The 39 golden eagles that first year at Hawk Mountain was an astonishing count at a time when the ornithological community believed the species to be a bird of western North America, not the Appalachians. Broun wondered whether the birds occurred each fall along the Kittatinny Ridge, and later devoted a chapter of his famous book *Hawks Aloft* to the golden eagle. In the years since 1934, long-term observations at Hawk Mountain and other Kittatinny sites have shown that golden eagles are indeed regular, albeit rather uncommon, fall migrants through Pennsylvania.

Since *Hawks Aloft* was published in 1948, a great deal has been learned about the eastern golden eagle, although much still remains to be discovered. We now know that a small population presently breeds in the wilds of northern Ontario, Quebec and Labrador, along the north shore of the St. Lawrence River, and on the Gaspé Peninsula. The few former breeding sites in the US Appalachians have apparently been abandoned for a decade or longer. We have learned that the bulk of the fall golden eagle migration through Pennsylvania occurs not on the famous Kittatinny Ridge, but rather along the western ridges and the Allegheny Front. The total number of golden eagles migrating through Pennsylvania represents a large fraction of the eastern population, a claim that cannot be made for any other raptor species. Furthermore, in recent years we discovered that there is a concentrated spring passage of golden eagles through central Pennsylvania that is unique among raptors. This chapter is devoted to a discussion of the current state of knowledge of this species in Pennsylvania and to identifying key management questions that should be answered to ensure its effective conservation.

BACKGROUND

Golden eagles are distributed throughout the northern hemisphere with six described subspecies, one of which occurs in North America (*Aquila chysaetos canadensis*; Watson, 1997). In eastern North America the species is considerably less abundant and less well known than in western North America. The population is thought to be small (perhaps <1500 individuals) and of great conservation concern. Here we review both what is known of the birds as a species and then focus on the limited understanding of their ecology and demography in eastern North America.

Diet

Golden eagles are a generalist predator that takes small to medium-sized avian and mammalian prey as well as carrion. In western North America their diet is composed of ptarmigan, grouse, rabbits, hares, ground squirrels and marmots (Collopy, 1983, McIntyre and Adams, 1999, Kochert et al., 2002). In other parts of their range the species exhibits largely similar patterns of generalist behavior, feeding on the most abundant and accessible prey. This approach to diet has consequences, as there is a well documented positive correlation between degree of dietary specificity and eagle reproductive output, such that birds with more specialized diets tend to produce more offspring (Watson, 1997, Katzner et al., 2005).

The diet of eastern golden eagles has never been studied in detail. Observations suggest that they take wild turkey in Pennsylvania (Todd, 1940), waterfowl in eastern Canada (Kirk, 1996) and geese, ducks, crows, gulls, marmots, hares, foxes and carrion on the Gaspé Peninsula (Équipe de rétablissement de l'aigle royal au Québec, 2005). On eastern breeding grounds in the far north the most likely prey are hares and ptarmigan, although carrion may also compose a significant component of their diet (Bent, 1961; Snow, 1973). In particular, one eagle being tracked with highly accurate GPS telemetry made repeated early spring trips to the middle of a large expanse of likely frozen water, the implication being that it was feeding there on a marine mammal carcass (T. Miller, personal observation). During winter, the massive eastern USA deer populations are probably critical in sustaining eagle populations. The thousands of road-killed deer that accumulate every winter are placed in carcass dumps. Recent camera-trapping evidence at these sites suggests that they are visited by large numbers of eagles, especially golden eagles, but also bald eagles (M. Lanzone, personal observation). Although these deer are a nuisance for drivers and gardeners, they may be a critical resource that allows eastern golden eagle populations to remain stable and potentially increase in the face of a loss of their more traditional prey base.

Breeding biology

Golden eagles breed in nests constructed on cliffs or, sometimes, in trees. When breeding birds are at carrying capacity, nests may be spaced as closely as 1–2 km, but more frequently are spaced 8–12 km apart (Watson, 1997). The birds breed approximately every other year, or two out of every three years, likely depending on climate, prey abundance, and the previous year's reproductive success. Territory defense is gender specific and early in the breeding season the birds perform elegant flight displays, often involving the pair flying together, wingtip to wingtip, in a so-called "undulating" flight. One or two eggs are laid early in the spring, between February and May, with the exact date depending on local climate and the condition of the individual birds. Incubation generally lasts about 43–45 days. Once the eggs hatch, chicks generally stay in the nest for approximately 70 days, until they are fully feathered and able to fly (Kochert et al., 2002). The female performs the bulk of the incubation duties, although both parents do participate. Likewise, the chicks are sheltered by the parents, largely the female, for the first 20 or so days of their life. During this period they are generally unable to thermoregulate and they rely on their parents for protection from climatic extremes. Throughout the nesting cycle the chicks are brought food by the parents; initially the parents feed them but once the chicks are able to feed themselves, the parents simply drop food in the nest and leave.

Little is known about how the breeding biology of eastern golden eagles differs from that of golden eagles elsewhere in their range. In the eastern USA, the last recorded breeding of golden eagles is from Maine in 2002, although adult birds have been reported in the southern Appalachians throughout the summer months. Golden eagles nest in both trees and on cliffs in western North America, but the majority of nests in eastern Canada are located on cliffs. In Québec, there is only one record of tree nesting, in a huge pine tree in the Gaspé Peninsula (Équipe de rétablissement de l'aigle royal au Québec, 2005) and there is a record of another pair using an abandoned fire tower in southern Québec (Brodeur and Morneau, 1999).

Migration and Winter Ecology

Throughout much of their range golden eagles are either non-migratory, holding a territory year-round, or they are short distance migrants. However, birds that breed in Canada and Alaska are generally longer-distance migrants. Alaskan eagles migrate through western Canada into the US Pacific Northwest; at one Alberta hawk watch site nearly 500 golden eagles have been recorded in a single day (Sherrington, 1993). In the eastern USA, one 1992 study tracked migratory golden eagles from Quebec into the USA and back (Brodeur et al., 1996). Three of the four telemetered individuals passed through Pennsylvania and all migrated relatively long distances to wintering grounds. Migration started in October, continuing through November and, in some cases into December. Birds stayed on wintering grounds until March, heading back on a four week migration to their breeding grounds.

Raptor migration has been well studied in Pennsylvania and golden eagles are known to pass through the state on a bi-annual basis. Because the vast majority of the eastern golden eagle population migrates along the Appalachians, it can be inferred that nearly all of the eastern golden eagle population passes through Pennsylvania twice each year en route to and from breeding grounds. Telemetry and observational data suggest that the vast majority of these birds winter in the Appalachians from New York to as far south as Georgia. Updates on recent research on winter and migration behavior of Pennsylvania golden eagles are provided in greater detail in the next section.

Comparison to western populations

Eastern golden eagles appear to be geographically separated from western populations on their breeding and wintering grounds. On their breeding grounds there are records of eastern golden eagles breeding as far west as the south coast of the Hudson Bay in Ontario (De Smet and James, 1987). Likewise, some eastern birds are known to pass west of the Great Lakes (Brodeur et al., 1996) and birds from both populations winter in the southern Mississippi River valley (Alabama, Oklahoma, etc.). The degree to which eastern and western populations are genetically separated is under study at Duquesne University and the National Aviary, both in Pittsburgh.

MIGRATION ECOLOGY

Golden eagles migrate between their breeding areas in Canada and their wintering range in the eastern USA. Hawk watches in Pennsylvania and neighboring states provide sufficient data to allow limited assessment of the general spatial and temporal pattern of golden eagle migration and preliminary identification of locations of concentrated migration passage. However, there are large gaps in the migration monitoring network, including the northern tier of Pennsylvania, the ridges to the north of Kittatinny Ridge in eastern Pennsylvania, and almost all of Maryland, West Virginia, and New York. Limited satellite telemetry data on golden eagle migration are also available (Brodeur et al.,1996; P. Nye, NYDEC) and much additional telemetry data is forthcoming by the authors. The importance of Pennsylvania's ridges to migrating golden eagles is clear, as the highest numbers of migrating golden eagles in eastern North America are recorded at ridge-top sites in Pennsylvania in both fall (at Waggoner's Gap near Carlisle) and spring (at Tussey Mountain near State College). However, golden eagle ecology – habitat and roosting requirements and social and feeding behavior – during migration is poorly understood.

Fall Migration

Fall golden eagle migration extends from October through December. Telemetry data suggest that most eastern golden eagles cross into the USA in northern New York, although some are deflected westward toward Detroit by Lake Ontario and Lake Erie. Little is known about fall golden eagle migration patterns through northern New York. The only New York site with high numbers of golden eagles is Franklin Mountain, a hawk watch on a bluff overlooking the East Branch of the Susquehanna River near Oneonta. This site regularly records annual totals of over 200 birds, with a peak flight of 71 on 11 November 2005. Farther south and east, at Mt. Peter near Warwick, very few have been recorded in spite of many years of hawk-watching. In northern New Jersey, golden eagles (generally less than 75 annually) are seen regularly at the Raccoon Ridge site on Kittatinny Ridge just east of Delaware Water Gap (HMANA, 2008).

Due to its long history of hawk-watching, migration count data are more complete in Pennsylvania than elsewhere in the eastern USA. However, there remain large gaps in spatial and temporal coverage of watch sites. Until the 1980s, the vast majority of golden eagle sightings in Pennsylvania were made during the fall migration, from mid- October through mid-November at sites along Blue Mountain and the associated Kittatinny Ridge, as well as at Tuscarora Mountain near Chambersburg. Since the 1980s, hawk watchers at ridge-top sites within the Valley and Ridge region (Second Mountain, Jacks Mountain, Stone Mountain, Tussey Mountain, and Bald Eagle Mountain) and on the Allegheny Front near Central City have greatly expanded knowledge of the spatial and temporal dynamics of eastern golden eagle migration.

It is now known that golden eagle migration extends across the Valley and Ridge region, with most of the flight occurring north and west of the Kittatinny Ridge (Van Fleet, 2001), particularly along the western ridges and Allegheny Front. Peak flights generally occur from late October through mid-November along the Kittatinny Ridge, and from mid-November to early December at the more western sites, such as Bald Eagle Mountain just west of State College. The largest recorded single-day autumn flights in Pennsylvania have been at the Allegheny Front site near Central City, with 51 on 23 November 2003 and 48 on 14 November 2005. No monitoring data exist regarding migration routes across the northern tier of the state, although telemetry data make clear that eagles do pass through this region. The total number of golden eagles counted at Pennsylvania hawk watches each fall, adjusted for potential double counting, is between 500 and 800.

Little is known about fall migration south of Pennsylvania, although existing telemetry data as well as continuity of topographic features suggest that golden eagles likely migrate down the ridges of western Maryland and eastern West Virginia.

Spring Migration

Prior to the mid-1990s, very little was known about spring migration of eastern golden eagles. Since then, full-time spring hawk watches have been implemented at the Allegheny Front and Tussey Mountain sites. When combined with anecdotal observations from Jacks Mountain, White Deer Ridge, and Sideling Hill, it is now understood that golden eagles pass through Pennsylvania from late February through early April each spring. Peak flights occur in early March and are equal in magnitude to the fall flights, making this species unique among the 16 species of diurnal raptors that pass through Pennsylvania. The current single-day record for golden eagles in Pennsylvania is 62 at Tussey Mountain on 03 March 2008. Pennsylvania's early spring flight is comprised almost exclusively of adult and subadult (i.e., age 2–4 years) birds that are almost certainly returning to breeding grounds in northeast Canada. Hawk watches on the southern shore of Lake Ontario in New York (Braddock Bay and Derby Hill) occasionally count golden eagles among large late April raptor flights, but these later birds are primarily pre-adults.

Brandes (1998) and Brandes and Ombalski (2004) summarized available spring hawk watch data and concluded that the early spring passage of adult golden eagles through Pennsylvania is highly concentrated, occurring in a narrow corridor west of Harrisburg. This contrasts with the wider migration pattern across the Valley and Ridge region observed in the fall. Data indicate that the area extending from the Allegheny Front eastward to Jacks Mountain is the primary spring migration corridor through southern and central Pennsylvania. To date, the authors' telemetry data has supported the existence of this narrow migration corridor. The flight appears to disperse somewhat as birds leave the ridges and cross over the Allegheny Plateau into New York, although some golden eagles are seen in March at the Mount Pleasant site near Ithaca and farther north at Valleyfield, Québec, where they cross the St. Lawrence River to the west of Montreal.

Gaps in study of golden eagle Migration Ecology

The large majority of data on golden eagle migration is of the kind reported above – that is, reports on where and when migration occurs. With the exception of several specific regions (the northern tier and the ridges of eastern PA north of the Kittatinny Ridge), hawk watch data provide a basic understanding of these broad scale patterns. Additional data on flight style, flight pattern, and behavior are now being collected for golden eagles passing Tussey Mountain, Allegheny Front, Waggoners Gap, and Hawk Mountain. These data have not yet been analyzed.

In contrast to the well-understood broad patterns, fundamental questions of conservation interest remain unanswered. Examples of these important questions include:

  (1) How often do golden eagles feed during migration and upon what?

  (2) How do golden eagles adjust to varying terrain and weather conditions during active migration?

  (3) What kind of habitats and roost sites are used during the migration period?

These ecological questions are particularly important to understanding the potential impact on golden eagles of extensive Appalachian ridge-top wind turbine development. Current eagle tracking research by the authors promises to provide answers to questions (2) and (3).

RECENT RESEARCH

While other populations of golden eagles have been well-studied (see Kochert et al., 2002 for an exhaustive list of publications), very little ecological research has focused specifically on the small population in eastern North America (Brodeur et al., 1996, Lee and Spofford, 1990, Millsap and Vana, 1984, Morneau et al., 1994, Spofford, 1971, Spofford, 1964a). However, in 2006 the authors initiated a telemetry study specifically to examine detailed habitat use and flight characteristics of eastern golden eagles throughout the Appalachian region and spanning the annual cycle. The main focus of the research is to locate areas of potential conflict with wind power development, however, we will also learn much about the ecology of this population.

Satellite Tracking

From November 2006 – October 2007, eight golden eagles (seven male and one female, both juveniles and adults) were captured in the USA and Canada. The three US birds were captured either on migration (near Central City, PA) or on the wintering grounds (near Scherr, WV). The five Canadian birds were captured on the breeding grounds or on the nest on the Gaspé Peninsula, Québec.

Each bird was fitted with a GPS-based satellite telemetry unit that obtains 10-15 GPS locations daily, as well as speed, altitude and heading. Data were obtained at 1–3 hour intervals on a seasonally varying cycle.

Migration Routes and Winter Locations

The general migratory routes we observed are similar to those noted by Brodeur et al. (1996). However, because of the increased data collection frequency and locational accuracy, the new information offers much greater detail. Brandes (1998) and Brandes and Ombalski (2004) suggested that during spring migration, raptors concentrate in a narrow 30–60 mi (50–132 km) corridor in the Valley and Ridge province of southern PA. Although a much larger sample size is necessary to accurately identify all migratory pathways, our preliminary data support this hypothesis. Not only during spring, but also during fall, the migration corridor is broader through eastern Canada and is markedly constricted through northeastern New York. The strong linear features of the mid-Appalachians in Pennsylvania concentrate migration even more, from just over 150 mi (330 km) in width in northern PA to 60 mi (132 km) as the birds leave southern PA.

These data also suggest that eastern golden eagles may exhibit a leap-frog migration pattern (Zink, 2003). Under such a scenario, birds from the southern portion of the range winter further north than birds from the northern portion of the range. Of the four birds from the Gaspé Peninsula, the two adults wintered in northern Pennsylvania, the juvenile female wintered in southeastern New York and the juvenile male wintered in West Virginia. Both juveniles took relatively more extended and circuitous migration routes before settling onto a localized wintering area. A similar behavior was also exhibited by sub-adult male #40. All adults and older sub-adults all traveled relatively more direct migration routes to a localized wintering area. However, regardless of the age of the bird or the relative directness of the migration, all routes through PA were direct (Figure 1) and stopovers of more than three days occurred only during extended periods of unfavorable weather. The average number of days spent in PA during migration for all birds and all seasons was 4.5 ± 3.4, ranging from 1–12 days (n = 6 birds and 13 migration tracks). These preliminary data suggest that the temporal length of migration varies annually, seasonally, and with age, though more information is needed to draw strong conclusions. However, as one might expect, the overall temporal duration of migration is dependent on the total distance traveled during migration (p = 0.007 F = 10.60, df = 13).

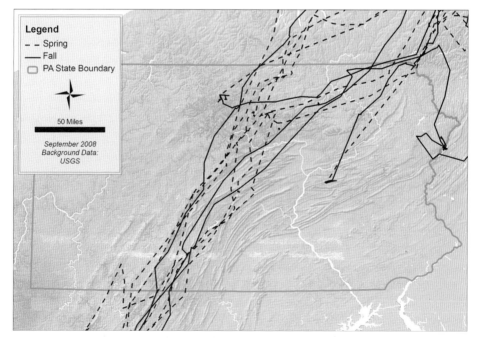

Figure 1:   General migration routes (n= 13 tracks) through and into Pennsylvania by six Golden Eagles during spring and fall 2007 and spring 2008. Tracks were interpolated using GPS locations collected every 1 – 2 hours using satellite telemetry.

Migratory distances can be described in two ways, 1) migration flight distance, which is the distance traveled between locations during active migration and does not include foraging or short forays during stopover, and 2) displacement distance, which is the straight-line distance between summer and winter ranges. Migration flight distance for all seasons for all birds ranged from 739–3364 mi (1183–5382 km), and displacement distance ranged from 569–1681 mi (910–2690 km). Birds from the Gaspé peninsula travelled 1154 ± 499 mi (1847 ± 798 km), while birds from farther north traveled 2274 ± 588 mi (3639 ± 940 km). Displacement distances from wintering to summering grounds for Gaspé birds averaged 749 ± 156 mi (1198 ± 249 km) and ranged from 569–944 mi (910–1510 km). As one might expect with leap-frog migration (Zink, 2003), displacement distances for northern latitude birds were greater than for southern latitude birds, averaging 1504 ± 154 mi (2407 ± 246 km) and ranging from 1406–1681 mi (2250–2690 km).

Interestingly, one juvenile that fledged from a nest on the Gaspé Peninsula, spent the winter in West Virginia, much further south than the other Gaspé birds, and migrated much further north to summer near Ungava Bay in northern Québec (Figure 2). Additionally, both juveniles wandered during fall migration before settling on a winter range. This is quite different behavior of the adult and sub-adult birds which moved more or less directly from summering grounds to wintering grounds.

Like migratory distance, departure dates appear to vary with latitude and age. Across both years, average spring departure date from wintering grounds was 15 March ±18 days (n = 7 birds and 14 journeys) and average spring arrival date upon summering grounds was 9 April ±23 days (6 birds, 8 journeys). Because fall departure dates of juveniles in the Gaspé coincided with departure dates of the high-latitude birds, fall departure dates are less variable. Average departure date from summering grounds was 21 October ±15 days and average arrival on wintering grounds was on 22 November ±11 days. These dates fall within the time frame during which high numbers of golden eagles are observed at hawk watches throughout Pennsylvania.

In contrast to geographic patterns, patterns of daily activity during migration did not vary significantly between seasons. Daily active migration began as early as 0500 EST and ended as late as 1900 EST, with the bulk of active migration occurring between 0800 and 1600 EST.

Flight Characteristics

Modern satellite transmitters provide information on flight altitude and speed in addition to location data. Flight altitudes averaged higher in spring (750 ± 307 m) than in fall (633 ± 277; p=0.001, alpha = 0.5, df = 434, t = –3.26). During active migration, the maximum altitude recorded by any of the transmitters was 1834 m. Conversely, average flight speeds were consistent across seasons, though slightly faster in spring than fall. Average flight speeds in spring were 46.3 ± 21.12 kph (n = 6 birds and 8 journeys) and in fall were 43.9 ± 18.6 kph (n = 6 birds and 6 journeys). The maximum speed recorded by any of the transmitters was 127 kph.

Migratory Roost Habitat Characteristics

Telemetry data are also being used to evaluate characteristics of roost sites used by eagles on migration. To do this we are integrating information on roost locations with that from remotely sensed land cover (The Pennsylvania State University, 2007) and topo-

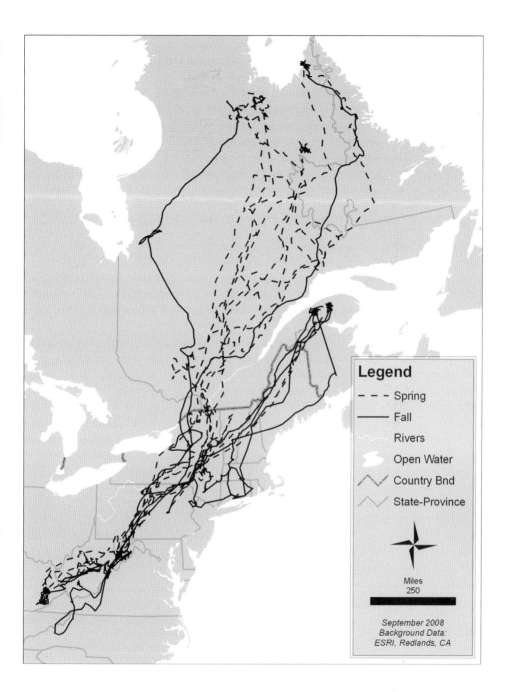

Figure 2: Complete migration routes (n = 13 tracks) of six Golden Eagles during spring and fall 2007 and spring 2008. Tracks were interpolated using GPS locations collected every 1 – 2 hours using satellite telemetry.

graphic data (United States Geological Survey, 2000). The golden eagles we tracked in Pennsylvania roosted at relatively high elevations, (524 ± 102 m), in densely forested habitats, on slight slopes (12.6 ± 6.6 degrees), away from roads and other types of human disturbances, and rarely roosted on west facing slopes (n = 6 and 13 journeys). The long distances between roost sites and barren habitat, such as those areas created by mining activities, suggests that these areas are avoided. Additionally, roost site selection did not appear to vary with season or age class. This suggests that protection of optimal and suitable habitat would protect the population as a whole. However, because the sample size was small, subsequent analyses are necessary to determine whether season, age or sex dependent differences exist. This is particularly important for age dependent differences because of the potential population level impacts and because hawk watch data suggest that there are age-related spatial and temporal differences in migration (Brandes and Ombalski, 2004).

PENNSYLVANIA AS A WINTERING AREA

Golden eagles have been described as either rare or occurring only occasionally in Pennsylvania during winter (Todd, 1940, McWilliams and Brauning, 2000). However, our recent data suggest that they are more common than previously known. These data, collected from remote camera traps and satellite telemetry suggest that the eagle's cryptic behavior and winter habitat selection may make them difficult to detect without new technologies.

Large numbers of eagles were detected by camera traps set over deer carcasses in remote areas of the state. Our conservative estimates suggest that 0–10 individual eagles were counted per day by camera traps in Westmoreland, Somerset and Bedford counties. We estimated the age ratio of birds photographed to be approximately 3:6:1 (adult:sub-adult:juvenile). This contrasts noticeably with observational accounts, which suggest that the majority of birds in Pennsylvania are juveniles. Anecdotal observations of golden eagles have also been reported to the authors by others who have placed camera traps on deer carcasses in other parts of the state.

In the winter 2007–08, two wintering eagles were tracked, in Potter and Northumberland Counties. Nearly all (99%) of the telemetry data point obtained from these eagles fell within contiguous forest. Eagle wintering areas were estimated at 431 and 229 km^2 (95% minimum convex polygon) or 182 and 329 ± km^2 (95% Fixed Kernel Density Estimates; Worton, 1987, Worton, 1989, Seaman and Powell, 1996). The majority of the habitat within the 95% fixed kernel winter home range estimates was forested. The home range of a Northumberland county bird was 81% forested and that of the Potter county bird 94% forested. All winter roost sites were located in forests.

Many of the birds we observed used the southern portions of Pennsylvania's Ridge and Valley Province. This area is heavily forested, thus corroborating our roost habitat data, which suggests that eagles use such areas frequently. Interestingly, this observation contrasts with observations of western birds, which are often thought to avoid forests in favor of open areas.

The large numbers of individual eagles that we detected indicate that Pennsylvania may fulfill a previously unrecognized role for eastern golden eagles – as wintering habitat. Although eagles are difficult to detect with standard observational techniques, newer technologies have provided insight into the important role contiguous forests within Pennsylvania may play in supporting wintering eagles. We suggest further winter studies to more completely evaluate the significance of Pennsylvania to wintering golden eagles.

CONSERVATION CONCERNS

The size of the golden eagle population in eastern North America is small, but its numbers are stable or increasing (Kochert and Steenhof, 2002, Farmer et al., 2008). Nevertheless, as US human populations grow and consumption increases, these birds continue to be at risk from anthropogenic threats. Threats to populations occur on two levels, either direct or indirect. Direct threats result in immediate mortality and tend to be obvious and more easily understood. Indirect threats are much less obvious and harder to quantify, but result in an overall decrease in fitness either at an individual or population level.

Direct Mortality Due to Human Activity

Direct mortality from humans is the single largest cause of golden eagle mortality in North America (Franson et al., 1995). Direct mortality results from illegal shooting, trapping, poisoning, and collisions with vehicles and man-made structures.

During the 19th and 20th Centuries, shooting of golden eagles was very common and sanctioned by the government. As many as 20,000 may have been shot from airplanes in Texas over a 20-year period from 1941–1961 (Spofford, 1964b) and more than 128,000 golden eagles were shot in Alaska during the first half of the 20th Century (Preston, 2004). Since then, mortality due to shooting has dramatically declined due to public education and the amendment of the Bald Eagle Protection Act in 1962 to include golden eagles. Nevertheless, it is estimated that 15% of all current golden eagle mortality in the USA is a result of illegal shooting (Franson et al., 1995). However, due to the secretive nature of the species, many shootings likely go undetected and actual mortality may be even higher.

Trapping for mammals results in accidental mortality of eagles throughout the USA. A ban on use of leg-hold traps has resulted in fewer incidental deaths in Pennsylvania. However, snares and leg-hold traps, which continue to be used in many other states, still kill many birds. A West Virginia game officer reported that many birds are likely taken each year and illegally disposed of by trappers. Therefore, as is the case for shooting, it is difficult to quantify the actually impact of trapping on the wintering population.

Poison-related deaths, like trapping, are often secondary, resulting from eagles consuming prey or carrion laced with lethal poisons intended for mammalian carnivores. Eagles are susceptible to a wide range of poisons including strychnine, phorate, carbofuran, heptachlor, and warfarin and other rodenticides (Henny et al., 1984, Kochert et al., 2002). Although information regarding poison-related deaths in the East is lacking, data from the western USA imply that eastern golden eagles are likely affected by secondary poisoning.

Lead poisoning can result in direct or indirect mortality. Necropsies of 31 western Canadian eagles suggest that 13% died of lead poisoning and 10% were sub-lethally poisoned (Wayland and Bollinger, 1999). Most lead poisoning in eagles is a result of scavenging on carcasses of hunter-shot game. Although lead waterfowl shot has been banned in Pennsylvania, lead ammunition is still used for other game including deer. Because eagles feed heavily on deer carcasses in the winter, lead poisoning may pose a significant threat to the population. Because lead shot residues in big game meat also poses a significant threat to human health, this issue should be addressed quickly (Cade, 2007).

Collision with human-made structures, including power-lines, wind turbines, cars, and fences are the leading cause of direct mortality for golden eagles in the western USA (Franson et al., 1995), and are likely significant causes of mortality in the east as well. With the boom in wind power plant installation across the migratory, wintering and southern breeding range of golden eagles in the eastern USA, collisions with turbines could pose a significant threat to the species. Studies at wind plants suggest that siting of turbines is a critically important factor relating to direct avian mortality (Barrios and Rodrigues, 2004). At the Altamont Pass Wind Resource Area 50–100 golden eagles, and many other birds of prey, are killed each year (Smallwood and Thelander, 2008). Conversely, other installations report few to no mortalities of raptors. At Altamont the majority of birds are killed during winter, when large numbers of hungry raptors are attracted to forage in this ground-squirrel rich habitat. Importantly, at the time of this writing there are no peer-reviewed publications regarding the impact of wind installations on migrating raptors anywhere in North America.

Indirect Effects of Human Activity

Indirect threats to golden eagles during winter and migration are not always obvious and can be difficult to measure. These threats include pesticide, mercury and lead poisoning, and habitat alteration, degradation and loss.

The impact of sub-lethal poisoning by contaminates such as pesticides, mercury, and lead often goes undetected. However, although it does not result in mortality, sub-lethal poisoning results in physically weakened birds. Weakened eagles are likely to have relatively less reproductive output, are predisposed to injury and are more likely to succumb to starvation, disease, or predation.

In contrast to other populations, eastern golden eagles are thought to regularly prey on large wading birds, such as Great Blue Heron and American Bittern (Spofford, 1971). This should make them relatively more impacted by organochlorine poisoning, and, indeed, earlier studies in Maine showed that these chemicals caused golden eagles to produce thin eggshells resulting in reproductive failure (Wheeler, 2003). Likewise, that same source notes that the Maine birds had high levels of mercury, which can result from pollution by coal-fired power plants. This contrasts markedly with western North America birds that usually have low levels of mercury (Harmata and Restini, 1995, Craig and Craig, 1998, Noble et al., 1993).

Although some harmful contaminants such as heptachlor and DDT have been banned, many others are still used. Decreasing their prevalence in the environment and implementation of clean coal technologies are important to reduce the known risks posed by environmental toxins. While little information exists on the dietary habitat of eastern golden eagles, anecdotal evidence of dietary differences between eastern and western birds illustrates that drawing conclusions about eastern eagles based on knowledge of western populations may not always be useful. Therefore, improving our knowledge of the dietary habits in the East is crucial to understanding the potential effects from environmental contaminants.

Golden eagles in the East tend to avoid humans and use large areas of undisturbed forested habitat with some openings. Telemetry data of seven birds wintering in Pennsylvania, southern New York, West Virginia and Kentucky between 2006–2008 suggest that high elevation deciduous forest and other large tracts of forest provide ideal wintering habitat. Current threats to these habitats include large scale clear cuts, surface mining, and wind power development, among others.

In addition to wintering habitat, Pennsylvania is a crucial migratory pathway for birds, with the majority of the eastern population of golden eagles passing through the state twice each year (Brandes, 1998, Brandes and Ombalski, 2004). Importantly, the majority of birds migrate late in the fall and early in the spring when thermal activity is low. Pennsylvania's ridges provide much needed updrafts to facilitate migration and to reduce the energetic costs of migration. Because of these updrafts, air movement atop ridges can power turbines, and it is for this reason that ridge tops have been sought for industrial wind power development. Ridges not only provide lift during migration, but also roosting and hunting habitat. In addition to loss of roosting and wintering habitat, wind power development at a large scale could result in indirect negative effects on fitness due to avoidance during migration.

Other possible threats to wintering habitat in the East include urban expansion, fire suppression, and reforestation. However, due to the secretive habits of golden eagles in the East, the true habitat requirements are yet to be adequately described.

CONCLUSIONS

It has long been recognized that Pennsylvania is an important state for migration of golden eagles. Recent telemetry data support this long-held view, and add considerable information on exactly how these birds move through our state. Likewise, these data also suggest that Pennsylvania may serve an important role as a key wintering habitat for the species. Together, these recent data provide a basic framework for protection of the species, in the face of current development on ridgetops and large forested areas that the species uses.

In spite of the significance of recent information on the ecology of this species, perhaps the greatest threat they face is the lack of knowledge humans have about their demography and ecology. Several key questions that should be addressed are as follows:

1. How many eastern golden eagles are there?

2. What proportion of this population passes through Pennsylvania each year?

3. What are the habitat features these birds use, on migration, on wintering grounds, and when foraging, during winter and on migration.

4. What are the dietary requirements of the species, on migration and during winter.

Because habitats are so different in eastern and western North America, it is also likely that the habits and habitat requirements between the two populations are significantly different. Therefore, although the western population is well known, those data are not an adequate basis for inference about Pennsylvania's eastern birds. Furthering our knowledge base will allow for the implementation of sound conservation plans that can decrease and mitigate the threats to this small population of birds.

LITERATURE CITED

Barrios L. and A. Rodriguez. 2004. Behavioural and environmental correlates of soaring-bird mortality at on-shore wind turbines. Journal of Applied Ecology. 41:72–81.

Bent, A. C. 1961. Life histories of North American birds of prey. Dover Publications, Inc. New York, New York. 409 pages.

Brandes, D.,1998. Spring Golden Eagle passage through the northeast U.S. – evidence for a geo-graphically concentrated flight? HMANA Hawk Migration Studies 23(2): 38–42.

_____, and D. Ombalski, 2004. Modeling raptor migration pathways using a fluid flow analogy. Journal of Raptor Research. 38(3):195–207.

Brodeur, S., R. Décarie, D. M. Bird, M. Fuller, 1996. Complete migration cycle of Golden Eagles breeding in northern Quebec. The Condor 98:293–299.

_____, and F. Morneau. 1999. Rapport sur la situation de l'aigle royal (Aquila chrysaetos) au Québec. Société de la faune et des parcs du Québec, Direction de la faune et des habitats, Québec.

Cade, T.J. 2007. Exposure of California Condors to lead from spent ammunition. Journal of Wildlife Management. 71:2125–2133.

Collopy, M. W. 1983. A comparison of direct observations and collections of prey remains in deter-mining the diet of Golden Eagles. Journal of Wildlife Management 47:360–368.

Craig, E. H. and T. H. Craig. 1998. Lead and mercury levels in Golden and Bald Eagles and annual movements of Golden Eagles wintering in east central Idaho 1990–1997. U.S. Department of Inte-rior, Bureau of Land Management, Idaho State Office, Boise, ID.

De Smet, K. D. 1987. Status report on the Golden Eagle Aquila chrysaetos . Status assigned in 1982, reviewed 1995. Comm. Status of Endangered Wildl. Can., Ottawa, ON.

Équipe de rétablissement de l'aigle royal au Québec. 2005. Plan de rétablissement de l'aigle royal (Aquila chrysaetos) au Québec 2005–2010. Ministère des Ressources naturelles et de la Faune du Québec, Secteur Faune Québec. 29 pages.

Farmer, C.J., R.J. Bell, B. Drolet, L.J. Goodrich, E. Greenstone, D. Grove, D.J.T. Hussell, D. Mizrahi, F.J. Nicoletti, and J. Sodergren, 2008. Trends in Autumn Counts of Migratory Raptors in Northeastern North America, 1974–2004, Pp. 176–216 in Bildstein, et al (Eds), State of North America's Birds of Prey. Series in Ornithology, No. 3, Nuttall Ornithological Club and the Amer-ican Ornithologist's Union.

Franson, J. C., L. Sileo and N. J. Thomas. 1995. Causes of eagle deaths. P. 68 in Our Living Resources, E. T. LaRoe, G. S. Farris, C. E. Puckett, P. D. Doran, and M. J. Mac, eds. U.S. Depart-ment of Interior, National Biological Service. Washington, D.C.

HMANA, Hawk Migration Association of North America, 2008. http://hawkcount.org. Accessed 28 September 2008.

Harmata, A. R. and M. Restani. 1995. Environmental contaminants and cholinesterase in blood of vernal migrant Bald and Golden Eagles in Montana. Intermountain Journal of Sciences. 1: 1–15

Henny, C. J., L. J. Blus and T. E. Kaiser. 1984. Heptachlor seed treatment contaminates hawks, owls, and eagles of Columbia Basin, Oregon. Journal of Raptor Research.18: 41–48.

Lee, D.S. and W.R. Spofford. 1990. Nesting of Golden Eagles in the central and southern Appalachi-ans. Wilson Bulletin. 102:693–698.

Katzner, T., E. Bragin, S. Knick and A. Smith. 2005. Relationship between demographics and dietary specificity of Imperial Eagles in Kazakhstan. Ibis 147:576–586.

Kirk, D. A. 1996. Updated status report on the Golden Eagle Aquila chrysaetos in Canada. COSEWIC.

Kochert, M.N. and K. Steenhof. 2002. Golden Eagles in the U.S. and Canada: Status, trends, and conservation challenges. Journal of Raptor Research. 36:32–40.

_____, _____, C.L. Mcintyre and E.H. Craig. 2002. Golden Eagle (Aquila chrysaetos), The Birds of North America Online (A. Poole, Ed.) Ithaca: Cornell Lab of Ornithology; Retrieved from the Birds of North America Online: http://bna.birds.cornell.edu/bna/species/684.

McIntyre, C.L. and L.G. Adams 1999. Reproductive characteristics of migratory Golden Eagles (Aquila chrysaetos) in Denali National Park, Alaska. The Condor 101:115–123.

McWilliams, G.M. and D.W. Brauning. 2000. The Birds of Pennsylvania. Cornell University Press. Ithaca, NY.

Millsap B.A. and S.L. Vana. 1984. Distribution of wintering Golden Eagles in the eastern United States. Willson Bulletin. 96: 692–701.

Morneau, F., S. Brodeur, R. Décarie, S. Carrière and D.M. Bird. 1994. Abundance and distribution of nesting Golden Eagles in Hudson Bay, Québec. Journal of Raptor Research. 28:220–225.

Noble, D. G., J. E. Elliott and J. L. Shutt. 1993. Environmental contaminants in Canadian raptors 1965–1989. Tech. Rep. Ser. no. 91. Canadian Wildlife Service, National Wildlife Research Centre, Ottawa, ON.

Preston, C.R. 2004. Golden Eagle: Sovereign of the Skies. Graphic Arts Publishing Company. Portland, OR.

Seaman, D.E. and R.A. Powell. 1996. An evaluation of the accuracy of kernel density estimators for home range analysis. Ecology 77:2075–2085,

Sherrington, P. 1993. Golden Eagle migration in the front ranges of the Alberta Rocky Mountains. Birder's J. 2: 195–204.

Smallwood, K.S. and C.G. Thelander. 2008. Bird mortality at the Altamont Pass Wind Resource Area, California. Journal of Wildlife Management 72:215–223.

Snow, C. 1973. Golden Eagle *Aquila chrysaetos* habitat management series for unique or endangered species. USDI Bureau of Land Management Tech. Note TN-239. 52 pages.

Spofford, W.R. 1964a. Golden Eagle 509-50214. Journal of Field Ornithology. 35:123.

————, W. R. 1964b. Golden Eagle in the Trans-Pecos and Edwards Plateau of Texas, Audubon Conservation Report no. 1. National Audubon Society, New York.

————, W.R. 1971. The breeding status of the Golden Eagle in the Appalachians. American Birds. 25:3–7.

The Pennsylvania State University. 2007. PAMAP Land Cover for Pennsylvania, 2005. The Pennsylvania State University. University Park, PA.

Todd, W.E.C. 1940. Birds of western Pennsylvania. University of Pittsburgh Press, Pittsburgh, PA.

United States Geological Survey. 2000. 7.5 minute digital elevation model for Pennsylvania (30 meter). United States Geological Survey. Reston, VA.

Van Fleet, K. 2001. Geography of diurnal raptors migrating through the valley-and-ridge province of central Pennsylvania 1991–1994, Pp. 23–41. In Hawkwatching in the Americas. (K.L. Bildstein and D. Klem, Jr., eds.) Hawk Migration Association of North America. North Wales, PA.

Wayland, M. and T. Bollinger 1999. Lead exposure and poisoning in bald eagles and golden eagles in the Canadian prairie provinces. Environmental Pollution. 104:341–350.

Watson, J. 1997. The Golden Eagle. London, T&AD Poyser. London.

Wheeler, B. K. 2003. Raptors of Eastern North America: The Wheeler Guides. Princeton University Press. Princeton, NJ, pp. 456.

Worton, B.J. 1987. A review of models of home range for animal movement. Ecological Modelling 38: 277–298.

————, B.J. 1989. Kernel Methods for Estimating the Utilization Distribution in Home-Range Studies. Ecology, 70:164–168.

Zink, R.M. Towards a framework for understanding the evolution of avian migration. Journal of Avian Biology. 33:433–436.

Avian Ecology and Conservation: A Pennsylvania Focus with National Implications. Edited by S. K. Majumdar, T. L. Master, M. C. Brittingham, R. M. Ross, R. S. Mulvihill and J. E. Huffman. © 2010. The Pennsylvania Academy of Science.

Chapter 9

Winter Raptor Survey

Gregory W. Grove
Pennsylvania Society for Ornithology
4343 McAlevys Fort Road
Petersburg, PA 16669
gwg2@psu.edu

INTRODUCTION

Goals of the Pennsylvania Winter Raptor Survey

Beginning in January 2001, birders in Pennsylvania have conducted annual, automobile-based Winter Raptor Surveys (WRS) directed at locating raptors and vultures. During the winter of 2001, over 50 WRS routes were run across the state, a total of 253 hours of effort. Since 2001, the number of routes has increased to over 125 with about 500 hours of effort annually (Table 1).

The WRS project was initiated with several goals in mind:

- *Assess mid-winter distribution of raptors and vultures in Pennsylvania.*
- *Detect long-term trends, if any, among wintering populations.*
- *Assess relationships between weather conditions and raptors.*
- *Involve as many experienced birders and beginners as possible.*

WRS Routes

Each WRS route is run once per winter, between mid-January and mid-February. Thus the WRS is a mid-winter survey of Pennsylvania's wintering raptors, in contrast to the early-winter Christmas Bird Count (CBC). Because the WRS effort is expended specifically on finding raptors, the number of raptors per hour of WRS effort is far higher than for CBC effort (see Summary), and therefore the WRS rate of detection is presumably a more accurate assessment of wintering raptor populations than is CBC data, which is obtained by observers searching for any and all species.

The various WRS routes were not determined randomly. Individual routes were designed by volunteers in each county to optimize the likelihood of locating raptors. The routes therefore emphasize coverage in open areas, which in turn favors detection of species that prefer open habitat. All raptors and vultures are recorded as well as age and sex when possible, and color morph in the case of rough-legged hawks (*Buteo lagopus*). Survey routes were designed to avoid busy roads as much as possible. (See Appendix for guidelines).

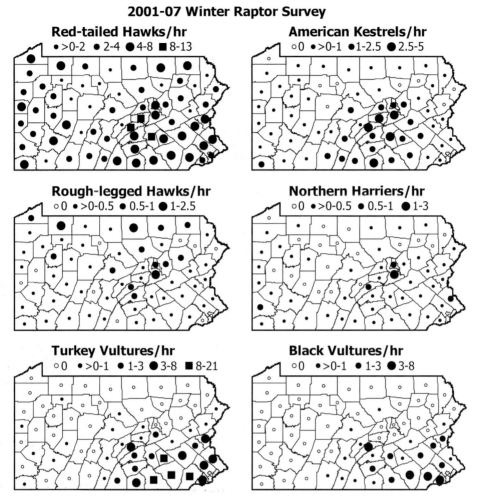

Figure 1: Distribution of raptors and vultures in Pennsylvania based on cumulative WRS data, 2001–2007. Data points are shown for each county. The 7-year cumulative total of each species in a given county was divided by the total hours of effort in that county to produce an annual average hourly rate.

Data Analysis and Comparison

For comparison between years and among counties, raptor numbers are normalized per hr of observation. The maps presented for common species (Fig. 1) are based on cumulative observations for each county over the 7 years of WRS. County maps for individual years have been published previously (Grove 2006, 2007).

The most abundant species reported by the WRS are those that favor open or semi-open habitat rather than forests. The following individual species accounts of WRS results are in order of abundance for the four most common raptors followed by the two vulture species.

ANALYSIS OF WRS RESULTS 2001–2007

Weather 2001–2007

The factors that regulate the annual numbers of wintering raptors in Pennsylvania are numerous and complex. Along with prey availability and the success of the previous breeding season, we may assume that weather, both in Pennsylvania and to the north, is also important. We might presume that a mild winter will result in high numbers of wintering raptors and a severe winter fewer. This may hold true for some or most species in some or most years, but often the relationship is not straightforward.

Year-to-year winter weather conditions in Pennsylvania vary considerably – some years are mild while others present a constant challenge of storms and extended periods of subfreezing weather. Such variation has been the case during the 7 years of the WRS. In summarizing certain WRS results I made some tenuous correlations between counts for individual species and the general weather conditions throughout the 7 years. For convenience, I have briefly summarized below the weather during each winter. Note that the generalization of "limited snowfall" in a given year may not apply to the traditional "lake-effect" areas in the northwest and the Laurel Highlands in the southwest.

2001, 2002– Mild; limited snowfall and snow cover.

2003, 2004– Cold (very cold in 2004), significant snow cover across the state.

2005, 2006– Mild; limited snowfall and snow cover.

2007– Very warm through mid-January, then very cold through remainder of season. Limited snowfall and cover over most of the state.

Red-tailed Hawks

Red-tailed hawks (*Buteo jamaicensis*) may be the most abundant wintering raptor in Pennsylvania and are certainly the most conspicuous. The WRS count of red-tailed hawks each year has been several-fold higher than all other raptors (excluding vultures) combined (Table 1).

Comparison of the weather conditions and the annual hourly detection rates of red-tailed hawks from 2001–2007 (Table 1) suggests that weather has some limited influence on wintering red-tail hawk numbers. The two lowest annual rates occurred during the two years with the most severe winters, 2003 and 2004. However the combined rates in those two years was only 25% lower than the average rate from the five years of milder weather, suggesting the effect of severe weather is not substantial.

Table 1. Results of Pennsylvania WRS, 2001–2007, for Open-country Raptors. The columns for each species are yearly statewide totals with birds per hour of effort in parentheses.

Year	Hrs	Northern Harrier	Red-tailed Hawk	Rough-legged Hawk	American Kestrel
2001	253	24 (0.09)	1141 (4.5)	44 (0.17)	343 (1.36)
2002	313	30 (0.10)	1399 (4.5)	21 (0.07)	392 (1.25)
2003	391	28 (0.07)	1182 (3.0)	99 (0.25)	357 (0.91)
2004	514	94 (0.18)	2052 (4.0)	341 (0.66)	265 (0.52)
2005	494	70 (0.14)	2610 (5.3)	200 (0.40)	433 (0.88)
2006	478	80 (0.17)	2184 (4.6)	93 (0.19)	488 (1.02)
2007	505	107 (0.21)	2218 (4.4)	87 (0.17)	511 (1.01)

Red-tailed hawks winter throughout Pennsylvania but more are found in southern coun-ties as expected given the milder weather and the abundance of open, agricultural habitat favored by red-tailed hawks. Red-tailed hawks are especially abundant in the central and lower Susquehanna River region (Fig. 1). This part of the state apparently has the best com-bination of extensive agricultural habitat and relatively mild winter weather. Southeastern and southwestern counties also host a significant number of red-tailed hawks in winter, as do cold northern counties with open habitat, even in years with severe weather (Grove 2006). In contrast, heavily forested counties have relatively few wintering red-tailed hawks (Fig. 1). In the west central area, the cluster of counties including Forest, Elk, Cameron, Clearfield, and Cambria has a collective detection rate of 0.86 per hr in comparison to the overall statewide average of 4.3 per hr. Counties in the heavily forested northeast also have detection rates well below the overall state average. This widespread distribution in all areas with appropriate habitat, along with the relatively small difference in detection rates regard-less of weather conditions, indicates that the winter range of red-tailed hawks in Pennsyl-vania may be defined primarily by habitat availability rather than climate.

During each WRS season, the age of about 75% of recorded red-tailed hawks was noted. The percentage of immature birds has been remarkably consistent from year-to-year, rang-ing between 9–16%.

American Kestrels

With the exception of 2004, American kestrels (*Falco sparverius*) have annually been the second most abundant raptor species recorded during the WRS (Table 1). Each year, about 85% of recorded American kestrels have been sexed. More males winter here than do females, the percentage of males annually varying within a range of 58–66%. Previous work has suggested that males are more likely than females to winter further north (Bird 1988), perhaps remaining on breeding territories rather than moving south.

Wintering American kestrels are far more abundant in the central and lower Susquehanna Valley than elsewhere in the state (Fig. 1). During some years, detection rates were high in scattered southwestern counties but much less consistently and uniformly than in the Susque-hanna Valley counties (Grove 2006). Thus American kestrels share with red-tailed hawks a preference for the Susquehanna Valley counties, but unlike red-tailed hawks they are not com-mon elsewhere in the state during the winter season despite the presence of seemingly appro-priate habitat. Therefore, in contrast to red-tailed hawks, the American kestrel winter range in Pennsylvania may be determined more by climate rather than by habitat availability.

Table 2. Results of Pennsylvania WRS, 2001–2007, for Black Vultures and Turkey Vultures. The columns for each species are yearly statewide totals with birds per hour of effort in parentheses.

Year	Black Vulture	Turkey Vulture
2001	112 (0.44)	528 (2.1)
2002	172 (0.55)	525 (1.7)
2003	206 (0.53)	502 (1.3)
2004	263 (0.51)	944 (1.8)
2005	199 (0.40)	1000 (2.0)
2006	477 (1.00)	1863 (3.9)
2007	542 (1.07)	1269 (2.5)

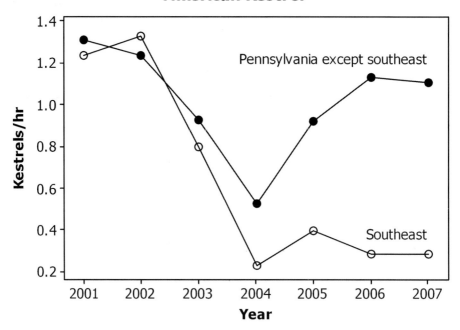

Figure 2: Pennsylvania WRS annual detection combined rate of American kestrel (birds/hour) in 6 contiguous southeastern counties vs. the combined rate in the remainder of counties. The 6 southeastern counties are Bucks, Chester, Delaware, Lehigh, Montgomery, and Northampton.

In 2004, a year with particularly deep and continual snow cover, the American kestrel detection rate was substantially lower than in any other year (Fig. 2). Presumably many birds moved south of the state, accounting for part, if not all, of the low detection rate.

Following the low count in 2004, the number of wintering American kestrels recovered over most of the state during the subsequent three years. However, American kestrel numbers in a cluster of six southeastern counties (Bucks, Chester, Delaware, Lehigh, Montgomery, and Northampton) did not recover and in fact decreased further despite substantially increased hours of effort in comparison to earlier WRS years (Fig. 2). Thus the winter American kestrel population in eastern Pennsylvania may be undergoing a somewhat different dynamic than elsewhere in the state.

Evidence from various sources indicates a declining American kestrel population in northeastern coastal states and New England (Sullivan and Wood 2004). For example, American kestrel CBC counts have declined significantly in New Jersey and Delaware (Walsh et al. 1999, Hess et al. 2000, Sullivan and Wood 2004), adjacent to the southeastern Pennsylvania counties analyzed in Figure 2. The sharp drop in the southeastern Pennsylvania WRS American kestrel counts beginning in 2004 coincides with an especially sharp drop noted in the New Jersey CBC American kestrel counts beginning in December 2003–January 2004 (Walsh 1999). Similarly, American kestrel counts on Breeding Bird Surveys in those states are declining as are American kestrel counts at the autumn Cape

May hawk watch in New Jersey (Walsh et al. 1999, Hess et al. 2000). If this trend is real, then in Pennsylvania it might be expected to be most evident in eastern counties where breeding and wintering American kestrel populations are presumably most likely to overlap with those in New England, New Jersey, and Delaware. Many causes for this decline have been suggested, including habitat loss, West Nile Virus, and predation by an increasing population of Cooper's hawks (*Accipiter cooperii*) (Sullivan and Wood 2004).

Rough-legged Hawks

Of the four open-country raptor species emphasized on WRS routes, the annual number of rough-legged hawks has varied most over the 7 years with hourly detection rates varying by a factor of nearly 10 (Table 1). Rough-legged hawks of course do not nest in Pennsylvania, the southern extent of their breeding range being approximately 1000 miles north of the state (Bechard and Swem 2002). Thus all rough-legged hawks in Pennsylvania are migrants. In agreement with previous observations in eastern North America (Wheeler 2003), the percentage of light morph rough-legged hawks recorded annually by WRS observers has been between 60–70%.

The extent of southward movement of rough-legged hawks in a given year varies widely, probably depending a combination of prey availability, breeding success, and weather conditions north of Pennsylvania. Rough-legged hawks are most often found in northern counties of the state (Fig. 1). However, they do regularly push into the Susquehanna Valley, the stronghold of other wintering raptors. The strongest movement south of the northern tier counties was in 2004, the year with the most severe winter weather (Grove 2006). In that year, rough-legged hawks were at least as abundant in middle latitude counties in the state as they were in northern counties. That year also saw by far the strongest movement into counties west of the Alleghenies. In no WRS year was there a strong incursion of rough-legged hawks into the far southeastern and southwestern corners of the state.

In some years, few rough-legged hawks come as far south as Pennsylvania. For example, in 2002 only 21 were counted during 313 hours of WRS effort, a rate of 0.07 per hour (Table 1). That year saw one of the mildest winters during the seven years of WRS. By contrast in 2004, the year of most severe weather, 341 rough-legged hawks were tallied in 514 hours, a rate of 0.66 per hour. Thus there may be some correlation between the influx of rough-legged hawks and weather, with the two most severe seasons producing the first (2004) and third (2003) highest hourly rates. The second highest rough-legged hawk detection rate, however, did not occur during a severe season, but in the mild winter of 2005. Possibly this was the result of an "echo" flight from the strong flight of the previous season.

The 2007 winter provided evidence of the influence of weather on the seasonal timing of movement of rough-legged hawks. Warm conditions prevailed through the first half of the 2007 winter. Very few rough-legged hawks were counted on WRS routes during the first two weeks of the survey period, as was also the case on Pennsylvania CBCs conducted earlier in the winter (Bolgiano 2007). As the WRS period began, the weather pattern turned intensely cold on January 20 and remained unusually cold through February (Grove 2007). During the latter part of the WRS period, higher numbers of rough-legged hawks were reported on several routes, especially in the northern half of the state, suggesting that some birds were seeking milder weather or experiencing prey shortages farther north. Several WRS observers unofficially repeated routes that had been conducted earlier during the survey period, and reported rough-legged hawks where none had been seen earlier; for example in Columbia, Schuylkill, Indiana, Berks, and Lancaster counties.

Northern Harrier

Northern harriers (*Circus cyaneus*) are found during winter in low numbers over most of Pennsylvania (Fig. 1). In five of seven years, northern harriers have been the least often recorded of the four "open-country" raptor species. Only in 2007 did the statewide WRS total exceed 100. Among birds identified by sex, there has been a consistent 40:60 ratio of males to females. The average fraction of birds in immature plumage has been approximately 30%.

In general, counties in the Susquehanna Valley have had the greatest cumulative numbers of northern harriers over all WRS years. Of the nine Pennsylvania counties with the highest cumulative WRS detection rates, six are in this region. Thus northern harriers share a preference with red-tailed hawks and American kestrels for this region. Northern harriers are reported in other counties with significant open habitat including cold, northern tier counties but are essentially absent from heavily forested counties, not surprising for this grassland specialist. For example, after 7 years of WRS efforts, no northern harriers have been reported in the contiguous counties of Cameron, Clearfield, Elk, and Forest, all of which have had surveys conducted in at least 5 of 7 years.

During 2001–2003, when WRS effort was lower, the annual statewide number of northern harriers did not exceed 30. Beginning in 2004, the number of northern harriers reported increased substantially. This was in part because of increased hours of effort. But the average hourly detection rate during 2004–2007 was double that during 2001–2003 (Table 1). Thus the increase in effort alone does not account for the increase in northern harrier counts beginning in 2004. Most of that increase occurred in counties of the Susquehanna Valley (Grove 2006), possibly in response to improved grassland habitat resulting from a land-set-aside begun in 2001, the Conservation Reserve Enhancement Program ("CREP").

Vultures

In the past century, turkey vulture (*Cathartes aura*) and black vulture (*Coragyps atratus*) ranges have expanded rapidly northward, with turkey vultures becoming established as breeders in Pennsylvania before 1900. Black vultures arrived in the latter half of the 20th century and are still largely confined to the southeastern counties as a breeding species. The spread of vultures northward has been attributed to availability of road-kill carrion, especially white-tailed deer (*Odocoilus virginianus*) (Brauning 1992, McWilliams and Brauning 2000).

The winter range of both species in Pennsylvania includes the Piedmont counties of the southeast as well as the adjacent counties of the southern Ridge and Valley region, a geographical pattern that has been consistently observed during the WRS (Fig. 1). Very few vultures are found outside of this area during winter. When they are observed elsewhere, the sighting is often of a single bird.

The WRS counts and distribution patterns of vultures suggest no strong or obvious correlation with the severity of the weather in a given year. Vulture numbers were highest in the mild years of 2006 and 2007, but in other mild years, vulture numbers were similar to those in years of severe weather.

Other raptor species

In addition to the raptor species' analyzed in detail above, surveyors also recorded 8 additional raptor species. These have not been the focus of this analysis for various reasons, including that they are not found primarily in the open habitats emphasized by WRS, are found in very limited areas within the state, or are present in only very small numbers. The 7-year annual average for these are as follows:

Bald Eagle (*Haliaeetus leucocephalus*)	35
Sharp-shinned Hawk (*Accipiter striatus*)	30
Cooper's Hawk (*Accipiter cooperii*)	55
Northern Goshawk (*Accipiter gentiles*)	2
Red-shouldered Hawk (*Buteo lineatus*)	19
Golden Eagle (*Aquila chrysaetos*)	1
Merlin (*Falco columbarius*)	2
Peregrine Falcon (*Falco peregrinus*)	3

SUMMARY

Comparison of WRS and CBC Results

The WRS is conducted during late January and early February, the mid-point of winter in Pennsylvania, a time when we expect winter resident bird populations to be relatively static. This contrasts with the early winter timing of the Audubon CBC, the major, national winter bird survey.

Participants in the CBC search for and count all birds of course, not focusing on raptors as do WRS counters. This is reflected in a large difference in numbers of raptors observed per hour of effort in the two surveys. Over the 7 years of WRS, the most abundant winter raptor, the red-tailed hawk, has been tallied at an hourly rate approximately 9 times higher than the CBC rate. Northern harriers and American kestrels are reported by WRS counters at a rate 6 times higher than CBC counters (Table 1 and CBC Website).

The greatest divergence in rates occurs for rough-legged hawks, which are found at a rate 20 times higher on WRS routes than from CBC effort. This might reflect the tendency of rough-legged hawks to move south very late, often after the end of the CBC period. Rough-legged hawks are also found in extensively open areas, where CBC effort is probably modest because of the lack of numbers and diversity of other birds. Thus, WRS is an especially effective means of assessing the winter population of rough-legged hawks in Pennsylvania. Given the high rates of detection for the other raptor species and the level of expertise of WRS observers, the WRS represents a superior means of monitoring wintering raptors in Pennsylvania in comparison to the CBC.

Species Summary

The Pennsylvania WRS, conducted beginning in 2001, has focused on four open-country raptors that are relatively easily detected and identified. The counties of the Susquehanna Valley host the greatest overall concentration of these four species in winter, yet each of the four species has unique features to their winter range and population status within the state (Fig. 1).

Red-tailed Hawks. WRS data indicate that the Pennsylvania winter range of the abundant red-tailed hawk may be determined primarily by availability of habitat, not regional climate differences. Although somewhat higher numbers are found in the Susquehanna Valley, red-tailed hawks nevertheless winter in substantial numbers throughout the state except in heavily forested counties. Long-term CBC data indicate that the number of wintering red-tailed hawks is increasing in Pennsylvania although this trend is not apparent in the shorter time span of the WRS (Goodrich and Senner 1988, CBC Website; N. C. Bolgiano, personal communication).

American Kestrels. American kestrels are seemingly linked to red-tailed hawks by their similar habitat preference and ease of detection. Like red-tailed hawks, their winter numbers are highest in the Susquehanna Valley. But the similarity with red-tailed hawk winter distribution ends there. American kestrels are not found in similar abundance in colder areas of the state despite the presence of appropriate habitat. Thus their winter status in Pennsylvania may be significantly more influenced by climate than is the case with red-tailed hawks. Furthermore, unlike red-tailed hawks, American kestrel numbers in winter may be declining in Pennsylvania. This apparent decline appears by far most acute in the southeast, where red-tailed hawks are doing well.

Rough-legged Hawks. WRS data for rough-legged hawks shows substantial annual variation in their winter population in the state, not surprising for a non-breeding species with no year-round residents. Also not surprising for this far-northern breeder, they are found most often in the northern half of the state, in areas where open habitat is present. Weather conditions and prey availability in northeast North America presumably dictate how many rough-legged hawks move south into Pennsylvania each year.

Given that rough-legged hawks come to Pennsylvania from the far north, it is not surprising that their winter distribution in the state does not exactly mirror that of the congeneric red-tailed hawk although both are open-country species and certainly they overlap in habitat and range. However, long-term CBC data for Pennsylvania shows opposite trends with wintering red-tailed hawks increasing steadily since the 1970s while wintering rough-legged hawks have declined (CBC Website; N. C. Bolgiano, personal communication). These opposite trends may be most easily explained as the result of northward range shifts in response to warmer weather in the past few decades. An additional element in the opposite trends, for which there is no strong supporting data, may be that as red-tailed hawks have expanded north in winter, they have exerted dominance over rough-legged hawks, as suggested previously (Bildstein 1987, Palmer 1988), in turn causing rough-legged hawks to also retract their wintering grounds farther to the north.

Northern Harriers. Northern harriers are the least abundant of the four raptor species discussed in detail above; they are widespread but sparse in winter throughout the state. This species could particularly benefit from land set-aside programs that result in unmowed grasslands. The data indicate an apparently favored winter region for northern harriers in the Susquehanna River valley.

Vultures. The WRS data for vultures reflect the well-established pattern of a strong winter presence in southeastern counties with a rather sharp delineation to the north and west where few vultures are found in winter. In this respect they show a clear contrast to the winter range of raptors, whose area of greatest concentration is not in the far southeast despite the milder weather there. If warm winters occur more often, as predicted from expected climate change, we can expect more vultures to winter in Pennsylvania and to expand their winter range beyond the southeast.

Expansion of WRS

The Pennsylvania WRS is the first statewide mid-winter survey of raptors in the U.S. involving a large number of observers and routes, covering over 60 of the state's 67 counties annually. As the WRS has become established in the state, many individual routes are now essentially unchanged from year-to-year, and I estimate that route coverage statewide is now approximately 85–90% identical annually.

Clearly the WRS has been successful in Pennsylvania both as a seasonal raptor survey and a method of involving many "citizen scientists" who are experts at raptor identification and of beginning birders as well, accompanying the experienced experts. An involvement and educational element is an important component of large-scale efforts requiring volunteers, the CBC being an obvious example.

In other states, as of this writing, there are no equivalent surveys on the scale of the Pennsylvania WRS, but individuals or small groups have been doing annual winter raptor surveys in various states. Given the success of the WRS in Pennsylvania, it is expected that this program could be expanded and our success indicates that experienced birders are willing to enthusiastically conduct such surveys at a time of the year outside of the migration periods. In fact, at the time of this writing, efforts to establish annual surveys of wintering raptors have begun in Illinois, Vermont, Nebraska, and California; and perhaps in other states as well.

Furthermore, the Hawk Migration Association of North America (HMANA) has begun an effort to expand the WRS concept nationally. At the least, it is hoped that many observers establish routes and run them once per year in mid-winter as is already done in Pennsylvania. In addition, interested participants will be encouraged to run their route 3–4 times per year and gather more extensive data than is currently done in the existing program in Pennsylvania. For example, willing observers will be asked to specify locations, perhaps via GPS, of each bird as well as certain aspects of behavior or activity. There are certainly interesting questions and issues that can be addressed through surveys that extend beyond the boundaries of any one state.

ACKNOWLEDGEMENTS

I thank Nick Bolgiano for comments on the manuscript and for creation of Figures 1 and 2. I also thank the well-over 100 volunteers; many from the Pennsylvania Society for Ornithology, whose data collection make the WRS a success.

REFERENCES

Bechard, M. J. and T. R. Swem. 2002. Rough-legged Hawk (*Buteo lagopus*). A. Poole and F. Gill, editors. The Birds of North America, No. 641. The Birds of North America, Philadelphia, Pennsylvania, USA.

Bildstein, K. L. 1987. Behavorial ecology of Red-tailed Hawks (*Buteo jamaicensis*), Rough-legged Hawks (*Buteo lagopus*), Northern Harriers (*Circus cyaneus*), and American Kestrels (*Falco sparverius*) in south central Ohio. Ohio Biological Notes no. 18.

Bird, D. M. and R. S. Palmer. 1988. American Kestrel. Pp. 253–290 in R. S. Palmer, editor. Handbook of North American birds. Volume 5: Diurnal raptors. Yale University Press, New Haven, Connecticut, USA.

Bolgiano, N. C. 2007. The 2006–2007 Christmas Bird Count in Pennsylvania. Pennsylvania Birds 21:2–20.

Brauning, D. W., editor. 1992. Atlas of Breeding Birds of Pennsylvania. University of Pittsburgh Press, Pittsburgh, Pennsylvania, USA.

CBC Website. http://www.audubon.org/bird/cbc/

Goodrich, L. J. and S. E. Senner. 1988. Recent Trends of Wintering Great Horned Owls (*Bubo virginianus*), Red-tailed Hawks (*Buteo jamaicensis*) and Two of their Avian Prey in Pennsylvania. Journal of the Pennsylvania Academy of Sciences 62: 131–137.

Grove, G. 2006. The 2006 Winter Raptor Survey in Pennsylvania with a Summary of Results from 2001–2006. Pennsylvania Birds 20:24–34.

Grove, G. 2007. The 2007 Winter Raptor Survey in Pennsylvania. Pennsylvania Birds 21:29–33.

Hess, G. K., R. L. West, M. V. Barnhill, III, L. M. Fleming. 2000. Birds of Delaware. University of Pittsburgh Press, Pittsburgh, Pennsylvania, USA.

McWilliams, G. M. and D. W. Brauning. 2000. The Birds of Pennsylvania. Cornell University Press, Ithaca, New York, USA.

Palmer, R. S., editor. 1988. Rough-legged Hawk in Handbook of North American birds. Volume 5: Diurnal raptors. Yale University Press, New Haven, Connecticut, USA.

Sullivan, B. L. and C. L. Wood. 2004. The Changing Seasons: A Plea for the Common Birds. North American Birds 59:18–30

Walsh, J., V. Elia, R. Kane, T. Halliwell. 1999. Birds of New Jersey. New Jersey Audubon Society, Bernardsville, New Jersey, USA.

Wheeler, B. K. 2003. Raptor of Eastern North America. Rough-legged Hawk. Pp 311–331. Princeton University Press, Princeton, New Jersey, USA.

APPENDIX. PENNSYLVANIA WRS GUIDELINES:

1. The most important consideration is safety. A designated driver is suggested.
2. Design your own route—a min of 10–20 miles and max of 100 miles. If possible, avoid busy roads and non-maintained back roads that may not be passable some years.
3. Dates: Volunteers choose the day within a designated period approximately mid-January through mid-February. Routes are run just one time.
4. Time of day: Mid-morning to mid-afternoon.
5. Avoid foggy, windy, rainy, snowy days.
6. Record hours of survey time and miles driven.
7. Record: average snow depth, temperature, % cloud cover, wind (calm, light, strong).
8. Record the following as possible: northern harrier (adult male or female; or immature), red-tailed hawk (adult or immature), rough-legged hawk (light or dark form), American kestrel (male or female), other raptors (record age). Don't linger over birds you can't easily age or sex—just record species.
9. Record vultures, owls, and shrikes.
10. You may leave your car to scope or get closer to a bird but do not hike looking for birds.
11. If possible, you may establish some optimal (and safe) stops (good vantage points) where you can scan more thoroughly.
12. Coordinate with others in your county to avoid route duplication.
13. For consistency sake, I will not accept routes that are primarily on interstate highways.

Avian Ecology and Conservation: A Pennsylvania Focus with National Implications. Edited by S. K. Majumdar, T. L. Master, M. C. Brittingham, R. M. Ross, R. S. Mulvihill and J. E. Huffman. © 2010. The Pennsylvania Academy of Science.

Chapter 10

Migration and Wintering Ecology of Northern Saw-whet Owls

Scott Weidensaul
Author and Naturalist
778 Schwartz Valley Rd.
Schuylkill Haven, PA 17972
sweidnsl@infionline.net

In 1928, state ornithologist George Miksch Sutton described the northern saw-whet owl (*Aegolius acadicus*) as "chiefly an irregular visitor in winter, in northern and central Pennsylvania." And for the remaining majority of the 20th century, that was about all we knew about this smallest and certainly most enigmatic of the Keystone State's owls.

Since the mid-1990s, however, an explosion of research, in Pennsylvania and across North America, has shown that saw-whet owls are far more widespread in migration than anyone had suspected. Yet despite these advances, there are still many fundamental questions to be answered about this long-neglected species.

RESIDENT OR MIGRANT?

Because they are highly nocturnal, rarely vocalize outside the breeding season and are extremely hard to detect in daytime, the presence of large numbers of migrant saw-whet owls in the autumn was overlooked for centuries. Even after evidence began to surface in the early 1900s that this species is a regular migrant in parts of North America, it was another 60 years before its migration was widely accepted.

Wilson referred to the saw-whet as "a general and constant inhabitant of the Middle and Northern States," (Brewer 1840) while Audubon believed it was a resident breeder as far south as Louisiana (Ford 1957). Coues, Bendire and other late nineteenth-century ornithologists, while by then holding a more accurate view of the saw-whet's breeding range, considered it either resident or at best weakly migratory at its northern limits (Coues 1874, Bendire 1892).

That assessment began to change in the early twentieth century, with reports from Lake Huron that a steamer boat captain experienced a fallout of "small owls" in the fall of 1903, and in October 1906, when an early snowstorm forced huge numbers of exhausted migrants to the water, where they drowned. Among the 1,845 birds counted by Saunders (1907) were 24 dead northern saw-whet owls, whose presence he called "a surprise… Evidently they migrate in considerable numbers."

Around the same time, ornithologists noted that saw-whets could be found commonly in autumn at Point Pelee and Long Point in Lake Erie, (the latter opposite the Pennsylvania shore) and concluded that "from the middle to the end of October the Saw-whet Owls migrate in considerable numbers, but from their nocturnal habits and secluded habitats while en route are seldom observed" (Taverner and Swales 1911). Not everyone was convinced, however. In 1938, Bent said only that the saw-whet "evidently migrates to some extent, or at least wanders widely, in fall" (Bent 1938), and a number of authors through the 1950s and 1960s continued to list the saw-whet as a permanent resident in regions like the upper Midwest (Wood 1951, Gromme 1963).

In the 1960s, Mueller and Berger (1967) at the Cedar Grove Ornithological Station in southern Wisconsin finally settled the question of migration status, showing that predictable numbers of saw-whets could be netted at night, even though the species was never detected there during the day, and vocalizations were never heard. The autumn of 1965 also marked what may still rank as the largest irruption of saw-whets ever recorded, with encounters as far south as Florida (Lesser and Stickley 1967). In the early 1970s, other banding sites in the upper Midwest followed Cedar Grove's lead. In 1986, Tom Erdman of Little Suamico Ornithological Station north of Green Bay, Wisconsin began using a tape-recording of the male saw-whet's advertising "toot" call, and experienced a more than 11-fold increase in the number of saw-whets caught versus passive netting (Erdman and Brinker 1997).

This audiolure technique spread to other saw-whet banding stations, with similar results, and researchers began to employ it in the East – at Cape May, N.J., where passive netting had begun in 1980, and where introduction of an audiolure in 1989 caused a six-fold rise in capture rates (Duffy and Kerlinger 1992, Duffy and Matheny 1997), and at Finzel Swamp, MD, where capture rates rose nearly four-fold (Erdman and Brinker 1997).

Interest in saw-whet owl banding increased in the southern mid-Atlantic region in the early 1990s, with stations opening on Sandy Point, MD, in 1990; Assateague Island, MD, in 1991; Casselman River, MD, in 1992; and Cape Charles, VA, in 1994 (Brinker et al 1997). At the time, saw-whets were generally considered rare or at best uncommon migrants to the region (Robbins and Van Velzen 1968).

The first well-documented irruption of saw-whets in 1995, however, changed that perception. The five sites operating in Maryland, New Jersey and Virginia accounted for an astounding 35% of the more than 7,400 saw-whets banded in North America that autumn. Cape May, which the previous year had netted 73 saw-whets, captured 637 and Cape Charles, which caught 52 in 1994, banded 1,007 in 1995 (Brinker et al, 1997). In all, the five mid-Atlantic sites reported 2,596 of these "rare" owls (Brinker et al 1997).

SAW-WHET OWL MIGRATION IN PENNSYLVANIA

As in much of the East, the saw-whet owl was long considered both a rare nesting species and an irregular migrant in Pennsylvania (Warren 1890, Sutton 1928).

As recently as the early 1990s, the ornithological literature suggested that saw-whets used only two major migration routes – south through the Great Lakes, and along the Atlantic coastal plain (Cannings 1993). There was no speculation that significant numbers of saw-whets might be using the Appalachian Mountains, despite that range's reputation as a globally significant flyway for diurnal raptors and other groups (Holroyd and Woods 1975, Cannings 1993, Zalles and Bildstein, 2000).

Most Pennsylvania records of saw-whets were scattered individuals located in fall and winter, almost always on daytime roosts, as roadkills, or the remains left by larger raptors. One interesting exception was 18 saw-whets "whistled up" at Hawk Mountain Sanctuary,

Berks/Schuylkill counties, on a single evening in October 1981 (S. Benz pers. comm., Urich 1997), during what was apparently a major irruption cycle. Although David Darney had begun capturing saw-whets on their daytime roosts on Presque Isle, Erie County, in 1991, and later as well at Moraine State Park, Butler County (Darney, pers. comm.), the lack of a more widespread banding effort meant that few data were available on the extent of migration; through 1971, only a single saw-whet owl banded in Pennsylvania had been recovered away from its banding site, a bird later found in central Georgia (Holroyd and Woods 1975).

In October and November 1996, biologists Eric and Melonie Atkinson and Todd Bauman began nightly banding with an audiolure near the Kittatinny Ridge in northern Lehigh County, capturing 78 saw-whets over the course of 34 nights, including one owl previously banded at Cape May, N.J. (Atkinson, pers. comm.). Armed with a small grant from the Wild Resource Conservation Fund, the Atkinsons, Bauman and Weidensaul subsequently recruited and equipped cooperators across Pennsylvania, and by autumn 1997, a network of seven stations stretching from Philadelphia to Crawford County was in place.

Although results were fairly poor that first season (144 owls banded in 619 hours of effort), new sites opened over the next several years, while Darney continued his independent work on Presque Isle and Moraine SP, and began netting at night in spring 2000. The number of banding sites across the state has remained around 12–13, although effort varies from sporadic backyard netting to nightly, constant-effort operations throughout the main two-month migration season in October and November (Fig. 1, Table 1). Most of these sites participate in Project Owlnet (www.projectowlnet.org), a collaborative effort involving nearly 100 owl banding stations across North America.

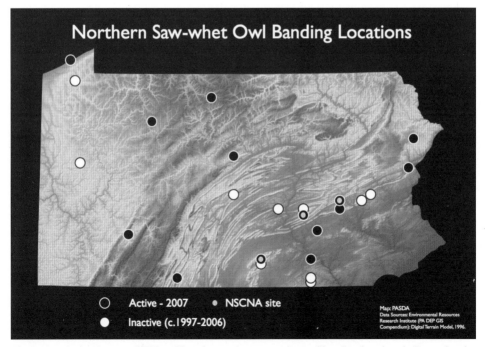

Figure 1:   Active (autumn 2007) and inactive northern saw-whet owl banding locations in Pennsylvania.

Table 1. Autumn 2007 results from northern saw-whet owl banding sites in Pennsylvania

SITE	COUNTY	NIGHTS OPEN	OWLS
Hidden Valley	Schuylkill	46	382
Small Valley	Dauphin	44	284
King's Gap	Cumberland	45	238
Allegheny Front	Bedford/Somerset	10	236
Wizard Ranch	York	13	124
Powdermill	Westmoreland	18	109
Roseto	Northampton	22	85
Skytop	Monroe	25	69
Bear Mountain	Clinton	11	18
Evitt's Mountain	Somerset	10	6
		TOTAL	**1,551**

Reports from three other sites were unavailable: Hebron, Potter Co.; Auburn, Schuylkill Co.; and Brockway, Jefferson Co. (Sources: S. Weidensaul, D. Darney, B. Fortman, R. Mulvihill, P. Karner, D. Speicher, W. Laubscher, J. Shaffer)

The largest saw-whet research program in Pennsylvania is operated by the Ned Smith Center for Nature and Art (NSCNA), which maintains constant-effort banding sites in northern Dauphin, western Schuylkill and southern Cumberland counties, manned by a crew of 19 licensed banders and about 85 volunteers. Since 1997, the NSCNA operation has netted 4,519 saw-whet owls, and since 2001 has conducted radio-telemetry studies aimed at determining roost site selection and habitat preferences, along with a variety of other collaborative ventures with researchers looking into the transmission of zoonotics like West Nile virus, avian influenza and Lyme disease. The following overview is based largely on NSCNA data from 1998–2007.

TIMING, WEATHER CONDITIONS AND ROUTES OF FALL MIGRATION

Unlike diurnal raptor migration, which can be observed directly, we are forced to infer the timing, intensity and routes of owl migration from capture data, with the inevitable risk of faulty conclusions based on spotty coverage and incomplete information. However, until methods like radar ornithology are further refined, it remains our only practical window into owl migration.

The NSCNA banding project begins 1 October each year and runs nightly through the end of November or early December. At each site, four 12-meter 60mm mist nets are opened from dusk until at least 2300 hr. EST, with an audiolure broadcasting a male "toot" call in a cycle of 30 seconds of calling and 15 seconds of silence. The net locations are in forested habitat atop or along major ridges, generally where there is a dense understory.

Usually few, if any owls, are captured during the first week of October, though in irruption years they may be caught as early as late September, and northern Pennsylvania banding stations often report their first saw-whets the last week of September or the first week of October. By mid-October, consistent numbers of birds are generally being netted across the state. In central and southern Pennsylvania, where most of the banding has been conducted, the median date for captures is 31 October. (Fig. 2)

The irruptions of 1995, 1999 and 2007 may reflect a four-year cycle in red-backed voles (*Clethrionomys gapperi*), a major prey item of northern saw-whet owls in boreal forests

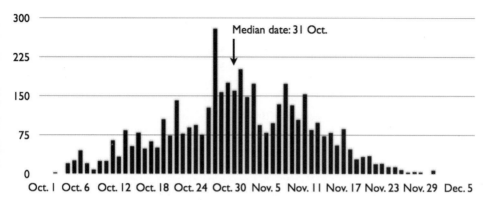

Figure 2: Phenology of northern saw-whet owl migration at three sites in central and southern Pennsylvania, 1998-2007. (S. Weidensaul)

(Cannings 1993). Similar four-year synchronization has been demonstrated between red-backed vole cycles and irruptions of the saw-whet's more northerly congener, the boreal owl (*Aegolius funereus*) (Cheveau et al 2004). The 2007 irruption followed a year of heavy tree mast production in 2006 across eastern Canada, high *Peromyscus* and *Clethrionomys* populations during the 2007 breeding season, and their subsequent collapse in autumn 2007 when trees in the region failed to produce much mast (Pittaway 2006 and 2007)

Based on 2,374 owls captured between 1998–2003, immature (hatching year, or HY) owls migrate significantly earlier than do adults (Caruna et al 2005). Although there appears to be no sexual difference in the timing of migration (Musilli et al 2005), there is a stark imbalance in the sex ratio of owls captured, with males making up just 6% of all netted saw-whets between 1998–2007. Saw-whets are sexed using a discriminant analysis of wing chord/mass values (Brinker et al 1997), and some cannot be assigned to gender; unknown-sex birds make up a further 17% of the total, with females comprising 77% of all captures. During irruption years, when the overall proportion of HY owls is much higher, males of all age classes comprise slightly higher percentages of the total – 8.9% in 1999, and 9.6% in 2007.

A comparison of passive netting versus use of an audiolure at Cape May, NJ, showed that females were more likely to be netted regardless of technique, but that a significantly higher percentage of females were captured using an audiolure (Duffy and Matheny 1997). It is unknown to what extent the skewed sex ratios seen in Pennsylvania represent a biased sample or, as Duffy and Matheny suggest, differential migration between sexes in this species.

Banding and radio-telemetry data, in Pennsylvania and elsewhere, have shown that saw-whets are remarkable languid migrants, with long periods of stopover that may last for weeks (Hurban et al 2004, 2005). As a result, it may be a week or two after sites in Potter or Clinton counties report their first saw-whets before banding stations in Dauphin or Schuylkill counties do, and another week before banders in Cumberland County net their first owls. Results from stations across the East bear this out; the migration peak is the third week of September in east-central Ontario; about 16 October in southern Maine; 31 October in central and southern Pennsylvania; 6 November in northern Maryland, 12 November at Assateague Island, MD, and 12–17 November at the southern tip of the

Delmarva Peninsula in Virginia (J. Camuso, D. Brinker and B. Murphy, pers. comm., Whalen et al 1997).

Not surprisingly, the same weather conditions that produce good flights of other fall migrants also produce the largest number of saw-whet owls at banding sites. The largest numbers of saw-whet owls are generally caught on calm nights following a frontal passage with strong northerly winds. Windy nights tend to be poor for netting; whether this is because the owls do not migrate under these conditions, or they detect billowing nets, or the reduced effectiveness of the audiolure in high wind, remains unclear, and attempts to use marine radar to answer this question have been unsuccessful.

Similarly, there is a close correlation between moonlight and the number of saw-whet owls netted; in general, the darker the night, the better the capture rate. While this may merely reflect the fact that saw-whets see and avoid mist nets better on moonlit nights, observations with night-vision equipment and detection of vocalizations both suggest that substantially fewer saw-whets respond to an audiolure on brightly lit nights. (One reason saw-whets were so long undetected in migration is that they are generally silent, even when responding to an audio recording, and rarely give the classic "toot" call when they do vocalize. The most common vocalizations in fall and winter are whines, *ksew* calls and bill-clacks).

In 1975, based on fall banding data, Holyrod and Woods outlined "two distinct routes" used by saw-whet owls, one running from central Ontario and the upper Midwest south through the Ohio River valley to Kentucky, the other along the Atlantic coast from Maine to North Carolina (Holyrod and Woods 1975). This view held sway through the early 1990s, but today it is clear that the Appalachians form a significant flyway for this species.

Recoveries and encounters of banded birds show that saw-whets passing through Pennsylvania are generally coming from eastern Canada and New England, passing around and through the eastern Great Lakes. The largest number of foreign birds encountered by the NSCNA project were originally banded in Ontario (42), most of those captured along the north shores of lakes Erie and Ontario, which form a significant migration barrier. Lesser numbers were banded in coastal Maine (6), New York (4), and western Vermont (2), although these numbers may reflect more the relative scarcity of banding sites in New England and New York, rather than an accurate picture of where most migrants are coming from.

A few owls from the western Great Lakes have been encountered by the NSCNA project, including three each from Michigan and Wisconsin. Some direct encounters suggest how widely these small owls can travel. For example, a saw-whet banded in juvenile plumage on 30 July 2007 at Whitefish Point, MI, was captured 7 October 2007 in Schuylkill County, more than 600 miles east-southeast.

It is unknown how far south migrant saw-whets routinely travel. Saw-whets banded in Pennsylvania are regularly recaptured in Maryland, Virginia and West Virginia, but a lack of banding coverage farther south hampers our understanding of their full migratory range. There are records as far south as the Gulf Coast and northern Florida (Lesser and Stickley 1967), but given the secretive nature of the species, it is likely to be overlooked unless netting with an audiolure is employed. In the fall and winter of 2007–08, a few banders reported catching small numbers of saw-whets in the Georgia piedmont and north Alabama (C. Muise, E. Soehren and B. Sargent, pers. comm.).

The details of how saw-whets respond to local and regional topography, especially their response to leading lines and barriers, remains equally murky. Of 36 direct banding recoveries between stations in Pennsylvania involving NSCNA birds, more than three-quarters (78%) involved birds traveling along the NE–SW trendline of the Appalachian ridge system. Darney's remarkable total of 236 saw-whets in just 10 nights of netting over several weeks (12 Oct.–11 Nov. 2007) during that year's irruption hints at the importance of the Allegheny Front as a major corridor for this species (D. Darney, pers. comm.).

Diurnal raptors follow ridges south in autumn because they offer energetic advantages, including lift from solar-generated thermals and deflection currents; at night, however, thermals are much reduced and the importance of deflection currents to nocturnal migrants is unknown. If saw-whets are indeed following ridge systems, they may be doing so because the mountains offer forested travel corridors among largely deforested valleys. Enough recoveries exist of owls moving directly south, crossing large areas of agricultural or urban land, to suggest that saw-whets are probably facultative migrants, either following the ridge system or moving broad-front depending on weather and wind.

As early 20th century records from Lake Huron indicate, saw-whet owls are capable of crossing the Great Lakes; in 1995, one was observed making a morning landfall there (Hall 1996). Darney (pers. comm.) has recaptured two saw-whets that made direct overwater crossings of Lake Erie.

STOPOVER AND WINTERING ECOLOGY

As little as we know about the migration dynamics of northern saw-whet owls, we know even less about their stopover and wintering ecology. However, seven years of radio-telemetry data, including five years in Michaux State Forest in Cumberland County, give some insight into roost site and habitat preferences of female saw-whets, which are large enough to support a 2g radio transmitter and harness.

Results confirm that, prior to leaf-fall, migrant saw-whets frequently roost in deciduous trees, usually picking large emergent canopy hardwoods, and perching well away from the trunk, often hidden among clusters of leaves. Once the hardwoods drop their leaves, the saw-whets switch to evergreen cover – most often conifers, but less frequently in thickets of mountain laurel (*Kalmia latifolia*) or, rarely, dense tree blowdowns (A. Stauffer and S. Weidensaul, unpub. data). Although not present on the study site, in other parts of the state saw-whets are commonly reported to use thickets of Japanese honeysuckle (*Lonicera japonica*) or dense stands of eastern redcedar (*Juniperus virginiana*). It seems likely that structure and density of cover are more important than species composition.

In Michaux State Forest, 90 of 103 roost sites located by radio-telemetry were in conifers—67 in pitch pine (*Pinus rigida*), 20 in eastern white pine (*P. strobus*), and one each in Scotch pine (*P. sylvestris*), Norway spruce (*Picea aibes*) and Douglas-fir (*Pseudotsuga menziesii*). Most roost sites were within pitch pine/mixed oak forest (Fike 1999). Four roost sites, all involving the same owl, were in thickets of mountain laurel. Most of the radio-tracking on this site occurred after major leaf-fall each year; those few roost sites located before leaf-fall showed relatively greater use of deciduous trees, including six roosts in chestnut oak (*Quercus montana*), two in scarlet oak (*Q. coccinea*) and one roost in northern red oak (*Q. rubra*).

Of 16 roosts located on Weiser State Forest and adjacent private land in Schuylkill County (located in dry oak-heath forest and dry white pine [hemlock]—oak forest communities [Fike 1999]), half were in conifers and half in shrubs or hardwoods—four in white pine, three each in pitch pine and mountain laurel, two in northern red oak, and one each in eastern hemlock (*Tsuga canadensis*), sassafras (*Sassafras albidum*), black gum (*Nyssa sylvatica*), and a leafless red maple (*Acer rubrum*) blowdown. The higher percentage of hardwoods may reflect the fact that much of this tracking took place before leaf-fall.

Roost locations tended to cluster in stands of pines, often in protected hollows or along ridgetop wind gaps, with owls moving between several favorite sites, sometimes changing roosts each night, sometimes remaining in one tree for up to five days in a row. Roost height varied from 1–32m, with average roost height 13m. Roost orientation was generally on the south or east side of the tree, presumably for sunlight and warmth. While many owls perched in thick cover (or in pitch pines whose large numbers of old cones make it surprisingly difficult to visually locate the owl), a few roosted regularly in fairly exposed locations, including the lower, open branches of pines, or in open laurel clumps (A. Stauffer and S. Weidensaul, unpub. data).

Although saw-whet owls are not believed to routinely use cavities for roosting, they will take shelter on some occasions. One wintering owl, tracked with telemetry in Michaux SF, may have used old squirrel nests and raptor stick nests on several occasions, although this did not correspond to unusually bad weather (Stauffer and Weidensaul, unpub. data). Another wintering saw-whet in Dauphin County was found to be using a newspaper delivery tube mounted in a stone column as a daytime roost, while disappearing at night to hunt. (B. Carricato, pers. comm.).

Essentially nothing is known about nightly activity range, foraging habitat preferences or hunting behavior in migrant and wintering saw-whets in the central Appalachians. An examination of collected pellets in the course of the Pennsylvania telemetry study confirms the importance of small mammals in their diet, especially *Peromyscus*, *Microtus*, *Clethrionomys* and *Blarina*.

AREAS FOR FURTHER RESEARCH

A great deal remains to be learned about the dynamics of northern saw-whet owl migration through the central Appalachians. For example, except for Darney's work on Presque Isle and two seasons (2000–2001) when netting occurred at the NSCNA's Hidden Valley site in Schuylkill County, very little has been done to investigate spring saw-whet migration in Pennsylvania.

The peak flight in central Pennsylvania appears to occur from early through mid-March, but the number of owls captured in spring is considerably lower than that netted in autumn. For example, following the autumn 1999 irruption, nets were operated at Hidden Valley from 3–26 March 2000. Although 52 saw-whet owls were netted, the capture rate was only slightly more than a third that of the previous autumn (.015 owls/net hour/m2 of net in the fall vs. .006 owls in spring). Results were similarly poor the following year, and spring netting was suspended thereafter. The much lower capture rate may reflect heavy overwinter mortality, lower susceptibility to the audiolure in spring or a different migration route north.

Darney's work focusing on wintering owls and spring migrants offers some clues on timing of migration along Lake Erie, including late dates of 11 May (two owls) and 12 May,

1996, following the previous autumn's irruption. The highest number of roosting spring saw-whets he found at Presque Isle was 14 on 14 April 2000 (D. Darney, pers. comm.).

Darney's work aside, the majority of Pennsylvania saw-whet research has been conducted in the Ridge-and-Valley and South Mountain sections of the state, with relatively little north or west of the Allegheny Front. Constant-effort netting in the piedmont would provide valuable comparisons to the mountainous regions, and much of the western Appalachian Plateau and Glaciated Low Plateau remain uninvestigated. Constant-effort mist-netting with an audiolure on Presque Isle, in both spring and fall, would document the extent of trans-lake migration, compliment a similar effort on the Canadian side at Long Point, and provide important information to guide the siting of wind turbines.

Similarly, the degree to which saw-whet owls follow Appalachian ridgelines, and the altitude at which they fly during migration, is of more than academic interest, given the extraordinary push to develop wind energy along known migration corridors like the Allegheny Front, Bald Eagle Ridge, Second Mountain and Tuscarora Mountain. In all of these places, the debate regarding wind development has focused largely on diurnal raptor migrants, with little attention paid to nocturnal migrants, including owls. Coupling netting, radio-telemetry and marine radar/ceilometers may shed light on these important questions.

ACKNOWLEDGMENTS

The author extends his deep appreciation to his long-time banding site coordinators Sandy Lockerman and Gary Shimmel, to telemetry project director Aura Stauffer, and to the NSCNA crew for their years of effort and collaboration. The staff of the Ned Smith Center for Nature Art have been extraordinarily supportive of this research. Sincere thanks are also due to his longtime collaborator Sara R. Morris of Canisius College, Buffalo, and to her students, for their work in analyzing banding results. Assistance in preparing this report was given by David F. Brinker, founder of Project Owlnet, and by Eric Atkinson, Seth Benz, Wayne Laubscher, David Darney, Paul Karner, Darryl Speicher, Janet Shaffer, Robert Mulvihill, Bruce Fortman, Judy Camuso, Charles Muise, Bob Sargent, Eric Soehren, Beth Carricato and Bruce Murphy.

REFERENCES

Bendire, Charles B. 1892. *Life Histories of North American Birds*, vol. 1. Government Printing Office. Washington, D.C., pp. 446.

Bent, Arthur Cleveland. 1938. *Life Histories of North American Birds of Prey*, vol. 2. Smithsonian Institution Bull. 170. Washington, D.C., pp. 482.

Brinker, D. F., K. E. Duffy, D. M. Whalen, B. D. Watts and K. M. Dodge. 1997. Autumn Migration of Northern Saw-whet Owls (*Aegolius acadicus*) in the Middle Atlantic and Northeastern United States: What Observations from 1995 Suggest. Pp. 74–89 in: J. R. Duncan, D. H. Johnson and T. H. Nicholls (Eds). *Biology and Conservation of Owls of the Northern Hemisphere*. Gen. Tech. Rep. NC-190. USDA Forest Service, North Central Research Station, St. Paul. MN, pp. 635.

Cannings, R. J. 1993. Northern Saw-whet Owl (*Aegolius acadicus*) in: A. Poole and F. Gill (Eds.). *The Birds of North America*, No. 42. The Academy of Natural Sciences, Philadelphia and The American Ornithologists' Union, Washington, D.C.

Caruna, E. A., S. M. Musilli, M. S. Hurban, S. Weidensaul, H. D. Sheets, and S. R. Morris. 2005. Age-related differences in the fall migration of Northern Saw-whet Owls. Wilson Ornithological Society and Association of Field Ornithologists, Beltsville, MD.

Cheveau, M., P. Drapeau, L. Imbeau and Y. Begeron. 2004. Owl winter irruptions as an indicator of small mammal population cycles in the boreal forest of eastern North America. *Oikos* 107: 190–198.

Coues, Elliott. 1874. *Birds of the Northwest.* U.S. Geological and Geographical Survey of the Territories. Washington, D.C., pp. 791.

Duffy, K. E., and P. E. Matheny. 1997. Northern Saw-whet Owls (*Aegolius acadicus*) captured at Cape May Point, N.J. 1980–1994: Comparison of two techniques. Pp. 131–137 in: J. R. Duncan, D. H. Johnson and T. H. Nicholls (Eds). *Biology and Conservation of Owls of the Northern Hemisphere.* Gen. Tech. Rep. NC-190. USDA Forest Service, North Central Research Station, St. Paul. MN, pp. 635.

Duffy, K. E., and P. Kerlinger. 1992. "Autumn owl migration at Cape May Point, New Jersey," *Wilson Bull.*, 104:312–320.

Erdman, T. C., T. O. Meyer, J. H. Smith and D. M. Erdman. 1997. Autumn populations and movements of migrant Northern Saw-whet Owls (*Aegolius acadicus*) at Little Suamico, Wisconsin. Pp. 167–172 in: J. R. Duncan, D. H. Johnson and T. H. Nicholls (Eds). *Biology and Conservation of Owls of the Northern Hemisphere.* Gen. Tech. Rep. NC-190. USDA Forest Service, North Central Research Station. St. Paul, MN, pp. 635.

Erdman, T. C., and D. F. Brinker. 1997. Increasing mist net captures of migrant northern saw-whet owls (*Aegolius acadicus*) with an audiolure. Pp. 533–544 in: J. R. Duncan, D. H. Johnson and T. H. Nicholls (Eds). *Biology and Conservation of Owls of the Northern Hemisphere.* Gen. Tech. Rep. NC-190. USDA Forest Service, North Central Research Station. St. Paul, MN, pp. 635.

Evans, D. L. 1997. Influence of broadcast tape-recorded calls on captures of fall migrant northern saw-whet owls (*Aegolius acadicus*) and long-eared owls (*Asio otus*). Pp. 173–174 in: J. R. Duncan, D. H. Johnson and T. H. Nicholls (Eds). *Biology and Conservation of Owls of the Northern Hemisphere.* Gen. Tech. Rep. NC-190. USDA Forest Service, North Central Research Station, St. Paul. MN, pp. 635.

Fike, J. 1999. *Terrestial and Palustrine Plant Communities of Pennsylvania.* Pennsylvania Natural Diversity Inventory. Harrisburg, PA, pp. 87.

Ford, Alice (Ed). 1957. *The Bird Biographies of John James Audubon.* Macmillan. New York, pp. 282.

Gromme, O. J., 1963. *The Birds of Wisconsin.* University of Wisconsin Press. Madison, WI, pp. 219.

Hall, G. A. 1996. Appalachian region. *National Audubon Society Field Notes* 50:53.

Holroyd, G. L., and J. G. Woods. 1975. Migration of the Saw-whet Owl in Eastern North America, *Bird-Banding* 46:101–105.

Hurban, M. S., E. A. Caruana, S. M. Musilli, H. D. Sheets, S. Weidensaul, and S. R. Morris. 2005. Stopover rates and durations of migrant Northern Saw-whet Owls in southern Pennsylvania. Wilson Ornithological Society and Association of Field Ornithologists, Beltsville, MD.

_____. 2004. Stopover ecology of Northern Saw-whet Owls in Pennsylvania. Wilson Ornithological Society and Association of Field Ornithologists, Ithaca, NY.

Korpimäki, E., P. R. Brown, J. Jacob and R. P. Pech. 2004. The puzzle of population cycles and outbreaks of small mammals solved? *Bioscience* 54:1071–1079.

Lesser, F. H., and A. R. Stickley. 1967. Occurrence of the Saw-whet Owl in Florida, *Auk* 84:3 425.

Mueller, H. C., and D. D. Berger. 1967. Observations on Migrating Saw-whet Owls, *Bird-Banding*, 38:120–125.

Musilli, S. M., M. S. Hurban, E. A. Caruana, S. Weidensaul, H. D. Sheets, and S. R. Morris. 2005. Sex-related differences in the migration of Northern Saw-whet Owls. Wilson Ornithological Society and Association of Field Ornithologists, Beltsville, MD

Pittaway, R. 2007. Ron Pittaway's winter finch forecast, 2007–2008. Ontario Field Ornithologists. http://ca.geocities.com/larry.neily@rogers.com/pittaway-new.htm.

_____. 2006 Ron Pitttaway's winter finch forecast, 2006–2007. Ontario Field Ornithologists. http://ca.geocities.com/larry.neily@rogers.com/pittaway06.htm.

Robbins, C. S., and W. T. Van Velzen. 1968. *Field List of the Birds of Maryland.* Maryland Ornithological Society. Baltimore, MD, pp. 44.

Saunders, W. E. 1907. A Migration Disaster in Western Ontario, *Auk* 24:108–110.

Sutton, G. M. 1928. *An Introduction to the Birds of Pennsylvania.* J. Horace McFarland Co. Harrisburg, PA, pp. 169.

Taverner, P. A., and B. H. Swales. 1911. Notes on the Migration of the Saw-whet Owl, *Auk* 28:329–334.

Urich, William D. 1997. *A Century of Bird Life in Berks County,* Pennsylvania. Reading Public Museum. Reading, PA, pp. 335.

Warren, B. H. 1890. *Report on the Birds of Pennsylvania.* Second edition. State Printing Office. Harrisburg, PA, pp. 432.

Whalen, D. M., B. D. Watts, M. D. Wilson and D. S. Bradshaw. Magnitude and timing of the fall migration of Northern Saw-whet Owls through the Eastern Shore of Virginia, 1994–1996. *The Raven* 68:97–104.

Wilson, Alexander, quoted in: T. M. Brewer. 1840. *Wilson's American Ornithology, with Notes by Jardine.* Otis Broaders and Co. Boston, pp. 746.

Wood, N. A. 1951. *The Birds of Michigan.* University of Michigan Museum of Zoology. Ann Arbor, MI, pp. 559.

Zalles, J. I., and K. L. Bildstein. 2000. *Raptor Watch.* BirdLife International and Hawk Mountain Sanctuary. Cambridge, UK, and Kempton, PA, pp. 420.

Avian Ecology and Conservation: A Pennsylvania Focus with National Implications. Edited by S. K. Majumdar, T. L. Master, M. C. Brittingham, R. M. Ross, R. S. Mulvihill and J. E. Huffman. © 2010. The Pennsylvania Academy of Science.

Chapter 11

The Christmas Bird Count

Nicholas C. Bolgiano
711 West Foster Avenue, State College, PA
Nbolgiano@minitab.com

The Christmas Bird Count (CBC) is more than an annual tradition. This is one of the largest and most successful of citizen-scientist projects. It is the primary data source for assessing winter bird distributions and with the data now computer-available, its role for assessing bird population trend is being discovered. This chapter relates CBC history in Pennsylvania; the value of CBC data for trend analysis; examples of distributions; and one of the wonders of winter bird study, irruptions.

CBC HISTORY

The CBC began in 1900, with 5 of the 26 reports from Pennsylvania. Although counts were once restricted to Christmas day, a CBC can now be conducted within December 14–January 5. (When I cite a year in reference to the CBC, it is the year in which Christmas occurs.) One practice that has remained standard is the reporting of all birds observed during a single day. Early reports were by single parties, but by 1932, multiple parties were reporting from the now traditional 15-mile diameter circle. Most of the growth occurred after World War II: party-hours by Pennsylvania observers reached the 500-hour level in 1946, the 1000-hour level in 1953, the 2500-hour level in 1972, and the 5000-hour level in 1992. Reporting of feeder-watch hours became customary in 1973, though yearly feeder watch effort in Pennsylvania has leveled off at around 1000 hours. Separate reporting of owling hours began in 1978 and this effort has continued to grow (Bolgiano 1997).

There are 67 current Pennsylvania count sites where the CBC has been conducted for 5 or more years. (I include Raccoon Creek State Park, where the count ended in 2006 after 44 years.) Some of these sites have a long history, as 20 were established by 1950, including West Chester in 1902, Pittsburgh in 1908, and Reading in 1911 (Table 1). A map of count site locations is shown in Figure 1, displaying the mean species count from the most recent 20-year period.

TREND ANALYSIS

For species that breed in the vast northern part of our continent, the CBC may be the primary means for assessing population trends (Niven et al. 2004). For species that commonly breed in Pennsylvania, the Breeding Bird Survey (BBS) is typically used for trend analysis. However, for some of these species, both CBC and the Breeding Bird Survey (BBS) provide valuable information on population trends, while for a few, the CBC is even superior. To illustrate, I compare Pennsylvania data from both sources for eight species. BBS data are expressed as mean count per route, while CBC data are expressed as mean count/10 party-hours from all count sites with at least 20 party-hours, thus giving equal weight to each site.

Table 1. Map abbreviation, Pennsylvania count site name, and year established.

AUDU	Audubon	1944	LWST	Lewistown	1983
BALD	Bald Eagle State Park	1980	LINE	Linesville	1947
BEAV	Beaver	1964	LITI	Lititz	1944
BEDF	Bedford County	1989	LOCK	Lock Haven–Jersey Shore	1967
BERN	Bernville	1985	MANS	Mansfield–Wellsboro	1953
BETH	Bethlehem–Easton	1951	NEWB	New Bloomfield	1949
BLOO	Bloomsburg	1971	NEWV	Newville	1991
BUFV	Buffalo Creek Valley	1966	PENN	Pennypack Valley	1953
BUSH	Bushy Run State Park	1963	PISH	Pittsburgh South Hills	2000
BUTL	Butler County	1964	PITT	Pittsburgh	1908
CBCK	Central Bucks County	1966	PLEA	Pleasantville	1966
CHAM	Chambersburg	1955	POCO	Pocono Mountain	1980
CLRN	Clarion	1987	RACC	Raccoon Creek State Park	1963
CLRK	Clarksville	1958	READ	Reading	1911
CULP	Culp	1969	RECT	Rector	1974
CURT	Curtin	1995	RYER	Ryerson	1998
DALL	Dallas Area	1958	SCRA	Scranton	1928
DELA	Delaware County	1922	SBCK	Southern Bucks County	1947
DING	Dingman's Ferry	1992	SLAN	Southern Lancaster Co.	1976
DUBO	Dubois	1983	SEBR	Southeastern Bradford Co.	1950
ELVE	Elverson	1939	STAT	State College	1940
EMPO	Emporium	1989	THOM	Thompson	1980
ERIE	Erie	1965	TUNK	Tunkhannock	1994
GETT	Gettysburg	1981	UBCK	Upper Bucks County	1968
HAMB	Hamburg	1965	WARR	Warren	1946
HARR	Harrisburg	1936	WASH	Washington	1974
HUNT	Huntingdon	1984	WCHE	Western Chester County	2003
INDI	Indiana	1983	WEST	West Chester	1902
JOHN	Johnstown	1983	WHIT	White Mills	1972
LAKE	Lake Raystown	1993	WILD	Wild Creek–Little Gap	1977
LANC	Lancaster	1938	WILL	Williamsport	1968
LEBA	Lebanon County	1980	WYNC	Wyncote	1928
LEHI	Lehigh Valley	1944	YORK	York	1941
LWBG	Lewisburg	1949			

Pileated woodpeckers (*Dryocopus pileatus*) and Carolina wrens (*Thryothorus ludovicianus*), both year-round residents, show remarkably similar trends in both surveys (correlation = 0.89 for the woodpecker and 0.96 for the wren). This imparts some confidence in the CBC data and suggests that the CBC can sometimes be used to discern a species' history before the BBS began in 1966. One can logically conclude that the woodpeckers started to take off in their recovery during the late 1940s and the wrens experienced minor peaks

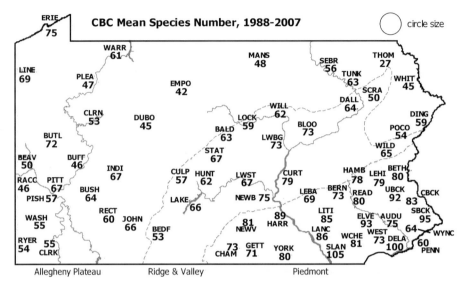

Figure 1:   CBC count sites and average species number, 1988–2007.

during the 1950s (Figure 2). (Minor wren peaks also occurred in 1904–13 and 1925–33. The woodpecker date also illustrates that first-year BBS data are sometimes anomalous.)

Eastern bluebirds (*Sialia sialis*) and Northern mockingbirds (*Mimus polyglottos*) are two more examples of how the CBC can be used to reconstruct population changes. Trends for bluebirds from both sources are similar (correlation = 0.93), with overall level differences partially attributable to some birds withdrawing southward during the winter. But why did wintering bluebirds drop off to nearly zero during 1959–77? This was the period when they apparently went through their crisis, which is not apparent in the BBS data. Similarly, extrapolating backward from the BBS cannot indicate how few mockingbirds there were until their population began to increase rapidly in the mid-1950s (Figure 2).

Among the next four species discussed, the CBC contains information unavailable from the BBS. I believe that the CBC is superior to the BBS for assessing the ruffed grouse (*Bonasa umbellus*) population. On the BBS, a total of 1–14 grouse were tallied per year, too few to represent anything but random noise. However, during the CBC, 61–313 grouse/year were tallied during 1970–2007, making this survey much more likely to be assessing the population trend. The downturn that began in the mid-1990s (Figure 3) coincides with fewer grouse being killed by Pennsylvania hunters. CBC data and the Pennsylvania Game Commission's game-take survey data from 1990–2006 (source: *Pennsylvania Game News*) showed very similar patterns (correlation = 0.87), suggesting that CBC's potential for assessing the grouse population. Among other species, many more raptors and water birds are tallied on the CBC than on the BBS, suggestive of the CBC's further potential (Butcher 1990).

The CBC gives a similar story for Northern bobwhites (*Colinus virginianus*) and ring-necked pheasants (*Phasianus colchicus*), with population peaks during 1960–70 and subsequent declines. The BBS captures only a portion of these peaks and gives different pictures of the two trajectories. For bobwhites, the two survey results since 1966 are similar (correlation = 0.87). For pheasants, though the trends from both surveys are downward

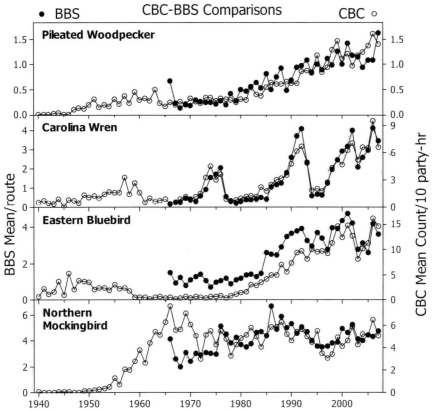

Figure 2: Pennsylvania CBC and BBS data for pileated woodpeckers, Carolina wrens, Eastern bluebirds, and Northern mockingbirds, 1940–2007.

(correlation = 0.61), there is a striking difference: the BBS data declined more gradually than did the CBC data (Figure 3). I suspect that the BBS trend was buoyed by the releases of many pen-reared birds and believe that the CBC trend more accurately reflects the wild pheasant population. If there was a wide distribution of male pen-reared birds that survived the winter, their spring cackling might over-represent the population size. The BBS shows steep declines after 1970 for ground-nesting birds of farmlands, including bobwhites, vesper sparrows (*Pooecetes gramineus*), grasshopper sparrows (*Ammodramus savannarum*), and Eastern meadowlarks (*Sturnella magna*), similar to the CBC data for bobwhites and pheasants and closely timed to the secure nesting habitat available from agricultural set-aside programs (Bolgiano 1999). As before, the CBC allows reconstruction of population cycles, with a downturn in bobwhites during the winter of 1944–45. This coincided with a nearly 90% loss of Pennsylvania's bobwhites from near low temperatures and drifting snow (Latham and Studholme 1952). Bobwhite numbers slowly recovered and both bobwhites and pheasants reached CBC peaks during 1960–1970 (Figure 3), when federal set-aside programs, such as the Soil Bank, provided them with secure nesting cover (Bolgiano 2000).

House finch (*Carpodacus mexicanus*) trends show the rapid rise in house finch numbers during the 1970s–1980s and the downturn in the 1990s related to the spread of house finch

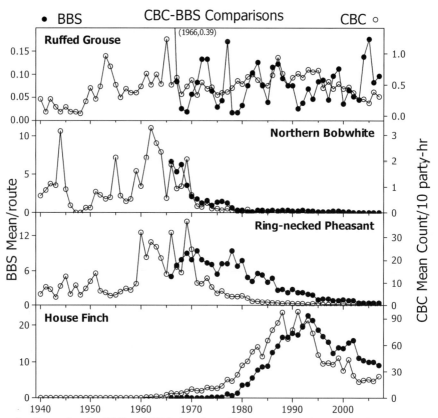

Figure 3:   Pennsylvania CBC and BBS data for ruffed grouse, Northern bobwhites, ring-necked pheasants, and house finches, 1940–2007.

conjunctivitis. However, the BBS data do not rise as rapidly or fall as sharply as do the CBC data (Figure 3). Possible explanations include a within-state regional effect or different dynamics between summering and wintering populations. Understanding why the two surveys differ is of interest to understanding house finch dynamics.

There are statistical issues to consider when using CBC data. Because its counting methodology is not uniform among count sites or between years, methodology changes could bias trends. During the early years, nearly all observations were made while observers were on foot, but there was a shift toward vehicle usage, especially during the 1930s to 1950s. Today, hours on foot and by vehicle are about equal (Bolgiano 1997). Such changes make it difficult to compare trends from the first half-century to more recent trends. Similarly, one must be careful when comparing owl trends before owling became popular to trends from recent decades. Unless these methodology changes can be corrected for, a good rule of thumb is to use the early data in a more descriptive manner.

How to adjust species counts by effort? When birds are well-distributed across the landscape, tallies tend to be proportional to effort and counts can be divided by units of effort. When birds are attracted to a landscape feature, such as a lake or roost, counts are often not proportional to effort and a different adjustment for effort is required (Butcher and

McCulloch 1990). If the counting protocol remains relatively unchanged at lakes or roosts, the unadjusted count may be a valid index. For example, the number of lesser black-backed gulls (*Larus fuscus*) tallied at Bucks County CBC count sites displays how they slowly increased at the Southern Bucks County site up to the mid-1990s, then rapidly increased while spreading to the central and the northern parts of the county (Figure 4).

A statistical model similar to the one used for BBS trend analysis has been applied to CBC data. It can be used to assess trends across large regions while adjusting for variation in effort (Sauer et al. 2004). Such methods should allow us to see that the strong signals present in the CBC data outweigh the noise, as has long been asserted (Drennan 1981).

WINTER DISTRIBUTIONS

For birds that remain in Pennsylvania during the winter, the odds of survival may be lowest during this season, as they struggle to find food or to keep warm and dry. The rigors of winter simplify the rules of distribution for many birds: fly to a location where survival is tenable or perish. Winter's southern boundary of ice and snow often falls across the state and many birds move accordingly. Pennsylvania's winter distribution of many birds is sufficiently tilted toward the south that two southeastern count sites, Southern Lancaster County and Delaware County, average 100 or more species per year, while northern count sites without expanses of open water average less than 50 species (Figure 1). Although birder participation in the CBC is typically higher at southern sites, the primary reasons for these differences are habitat and climate.

Pennsylvania's winter climate largely follows a north-to-south gradient related to the earth's seasonal tilt. Regional departures from this pattern are caused by the state's topography and its proximity to large bodies of water. Temperatures are cooler at high elevations and Lake Erie contributes moisture for higher snowfall in northwestern Pennsylvania, while the Atlantic Ocean moderates the temperature of southeastern Pennsylvania (Yarnal 1995). This is shown in contour plots of average January temperatures and annual snowfall. The January

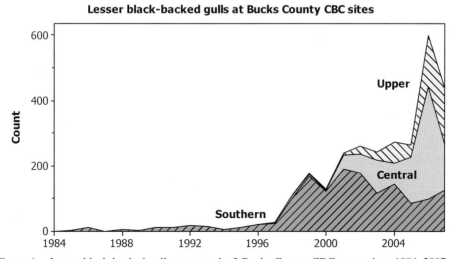

Figure 4:   Lesser black-backed gull counts at the 3 Bucks County CBC count sites, 1984–2007.

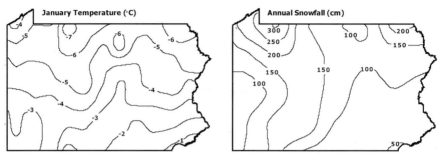

Figure 5:   Contour plots of mean Pennsylvania January temperatures and annual snowfall, 1961–90.

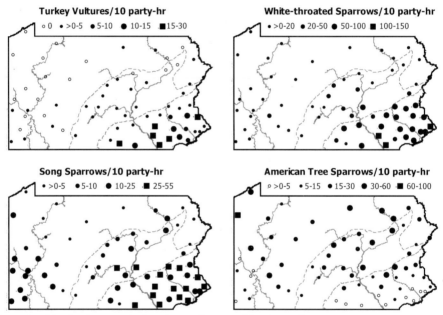

Figure 6:   Distribution maps of turkey vultures, white-throated sparrows, song sparrows, and American tree sparrows at Pennsylvania CBC count sites, 1988–2007.

temperatures range from a low of –7 degrees Celsius at Bradford to a high of –1 at Philadelphia. Annual snowfall exhibits a 6-fold difference statewide, with a high of 300 cm east of Lake Erie to a low of 50 cm at Philadelphia. More snow also falls at the higher elevations of the Alleghenies southeast of Lake Erie (Figure 5, data from National Climatic Data Center).

Distribution maps of turkey vultures (*Cathartes aura*), white-throated sparrows (*Zonotrichia albicollis*), and song sparrows (*Melospiza melodia*) reflect the climate pattern. Most of these birds move south when it turns colder in the fall. By the CBC period, those that remain in Pennsylvania are concentrated in the warmer and more sheltered areas. The vultures are apparently the most sensitive to cold while song sparrows are the least sensitive. All three are commonly found in southeastern Pennsylvania, while song sparrows remain fairly common in the southwest and in the central valleys (Figure 6). A

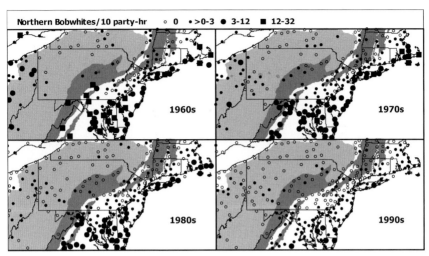

Figure 7: Four decades of Northern bobwhite CBC counts from Pennsylvania and a surrounding region, 1960–1999.

wider view across eastern North America shows that turkey vultures and white-throated sparrows winter primarily southeast of the Appalachians to the Atlantic and Gulf coasts, while song sparrows are primarily found across the southern two-thirds of the United States, as far north as the Ohio Valley and southern New England. In contrast, American tree sparrows (*Spizella arborea*) are sufficiently hardy to thrive in northern parts of the state (Figure 6). Among Pennsylvania's wintering avifauna, more distributions resemble the vultures, white-throated sparrows, and song sparrows than they do the tree sparrows (Root 1988; Sauer et al. 1996; BirdSource 2008).

Distribution changes can reflect large-scale landscape changes. For example, Figure 7 shows four decades of bobwhite CBC distributions in Pennsylvania and the surrounding region. During the 1960s, high bobwhite densities were found in eastern Ohio, in south-central Pennsylvania, and along the eastern seaboard, including southeastern Pennsylvania (Figure 7). During Pennsylvania's first breeding bird atlas, many of the bobwhites observed in the lower portions of the Great and Susquehanna Valleys and possibly in southwestern Pennsylvania were likely from wild populations. As these populations retracted, small numbers of bobwhites have been recorded on both the CBC and the BBS in a more random fashion, a pattern replicated during Pennsylvania's second breeding bird atlas. I believe that these are primarily released pen-reared bobwhites.

IRRUPTIONS

An "irruption" is the movement of an unusually large number of individuals from their usual post-breeding range. Avian irruptions into Pennsylvania usually originate in northern regions when food becomes scarce. Discussed here are 10 seed- and fruit-eating species, including 2 chickadees, a nuthatch, and 7 finches. Irruptions of these birds from Canada and the northern United States southward during fall and winter were once thought to be irregular events. However, Bagg (1969) noted that large alternate-year movements of black-capped chickadees (*Poecile atricapillus*) in Ontario during 1951–1968 coincided with Chapman's observations of low natural food supplies in Maine. Subsequently, Bock and Lepthien (1972, 1976), and later Koenig (2001), in analyses of CBC data, found North American counts of red-breasted nuthatches (*Sitta canadensis*) and some of the northern finches synchronized with the black-capped chickadee irruptions. These irruptions are related to levels of tree masting, or seed production, which can synchronously occur over vast areas, up to 2500 km in span (Koenig and Knops 1998, 2000). In winters when there are sufficient seeds, many boreal seed-eating birds remain in northern areas; when seed production is low, they irrupt in search of food (Newton 1973, Bock and Lepthien 1976, Koenig and Knops 2001).

For most of these birds, the region just south of the boreal forest, including New York and southern New England, is a good place to assess the size of irruptions. Pennsylvania counts show the same patterns, though generally with fewer birds. There are two exceptions to this general rule: black-capped chickadees, for which Pennsylvania data may constitute the best irruption measures, and purple finches (*Carpodacus purpureus*), which winter as far south as the southern Appalachians (Bolgiano 2004b).

Large numbers of irrupting black-capped chickadees usually disperse by the CBC period, but there are three places in eastern North America where apparently irrupting black-capped chickadees have regularly congregated in winter, each near geographical migrant funnels and the contact zone between black-capped chickadees and Carolina chickadees (*Poecile carolinensis*): in southeastern Pennsylvania, along the western end of Lake Erie, and at the southern end of Lake Michigan. Southeastern Pennsylvania is where the most regular irruptions have occurred (Bolgiano 2004a); black-capped chickadee CBC counts there during 1954–1983 showed the see-saw pattern of alternate-year irruptions. However, an abrupt change occurred after 1983. North of the contact zone as of the mid-1980s (region A), the see-saw pattern appears to have dampened. South of the contact zone (region B), few black-capped chickadees were observed after 1983 (Figure 8, Bolgiano 2004a).

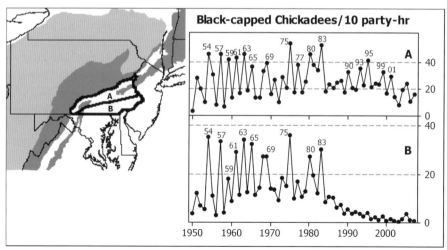

Figure 8:   CBC black-capped chickadee mean count/10 party-hours from southeastern Pennsylvania sites, above (A) and below (B) the contact zone between chickadee species, 1950–2007. Gray shading indicates mountainous or upland physiographic provinces; numbers next to symbols are two-digit year values.

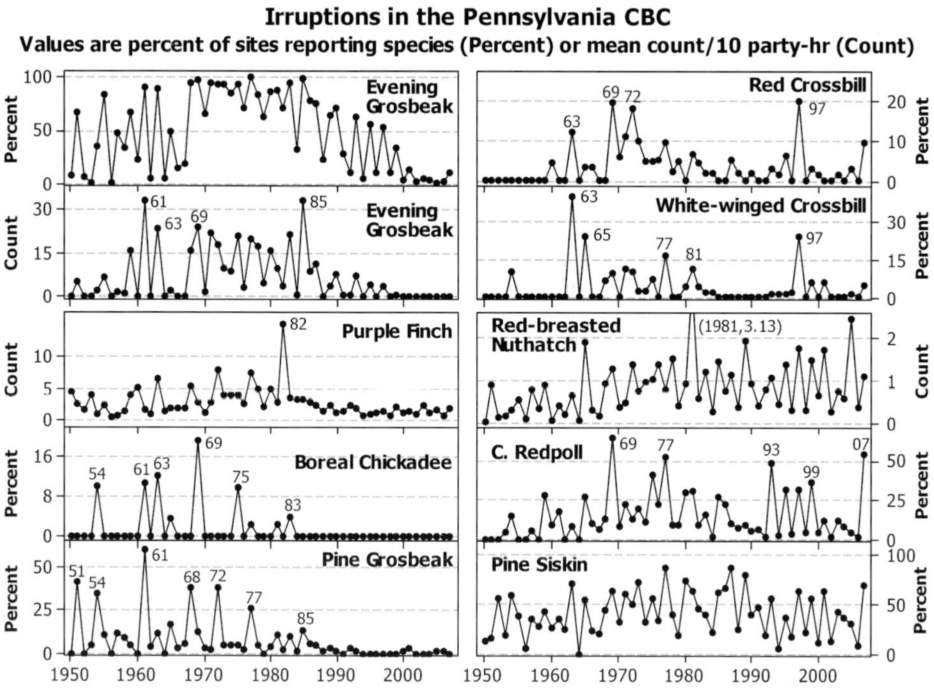

Figure 9:   Pennsylvania CBC data for nine species, expressed either as percent of sites reporting the species or as mean count/10-party hours, 1950–2007. Numbers next to symbols are two-digit year values.

Evening grosbeaks (*Coccothraustes vespertinus*) were infrequently found in eastern North America until the late 1800s, when they began an eastward range expansion. Beginning around the middle of the twentieth century, the see-saw pattern of alternate-year irruptions appeared in CBC data, as measured in the percent of sites reporting grosbeaks (Figure 9). During the winters of 1969–85, grosbeak irruptions became the norm throughout Pennsylvania. After 1985, increasingly fewer grosbeaks were observed, as measured in the count/10 party-hours (Figure 9). The same pattern was observed throughout the northeast. In recent years, evening grosbeaks have been consistently found during the CBC only at sites in or near boreal forest, while at many locations to the south, including Pennsylvania, they have become difficult to find (Bolgiano 2004b).

Purple finches differ from the other species discussed here not only in their winter distributions, but also in their historical irruption pattern. They are found regularly in Pennsylvania every winter, but only occasionally in very large numbers. The last such CBC count was in 1982. Since the mid- to late-1980s, CBC purple finch counts have been consistently lower than in previous years (Figure 9).

Boreal chickadees (*Poecile hudsonicus*) and pine grosbeaks (*Pinicola enucleator*) irrupted about every 2–7 years during the 1950s to mid-1980s, according to CBC data. However, no boreal chickadees have been reported in Pennsylvania since the winter of 1983–84 and pine grosbeaks have become increasingly scarce since 1985 (Figure 8, McWilliams and Brauning 2000). Irruptions of red crossbills (*Loxia curvirostra*), and white-winged crossbills (*Loxia*

Table 2. An irruption history since 1950 of 10 seed- and fruit-eating birds.

Black-capped Chickadee	Tends toward alternate years, many fewer after 1983
Boreal Chickadee	About every 2–7 years during 1961–83, absent since
Red-breasted Nuthatch	Tends toward alternate years
Pine Grosbeak	About every 2–7 years during 1951–85, uncommon since
Purple Finch	Least synchronous, 1982 was last big year
Red Crossbill	Periodically during 1963–81, again in 1997
White-winged Crossbill	Periodically during 1963–81, again in 1997
Common Redpoll	Sometimes alternate years, but erratic
Pine Siskin	Tends toward alternate years
Evening Grosbeak	Tends toward alternate years, more commonly in 1969–85, less common since 1985

leucoptera) occurred periodically during the 1960s to early 1980s. The irruption of 1997 may have been an anomaly, the only crossbill irruption in a span of 25 years (Figure 9).

Unlike the other species, the irruption patterns in the CBC of red-breasted nuthatches, pine siskins (*Carduelis pinus*), and common redpoll (*Carduelis flammea*) did not appear to change in the mid-1980s. The nuthatch and siskin, in particular, have continued to irrupt regularly (Figure 9). An irruption history of the ten species is given in Table 2.

What could have changed the irruptions of 7 of these 10 species during the mid-1980s? One event stands out as a plausible cause: a large spruce budworm (*Choristoneura fumiferana*) infestation in eastern Canada and the resulting forest destruction. The strong association of budworm warblers, evening grosbeaks, and purple finches with the budworm infestation implies a direct response. The abrupt irruption drop-off by the chickadees, pine grosbeaks, and the crossbills near the end of the budworm infestation suggests that the widespread forest destruction may have been the main cause (Bolgiano 2004b).

CONCLUSION

The Christmas Bird Count's long history and enthusiastic participation of the birding community have made it an important ornithological record of Pennsylvania's avifauna. During its span of more than a century, dramatic changes have occurred to the landscape, from the end of the logging era to reforestation, from farms dominating large regions to farms becoming fewer in number and more intensively farmed, and from human populations expanding into suburban tracts surrounding cities. Probably no other data source can reflect how North American avifauna populations have changed with respect to such landscape transformations.

Although the CBC's protocol is not as statistically rigorous as the BBS, its large sample overcomes some of its potential weaknesses. It can be a valid assessment and monitoring tool for some species, particularly for those infrequently observed on the BBS, either because the birds are uncommon or are difficult to find, or because their summer distributions are predominantly in the far north.

Pennsylvania's geography and topography produce large gradients in winter temperature and snowfall and therefore affect the winter distribution of many birds. Until now, the effects of a warming climate upon Pennsylvania's wintering birds have been relatively modest. However, winter temperatures appear to be increasing faster than summer temperatures (Vose et al. 2005). Because Pennsylvania has frequently been on the southern edge of severe winter weather, future climate warming could have a dramatic effect upon our winter bird distributions and the CBC will be a primary tool for making such conclusions.

Some readers may remember the frequent boreal bird irruptions that occurred during the 1950s to the 1980s. However, for seven of those species, the irruption frequency and the number of birds observed were much diminished after the mid-1980s. The CBC data are our best records of such irruptions, with their patterns being sufficiently regular to link them to an event that transformed the northern landscape.

REFERENCES

Bagg, A. M. 1969. The changing seasons—A summary of the fall migration season, 1968, with special attention to the movements of black-capped chickadees. Audubon Field Notes 23:4–12.
BirdSource. 2008. Christmas Bird Count website. http://www.birdsource.org
Bock, C. E., and L. W. Lepthien. 1972. Winter eruptions of red-breasted nuthatches in North America, 1950–1970. American Birds 26:558–561.
_____ and _____. 1976. Synchronous eruptions of boreal seed-eating birds. The American Naturalist 110:559–571.
Bolgiano, N. C. 1997. Examining the Christmas Bird Count in Pennsylvania, 1900–1995. Pennsylvania Birds 11:50–54.
_____. 1999. The story of the ring-necked pheasant in Pennsylvania. Pennsylvania Birds 13:2–10.
_____. 2000. A history of Northern bobwhites in Pennsylvania. Pennsylvania Birds 14:58–68.
_____. 2004a. Black-capped chickadee irruptions in Pennsylvania. Pennsylvania Birds 17:174–178.
_____. 2004b. Changes in boreal bird irruptions in eastern North America relative to the 1970s spruce budworm infestation. American Birds 58:26–33.
Butcher, G. S. 1990. Audubon Christmas Bird Counts. Pages 5–14 in J. Sauer and S. Droege editors. Survey designs and statistical methods for the estimation of avian population trends. U.S. Fish and Wildlife Service Biological Report 90(1).
Butcher, G. S., and C. E. McCulloch. 1990. The influence of observer effort on the number of individual birds recorded on Christmas Bird Counts. Pages 120–129 in J. Sauer and S. Droege, editors. Survey designs and statistical methods for the estimation of avian population trends. U.S. Fish and Wildlife Service Biological Report 90(1).
Drennan, S. R. 1981. The Christmas Bird Count: an overlooked and underused sample. In J. M. Scott and C. J. Ralph, editors. Studies in Avian Biology 6:24–29.
Koenig, W. D. 2001. Synchrony and periodicity of eruptions by boreal birds. Condor 103:725–735.
_____, and J. M. H. Knops. 1998. Scale of mast-seeding and tree-ring growth. Nature 396:225–226.
_____ and _____. 2000. Patterns of annual seed production by northern hemisphere trees: A global perspective. The American Naturalist 155:59–69.
_____ and _____. 2001. Seed-crop size and eruptions of North American boreal seed-eating birds. Journal of Animal Ecology 70:609–620.
Latham, R. M., and C. R. Studholme. 1952. The bobwhite quail in Pennsylvania. Pennsylvania Game News Special Issue No. 4.
McWilliams, G. M., and Brauning, D. W. 2000. Birds of Pennsylvania. Cornell University Press, Ithaca, New York, USA.
Newton, I. 1973. Finches. Taplinger Publishing Company, New York, New York, USA.
Niven, D. K., J. R. Sauer, G. S. Butcher, and W. A. Link. 2004. Christmas Bird Count provides insights into population change in land birds that breed in the boreal forest. American Birds 58:10–20.

Root, T. 1988. Atlas of wintering North American birds. An analysis of Christmas Bird Count data. The University of Chicago Press, Chicago, Illinois, USA.

Sauer, J. R., S. Schwartz, and B. Hoover. 1996. The Christmas Bird Count Home Page. Version 95.1. Patuxent Wildlife Research Center, Laurel, Maryland, USA. http://www.mbr-pwrc.usgs.gov/bbs/cbc.html

Sauer, J.R, D.K. Niven, and W.A. Link. 2004. Statistical analyses make the Christmas Bird Count relevant for conservation. American Birds 58: 21–25.

Vose, R.S, D.R. Easterling, and B. Gleason. 2005. Maximum and minimum temperature trends for the globe: an update through 2004. Geophysical Research Letters 32, L23822, doi:10.1029/2005GL02439.

Yarnal, B. 1995. Climate. Pages 44–55 in E.W. Miller, editor. A geography of Pennsylvania. The Pennsylvania State University Press, University Park, Pennsylvania, USA.

Avian Ecology and Conservation: A Pennsylvania Focus with National Implications. Edited by S. K. Majumdar, T. L. Master, M. C. Brittingham, R. M. Ross, R. S. Mulvihill and J. E. Huffman. © 2010. The Pennsylvania Academy of Science.

Chapter 12

Stopover Ecology of Landbird Migrants in Pennsylvania

Robert J. Smith
Department of Biology
The University of Scranton
Scranton, PA 18510
smithr9@scranton.edu

Margret I. Hatch
Penn State Worthington
120 Ridge View Drive
Dunmore, PA 18512
mih10@psu.edu

INTRODUCTION

Over two-thirds of all landbirds breeding in the United States and Canada migrate to tropical wintering areas in Mexico, Central and South America, as well as the islands in the Caribbean (Rappole 1995). Through the course of their movement, migrants travel hundreds, if not thousands of kilometers, often through unfamiliar habitats and uncertain weather, stopping at periodic intervals to rest and rebuild energy stores necessary for fueling a continued migration (see Moore et al. 1995). How migrants respond to the energy demand of long-distance flight and cope with exigencies that arise throughout the migratory period depends largely on habitat quality at stopover sites (Moore et al. 1995) and is key to their survival and successful reproduction. Individuals able to restore fat loads quickly minimize time spent *en route*, arriving earlier at the breeding grounds and in better condition, which translates into enhanced reproductive performance (Smith and Moore 2005).

Long-term data sets reveal population declines in many landbird migrant species (Askins et al. 1990), including a number of species that breed in or migrate through Pennsylvania (Pashley et al. 2000). While these declines have inspired increased activity to conserve migratory landbirds (see Mehlman et al. 2005), significant challenges continue to exist for their protection such as a lack of basic information on population sizes, interseasonal connectivity and demography (Webster et al. 2002) and assessment of population viability (Donovan et al. 2002). Especially lacking is information pertaining to the *en route* ecology of migratory landbirds (Mehlman et al. 2005), even as it becomes increasingly clear that the migratory period plays an important role in population limitation. Indeed, recent work by Sillet and Holmes (2002) suggests that mortality rates for songbird migrants may be up to 15 times higher during migration than the other, stationary periods of the annual cycle. Until recently attention has mainly focused on events associated with the breeding and wintering phases of the annual cycle (Sherry and Holmes 1995). Consequently, the importance of stopover habitat has been largely overlooked in the development of conservation strategies (Moore et al. 1995, Ewert et al. 2005).

Overviews of avian migration, including aspects unique to different groups of birds (e.g., waterfowl, raptors, songbirds) are presented throughout this section on Migration and Wintering Ecology. Our purpose for this chapter is not to present a general discussion of songbird migration but rather to provide the reader with a basic understanding of landbird migrant stopover ecology as well as conservation issues associated with landbirds using Pennsylvania habitats during migration. We emphasize that due to the transient nature of migration, the presence and quality of stopover habitat is important to <u>numerous</u> populations of landbirds, including millions of individuals from breeding populations that only use Pennsylvania habitats during spring or fall migration. As we will see, the existence of high quality stopover habitat is critical to ensuring a successful migratory journey, and Pennsylvania provides migrating landbirds with an array of habitats that contribute to their migratory fitness.

THE ECOLOGY OF LANDBIRD MIGRATION

Benefits and Costs of Migration—Why Migrate?

Migration allows birds to take advantage of different habitats in response to annual variation in life-history requirements or seasonally abundant resources as well as avoiding habitats or locations during times of insufficient resources or unsuitable weather (Kerlinger 1995, Moore et al. 1995). Migration will be favored if the fitness advantages arising from migration exceed the costs of passage. These costs include: 1) fulfilling the energetic demands of transport (Blem 1980), 2) encountering and adjusting to unfamiliar habitats (Moore et al. 1995), 3) conflicting demands between avoiding predators and finding food (Cimprich and Moore 2006), 4) competition with other migrants and with resident birds for limited resources (Moore and Yong 1991), 5) unfavorable weather (Richardson 1978) and orientation errors (Alerstam 1990). Most of these costs are associated with habitat use during passage (Moore et al. 2005) which can be minimized through selection of quality habitat.

Population Implications

While we have a reasonable idea of how factors occurring during both the breeding and wintering seasons influence populations of migratory landbirds, we have only recently begun to consider how migratory events may influence North American landbird populations. Moreover, given the transient nature of migrant landbirds (generally staying at stopover sites for no more than a few days) and because they exhibit a broad-front migration, the difficulties associated with studying migrating landbirds have so far limited the number of studies investigating how *en route* events affect population levels. To date, most research has examined the ecology of migrant landbirds at specific stopover sites (Newton 2006, but see Buler et al. 2007) with many researchers then making inferences about how migratory events influence population size.

Regardless, it would be surprising if landbird populations were unaffected by migratory events. In addition to the documentation of numerous mass mortality events *en route* (see review by Newton 2007), an increasing number of studies are providing evidence of linkages between the different phases of the avian annual cycle (Marra et al. 1998, Smith and Moore 2004, Norris and Marra 2007). That is, events encountered by a landbird prior to the breeding season, including during migration, influence reproductive performance. Therefore, a migrant who performs or functions poorly *en route*, perhaps due to an inability to find suitable stopover habitat, may in turn suffer fitness consequences after arriving at its migratory destination. Consequently, if persistence of migrant populations depends on locating favorable conditions throughout the annual cycle, factors associated with *en route* ecology of migrants must figure prominently in any analysis of population change and in the development of a comprehensive conservation plan for migrant species. Unless habitat requirements during migration are met, conservation measures focused on temperate breeding grounds and/or neotropical wintering areas will be compromised (Moore and Simons 1992).

STOPOVER ECOLOGY

Researchers who study stopover ecology are concerned with understanding the interactions of migrants with the abiotic (nonliving) and biotic (e.g., predators, competitors) components of their environment while they are using habitats *en route*. We are especially concerned with understanding intrinsic factors (see below) driving habitat selection along with fitness consequences associated with that selection. Typical questions confronting researchers include: what types of habitats or habitat elements are important to migrating landbirds (Rodewald and Brittingham 2007, Smith et al. 2007)? Does competitor density affect fat deposition rate (Moore and Yong 1991)? How does a bird trade off the need to forage quickly to deposit fat stores while at the same time avoid getting eaten by a raptor (Cimprich and Moore, 2006)? Outcomes of this research contribute to our overall understanding of the avian annual cycle along with how the migratory period might limit populations of migratory birds, ultimately providing insight into how we might focus conservation efforts concerned with enhancing populations of migratory birds (Mehlman et al. 2005).

Landbirds spend up to four months of each year migrating. During their transit, individuals frequently stop to rest and rebuild energy stores (fat) as they prepare to continue migrating. A stopover site can generally be defined as where a bird pauses for some length of time between migratory flights. During these stopovers, individual migrants may be found in a surprising number of different habitats, ranging from city parks (e.g., Central Park in New York City) to large blocks of contiguous forest. Stopover frequency and duration vary on the basis of some combination of at least four factors: 1) weather, 2) physiological condition of the individual migrant, 3) mortality risk associated with predation and 4) resource abundance at current, past and possibly future stopover sites. The intrinsic (e.g., resource abundance, density of predators) and extrinsic (e.g., landscape features such as proximity to a large water body) characteristics of a stopover site, combined with weather and an individual migrant's energetic (Blem 1980) and immunological (Owen 2004) condition combine to determine how a particular stopover site contributes to a successful migration (Mehlman et al. 2005). Moreover, a stopover site may serve a different suite of purposes depending upon context. In light of this, Mehlman et al. (2005) recently proposed defining stopover sites on the basis of how and the extent with which that site meets the needs of migrants at a given point in space and time. They suggest considering stopover sites as ranging along a continuum from infrequently used but vital sites in emergency situations ('fire escapes') through habitat patches of varying size that fulfill some, though not all needs of migrating landbirds ('convenience stores') to sites that contain extensive habitat sufficient to fulfill most/all the needs of many landbird species ('full-service hotels'). Fire escapes are often found within or adjacent to significant ecological barriers such as large bodies of water, deserts or human altered landscapes and are composed of small, isolated patches surrounded by inhospitable habitat. These habitats are typically resource poor, used principally as cover in the face of poor weather. Examples include islands in the Gulf of Mexico or even patches of shade behind isolated rocks in the middle of the desert (Biebach et al. 1986). Convenience stores provide cover but also contain sufficient resources to permit regeneration of some fat and muscle, though not at optimal rates. These sites also tend to be small and isolated. Thus, migrants using these sites may be vulnerable to density-dependent limits on food and shelter (Mehlman et al. 2005). Examples of this type of stopover site can be seen as parks and cemeteries in many large cities, including Scranton's Nay Aug Park, Fairmount Park in Philadelphia and Pittsburgh's Schenley Park, as well as small forested patches characteristic of agricultural areas.

At the other end of the continuum, full service hotels are places where migrants can find all necessary resources (e.g., food, water, cover) in amounts sufficient to maximize migration rate. Examples include large blocks of contiguous habitat, such as in the Great Smoky Mountains National Park, Allegheny National Forest, and the Pennsylvania Wilds area. Indeed, relative to parts of Illinois, Ohio, Indiana and Michigan, Pennsylvania, due to the presence of large blocks of habitat, especially in the northern part of the state, may provide migrating landbirds with a much better suite of high quality habitat choices.

Habitat Use During Stopover

Given the high energetic cost of transport (Blem 1980) in addition to the numerous other exigencies faced by a migrating landbird, the ability to find suitable *en route* habitat is critical to ensuring a successful migration. Moreover, the extent to which a migrant solves these *en route* problems is measured in units of time and condition during both the migratory event (Alerstam and Lindström 1990) and upon arrival at the migratory destination (Moore et al. 2005). For example, Smith and Moore (2003, 2004) demonstrated that American redstarts arriving at breeding sites in northern Michigan earlier and in superior energetic condition enjoyed fitness advantages. The implication is that a migrant's ability to locate quality stopover habitat permits effective and timely solutions to migratory exigencies. Hence the presence of suitable habitat has fitness consequences both during migration as well as other stages of the annual cycle.

En route habitat use is driven by the interaction of extrinsic and intrinsic factors. Extrinsic factors are largely unrelated to habitat, affecting large scale movements between the migratory origination and destination points (e.g. prevailing and synoptic weather patterns), whereas intrinsic constraints reflect factors related to habitat quality (Moore et al. 1995). During stopover, migrants evaluate numerous intrinsic factors, selecting among available habitats to maximize fitness. That is, given the diversity of habitats encountered during migration some are preferred over others. Several lines of evidence indicate *en route* migrants select habitat (for an overview see Moore et al. 1995), including: 1) use of habitat disproportional to its availability, 2) migrant distribution among habitat types related to changes in food availability, and 3) repeated distributional patterns of migrants among different habitats. For example, at our study site in northeastern Pennsylvania spring transients show year-to-year constancy of habitat use—we captured and counted more individuals of more species in shrubland habitat than nearby forested habitat over multiple years (Figure 1). Mizrahi et al. (2006), using radar data to examine landbird migration through Pennsylvania, demonstrated year-to-year constancy in use of deciduous and mixed forest.

Selection of habitat implies variation in habitat suitability. But what are the determinants of habitat suitability for a migrating landbird? Arguably the single most significant *en route* constraint faced by a migrant is finding sufficient food to meet energetic requirements (Moore et al. 1995). Moreover, because large numbers of migrants with similar food requirements and heightened energy demand often concentrate in areas during stopover, competition for food resources may occur (Moore and Yong 1991). Consequences of resource competition include a decreased rate at which individuals replenish lipid stores either due to depressed resource availability (Moore and Yong 1991) or because migrants directly influence each other's intake rates (Carpenter et al. 1993). Further, even when resource availability is not depressed to the point where it affects mass gain, this depression may increase search time, conflicting with migratory timing (Moore et al. 1995) and delaying arrival at the migratory destination.

Predation may pose a significant hazard to a migrating landbird, and stopover habitats certainly vary with respect to predation risk. While numbers of migrating raptors are relatively low at our site in northeastern Pennsylvania (Smith and Hatch, unpublished), other

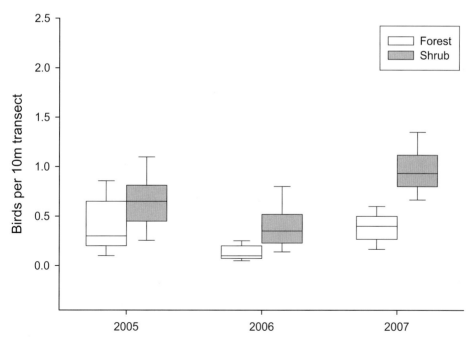

Figure 1: Bird detections per 10 meter transect by habitat type as estimated by transect census. Line represents median, box encompasses the interquartile range which contains 50% of the values and whiskers encompass 5th and 95th percentiles. We detected more birds in shrub than forested habitat in all years ($F_{1,494} = 432.3$, $P < 0.001$).

sites such as Hawk Mountain, Pennsylvania or coastal areas such as Cape May, New Jersey are well known for high hawk numbers. In fact, Kerlinger (1989) speculated that some raptors follow coastlines during migration due to seasonal concentrations of migrating landbirds. When stopover habitat also contains predators, individual migrants must trade off energy gains against mortality risks (Cimprich and Moore 2006), often reducing the rate at which fat is deposited. Presence of predators may also influence habitat use, lowering food acquisition rate as birds are forced to use less suitable habitat, depressing rate of lipid gain and in turn affecting migration rate (Cimprich et al. 2005).

Habitat and plant physiognomy as well as plant species composition may influence habitat suitability by affecting movement through the habitat, how a migrant perceives and captures prey and what prey are available (Rodewald and Brittingham 2004, 2007). For example, birds who characteristically glean from nearby substrates might be expected to forage more readily in vegetation with leaves on short petioles, whereas birds that often fly and hover for prey at distant leaf surfaces may be efficient at foraging in vegetation with leaves placed on longer petioles (Holmes and Robinson 1981). We found differences in invertebrate abundance by plant species in northeastern Pennsylvania with red maple (*Acer rubrum*), hawthorn (*Crataegus* spp.) and arrow wood viburnum (*Viburnum dentata*) being relatively resource rich, whereas invasive exotics such as honeysuckle (*Lonicera* spp.) were resource poor (Figure 2). Further, foraging birds spent more time in vegetation

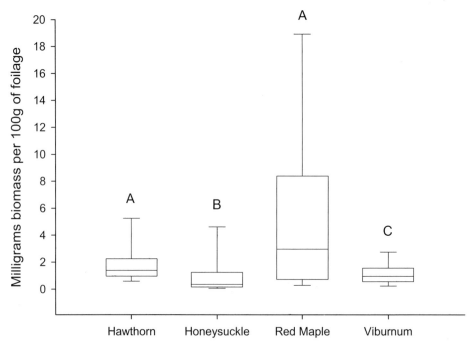

Figure 2:   Substrate arthropod abundance by common plant species, as estimated by grab sampling for the years 2005–2007. Lines represent the median, boxes encompass the interquartile range which contains 50% of values and whiskers encompass 5th and 95th percentiles. Different letters indicate statistical significance at $P < 0.002$.

which appeared to contain more food resources (Smith and Hatch, unpublished; see Ewert et al. 2005). Finally, the physical structure of habitat may influence a migrant's suscepti-bility to predator attack. Dense, structurally complex habitats may reduce predator suc-cess, providing a landbird with an increased margin of safety (Cimprich et al. 2005).

Habitat loss/fragmentation effects may influence habitat suitability for migrating land-birds, though perhaps not to the extent we see during the breeding or wintering periods. For example, Mizrahi et al. (2006) found negative relationships between migrant abun-dance and areas suffering from extreme habitat loss/fragmentation (urban areas with little to no vegetation), whereas Rodewald and Brittingham (2004, 2007) demonstrated the use of edge-dominated forests during both spring and fall migration through central Pennsyl-vania. Similar to species-related variation in area sensitivity of breeding landbirds (see Chapter 3) *en route* landbirds may have different threshold levels of habitat area below which they find the habitat unsuitable (Martin 1980). Area sensitivity may influence *en route* habitat use and consequently the rate at which energy stores are replenished (Moore et al. 1995). Further, a migrant moving through a fragmented landscape encounters blocks of potentially suitable habitat separated by an inhospitable matrix (e.g., agricultural fields). These small habitat blocks may concentrate landbirds, increasing competition for limited resources while movement between blocks may augment the likelihood of predation through increased exposure.

While fragmentation effects on resource abundance during migration have not been examined in detail, evidence from breeding season work suggests that fragmentation may negatively affect resource abundance, as demonstrated for ground invertebrates by Burke and Nol (1998). Fragmentation also adds to the time and energy a migrant devotes to search-ing for quality habitat which likely comes at a cost of depressed gain rates and overall increasing time spent *en route*. Consequently, a migrant's ability to gain access to blocks of habitat where fat stores can be safely replenished is restricted if fragments of suitable habi-tat are widely dispersed. In summary, suitability of stopover habitat will vary dependent upon context. However, the highest quality habitats will provide landbird migrants with suf-ficient resources and cover to maximize lipid gain in the face of competition and predation.

Significance of Pennsylvania Habitats to *En Route* Landbird Migrants

Many migrant landbirds using habitats in Pennsylvania remain to breed. However, many individuals also continue on to habitats outside of the state, emphasizing the role Pennsyl-vania plays in the overall conservation of migratory landbirds. For example, Powdermill Avian Research Center in western Pennsylvania, bands thousands of birds annually, many of which pass through the state *en route* to northerly breeding grounds or southerly win-tering areas. At our study area in Northeastern Pennsylvania we captured a white-throated sparrow (*Zonotrichia albicollis*) that was recaptured the following year near Quebec City, Canada (distance is approximately 550 miles by car).

Many species using Pennsylvania habitats during migration are listed as priority species in Partners in Flight Conservation Plans for physiographic regions immediately to the north. At our site we routinely capture wood thrush (*Hylocichla mustelina*), veery (*Catharus fuscescens*), rose-breasted grosbeak (*Pheucticus ludovicianus*), Canada warbler (*Wilsonia canadensis*), chestnut-sided warbler (*Dendroica pensylvanica*), and black-throated blue warbler (*Dendroica caerulescens*) (species of concern in the Boreal Hardwood Transition Region, Adirondack Mountain Region and the Allegheny Plateau Region (Pashley et al. 2000). The large amount of contiguous vegetative cover, along with the wide diversity of habitat types present throughout Pennsylvania no doubt contribute significantly to the fitness of migrant landbirds. Preservation of these habitats is critical to conservation efforts focused on migratory landbirds throughout eastern North America.

Conservation Issues Faced By Landbirds Using Stopover Habitats In Pennsylvania

There are a number of conservation-related issues associated with landbird migration. We are already beginning to see the effects of global climate change on migration phenology (see Møller et al. 2006), especially with respect to the timing of arrival at the migratory destination and onset of breeding relative to emergence of invertebrates (Dunn 2006). Further, in Pennsylvania and elsewhere, there is concern about the effects of wind turbines and transmission towers contributing to the mortality of *en route* migrants. Other potential threats include window glass impacts, domestic cat predation, and pesticides. All of these issues are of relevance to birds both breeding in and moving through Pennsylvania. Each is treated in more detail elsewhere in this volume. Here we focus on conservation issues more directly related to stopover ecology. These issues are primarily associated with loss, fragmentation or alteration of habitats used by landbirds during stopover.

We have already outlined possible effects of habitat loss and the associated fragmentation effects on migrating landbirds. While Pennsylvania is not without significant habitat fragmentation, compared to many other states, especially those in the Midwest, fewer habitats are fragmented in Pennsylvania. There are, however, issues associated with loss of habitat or habitat quality that are of concern. For example, the negative influence of white-tailed deer (*Odocoileus virginianus*) on breeding bird populations is well known (see e.g., McShea and Rappole 1997), and deer are having a significant effect on forest communities throughout Pennsylvania (see chapter on Emerging Conservation Issues). Overbrowsing contributes to habitat loss by reducing/eliminating understory vegetation important to a suite of both avian and nonavian species. While we are unaware of any research that has explicitly focused on how loss of forest understory affects migrant landbirds, species such as black-throated blue warblers that require understory while breeding may also require it during migration (Moore and Aborn 2000). Additionally, given the importance of habitat diversity and structure to a migrant (Rodewald and Brittingham 2004, Smith and Hatch unpublished), either through providing cover to reduce predation or providing resources (invertebrates in the spring, invertebrates and fruit in the fall), loss of this diversity in overbrowsed forests is likely to impact migrants.

White-tailed deer have also been linked to widespread failure of eastern hemlock (*Tsuga canadensis*) in the Upper Great Lakes Region (Alverson and Waller 1997) and are influencing hemlock regeneration in areas throughout Pennsylvania (Benner 2006). This, in conjunction with the impact of hemlock woolly adelgid (*Adelges tsugae*), an exotic invertebrate that feeds on hemlock, may affect migrating landbirds. As of this writing, 47 counties in Pennsylvania have infestations of this insect (Pennsylvania Department of Conservation and Natural Resources 2008a). Loss of hemlock may have species-specific consequences for birds migrating through Pennsylvania. For example, at our study site in northeastern Pennsylvania we counted more black-throated green warblers (*Dendroica virens*) in hemlock stands during spring migration than in deciduous stands (Smith and Hatch, unpublished), suggesting that hemlocks may be important to this species during spring migration.

Other potential threats associated with habitat loss include exotic invertebrates such as the emerald ash borer (*Agrilus planipennis*) and the gypsy moth (*Lymantria dispar*). Both insects severely influence habitat that may be used during stopover. Emerald ash borer generally kills ash trees (*Fraxinus* spp.) within three years of infestation and since it was first detected in Michigan in 2002 it has killed over 20 million trees (Pennsylvania Department of Conservation and Natural Resources 2008b). Moreover, migrants moving through northeastern Pennsylvania use ash as a foraging substrate during spring migration (Smith and Hatch, unpublished). Fortunately, to date this insect has not been influential in Pennsylvania forests, though it was detected for the first time in Butler County in 2007 (Pennsylvania Department of Conservation and Natural Resources 2008b).

Gypsy moth infestation is perhaps thought to have more of an influence on breeding landbirds, primarily through reduction/elimination of forest cover and substrate-dwelling invertebrates important as forage. However, larvae hatch and begin feeding on growing foliage while many spring migrants are passing through Pennsylvania (Whelan et al. 1989). While a number of landbird species do consume gypsy moth larvae, they are likely not a preferred food item relative to native larvae (Whelan et al. 1989). Thus, the reduction/elimination of cover and the associated native invertebrates may negatively influence *en route* fitness.

Invasive, exotic species are also greatly affecting wild areas throughout Pennsylvania, especially early successional shrublands. In Pennsylvania, exotic shrubs such as honeysuckle (*Lonicera* spp.), multiflora rose (*Rosa multiflora*) and autumn olive (*Elaeagnus umbellata*) are considered serious threats to native ecosystems (Pennsylvania Department of Conservation and Natural Resources 2008c). Unfortunately, study of the influence of invasive species on avian communities is in its infancy. To date, most research has focused on the influence of exotic vegetation on breeding birds with surprisingly few studies examining invasive use by *en route* migrants. For example, studies such as those by Johnson et al. (1985) and Parrish (1997) demonstrated that fall migrating landbirds incorporated fruits of exotic shrubs into their diet while Suthers et al. (2000) demonstrated higher numbers of birds captured in habitats with high fruit abundance.

Results of our research on migrant habitat use in northeastern Pennsylvania suggest that early leaf development of honeysuckle relative to native species may attract early spring migrants but that overall honeysuckle contains fewer invertebrates than native species (Figure 2). Further, honeysuckle berries make up a significant portion of the diet of fall migrating gray catbirds (Figure 3) even as there is evidence that nonnative berries, including honeysuckle, provide suboptimal forage relative to native berries (Ingold and Craycraft 1983).

Habitat alteration as a consequence of climate change is certain to impact landbirds using Pennsylvania habitats during stopover. However, due to a lack of detailed studies and the uncertainty of climate models, proposed effects of climate change on landbird stopover ecology are currently quite speculative. There are a number of projected effects of climate change in Pennsylvania (Frumhoff et al. 2007) including warmer summers and winters, spring arriving earlier with summer extended by up to three weeks, wetter winters and springs, drier summers and falls, increases in the likelihood and severity of heavy rainfall events and possibly an increase in short and medium-term droughts. These effects will no doubt alter the vegetation composition of habitats available to migrants during

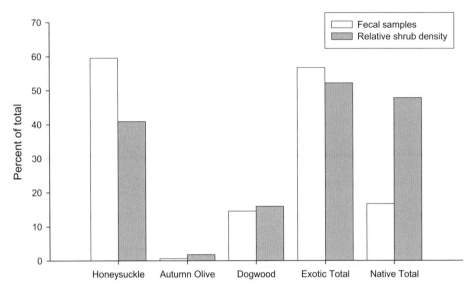

Figure 3:   Examination of diet in fall migrating Gray Catbirds, 2006. Fecal samples indicated birds
foraged on fewer native and more exotic fruits than expected by chance ($\chi^2 = 8.9$, df =
1, $P = 0.003$) with the predominate fruit being invasive honeysuckle.

stopover. For example, the beech, maple and birch forests typical of northern Pennsylvania are projected to move northward and be replaced by forests dominated by oak, ash,
hickory and pine (U.S. Environmental Protection Agency 1997). These habitat responses
will likely result in species-specific migrant responses in use and the fitness consequences
associated with using these habitats.

Suitable stopover habitats may deteriorate due to climate change induced drought or
vegetation shifts (Bairlein and Hüppop 2006), both of which are projected for Pennsylvania. The resulting depressed food abundance may in turn reduce the carrying capacity of
stopover sites (Ottich and Dierschke 2003). However, the considerable plasticity in migratory performance exhibited by landbirds may enable them to counteract adverse conditions
(Bairlein and Hüppop 2006). Further, similar to concerns associated with mistiming of
breeding events and arthropod emergence, there are concerns about a mismatch between
the timing of landbird migration and temporal availability of food because endogenous
mechanisms play a major role in the onset of migration whereas food availability is strongly temperature and precipitation dependent (Bairlein and Hüppop 2006). Finally, even as
many species may be negatively affected there may be benefits. For example, migrants
may encounter more favorable tail-wind conditions, thus lowering flight costs (Bairlein
and Hüppop 2006) while warmer spring temperatures may reduce thermoregulatory costs
during stopover (Wikelski et al. 2003).

Recommendations

Increasing evidence implicates *en route* events as contributing factors in the population
limitation of migratory landbirds. It is imperative that we increase our efforts to better

understand landbird migrant stopover ecology and then incorporate this information into future conservation efforts focused on migratory landbirds. Pennsylvania, due to its extensive wilderness areas, is and will continue to have a significant role to play in the conservation of landbird migrants.

While efforts to conserve a diverse set of habitats for breeding landbirds within Pennsylvania will benefit *en route* migrants, there is mounting evidence that migrants prefer structurally complex habitats, including forests with a mixed shrub layer (Rodewald and Brittingham 2004, 2007) or early-successional habitats (Smith and Hatch, unpublished). Given the potential negative consequences of nonnative vegetation to migrating landbirds, efforts to maintain both floristic and structural diversity using native species should be habitat management goals (Moore et al. 1995). Maintenance of native shrub communities, even within urban and agricultural landscapes, should also improve habitat quality for migrants. Further, *en route* migrants benefit from an ability to access a variety of foods, including both fruit and insects during the fall as fruit facilitates fat deposition (Bairlein and Simons 1995). Consequently, management activities that reduce food abundance, such as pesticide application, should be carefully considered.

A landbird migrating through Pennsylvania arguably finds itself with a greater diversity and abundance of quality habitats than if it had stopped over in several other states in the eastern United States and especially those in highly fragmented portions of Midwestern states. The presence of large blocks of habitat clearly benefit both those birds migrating to Pennsylvania to breed as well as the millions of individuals that pass through the state on their way to northerly breeding or southerly wintering grounds. Consequently, efforts to conserve this diverse set of habitats for breeding and migrating landbirds will have broad impacts both within Pennsylvania and beyond.

ACKNOWLEDGEMENTS

We are grateful to the Pennsylvania Academy of Science for the opportunity to contribute to this volume. Further, funding from The Pennsylvania Department of Conservation and Natural Resources Wild Resource Conservation Program, the University of Scranton and support from Penn State Worthington Scranton has greatly added to our ability to answer questions on the stopover ecology of landbird migrants. The comments of Drs. Michael Carey, David Ewert, Michael Hamas, Terry Master, Frank Moore and Paul Rodewald significantly improved the manuscript. We thank Ms. Anna Bushko and Lackawanna State Park for permission to census and capture birds and invertebrates on their properties. We also thank Mike Carey for permitting use of his study area and for providing insight into the ecology of this system. Finally, we thank the many field assistants, including numerous undergraduates from the University of Scranton, who contributed to this work.

LITERATURE CITED

Alerstam, T. 1990. Ecological causes and consequences of bird orientation. Experientia 46:405–415.
Alerstam, T., and A. Lindström. 1990. Optimal bird migration: the relative importance of time, energy and safety. Pages 331–351 in E. Gwinner [editor], Bird migration: physiology and ecophysiology. Springer-Verlag, New York.

Alverson, W. S., and D. M. Waller. 1997. Deer populations and the widespread failure of hemlock regeneration in northern forests. Pages 280–297 in W. J. McShea, H. B. Underwood and J. H. Rappole [editors], The science of overabundance: deer ecology and population management. Smithsonian Institution Press, Washington.

Askins, R. A., J. F. Lynch, and R. Greenberg. 1990. Population declines in migratory birds in eastern North America. Pages 1–57 in D. M. Power [editor], Current ornithology. Plenum Press, New York.

Bairlein, F., and O. Hüppop. 2006. Migratory fueling and global climate change. Pages 33–47 in A. P. Møller, W. Fiedler and P. Berthold [editors], Birds and climate change. Elsevier, Amsterdam.

Bairlein, F., and D. Simons. 1995. Nutritional adaptations in migrating birds. Israel Journal of Zoology 41:357–367.

Benner, J. M. 2006. Browsing impact report for the Pennsylvania State Forests. Pennsylvania Department of Conservation and Natural Resources Bureau of Forestry.

Biebach, H., W. Friedrich, and G. Heine. 1986. Interaction of bodymass, fat, foraging and stopover period in trans-Sahara migrating passerine birds. Oecologia (Berl) 69:370–379.

Blem, C. R. 1980. The energetics of migration. Pages 175–224 in S. A. J. Gauthreaux [editor], Animal migration, orientation, and navigation. Academic Press, New York.

Buler, J. J., F. R. Moore, and S. Woltmann. 2007. A multi-scale examination of stopover habitat use by birds. Ecology 88:1789–1802.

Burke, D. M., and E. Nol. 1998. Influence of food abundance, nest-site habitat, and forest fragmentation on breeding ovenbirds. Auk 115:96–104.

Carpenter, F. L., M. A. Hixon, D. Russell, C. Paton, and E. J. Temeles. 1993. Interference asymmetries among age-classes of rufous hummingbirds during migratory stopover. Behavioral Ecology and Sociobiology 33:297–304.

Cimprich, D. A., and F. R. Moore. 2006. Fat affects predator-avoidance behavior in Gray Catbirds (*Dumetella carolinensis*) during migratory stopover. Auk 123:1069–1076.

Cimprich, D. A., M. Woodrey, and F. R. Moore. 2005. Passerine migrants respond to variation in predation risk during stopover. Animal Behaviour 69:1173–1179.

Pennsylvania Department of Conservation and Natural Resources. 2008a. Hemlock Woolly Adelgid. http://www.dcnr.state.pa.us/forestry/woollyadelgid/index.aspx. Accessed: (2/13/08).

_____. 2008b. Emerald Ash Borer. http://www.dcnr.state.pa.us/forestry/fpm_invasives_EAB.aspx. Accessed: (2/13/08).

_____. 2008c. Invasive Plants in Pennsylvania. http://www.dcnr.state.pa.us/forestry/wildplant/invasivelist.aspx. Accessed: (2/13/08).

Donovan, T. M., C. J. Beardmore, D. N. Bonter, J. D. Brawn, R. J. Cooper, J. A. Fitzgerald, R. Ford, S. A. Gauthreaux, T. L. George, W. C. Hunter, T. E. Martin, J. Price, K. V. Rosenberg, P. D. Vickery, and T. B. Wigley. 2002. Priority research needs for the conservation of Neotropical migrant landbirds. Journal of Field Ornithology 73:329–450.

Dunn, P. 2006. Breeding dates and reproductive performance. Pages 69–87 in A. P. Møller, W. Fiedler and P. Berthold [editors], Birds and climate change. Elsevier, Boston.

U.S. Environmental Protection Agency. 1997. Climate change and Pennsylvania. Office of Planning and Evaluation. U.S. EPA publication 230-F-97-008II.

Ewert, D. N., G. J. Soulliere, R. D. Macleod, M. C. Shieldcastle, P. G. Rodewald, J. Fujimura, E. Shieldcastle, and R. J. Gates. 2005. Migratory bird stopover site attributes in the western Lake Erie basin. Final report to The George Gund Foundation, p. 71.

Frumhoff, P. C., J. J. McCarthy, J. M. Melillo, S. C. Moser, and D. J. Wuebbles. 2007. Confronting climate change in the U.S. Northeast: science, impacts, and solutions, Synthesis report of the Northeast Climate Impacts Assessment (NECIA). Union of Concerned Scientists (UCS), Cambridge, MA.

Holmes, R. T., and S. K. Robinson. 1981. Tree species preferences of foraging insectivorous birds in a northern hardwoods forest. Oecologia (Berl) 48:31–35.

Ingold, J. L., and M. J. Craycraft. 1983. Avian frugivory on honeysuckle (*Lonicera*) in southwestern Ohio in fall. Ohio Journal of Science 83:256–258.

Johnson, R. A., M. F. Willson, J. N. Thompson, and R. I. Bertin. 1985. Nutritional values of wild fruits and consumption by migrant frugivorous birds. Ecology 66:819–827.

Kerlinger, P. 1989. Flight strategies of migrating hawks. University of Chicago Press, Chicago, IL.

_____. 1995. How birds migrate. Stackpole Books, Mechanicsburg, PA.

Marra, P. P., K. A. Hobson, and R. T. Holmes. 1998. Stable-carbon isotopes link winter and summer events in a migratory bird. Science (Washington, D.C.) 282:1884–1886.

Martin, T. E. 1980. Diversity and abundance of spring migratory birds using habitat islands on the Great Plains. Condor 82:430–439.

McShea, W. J., and J. H. Rappole. 1997. Herbivores and the ecology of forest understory birds. Pages 402 in W. J. McShea, H. B. Underwood and J. H. Rappole [editors], The science of overabundance: deer ecology and population management. Smithsonian Institution Press, Washington.

Mehlman, D. W., S. E. Mabey, D. N. Ewert, C. Duncan, B. Abel, D. Cimprich, R. Sutter, and M. Woodrey. 2005. Conserving stopover sites for forest-dwelling migratory landbirds. Auk 122: 1281–1290.

Mizrahi, D. S., P. Hodgetts, V. Elia, and K. Peters. 2006. Oases along the flyway: preserving critical stopover habitat for migrating songbirds in Pennsylvania. Final Report submitted to the Pennsylvania Game Commission, p. 92. New Jersey Audubon Society, Harrisburg, PA.

Møller, A. P., W. Fiedler, and P. Berthold [editors]. 2006. Birds and Climate Change. Elsevier, Boston.

Moore, F. R., and D. A. Aborn. 2000. Mechanisms of *en route* habitat selection: how do migrants make habitat decisions during stopover? Studies in Avian Biology 20:34–42.

Moore, F. R., S. A. J. Gauthreaux, P. Kerlinger, and T. R. Simons. 1995. Habitat requirements during migration: important link in conservation. Pages 121–144 in T. E. Martin and D. M. Finch [editors], Ecology and management of neotropical migratory birds. Oxford University Press, New York.

Moore, F. R., and T. R. Simons. 1992. Habitat suitability and stopover ecology of Neotropical landbird migrants. in J. M. I. Hagan and D. W. Johnson [editors], Ecology and conservation of Neotropical migrant landbirds. Smithsonian Institution Press, Washington, D.C.

Moore, F. R., R. J. Smith, and R. Sandberg. 2005. Stopover ecology of intercontinental migrants: En route problems and consequences for reproductive performance. Pages 251–261 in P. P. Marra and R. Greenberg [editors], Birds of two worlds: the ecology and evolution of migration. The Johns Hopkins University Press, Baltimore.

Moore, F. R., and W. Yong. 1991. Evidence of food-based competition among passerine migrants during stopover. Behavioral Ecology and Sociobiology 28:85–90.

Newton, I. 2006. Can conditions experience during migration limit the population levels of birds? Journal of Ornithology 147:146–166.

_____. 2007. Weather-related mass-mortality events in migrants. Ibis 149:453–467.

Norris, D. R., and P. P. Marra. 2007. Seasonal interactions, habitat quality, and population dynamics in migratory birds. Condor 109:535–547.

Ottich, I., and V. Dierschke. 2003. Exploitation of resources modulates stopover behaviour of passerine migrants. Journal of Ornithology 144:307–316.

Owen, J. C. 2004. Avian immune function and the energetic demands of long-distance migration. Dissertation, The University of Southern Mississippi, Hattiesburg.

Parrish, J. D. 1997. Patterns of frugivory and energetic condition in nearctic landbirds during autumn migration. Condor 99:681–697.

Pashley, D. N., C. J. Beardmore, J. A. Fitzgerald, R. P. Ford, W. C. Hunter, M. S. Morrison, and K. V. Rosenberg. 2000. Partners in Flight: Conservation of the Land Birds of the United States. American Bird Conservancy, The Plains, VA.

Rappole, J. H. 1995. The ecology of migrant birds: A neotropical perspective. Smithsonian Institution Press, Washington, D.C.

Richardson, W. J. 1978. Timing and amount of bird migration in relation to weather: a review. Oikos 30:224–272.

Rodewald, P. G., and M. C. Brittingham. 2004. Stopover habitats of landbirds during fall: use of edge-dominated and early-successional forests. Auk 121:1040–1055.

_____. 2007. Stopover habitat use by spring migrant landbirds: the roles of habitat structure, leaf development, and food availability. Auk 124:1063–1074.

Sherry, T. W., and R. T. Holmes. 1995. Summer versus winter limitation of populations: what are the issues and what is the evidence? Pages 85–120 in T. E. Martin and D. M. Finch [editors], Ecology and management of neotropical migratory birds. Oxford University Press, New York.

Sillett, T. S., and R. T. Holmes. 2002. Variation in survivorship of a migratory songbird throughout its annual cycle. Journal of Animal Ecology 71:296–308.

Smith, R. J., and F. R. Moore. 2003. Arrival fat and reproductive performance in a long-distance passerine migrant. Oecologia 134:325–331.

_____. 2004. Arrival timing and seasonal reproductive performance in a long-distance migratory landbird. Behavioral Ecology and Sociobiology.

_____. 2005. Arrival timing and seasonal reproductive performance in a long-distance migratory landbird. Behavioral Ecology and Sociobiology 57:231–239.

Smith, R. J., F. R. Moore, and C. May. 2007. Stopover habitat along the shoreline of Lake Huron, Michigan: Emergent aquatic insects as a food resource for spring migrating landbirds. Auk 124:107–121.

Suthers, H., B., J. M. Bickal, and P. G. Rodewald. 2000. Use of successional habitat and fruit resources by songbirds during autumn migration in central New Jersey. Wilson Bulletin 112: 249–260.

Webster, M. S., P. P. Marra, S. M. Haig, S. Bensch, and R. T. Holmes. 2002. Links between worlds: Unraveling migratory connectivity. Trends in Ecology and Evolution 17:76–83.

Whelan, C. J., R. T. Holmes, and H. R. Smith. 1989. Bird predation on gypsy moth (Lepidoptera: Lymantriidae) larvae: an aviary study. Environmental Entomology 18:43–45.

Wikelski, M., E. M. Tarlow, A. Raim, R. H. Diehl, R. P. Larkin, and G. H. Visser. 2003. Costs of migration in free-flying songbirds. Nature 423:704.

Avian Ecology and Conservation: A Pennsylvania Focus with National Implications. Edited by S. K. Majumdar, T. L. Master, M. C. Brittingham, R. M. Ross, R. S. Mulvihill and J. E. Huffman. © 2010. The Pennsylvania Academy of Science.

Chapter 13

Use of Genetic Markers and Stable Isotope Technology to Determine Migratory and Dispersal Patterns and Geographical Variations in Avian Populations

Shawn M. Rummell
School of Forest Resources, 136 Land and Water Resources Building
The Pennsylvania State University, University Park, Pennsylvania 16802

Fred J. Brenner and Christina A. Genareo
Biology Department, Grove City College, 100 Campus Drive,
Grove City, Pennsylvania 16127
fjbrenner@gcc.edu

INTRODUCTION

The dispersal of organisms is important to the demographic and evolutionary dynamics of populations. The dispersal of birds is of particular interest to researchers due to the long distance migrations of many species. For the purpose of this chapter, migration will be defined as the regular dispersal of birds between the breeding grounds and the wintering grounds (Thomson, 1964). An understanding of the movements and the geographic origin of migratory and resident populations have implications for individual ecology, population biology, and conservation biology.

For an individual species, dispersal allows individuals to escape unfavorable conditions, avoid predators, locate potential mates, avoid inbreeding or locate unoccupied habitat, and decrease competition for available resources. The environmental conditions and habitat quality in wintering and breeding areas used by migratory bird species may influence the fitness and survival of individuals (Webster et al., 2002; Moller and Hobson, 2003; Norris et al., 2003). This link between wintering and breeding areas is referred to as migratory connectivity (Webster and Marra, 2005).

Among populations, migratory behavior may allow for heightened gene flow through increased interaction between populations. The emigration and immigration of migrating individuals between populations are as important as birth and death rates in population biology. However, emigration and immigration rates are often overlooked in population studies, primarily due to the difficulty in estimating these parameters. In addition, population ecology is becoming increasingly focused on the individual organism. An understanding of the demographic implications of migratory behavior adopted by individuals and the variation between individuals in terms of behavior is vital in determining how changes in environmental conditions will impact populations (Sutherland, 1996; Grimm and Uchmanski, 2002; Ydenber et al., 2002; Stillman et al. 2003).

The geographic origin of populations and migratory connectivity may also influence conservation biology. The effective management of migratory bird populations is currently limited by a lack of knowledge concerning migratory connectivity (Hobson, 1999). With a more complete understanding of migratory connectivity and which habitats populations are utilizing, conservation efforts could assign higher priority to the most demographically critical habitats for migratory bird populations (Lovette et al., 2004). Nuisance species management, such as Canada geese (*Branta canadensis*), could also be improved with the ability to determine the geographic origin of populations (Caccamise et al., 2000). Finally, disease transmission may be an issue because many diseases and parasites are transported among geographic regions by migratory birds. Wildlife managers and public health officials could specifically manage populations with the highest risk for carrying diseases such as Lyme disease, (Alekseev et al., 2001; Scott et al., 2001), West Nile virus (Rappole et al., 2000), and avian influenza, with an understanding of the habitats being used by birds on the breeding or wintering grounds. However, the commonly used methods to study migration may not allow for accurate identification of geographic origin or migratory connectivity.

METHODS OF STUDY

For over 100 years, several methods have been used to study bird migration patterns and attempt to determine the geographic origin of populations. The majority of these methods require tracking movement patterns of individuals for extended periods of time over potentially long distances. A review of the ornithological literature reveals that four main methods have been used to study bird migration and dispersal patterns. The majority of these studies involved using morphological differences, extrinsic markers, radio/satellite transmitters, and intrinsic markers to track bird movements. Morphological differences among populations may be used to identify the geographic origin of individuals and if these differences are significantly different from one location to the next (James, 1983). However, in most cases it is difficult to differentiate between populations using morphological differences alone (Wennerberg, 2001).

The use of extrinsic markers has been a commonly used method to study migration (Boulet and Norris, 2006). Extrinsic markers include leg bands, neck collars, patagial tags, and plumage marking with dyes or picric acid. Mark-recapture designs are typical for studies using extrinsic marking techniques. Therefore, marked individuals must either be resighted or recaptured. The distance of migration movements, variability in habitat selection, and large geographic scale complicate the task of resighting or recapturing individuals and often results in sample sizes too small for statistical analysis (Nichols, 1996). In addition, extrinsic markers may be biased toward conspicuous species that are more easily observed (Hobson, 1999).

Radio and satellite transmitters have been and are currently used to examine bird migration and dispersal patterns among non-migratory species. While these methods provide good results, they may not be economical or viable for all species. Transmitters are expensive, which may limit sample size and moreover, transmitters can only be installed on large species, thereby excluding their use on many species of neotropical migrants.

The most promising methodology for studying migration movements and population origins are intrinsic methods. These include genetic markers and stable isotopes that have several benefits over conventional methods described previously. These intrinsic methods do not require the recapture of individuals, thereby allowing for potentially larger sample sizes. These methods make it possible to study migratory connectivity over large geographic scales and have the potential to provide valuable insight into the links between animal behavior and population ecology.

GENETIC MARKERS

Genetic markers were traditionally used in the identification of the phylogenetic origin of species or populations (Sibley and Ahlquist, 1990) and to determine the historical origin of populations colonizing new habitats via dispersal (Cann et al., 1987; Avise and Nelson, 1989; Quinn et al., 1991). Recently, genetic markers have been used to trace the geographical origin of migrating species (Milot, 2000; Wennerberg, 2001; Kimura et al., 2002; Lovette et al., 2004). They are most useful for assigning broad geographical ranges rather than finer scales (Haavie et al., 2000; Hansson et al., 2000, Nesje et al., 2000; Helbig et al., 2001; Irwin et al., 2001). Genetic markers are most powerful and straightforward when they are specific to particular populations or subsets of migratory and non-migratory populations (Webster et al., 2002). Effective use of genetic markers requires an adequate knowledge of the genetic differences between populations, as well as a limited amount of gene flow between populations.

Three types of genetic markers, namely microsatellites, dominant nuclear markers, and mitochondrial DNA have been used to study animal migration, dispersal patterns, and/or geographic origin of avian populations. Microsattelites, also known as simple sequence repeats (SSRs), are polymorphic loci present in both nuclear DNA and organellar DNA. Microsattelites typically consist of repeating units 1–4 base pairs in length. They are typically neutral, codominant, and functional as molecular markers. Microsattelites have been useful for answering questions at both the individual and population level because of their prominent polymorphism (Dawson et al., 2000). Although they have been effective in other wildlife studies (Anderson et al., 2002), microsatellites appear to be relatively rare in the avian genome and therefore have not been used extensively in migratory bird studies (Primmer et al., 1997). In addition, microsattelites often show weak differentiation between populations (Helbig et al, 2001; Nesje et al., 2000).

Dominant nuclear markers include randomly amplified polymorphic DNA (RAPD) and arbitrary fragment length polymorphisms (AFLP). Both techniques are polymerase chain reaction based (PCR) and amplify random DNA fragments. Therefore, little or no prior knowledge of the genome is required for these methods, making the study of new or previously unstudied species possible. Burlando et al. (1996) used RAPD to differentiate populations of Eurasian woodcocks (*Scolopax rusticola*) and Haig et al. (1997) used RAPD to identify exclusive genetic markers in populations of two species of shorebirds. Busch et al. (2000) and de Knijff et al. (2001) identified statistically significant, but weak, population differentiation among willow flycatchers (*Empidonax traillii*) and herring gulls

(*Larus argentatus*) using AFLP. Although studies using RAPD and AFLP are few, the results of these studies have been encouraging.

Mitochondrial DNA (mtDNA) is another genetic marker that has been used to differentiate populations and study migratory and non-migratory dispersal patterns, as well as differences in different geographic populations of birds. Mitochondrial DNA haplotypes, a combination of alleles at multiple linked loci that are transmitted together, have been the most prevalent genetic markers used in avian research. It has become a popular technique because genetic differentiation and population specific markers are likely to arise in mtDNA relatively quickly. This occurs because the effective population size for mtDNA is smaller than that for nuclear markers (Webster et al., 2002). Both regional and subspecific markers have been identified among avian populations and have been effectively used to track migratory movements (Bensch and Hasselquist, 1999; Wennerberg, 2001).

Genetic markers, predominantly mtDNA, have been used in many studies concerning migratory connectivity, differentiation of subspecies, and geographic origins of populations over the last 15 years. Wenink et al. (1994) was able to partly or wholly distinguish between different subspecies of shorebirds using mtDNA haplotypes. Similarly, Clegg et al. (2003) used microsatellite DNA variation to characterize the population structure of the Wilson's warbler (*Wilsonia pusilla*). In addition, Clegg et al. (2003) was able to infer migration patterns and population connectivity between breeding and wintering grounds of Wilson's warbler. Migratory connectivity has been studied using genetic markers in several species, including the yellow warbler (*Dendroica petechia*) (Milot et al., 2000), Wilson's warbler (Kimura et al., 2002), Swainson's thrush (*Catharus ustulatus*) (Ruegg and Smith, 2002), the yellow breasted chat (*Icteria virens*), the common yellowthroat (*Geothlypis trichas*), and the Nashville warbler (*Vermivora ruficapilla*) (Lovette et al., 2004).

Genetic markers have also allowed for the identification of the geographic origin of populations. Buerkle (1999) determined that genetic variation in prairie warblers (*Dendroica discolor*) paralleled behavioral and morphological differences between two subspecies that exhibit differences in migratory behavior, habitat use, and morphology. Tiedemann (1999) and Wennerberg (2001) used mtDNA to trace the geographic origin of dunlins (*Calidris alpina*). Finally, Wennerberg et al. (2002) was able to separate geographic populations of white-rumped sandpipers (*Calidris fuscicollis*). Lamborn et al. (in preparation) used mtDNA to determine the phylogenetic relationships among four species of the order Galliformes.

Procedures for DNA Preparation and Sequencing

For the study of bird migration, both nuclear genome (ncDNA), where DNA is linear and embodied in separate chromosomes, and mitochondria (mtDNA) genome, where DNA is packaged in a circular fashion comparable to bacteria, are available options. The mitochondrial genome is much smaller than the nuclear genome, possessing at most 19,000 base pairs. Consequently, the genome of the mitochondria has less non-coding regions of DNA; however, the non-coding D-loop region, where replication originates, is an important genetic marker. The considerably larger nuclear genome with a size greater than 1 billion base pairs thus has a vast quantity of extragenic DNA defined into categories, depending on the size of the repetitive sequence, including SINE, LINE, microsatellite, and minisatellite DNA. Of these categories, mini-satellite and microsatellite DNA have been identified as providing adequate means to study population genetics as well as pedigree and paternity tracing. Mini-satellite DNA, or variable number tandem repeats (VNTR), include up to 50 repetitions of 15 to 100 base pair long sequences. Alternatively, microsatellite DNA includes only two to five nucleotides in repetition of 10 to 50 times, thus giving microsatellites the acronym STR to describe their short tandem repeats. Slippage of DNA polymerase and uneven meiotic recombination crossing-over events lead to polymorphic alleles on the VNTR and STR loci. Consequently, VNTR and STR studies show a less than one in a million chance of matching VNTR or STR profiles between specimens. Thus VNTR and STR profiles serve as excellent markers of evolution for the molecular clock as applicable to bird migration, dispersal and phylogenetic studies (Wink, 2006).

In order to obtain DNA for profile analyses in bird migration studies, DNA samples can be obtained from a variety of sources, including direct tissue samples, blood samples, feathers, and eggs. Additionally, the tissue sample that serves as the DNA providing agent can be either fresh, frozen, or formalin fixed. After undergoing microtome processing to prepare thin sample slices, the tissue samples can then be studied for immunohistochemistry or applied to *in Situ* Hybridization and Single-Fiber Polymerase Chain Reaction processing. Microscopic optical imaging techniques can also provide further insight into genetic analysis of tissues (Ray et al., 2005). Similarly, blood can be collected for DNA analysis and stored in an EDTA buffer as described in detail in a previous study by Wink (2006).

DNA analysis can additionally utilize eggs and feathers in situations where tissue and blood samples are difficult or impossible to obtain. Therefore, gene analysis can be performed on eggs; however, this procedure is difficult due to eggs containing one haploid nucleus, or if fertilized, one diploid nucleus. When preparing samples for the genetic analysis of eggs, procedures outlined by Ray et al. (2005) concerning tissue DNA isolation are applicable. Similarly, established processes exist for DNA extraction from dropped or freshly plucked feathers. These methods are specified in detail in Ray et al. (2005) and include soaking the feathers briefly in ethanol so that a 1 cm sterile root tip of the feather can be removed and pulverized in liquid nitrogen. The sample is then utilized in a centrifuge incubation pattern and can then be stored on ice (Ray et al., 2005). In all DNA samples, however, contamination must be prevented between bird specimens, so that PCR processing produces adequate samples for accurate DNA analysis (Wink, 2006).

Once DNA is extracted from any source, the regions of marker genes, such as protein coding mtDNA and non-coding ncDNA, should be examined. Examples of intron regions that merit study on ncDNA include the genes RAG, LDH, and ODC-6. Mitochondrial genes such as cytochrome b, ND2, and COI are additional examples of genes commonly studied in comparing bird genomes; however, these genes require that the species being studied evolved at least two million years ago. Furthermore, the D-loop of mtDNA, which is highly variable between genomes, provides a higher resolution of genetic testing, though the D-loop region proves difficult to amplify by PCR sequencing. This results from the failure to match primers to mutated target sequences. Additionally, when studies require high resolution testing on recently emerged breeding populations, such as those in the Northern hemisphere that were established 20,000 years ago at the end of the glaciation period, mtDNA is inferior to molecular markers of ncDNA, as a result of it being inherited maternally. For both species with similar intraspecific sequences and for older, well-established species, with a mitochondrial lineage or haplotype, of a bird can reveal its geographic origin. However, it must be noted that gene flow, even that which occurred in the past, often complicates mitochondrial lineage studies, as populations share haplotypes with other populations. This results in multiple haplotypes to exist within genomes of bird species (Wink, 2006).

In order to study a specified genome region, such as the varying regions of protein coding mtDNA and non-coding ncDNA defined earlier, the base pair sequence upstream and downstream from this sequence must be known to allow primer design. If the target region has an unknown nucleotide sequence, it is still possible to design a primer for this sequence following the process outlined by Ray et al., (2005). This procedure must be reverted to which involves insertion of the unknown target sequence into a plasmid vector with a known sequence prior to cloning the plasmid. However, for those target regions with known base pair sequence upstream and downstream from the desired amplification site, criteria exist as to how to choose an adequate primer for amplification. An overview of these criteria include picking a primer that includes at least 18 nucleotides and has two G/C match ups on the end of the 3' end, and contains 45–55% GC base content. Further explanation of primer criteria, such as how to avoid primer dimer amplification, is explained in detail by Ray et al., (2005). Furthermore, primers can be designed to compare the amplicon products from a polymerase chain reaction to the target region of closely related species by performing a BLAST analysis at the NCBI website http://www.NCBI.gov (Ray et al., 2005).

Following the establishment of the primers for the targeted sequence region of study, the polymerase chain reaction (PCR) can be used to amplify the desired area of polymorphic DNA (Wink, 2006). Ray et al. (2005) provides extensive information as to how to complete PCR including temperatures and descriptions of each section of the process. Additionally, Ray et al. (2005) specifically addresses mtDNA D-loop regions and the unique process used to amplify mtDNA, which makes use of the fact that mitochondria are similar to a large plasmid and therefore can be amplified in a similar fashion. The amplicons produced by such PCR testing can then be separated by gel or capillary electrophoresis (Wink, 2006).

Molecular sexing, which depends on targeting the introns of the CHD gene on the sex chromosomes and then comparing PCR products, is one specific example of PCR methods being applied in research on migratory studies and geographic variation in non-migratory species. For instance, if two PCR products are obtained, it can be concluded that the bird is female, as female birds have the heterogametic ZW chromosomes. On the contrary, if only one PCR product is observed, the sex of the specimen can be established as male, due to male birds having the homogametic sex chromosomes of WW. Therefore, molecular sexing, which makes use of PCR amplicon comparisons, allows sexing outside of the breeding period of monomorphic species (Wink, 2006).

Additionally, phenograms, which analyze the presence and absence of alleles to establish clades through cluster analysis, are yet another example of bird migratory tracking methods made possible by PCR techniques. For instance, in order to establish data on which to perform a cluster analysis, at least ten polymorphic STR loci are required to identify an individual. Therefore, a multplex PCR system can minimize the number of PCR sequencing samples and produce data that can be analyzed for allele distribution and frequencies. For example, these data can be compiled with any private alleles in the bird population and to the migratory profile of a species this establishes the clade of a bird in question in order to track the bird migratory patterns (Wink 2006). These same procedures may be used to compare populations of resident and migratory populations of species, such as Canada Geese, or to analyze differences in a species from different geographic locations.

Similar to most methods, genetic markers have limitations. The limitations of genetic markers generally include gene flow between populations and recently diverged populations. For example, post-pleistocene populations are generally too recently diverged to be positively identified using genetic markers (Baker, 2002). Additionally, genetic markers are also of limited use in populations with higher amounts of gene flow (i.e. less reproductively isolated populations) between populations (Lovette et al., 2004). Increased gene flow causes homogenization of mtDNA diversity, making it more difficult to detect subtle differences between populations. This is often an issue among bird populations because of their capability of widespread dispersal.

STABLE ISOTOPES

Elements typically have several different forms, each of which has a different atomic mass. These different forms are known as isotopes. Stable isotopes are those chemical isotopes that are not radioactive and occur naturally. Ratios of stable isotopes of naturally occurring elements, such as carbon (C), hydrogen (H), oxygen (O), nitrogen (N) and sulfur (S), vary across the landscape, often in systematic patterns (Webster et al., 2002). For example, carbon and nitrogen isotopes are more enriched in marine systems than terrestrial systems (Hobson, 1999); $_{-}C^{13}$ is typically more depleted in moist, cool environments (Marra et al., 1998); deuterium (H^2) shows a continent-wide pattern in North America (enriched values in the southeast to depleted values in the northwest) (Sheppard et al., 1969; Taylor, 1974) and is also variable in a predictable manner in rainfall (Bowen et al., 2005); and hydrogen and oxygen isotope composition of environmental water varies widely and systematically across the world (Kendall and Coplen, 2001).

The use of stable isotopes for the study of migration and the geographic origin of migrating and resident populations is based on the fact that the stable isotope signatures in animal tissues reflect those of local food webs. This technique uses naturally occurring stable isotopes of various elements occurring in organisms (Chamberlain et al., 1997; Hobson 1999; Webster et al., 2002). The most commonly used stable isotopes are $_{-}C^{13}$, $_{-}N^{15}$, and $_{-}S^{34}$. Stable isotopes, like genetic markers, have the potential to provide insight into the links between animal behavior and population ecology. In addition, stable isotopes have been used successfully in studying migratory connectivity over large geospatial scales.

By using different tissues, a researcher may be able to infer diet from several days to several years, trace diet over different seasons, determine migration patterns, geographical origins, population-specific demographies, or conduct multispecies comparisons (Atkinson et al., 2005). Keratinous tissue and metabolically active tissue are two commonly analyzed types of tissues. Keratinous tissues include hair, feather, and nails. These tissues retain a stable isotope signature indicative of where that tissue was synthesized. For example, feather proteins formed during a molt assimilate an isotopic signature that is determined by diet and consequently reflects that of the environment. If birds molt in different areas across a stable isotope gradient or in areas which have different isotopic signatures, it may be possible to infer where the feather was molted (Schell et al. 1989; Mizutani et al., 1990, 1991). Metabolically active tissue may be variable in terms of how far back in time inferences can be made. Liver and blood plasma may provide accurate inferences up to a few days (Hobson and Clark, 1993), muscle tissue and whole blood reflect diet/habitat for several weeks (Ayliffe et al., 2004; Evans-Ogden et al., 2004), and bone collagen may provide estimates throughout the lifetime of the individual (Hobson and Clark, 1993).

Fry (1981) was among the first to determine that isotopic variation in an organism could be associated with migration using stable isotope analysis. This pioneering work used $\_C^{13}$ concentrations in brown shrimp (*Panaeus aztecus*). Based on the initial study by Fry (1981), numerous investigators have examined the geographic origin and migration of organisms including invertebrates (Fry, 1981; Hobson et al., 1999), fish (Tietje and Teer, 1988; Nelson et al. 1989; Harrington et al., 1998), reptiles and amphibians (Killingley and Lutcavage, 1983), mammals (Schell et al., 1989; Vogel et al., 1990; Ben-David et al., 1997), and birds (Mizutani et al., 1990, 1991; Alisauskas and Hobson, 1993; Alisauskas et al., 1998).

There is a large body of literature that exists documenting the use of stable isotopes among a variety of bird species. Stable isotope analysis has also been used for a variety of purposes among bird populations, including determining the geographical origin of migrating bird populations (Chamberlain et al., 1997; Hobson and Wassenaur, 1997; Atkinson et al., 2005; Bowen et al., 2005; Mazerolle and Hobson, 2005; Hobson et al. 2006; Hobson et al. 2007). These studies have examined a variety of species, including the red knot (*Calidris canutus*) (Atkinson et al. 2005), sandhill crane (*Grus canadensis*) (Hobson et al., 2006), Swainson's thrush (*Catharus ustulatus*), wood thrush (*Hylocichla mustelina*), and gray catbird (*Dumetella carolinensis*) (Hobson et al., 2007). Several aspects of bird migration have also been examined using stable isotope analysis. Marra et al. (1998) examined differences in the timing of migratory movements between birds occupying two types of habitats, while Alisauskas and Hobson (1993) tracked migratory movements in lesser snow geese (*Chen caerulescens*). Migratory connectivity and habitat use has also been documented utilizing stable isotopes (Kelly, 2002; Hobson et al., 2004a,b; Norris et al., 2005; Gladbach et al., 2007; Paxton et al., 2007). Caccamise et al., (2000) was able to distinguish between resident and migratory Canada goose populations, a study with implications for management of resident geese.

SUMMARY AND DIRECTION OF FUTURE RESEARCH

Wennerberg et al. (2002) indicated that both genetic markers and stable isotope analysis provide similar results in examining the origin of migratory populations. However, genetic markers have limited use among populations with high amounts of gene flow between populations. One alternative that has been suggested to avoid this issue is to utilize genes from avian parasites rather than genes from the birds themselves (Rintamaki et al., 1998; Bensch et al. 2001, Sehgal et al., 2001). Geographic location and specific genetic signatures might be traceable from avian parasites because these parasites can only be transmitted in areas where they coexist with the host, providing information about the breeding or wintering location of a bird at a finer scale than its own genotype would allow (Rintamaki et al., 1998, Bensch et al., 2001; Sehgal et al., 2001).

In general, there is a need for studies that provide techniques capable of examining species at a finer geographic scale than is currently available. Trace element analysis may allow for more specific sites than genetic markers or stable isotope analysis (Norris et al., 2007). This technique uses inductively coupled plasma mass spectrometry (ICP-MS) and inductively coupled plasma atomic emission spectrometry (ICP-AES) to quantify element levels within an organism's tissue. Neither ICP-MS nor ICP-AES rely on stable isotopes and instead use commonly occurring trace elements. This technique should be used along with stable isotope analysis and genetic markers to validate the results of each type of study (Donovan et al., 2006; Norris et al., 2007).

As with most research, there is a need for larger studies incorporating both larger sample sizes and at a various spatial scale. The combination of data from genetic marker and stable isotope analysis with geographic information systems (GIS) tools, to provide a long-term data base as well as better visualization of migratory and geographic population record, has also been suggested as a direction for future work (Hobson et al., 2007). Overall, genetic markers and stable isotope analysis provide the potential to begin to examine links between individual behavioral patterns and population ecology. In addition, these techniques will continue to enhance our understanding of migratory patterns, dispersal patterns, and the geographical origin of populations.

LITERATURE CITED

Anderson, J. D., R. L. Honeycutt, R. A. Gonzales, K. L. Gee, L. C. Skow, R. L. Gallagher, D. A. Honeycutt, R. W. DeYoung. 2002. Development of microsatellite DNA markers for the automated genetic characterization of white-tailed deer populations. *J. Wildlife Management* 66: 67–74.

Alekseev, A. N., H. V. Dubinina, A. V. Semenov, and C. V. Bolshakov. 2001. Evidence of Ehrlichiosis agents found in ticks collected by migratory birds. *J. Medicinal Entomology* 38: 471–474.

Alisauskas, R. T., and K. A. Hobson. 1993. Determination of lesser snow goose diets and winter distribution using stable isotope analysis. *J. Wildlife Management* 57: 49–54.

Alisauskas, R. T., E. E. Klaas, K. A. Hobson, and C. D. Ankney. 1998. Stable carbon isotopes support use of adventitious color to discern winter origins of lesser snow geese. *J. of Field Ornithology* 69: 262–268.

Atkinson, P. W., A. J. Baker, R. M. Bevan, N. A. Clark, K. B. Cole, P. M. Gonzalez, J. Newton, L. J. Niles, R. A. Robinson. 2005. Unraveling the migration and moult strategies of a long-distance migrant using stable isotopes: red knot movements in the Americas. *Ibis* 147: 738–749.

Avise, J. C., and W. S. Nelson. 1989. Molecular genetic relationships of the extinct dusky seaside sparrow. *Science* 243: 646–648.

Ayliffe, L. K., T. E. Cerling, T. Robinson, A. G. West, M. Sponheimer, B. H. Passey, J. Hammer, B. Roeder, M. D. Dearling, and J. R. Ehleringer. 2004. Turnover of carbon isotopes in tail hair and breath CO_2 of horses fed an isotopically varied diet. *Oecologia* 139: 11–22.

Baker, A. J. 2002. The deep roots of bird migration: inferences from the historical record preserved in DNA. *Ardea* 90: 503–513.

Ben-David, M., T. A. Hanley, D. R. Klein, and D. M. Schell. 1997. Seasonal diets of coastal and riverine mink: the role of spawning Pacific salmon. *Canadian J. Zoology* 75: 803–811.

Bensch, S., and D. Hasselquist. 1999. Phylogeographic population structure of great reed warblers: an analysis of mtDNA control region sequences. *Biological J. Linnean Society* 66: 171–185.

Bensch, M. Stjernman, D. Hasselquist, O. OStman, B. Hansson, H. Westerdahl, and R. T. Pinheiro. 2001. Host specificity in avian blood parasites: a study of *Plasmodium* and *Haemoproteus* mitochondrial DNA amplified from birds. Proceed. *Royal Society of London Biological Science* 267: 1583–1589.

Boulet, M., and D. R. Norris. 2006. The past and present of migratory connectivity. *Ornithological monographs* 61: 1–13.

Bowen, G. J., L. I. Wassenaar, and K. A. Hobson. 2005. Global application of stable hydrogen and oxygen isotopes to wildlife forensics. *Oecologia* 143: 337–348.

Buerkle, C. A. 1999. The historical pattern of gene flow among migratory and non-migratory populations of prairie warblers. *Evolution* 53: 1915–1924.

Burlando, B., A. Arillo, S. Spano, and M. Machetti. 1996. A study of the genetic variability in populations of the European woodcock by random amplification of polymorphic DNA. *Italian J. Zoology* 63: 31–36.

Busch, J. D., M. P. Miller, E. H. Paxton, M. K. Sogge, and P. Keim. 2000. Genetic variation in the endangered southwestern willow flycatcher. *Auk* 117: 586–595.

Caccamise, D. F., L. M. Reed, P. M. Castelli, S. Wainright, and T. C. Nichols. 2000. Distinguishing migratory and resident Canada geese using stable isotope analysis. *J. Wildlife Management* 64: 1084–1091.

Cann, R. L., M. Stoneking, and A. C. Wilson. 1987. Mitochondrial DNA and human evolution. *Nature* 325: 31–36.

Chamberlain, C. P., J. D. Blum, R. T. Holmes, X. Feng, T. W. Shery, and G. R. Graves. 1997. The use of isotope tracers for identifying populations of migratory birds. *Oecologia* 109: 132–141.

Clegg, S. M., J. F. Kelly, M. Kimura, and T. B. Smith. 2003. Combining genetic markers and stable isotopes to reveal population connectivity and migration patterns in a neotropical migrant, Wilson's warbler. *Molecular Ecology* 12: 819–830.

Dawson, D. A., O Hanotte, C. Greig, I. R. K. Stewart, and T. Burke. 2000. Polymorphic microsatellites in the blue tit and their cross species utility in twenty songbird families. *Molecular Ecology* 9: 1941–1944.

de Knijff, P., F. Denkers, N. D. van Swelm, and M. Kuiper. 2001. Genetic affinities within the herring gull assemblage revealed by AFLP genotyping. *J. Molecular Evolution* 52: 85–93.

Donovan, T., J. Buzas, P. Jones, and H. L. Gibbs. 2006. Tracking dispersal in birds: assessing the potential of elemental markers. *Auk* 123: 500–511.

Evans-Ogden, L. J., K. A. Hobson, and D. B. Lank. 2004. Bood isotopic turnover and diet-tissue fractionation factors in captive dunlin. *Auk* 121: 170–177.

Fry, B. 1981. Natural stable carbon isotope tag traces Texas shrimp migrations. Fisheries Bull. *United States* 79: 337–345.

Gladbach, A., R. A. R. McGill, and P. Quillfeldt. 2007. Foraging areas of Wilson's storm-petrel in the breeding and inter-breeding period determined by stable isotope analysis. *Polar Biology* 30: 1005–1012.

Grimm, V., and J. Uchmanski. 2002. Individual variability and population regulation: a model of the significance of within generation density dependence. *Oecologia* 131: 196–202.

Haavie, J., G. P. Saetre, and T. Mourn. 2000. Discrepancies in population differentiation at microsatellites, mitochondrial DNA and plumage colour in the pied flycatcher: inferring evolutionary processes. *Molecular Ecology* 9: 1137–1148.

Haig, S. M., C. L. Gratto-Trevor, T. D. Mullins, and M. A. Colwell. 1997. Population identification of western hemisphere shorebirds throughout the annual cycle. *Molecular Ecology* 6: 413–427.

Hansson, M. C., S. Bensch, and O. Brannstrom. 2000. Range expansion and the possibility of an emerging contact zone between two subspecies of Chiffchaff. *J. Avian Biology* 31: 548–558.

Harrington, R. R., B. P. Kennedy, C. P. Chamberlain, J. D. Blum, and C. L. Folt. 1998. [15]N enrichment in agricultural catchments: field patterns and applications to tracking Atlantic salmon. *Chemical Geology* 147: 281–294.

Helbig, A. J., M. Salomon, S. Bensch, and I. Seibold. 2001. Male-biased gene flow across an avian hybrid zone: evidence from mitochondrial and microsatellite DNA. *J. Evolutionary Biology* 14: 277–287.

Hobson, K. A., and R. W. Clark. 1993. Turnover of ^{13}C in cellular and plasma fractions of blood: implications for nondestructive sampling in avian dietary studies. *Auk* 110: 638–641.

Hobson, K. A., and L. I. Wassennaar. 1997. Linking breeding and wintering grounds of neotropical migrant songbirds using stable hydrogen isotopic analysis of feathers. *Oecologia* 109: 142–148.

Hobson, K. A. 1999. Tracing origins and migration of wildlife using stable isotopes: a review. *Oecologia* 120: 314–326.

Hobson, K. A., L. I. Wassenaar, and O. Taylor. 1999. Stable isotopes are geographic indicators of monarch butterfly natal origins in eastern North America. *Oecologia* 120: 397–404.

Hobson, K. A., Y. Aubry, and L. I. Wassenaar. 2004(a). Migratory connectivity in Bicknell's thrush: locating missing populations with hydrogen isotopes. *Condor* 106: 905–909.

Hobson, K. A., G. J. Bowen, L. I. Wassenaar, Y. Ferrand, and H. Lormee. 2004(b). Using stable hydrogen and oxygen isotope measurements of feathers to infer geographical origins of migrating European birds. *Oecologia* 141: 477–488.

Hobson, K. A., S. V. Wilgenburg, L. I. Wassenaar, H. Hands, W. P. Johnson, M. O'Meillia, and P. Taylor. 2006. Using stable hydrogen isotope analysis of feathers to delineate origins of harvested sandhill cranes in the central flyway of North America. *Waterbirds* 29: 137–147.

Hobson, K. A., S. V. Wilgenburg, L. I. Wassenaar, F. Moore, and J. Farrington. 2007. Estimating origins of three species of newtropical migrant songbirds at a Gulf coast stopover site: combining stable isotope and GIS tools. *Condor* 109: 256–267.

Irwin, D. E., S. Bensch, and T. D. Price. 2001. Speciation in a ring. *Nature* 209: 333–337.

James, F. C. 1983. Environmental component of morphological differentiation in birds. *Science* 221: 184–186.

Kendall, C., and T. B. Coplen. 2001. Distribution of oxygen-18 and deuterium in river waters across the United States. *Hydrological Processes* 15: 1363–1393.

Kelly, J. F., V. Atudorei, Z. D. Sharp, and D. M. Finch. 2002. Insights into Wilson's warbler migration from analyses of hydrogen stable-isotope ratios. *Oecologia* 130: 216–221.

Killingley, J. S., M. Lutcavage. 1983. Loggerhead turtle movements reconstructed from ^{18}O and ^{13}C profiles from commensal barnacle shells. *Estuarine Coastal Shelf Science* 16: 345–349.

Kimura, M., S. M. Clegg, I. J. Lovette, K. R. Holder, D. J. Girman, B. J. Mila, P. Wade, and T. B. Smith. 2002. Phylogeographic approaches to assessing demographic connectivity between breeding and overwintering sites in a nearctic-neotropical warbler. *Molecular Ecology* 11: 1605–1616.

Lamborn, I. T., P. Mcpherson, M. R. Latini, J. P. Haggan, F. J. Brenner and D. B. Ray. Resolution of the phylogenetic position of the northern bobwhite (*Coronis virginianus*): Using the complete D-Loop sequences of the chukar partridge, ruffed grouse and ring-necked pheasant to reconstruct a phylogeny (In Preparation),

Lovette, I. J., S. M. Clegg, and T. B. Smith. 2004. Limited utility of mtDNA markers for determining connectivity among breeding and overwintering locations in three neotropical migrant birds. *Conservation Biology* 18: 156–166.

Marra, P. P., K. A. Hobson, and R. T. Holmes. 1998. Linking winter and summer events ina migratory bird by using stable carbon isotopes. *Science* 282: 1884–1886.

Mazerolle, D. F. and K. A. Hobson. 2005. Estiamting origins of short-distance migrant songbirds in North America: contrasting inferences from hydrogen isotope measurements of feathers, claws, and blood. *Condor* 107: 280–288.

Milot, E. M., H. L. Gibbs, and K. A. Hobson. 2000. Phylogeography and genetic structure of northern populations of the yellow warbler. *Molecular Ecology* 9: 667–681.

Mizutani, H., M. Fukuda, Y. Kabaya, and E. Wada. 1990. Carbon isotope ratio of feathers reveals feeding behavior of cormorants. *Auk* 107: 400–403

Mizutani, Y. Kabaya, and E. Wada. 1991. Nitrogen and carbon isotope compositions relate linearly in cormorant tissues and its diet. *Isotopenpraxis* 27: 166–168.

Moller, A. P., and K. A. Hobson. 2003. Heterogeneity in stable isotope profiles predicts coexistence of two populations of barn swallows differing in morphology and reproductive performance. *Proceedings of the Royal Society of London B* 271: 1355–1362.

Nelson, C. S., T. G. Northcote, and C. H. Hendy. 1989. Potential use of oxygen and carbon isotopic composition of otiliths to identify migratory and non-migratory stocks of the New Zealand common smelt: a pilot study. *New Zealand J. Marine and Freshwater Research* 23: 337–344.

Nesje, M., K. H. Roed, D. A. Bell, P. Lindberg, and J. T. Lifjeld. 2000. Microsatellite analysis of population structure and genetic variability in peregrine falcons. *Animal Conservation* 3: 267–275.

Nichols, J. D. 1996. Sources of variation in migratory movements of animal populations: statistical inference and a selective review of empirical results for birds. Pages 147–197 in O. E. Rhodes, editor. *Population dynamics in ecological space and time.* University of Chicago Press, Chicago, Illinois, USA.

Norris, D. R., P. P. Marra, T. K. Kyser, T. W. Sherry, and L. M. Ratcliffe. 2003. Tropical winter habitat limits reproductive success on the temperate breeding grounds in a migratory bird. Proceed. *Royal Society of London B* 271: 59–64.

Norris, D. R., P. P. Marra, T. K. Kyser, T. W. Sherry, and L. M. Ratcliffe, 2005. Tracking habitat use of a long-distance migratory bird, the American redstart using stable-carbon isotopes in cellular blood. *J. Avian Biology* 36: 164–170.

Norris, D. R., D. B. Lank, J. Pither, D. Chipley, R. C. Ydenberg, and T. K. Kyser. 2007. Trace element profiles as unique identifiers of western sandpiper populations. *Canadian J. Zoology* 85: 579–583.

Paxton, K. L., C. Van Ripper III, T. C. Theimer, and E. H. Paxton. 2007. Spatial and temporal migration patterns of Wilson's warbler in the southwest as revealed by stable isotopes. *Auk* 124: 162–175.

Primmer, C. R., T. Raudsepp, B. P. Chowdhary, A. P. Moller, and H. Ellegren. 1997. Low frequency of microsatellites in the avian genome. *Genome Research* 7: 471–482.

Quinn, J. W., G. F. Shields, and A. C. Wilson. 1991. Affinities of the Hawaiian goose based on two types of mitochondrial DNA data. *Auk* 108: 585–593.

Rappole, J. H., S. R. Derrickson, and A. Hubalek. 2000. Migratory birds and spread of West Nile virus in the western hemisphere. *Emerging Infectious Diseases* 6: 319–328.

Ray, D., F. Brenner, M. Show, A. Baker, K. Gleason, J. Gressley, A. Pyle, L. Hubiak, P. Tobelmann, J. Snyder, and P. Barry. 2005. Diagnosis of diseases: Sample collection, record keeping, processing techniques for molecular analysis of protein, nuclear, and mitochondrial DNA and RNA. Pages 415–427 in S. K. Majumdar, J. E. Huffman, F. J. Brenner, and A. I. Panah, editors. Wildlife diseases: landscape, epidemiology, spatial distribution and utilization of remote sensing technology. *Pennsylvania Academy of Science*, Easton, Pennsylvania, pp. 506, 2005.

Rintamaki, P. T., M. Ojanen, H. Pakkala, and M. Tynjala. 1998. Blood parasites of migrating willow warblers at a stopover site. *Canadian J. Zoology* 76: 984–988.

Ruegg, K. C., and T. B. Smith. 2002. Not as the crow flies: an historical explanation for circuitous migration in the Swainson's thrush. Proceed. *Royal Society of London Series B* 269: 1375–1381.

Schell, D. M., S. M. Saupe, and N. Haubenstock. 1989. Bowhead whale growth and feeding as estimated by $\_C^{13}$ techniques. *Marine Biology* 103: 433–443.

Scott, J. D., K. Fernando, S. N. Banerjee, L. A. Durden, S. K. Byrne, M. Banerjee, R. B. Mann, and M. G. Morshed. 2001. Birds disperse Ixodid and *Borrelia burgdorferi*-infected ticks in Canada. *J. Medical Entomology* 38: 493–500.

Sehgal, R. N. M., H. I. Jones, and T. B. Smith. 2001. Host specificity and incidence of *Trypanosoma* in some African rainforest birds: a molecular approach. *Molecular Ecology* 10: 2319–2327.

Sheppard, S. M. F., R. L. Neilsen, and H. P. Taylor. 1969. Oxygen and hydrogen isotope ratios of clay minerals from porphyry copper deposits. *Economic Geology* 64: 755–777.

Sibley, C. G., and J. E. Ahlquist. 1990. *Phylogeny and classification of birds.* Yale University Press, New Haven, Connecticut, USA.

Stillman, R. A., A. D. West, J. D. Goss-Custard, R. W. G. Caldow, S. McGrorty, S. E. A. LeV. Dit Durell, M. G. Yates, P. W. Atkinson, N. A. Clark, M. C. Bell, P. J. Dare, and M. Mander. 2003. An individual behaviour-based model can predict shorebird mortality using routinely collected shellfishery data. *J. Applied Ecology* 40: 1090–1101.

Sutherland, W. J., editor. 1996. *From individual behaviour to population ecology.* Oxford University Press, Oxford, UK.

Taylor, H. P., Jr. 1974. An application of oxygen and hydrogen isotope studies to problems of hydrothermal alteration and ore deposition. *Economic Geology* 69: 843–883.

Thomson, A., editor. 1964. Migration. Pages 465–472. in *A new dictionary of birds.* London, UK.

Tiedemann, R. 1999. Seasonal changes in the breeding origin of migrating dunlins as revealed by mitochondrial DNA sequencing. *J. Ornithology* 140: 319–323.

Tietje, W. D., and J. G. Teer. 1988. Winter body condition of northern shovelers on freshwater and saline habitats. pages 353–377 in D. J. batt, R. H. Chabreck, L. H. Fredrickson, and D. G. Raveling, editors. *Waterfowl in winter.* University of Minnesota Press, Minneapolis, MN, USA.

Vogel, J. C., B. Eglington, and J. M. Auret. 1990. Isotope fingerprints in elephant bone and ivory. *Nature* 346: 747–749.

Webster, M. S., P. P. Marra, S. M. Haig, S. Bensch, and R. T. Holmes. 2002. Links between worlds: unraveling migratory connectivity. *Trends in Ecology and Evolution* 17: 76–82.

Webster, M. S., and P. P. Marra. 2005. The importance of understanding migratory connectivity and seasonal interactions. in: R. Greenberg, and P. P. Marra, editors. *Birds of two worlds: the ecology and evolution of migration.* JHU Press, Baltimore Maryland, USA.

Wenink, P. W., A. J. Baker, and M. G. J. Tilanus. 1994. Mitochondrial control-region sequences in two shorebird species, the turnstone and the dunlin, and their utility in population genetic studies. *Molecular Biology and Evolution* 11: 22–31.

Wennerberg, L. 2001. Breeding origin and migration pattern of dunlin revealed by mitochondrial DNA analysis. *Molecular Ecology* 10: 1111–1120.

Wennerberg, L., M. Klaassen, and A. Lindstrom. 2002. Geographical variation and population structure in the white-rumped sandpiper as shown by morphology, mitochondrial DNA and carbon isotope ratios. *Oecologia* 131: 380–390.

Wink, M. 2006. Use of DNA markers to study bird migration. *J. Ornithology* 147: 234–244.

Ydenberg, R. C., R. W. Butler, D. B. Lank, C. G. Guglielmo, M. Lemon, and N. Wolf. 2002. Trade-offs, condition dependence and stopover site selection by migrating sandpipers. *J. Avian Biology* 33: 47–55.

Avian Ecology and Conservation: A Pennsylvania Focus with National Implications. Edited by S. K. Majumdar, T. L. Master, M. C. Brittingham, R. M. Ross, R. S. Mulvihill and J. E. Huffman. © 2010. The Pennsylvania Academy of Science.

SECTION III

Conservation Issues and Challenges

Section Overview

Margaret C. Brittingham
The School of Forest Resources, The Pennsylvania State University,
409 Forest Resources Building, University Park, PA 16802
mxb21@psu.edu

The conservation of biodiversity and the maintenance of healthy functioning ecosystems in the face of an ever-growing human population is one of the greatest challenges we face here in Pennsylvania and around the world. An increasing human population has resulted in higher demands on our natural resources for goods and services. Oftentimes, conservation of natural resources is portrayed as an impediment to economic growth. Yet, sustainable economic growth is, in fact, dependent on the quality and supply of natural resources, including clean water, clean air, productive soils, healthy forests capable of regenerating, and the complex complement of species that work together to provide innumerable ecological services.

Birds have been used as indicators of environmental health throughout time because many are visually and vocally conspicuous, they are familiar to scientists and lay persons alike, and they can be found across a broad range of habitats and environmental conditions. As a result, they can serve as visible indicators of environmental change. In fact, birds often give the first alert that changes are occurring in the environment, changes that could be detrimental to other living organisms that share the same space. It is their greater inherent sensitivity to environmental change (a consequence of their higher metabolic rate and some unique aspects of their physiology compared to humans and other mammals) that enables birds to serve, both literally (at one time in our early coal-mining history) and figuratively, as life-saving canaries-in-a-cage for human beings who share those same environments. For many species, our understanding of their ecology and biology enables us to use them to unravel how environmental changes are impacting, or might impact, a broad range of organisms. Equally important is that there is great public interest in birds, so changes in populations of birds can be used to illustrate changes to the environment in a way that is likely to garner public support.

Conservation of avian populations in the state involves multiple steps. Large scale monitoring programs such as the Breeding Bird Survey and Pennsylvania Breeding Bird Atlas, in combination with surveys targeted at specific groups of species or specific locations, are used to identify species or groups of species that are declining. Research hypotheses are generated, and research is conducted to determine the cause or causes of declines. Based on research results, potential solutions or ways to mitigate declines are proposed. These can range from habitat management and manipulation to direct protection, regulations and legislation. Monitoring and evaluation occur throughout the process, and changes and adjustments are made as we learn more about the causes and consequences of declines, the effectiveness of attempted solutions, and the tools we have to implement them.

The following section on conservation issues provides a window into this process. It is an eclectic section which covers everything from policy and tools associated with the management and recovery of threatened and endangered species to chapters focused on major causes of species decline such as habitat loss and fragmentation. Other chapters address current causes of habitat degradation including invasive species (hemlock woolly adelgid), pollution (acid pollution from deposition and abandoned mine drainage), and the threat posed by the ubiquitous presence of plate glass (e.g. windows) in our environment. Two of the chapters deal specifically with guilds of species (colonial nesters, farmland species) that are of immediate and significant conservation concern. All of the chapters are authored by individuals who have worked extensively in Pennsylvania and have a close working knowledge of the conservation issues and challenges we face in Pennsylvania and the relevance of these issues, challenges, and solutions to avifauna at the regional and national scale.

The lead chapter in this section deals with the management and recovery of threatened and endangered species. Dan Brauning and Jerry Hassinger address the policies and regulations that have guided the protection and conservation of threatened and endangered species, and the process used at the state level to list species. The states have a trust responsibility to conserve and sustain wildlife populations for future generations, and state lists can serve as early warnings with the hope that management at the state level can prevent species from becoming federally endangered. The authors review a few successes such as the case of the bald eagle (*Haliaeetus leucocephalus*) which shows what can be done when we can identify a threat (in this case DDT) and then eliminate or reduce that threat. They also point out the lack of success particularly in relation to the suite of declining species associated with wetland habitats and the extreme difficulty of reversing habitat loss and fragmentation.

The next chapter focuses on the issue of habitat fragmentation with a specific emphasis on forest habitat. Margaret Brittingham and Laurie Goodrich review the causes and extent of fragmentation of Pennsylvania forests and the consequences to forest specialists. They review the causes of fragmentation that have affected forests throughout the Northeast in the past and speculate on new and emerging causes of fragmentation. They caution that fragmentation affects entire communities and is something we must strive to minimize if we hope to retain the structure of bird communities found in our forests today.

Andy Wilson addresses the plight of farmland and grassland birds in Pennsylvania and the Northeast. He examines trends in farmland birds and shows that our grassland obligates and field nesters have declined precipitously at the same time that farmland generalists, like Eastern bluebirds, *Sialia sialis*, have fared much better. The decline of field-nesting birds in Pennsylvania is being replayed across the United States and is particularly extreme in the Midwest. The result is that states like Pennsylvania, historically on the periphery of the range for many of these species, are now increasingly important to their global survival. Maintaining populations of ground nesting birds in Pennsylvania will require active management, and these management practices will need to be modified and revised as we learn more about the habitat needs of this important group of species.

Eastern hemlock (*Tsuga canadensis*) decline is a relatively new conservation issue with the potential to have major impacts on hemlock-associated species. Michael Allen and James Sheehan describe the arrival and spread of the hemlock woolly adelgid, its direct effects on hemlock stands, and the indirect effects on birds dependent on the Eastern hemlock ecosystem for food and cover. They end by reviewing the pros and cons of potential methods of control; none of which has proven very successful so far. It will be important to continue to monitor and conduct research on hemlock-associated birds to determine which ones are able to persist and adapt and which may be in real trouble.

Acidification of terrestrial and freshwater ecosystems from human causes is a conservation issue for Pennsylvania, as well as regionally, nationally and even worldwide. Steven Latta and Bob Mulvihill provide a case study looking at the effects of acidification on the Louisiana waterthrush (*Seiurus motacilla*), the only stream-dependent songbird in eastern North America. They discuss a range of indirect (negative) impacts of acid pollution on the waterthrush through its direct impacts on the aquatic invetebrate food supply that constitutes the bulk of a waterthrush's diet.

Bob Ross writes about another group of species closely tied to riparian habitats, the colonially nesting wading birds. This group includes eight species that have previously or are currently nesting in the state. All eight species are globally secure, but three have been extirpated from the state and three are listed as state endangered species. Because of small population sizes and high levels of site fidelity, the three endangered species face a host of threats including loss of nest sites to floods and invasive species, competition from double-crested cormorants (*Phalacrocorax auritus*), a recent addition to Pennsylvania avifauna, and in some cases direct persecution.

In the final chapter, Dan Klem addresses a conservation issue that is often overlooked. He discusses the importance of sheet glass or windows as an avian mortality factor. Clear glass is associated with buildings and structures throughout the world, and the amount of glass increases with urban sprawl and development. This killer is indiscriminate and affects birds of all species, ages, and status. Unlike other sources of mortality, it does not have a larger impact on birds that are in poorer physical condition. The author provides guidelines for making plate glass less hazardous to birds and ends with a plea for the US Green Building Council to incorporate bird-safe designs into their evaluation system.

Collectively, the conservation section provides a picture of the range of conservation issues facing birds in Pennsylvania, the Northeast, and in many cases, birds around the world. It also provides guidelines and suggestions for reversing these declines if we are willing to make the effort. Researchers, managers, and conservationists must work together to develop creative strategies to reverse declining trends in all habitats from the urban core to working farmlands to our rural forest lands and the streams running through them.

Avian Ecology and Conservation: A Pennsylvania Focus with National Implications. Edited by S. K. Majumdar, T. L. Master, M. C. Brittingham, R. M. Ross, R. S. Mulvihill and J. E. Huffman. © 2010. The Pennsylvania Academy of Science.

Chapter 14

Management and Recovery of Threatened and Endangered Bird Species

Dan Brauning
Wildlife Biologist, Pennsylvania Game Commission,
2001 Elmerton Ave., Harrisburg, PA 17110
dbrauning@state.pa.us

Jerry Hassinger
Wildlife Biologist, 105 Adams Lane, Millersburg, PA 17061

INTRODUCTION

This chapter focuses primarily on the management and recovery, or the lack thereof, of threatened and endangered (T&E) bird species in Pennsylvania during the period subsequent to publications that addressed the initial results of T&E programs (Genoways and Brenner 1985, Majumdar et al. 1986) or in particular T&E birds (Gill 1985, Clark and Klem 1986). However, some background and historical insight is also provided to emphasize the value of reactive legislation as a first-step management tool, or conversely, to point out that the "inadequacy of existing regulatory mechanisms" (O'Grady 2002) is a potentially correctable threat to the continued existence of some species in Pennsylvania.

BACKGROUND

Historically, Species Declines Have Stimulated Legislation and Action

Birds and mammals, notably game species, were in decline at the end of the 1800s (Warren 1890). Coincident with major conversions of vegetative cover types (forest to farmland) and tree age-class distribution, major reasons for these declines were the lack of adequate laws and regulations to protect wildlife and scant enforcement of the few laws that were on the books. By 1895 the need for the management and recovery of wild birds and mammals was obvious; if nothing was done a rich heritage would be lost and future generations would suffer the consequences. This was the year that legislation created the Pennsylvania Game Commission (PGC) and designated this new agency as trustee of the Commonwealth's wild birds and mammals. This act proved to be too late to help the endangered passenger pigeon. The last reports of this species in Pennsylvania were in the first decade of the 20th Century and the species became extinct in 1914 (French 1919).

With the legislated, financial assistance of hunters and resultant enforcement of laws, and given that habitat was in a state of flux but was not lost or irreparably degraded, other birds eventually recovered. This history of recovery and conservation of wild birds, primarily game species, is not the subject of this paper; but it exemplifies the potential impact of laws and regulations designed to conserve wildlife, and it does inform the process of prioritizing concern.

Despite the distraction of major wars, the 1900s were an era of human population growth and unprecedented development. The need for more food production from fewer and fewer acres of farmland stimulated the production and widespread use of herbicides and pesticides. By mid-century, these trends resulted in a different set of threats, namely the environmental contamination, degradation, and loss of habitat. The consequence was a new set of declining bird species and the threat of their eventual extinction or extirpation from the state. Mounting concern resulted in new laws and regulations culminating at the national level in 1972 when DDT was banned from use and in 1973 with the passage of the federal Endangered Species Act (ESA). These are arguably two of the more important legal actions ever taken for wildlife in North America.

In 1971, Pennsylvania passed a constitutional amendment (Section 27, Article 1): *"The people have a right to clean air, pure water, and to the preservation of the natural, scenic, historic and esthetic values of the environment. Pennsylvanian's public natural resources* [this includes all free-ranging wildlife species (Bean 1977)] *are the common property of all the people, including generations yet to come. As trustee of these resources, the Commonwealth shall conserve and maintain them for the benefit of all the people."*

The state has a trust responsibility to conserve and sustain our wildlife heritage for the benefit of all people including generations yet to come. Inherently this daunting task requires us to prevent the regional loss of our most troubled species (labeled T&E). While states are obligated to protect those federal T&E species that are found within their borders, most states, including Pennsylvania, established state regulations and began (post-1973) formulating their own lists of T&E species in order to sustain the wildlife within their own jurisdictions. A few states, e.g., Florida (http://www.animallaw.info/statutes/stusfl372_072.htm) and New York (http://www.animallaw.info/statutes/stusny11_0535.htm), but not Pennsylvania, went even further and passed their own state version of the federal ESA. State lists naturally include the federal T&E species found within their borders, but in addition include species that are threatened with extirpation (regional extinction) from the state but not necessarily global extinction. In essence, T&E species found on multiple state lists have functioned, over time and informally, as an early warning system for broader declines (Table 1). Focusing management on state-listed species, to the extent that it is successful, prevents these species from becoming candidates for potential federal listing and helps fulfill the state's role as trustee of the public's wildlife resources. The value of these state efforts was recently recognized when Congress created the State Wildlife Grants Program in 2001. This program required each state to develop a Wildlife Action Plan (WAP), and is aimed at species of greatest conservation need, with the ultimate goal of preventing species from declining to the point where they become candidates for federal listing as Threatened or Endangered. Similarly, a core component of the mission of the "Partners in Flight" initiative is to "Keep Common Birds Common" (PIF 2008). The process of status determination, listing (including

Table 1. Insular and linear habitats used by breeding Threatened and Endangered bird species common to Pennsylvania and neighboring states.[1]

Threatened and Endangered Bird Species	Wetlands[2]	Forested Islands[3]	Cliffs and Structures	Upland Fields
Bald Eagle[4]	PA, NY, NJ, OH, MD, WV			
Osprey[4]	PA, NJ, OH, WV			
Peregrine Falcon[4]			PA, NY, NJ, OH, WV	
Black-crowned Night Heron	PA, OH, NJ, WV			
Yellow-crowned Night Heron	PA, OH, NJ, WV			
Great Egret	PA			
Black Tern	PA, OH, NY			
Common Tern	PA, OH, NY			
American Bittern	PA, OH, NJ, WV			
Least Bittern	PA, OH, NY, WV			
King Rail	PA, OH, NY, WV			
Dickcissel				PA, WV
Upland Sandpiper				PA, OH, NJ, NY, WV
Loggerhead Shrike				PA, OH, NJ, NY, MD, WV
Yellow-bellied Flycatcher	PA, WV	PA-D		
Sedge Wren	PA, NJ, NY, MD, WV			
Blackpoll Warbler	PA	PA-D		
Short-eared Owl	PA, NJ, NY, MD, WV			PA, NJ, NY, MD, WV

[1]West Virginia does not have a state T&E list; information from WV is from the WV Wildlife Action Plan: "Species in Greatest Need of Conservation."
[2]U.S. Fish and Wildlife Service Classification (Tiner 1989)
[3]Forested Islands: A – Seedling/Sapling Stands; B – Old Growth Stands; C – Interior Forest; & D – Limited Forest Cover Type
[4]Breeding populations are trending upward

the assessment of "deleterious factors"), and determining "species of greatest conservation need" starts with surveys, inventories and monitoring.

Surveys, Inventories and Monitoring

Prioritizing and tracking the progress of species management depends on surveys, inventories and monitoring. Determining species status for 189 breeding bird species in Pennsylvania (about 80% of which are not hunted), delineating critical habitats, analyzing threats, and developing adaptive management require that a variety of ecological parameters be measured (Hassinger et al. 1998). However, the PGC has never had the funds or staff to adequately measure and assess these parameters for all species under its jurisdiction. This perennial shortcoming was the impetus in 1979 for the formation of the Pennsylvania Biological Survey (PABS), a nonprofit organization of volunteers comprised largely of interested and knowledgeable professional scientists, amateur naturalists and agency representatives. PABS is comprised of taxon-specific committees, one of which is the Ornithological Technical Committee (OTC) (Dunstan 1985). Since 1979 the OTC has conducted the bird status determination process (Brauning et al. 1994). The OTC serves the PGC in an official advisory capacity through a Memorandum of Understanding. In turn the PGC and OTC depend on the state's active birding community for basic survey data, such as the breeding bird atlas (Brauning 1992).

Gross (1998), in a review of the status of birds in Pennsylvania, lists 18 "Pennsylvania bird inventory and monitoring programs," most of which are repeated annually, most notably the Breeding Bird Survey (BBS 2007). Five of these 18 programs are PGC initiatives; the remainder are supervised by other organizations. The majority of these programs depend on volunteer birders for basic data.

While recreational birders put their knowledge to good use in surveys, it is primarily land management agencies and researchers supported by grants that survey and monitor habitats. Goodrich et al. (2006) provide a comprehensive overview of wildlife habitats in Pennsylvania. A relevant conclusion was that the "critical habitat" required by many wildlife species for their continued existence in Pennsylvania is not adequately monitored. It follows that insular wetlands, grasslands, and limited cover types (e.g. spruce/hemlock), all habitats associated with T&E birds, are not systematically monitored. These largely fragmented habitats are, nevertheless, periodically surveyed and assessed (Myers and Bishop 1999, Goodrich et al. 2006, Bishop 2008). The classification and monitoring of cover types and habitats continue to be a challenge. However, evolving technology (e.g. satellite imagery with resolutions of $1m^2$, global positioning systems, and geographic information systems) is stimulating large-scale surveys of important habitat changes (Warner et al. 2007, Bishop 2008).

The PGC is developing plans that will result in the systematic monitoring of habitat on 1.4 million acres of State Game Lands. The Pennsylvania Department of Conservation and Natural Resources Bureau of Forestry, and the U.S. Forest Service monitor forest condition on 21,000,000 acres of State Forest and 500,000 acres of the Allegheny National Forest, respectively. These agencies cooperate with the USDA Forest Service's Northeastern Forest Inventory, which includes the measurement of wildlife habitat and forest fragmentation (USDA 2008). Current plans and inventories notwithstanding, these management agencies lack the guidance of T&E species' recovery plans, which define critical habitat for each species. It follows that with some obvious exceptions (e.g. large wetlands), critical habitats for T&E birds, to the extent they exist, have not been delineated on our public lands. Species and habitat survey, inventory, and monitoring data and the research projects deriving therefrom, help to prioritize species management.

Prioritizing Species Management, a Progression of Definitions

Species-specific survey and inventory data initiate the status determination and regulatory listing processes. These processes and the dictates of the Wildlife Action Plan result in conservation priorities for bird species. Excluding prioritized "conservation tiers," defined in and unique to the PGC's Wildlife Action Plan (http://www.pgc.state.pa.us/pgc/cwp), a complete listing of federal, state and NatureServe status and rank definitions is available on the Pennsylvania Natural Heritage Program's (PNHP) web site: http://www.naturalheritage.state.pa.us/RankstatusDef.aspx .

Following are federal and state legal definitions for T&E species: the 1973 ESA defines a Federal Endangered Species as "a species which is in danger of extinction throughout all or a significant portion of its range"; a Federal Threatened Species is "any species which is likely to become an endangered species within the foreseeable future throughout all or a significant portion of its range." Pennsylvania and most neighboring states have no equivalent of the federal ESA. To partially compensate for this, the legal definitions for state T&E species incorporate categories of deleterious factors and penalties for take of listed species are elevated here.

Pennsylvania Endangered - Species in imminent danger of extinction or extirpation throughout their range in Pennsylvania if the deleterious factors affecting them continue to operate. These are: 1) species whose numbers have already been reduced to a critically low level or whose habitat has been so drastically reduced or degraded that immediate action is required to prevent their extirpation from the Commonwealth; or 2) species whose extreme rarity or peripherality places them in potential danger of precipitous declines or sudden extirpation throughout their range in Pennsylvania; or 3) species that have been classified as "Pennsylvania Extirpated", but which are subsequently found to exist in Pennsylvania as long as the above conditions 1 or 2 are met; or 4) species determined to be "Endangered" pursuant to the Endangered Species Act of 1973, Public Law 93 205 (87 Stat. 884), as amended.

Pennsylvania Threatened - Species that may become endangered within the foreseeable future throughout their range in Pennsylvania unless the casual factors affecting the organism are abated. These are: 1) species whose populations within the Commonwealth are decreasing or have been heavily depleted by adverse factors and, while not actually endangered, are still in critical condition; 2) species whose populations may be relatively abundant in the Commonwealth but are under severe threat from serious adverse factors that have been identified and documented; or 3) species whose populations are rare or peripheral and in possible danger of severe decline throughout their range in Pennsylvania; or 4) species determined to be "Threatened" pursuant to the Endangered Species Act of 1973, Public Law 93205 (87 Stat. 884), as amended, that are not listed as "Pennsylvania Endangered".

Status determination protocol: For our purposes, "status determination" as a risk assessment, is defined as a process by which the OTC, in an advisory capacity to the PGC, uses an established procedure (objective science and expert opinion) to evaluate a species' risk of extirpation from Pennsylvania and recommends or petitions that the species or population be given special attention for regulatory listing as provided by the PGC. While the list maintained by the OTC is non-regulatory, there is every effort, short of violating biological criteria for status determination, to maintain consistency between the OTC's non-regulatory and agency regulatory lists. "Established procedure" includes regulatory criteria here defined as definitions and criteria in rule or code (see above) for qualifying a species for listing, and non-regulatory criteria (often referred to as guidelines), which are written descriptions of factors considered or data requirements to be met in determining the status of a species.

Regulatory Listing Protocol: "Regulatory listing" is the process by which the PGC, building on the independent and scientifically objective status determination process, uses regulatory criteria (i.e. definitions in rule or code as influenced by policy, cost-benefits, a current protection profile, recoverability, and other considerations) and an established procedure (specifying, among other items, petition-documentation requirements and public participation) to officially classify and list species as Threatened or Endangered in the Game and Wildlife Code, Title 58. The PGC adopted, through policy, this current listing protocol in 2006 (Roe 2006).

FACTORS AFFECTING STATUS DETERMINATION

The ESA lists 5 historical threats that have contributed to the decline and listing of T&E bird species (ESA 2008, Table 2). The relative roles of these 5 factors vary among species and have changed over time. Overutilization, a consequence of few laws and regulations and little enforcement, historically contributed to the decline and listing of birds in Pennsylvania and its neighboring states (Warren 1890, Kosack 1995). But this changed in the 20th Century (Clark and Klem 1986). With passage of the Lacey Act by the U.S. Congress in 1900 and the Migratory Bird Treaty Act of 1918 and their attendant regulations and aggressive enforcement, direct killing of birds is not thought to be a contributory factor behind the listing of any of the birds in Table 1. Nevertheless, when a T&E bird is killed or wounded, the incident is frequently reported in local papers and extra efforts are made to apprehend violators.

By the mid-1900s, uncontrolled shooting was replaced by pesticide contamination as the predominant factor which threatened, among other bird species, at least 3 charismatic rap-

Table 2. Pennsylvania's current list of Endangered or Threatened bird species and listing factors.

Bird Species*	Year First State Listed and Status	Most Recent Recovery Plan**	Current Status F = Federal S = State	Current Species Applicable Threat Categories or Listing Factors***				
				A	B	C	D	E
Bald Eagle	1974 - E	2000	S -Threatened					X
Osprey	1989 - E		S - Threatened					X
Peregrine Falcon	1974 - E		S - Endangered					X
Black-crowned Night Heron	1990 - T	1995	S - Endangered	X			X	X
Yellow-crowned Night Heron	1990 - T	1995	S - Endangered	X				
Great Egret	1990 - T	1995	S - Endangered	X			X	
Black Tern	1983 - T	1995	S - Endangered	X				X
Common Tern	1983 - E		S - Endangered	X		X		X
American Bittern	1983 - T	1995	S - Endangered	X				
Least Bittern	1983 - T	1995	S - Endangered	X				
King Rail	1983 - E	1995	S - Endangered	X				
Dickcissel	1983 - E		S - Endangered	X			X	
Upland Sandpiper	1983 - T	1995	S - Endangered	X			X	
Loggerhead Shrike	1983 - E	1995	S - Endangered	X			X	X
Yellow-bellied Flycatcher	1989 - T	1995	S - Endangered	X			X	
Sedge Wren	1983 - T	1995	S - Endangered	X			X	
Blackpoll Warbler	2005 - E	1995	S - Endangered	X			X	
Short-eared Owl	1983 - E	1995	S - Endangered	X			X	

* Species with notable increases in nesting pairs since their initial listing are bolded.

** The most recent management/recovery plans were prepared or revised in the year indicated.

*** The five listing factors as outlined in section 4 of the federal ESA.

  A – The present or threatened destruction, modification, or curtailment of its habitat or range.

  B – Overutilization for commercial, recreational, scientific or educational purposes.

  C – Disease or predation.

  D – The inadequacy of existing regulatory mechanisms.

  E – Other natural or manmade factors affecting its continued existence.

tors: bald eagle, osprey and peregrine falcon. The decline of these large birds lent urgency to the passage of the ESA in 1973 and expedited the removal of chlorinated hydrocarbons (e.g. DDT) from the U.S. market, setting the stage to recover these species.

But other species began to find their way onto federal and state T&E lists (Tables 1 and 2), primarily as a result of the cumulative loss, fragmentation, and/or degradation of insular habitats. These habitats include wetlands, young growth or old growth forest age classes, limited cover types (e.g. red spruce), and undisturbed grasslands (Gill 1985, Majumdar et al. 1989, Goodrich et al. 2006). Loss of habitat (exacerbated by the insular nature of wetlands in Pennsylvania) now is the primary factor that has resulted in widespread (multistate) and to date intractable declines for the 15 wetland and grassland breeding bird species (Tables 1 and 2). By comparison, the 3 listed raptors did not suffer the sustained loss of their habitat. To the contrary, the habitats used by these species have increased in extent, sometimes at the expense of habitat needed by other T&E species (Goodrich et al. 2002).

Pennsylvania's status determination process focuses on population size and trend, but considers the diverse range of potential threats described above. A quantitative ranking procedure has been employed since the 1980s that evaluates the relative impact of these and other threat factors for birds and mammals (Kirkland and Krim 1990). In this procedure, population condition, including historic status and trends, contributes up to 50% of the ranking score. Habitat availability, condition, and loss are weighted to contribute up to 28% of the score, while environmental hazards, the historic factor in many high-profile declines, contributes at most 2.25%. The resulting ranking scores were used as one piece of information in the status consideration for birds (Brauning et al. 1994), but the scoring reflects the strong habitat orientation of late-20th Century status considerations.

Because most threats are not distinct to Pennsylvania, the resulting lists of birds classified as T&E in Pennsylvania are similar to those of neighboring states (Table 1). Fourteen (78%) of Pennsylvania's 18 T&E bird species breed in wetland habitats. The peregrine falcon historically nested primarily on cliffs; today this species nests on bridges, buildings and cliffs. Four T&E species nest in the limited and largely unsafe/transient cover types that characterize upland grassy fields. Specific information for each of Pennsylvania's 18 listed T&E bird species may be found on the PGC 's web site http://www.pgc.state.pa.us/pgc/cwp/view.asp?a=458&q=150321

MANAGEMENT AND RECOVERY PLANNING

Regulatory listing is designed to trigger conservation through: 1) increased funds for research and management, 2) targeted law enforcement and an increase in regulatory penalties, 3) environmental reviews to reduce impacts of permitted activities on wildlife species, 4) recovery-related planning and action, and 5) adaptive management. The history of success of these initiatives also varies considerably among taxa and across time.

ESA provides not only regulatory penalties, but also financial resources for research and recovery of listed species in the form of Section 6 grants. Section 6 provides grants to states and territories for implementation of conservation actions, land acquisition, and conservation planning (USFWS 2008a). This has provided an important source of funds for federally listed species. Newly available federal funds and state listings also spurred the establishment of state non-game (or wildlife diversity) programs in the 1980s.

Three listed species have been beneficiaries of increased funds and considerable recovery attention: the bald eagle, peregrine falcon and osprey. But virtually no funds have been earmarked to mitigate the threats (Table 2) contributing to the status of the remaining 15 T&E bird species, 10 of which have been listed for 25 years. Other regulation and expenditures have been made, however, that incidentally favored species using wetlands. For instance, compared to other public lands, a disproportionate number of recent records of T&E birds using wetlands are on State Game Lands primarily because the PGC has a history of acquiring and conserving wetlands for waterfowl hunting. Hunting may have been the primary stimulus behind these acquisitions but there is little question that T&E bird species have benefited.

An assessment of the impacts on habitat and their associated listed wildlife species by human activities requiring regulatory permits is carried out through a process of environmental reviews. This is a carried out at the federal level for all activities using federal funds through Section 7 reviews (ESA) and through the National Environmental Policy Act (NEPA). In Pennsylvania, environmental review personnel in each of the state agencies are linked to Department of Environmental Protection permitting through an on-line application of the Pennsylvania Natural Diversity Inventory (PNDI). Projects that come within specified distances of known occurrences of listed species require a review by the jurisdictional agency. Like penalties for take of a listed species, environmental review is a defensive strategy that may at best slow decline of T&E species, to avoid, minimize, or mitigate deleterious effects on these species. For example, from July 2005 through June 2007, the PGC Environmental Review Section looked at nearly 3,000 permit applications to ensure compliance with federal and state regulations and to recommend measures to avoid unnecessary losses to wildlife and their habitats (PGC 2007, 2008). One-third (1,018) of these proposed projects had potential impacts on species of special concern. Out of a subset of 800 projects, i.e., private development projects with potential impacts on special concern species, 56 required measures to avoid or minimize impacts on federally and state listed species. Among the T&E bird species mentioned that required surveys were the bald eagle, osprey, and upland sandpiper. To date these reviews have resulted primarily in reactive avoidance or mitigation at or near a proposed project site. The effectiveness and efficiency of this strategy has yet to be evaluated in Pennsylvania. Several countries and states, however, have adopted the compensation principle based on their experience that impacts may still persist after mitigation (Cuperus et al. 1999).

The PGC recognizes that off-site compensation for the loss, degradation, and isolation of species specific habitat has more potential to counteract the adverse impacts of infrastructure projects on T&E species than site-related avoidance and mitigation. To this end, working with the Federal Highway Administration and PennDOT, they have drafted a State Game Lands Banking Agreement that offsets permanent, transportation related impacts to Game Lands. Basically, PennDOT purchases and deeds over property to the PGC prior to project-related impacts (PGC 2008). A major advantage of this approach is that instead of expending funds on sites dictated by the nature and location of a development project, they are instead used to purchase or improve habitat on sites chosen by wildlife managers.

Listing also leads to a recovery planning process that includes the development of a strategy and action plan to accomplish tasks and goals with the ultimate objective of

Table 3. Sample Table of Contents from a Recovery Plan (National Marine Fisheries Service 2006).

returning the listed species to a self-sustaining state in its native ecosystem. While plans were drafted for most listed species in the late 1990s, formal adoption of the state's management plans for bald eagle and peregrine falcon is underway.

A central aspect of recovery is mitigating the threats affecting the continued existence of a listed species. This involves knowledge of the factor(s) that contributed to the species decline, essentially a threats analysis. These provisional threat analyses help guide the development of a recovery plan. Recovery planning can be a complex and time-consuming process.. Nowhere is this more evident than in the interim recovery planning guidance document recently released by the National Marine Fisheries Service in conjunction with the U.S. Fish and Wildlife Service (National Marine Fisheries Service 2006). Table 1 provides a sample "table of contents" of a recovery plan for a federally listed species.

IMPLEMENTING RECOVERY, TWO EXAMPLES

Following are two case studies that compare how suites of species have faired under Pennsylvania's listing process.

A Case of Degraded Habitat

The majority of the listed species in Pennsylvania are wetland or grassland obligates because of the destruction, modification, or curtailment of these habitats (Table 2). The most dramatic loss of wetland habitat happened prior to 1970 (Tiner 1989). While native grassland habitats existed prior to European settlement, grassland bird populations declined drastically over the past 200 years, primarily in response to conversion of grassland habitats for agricultural activity.

The wetland bird community is striking for its diversity; many wetland-breeding birds are obligate to emergent wetland habitats, and a larger list of species benefit from the variety of wetland habitats. So, while not representing substantial portions of non-coastal land areas of the Mid-Atlantic States, the local diversity of birds through the year is strongly influenced by the presence of wetlands. But, the suite of wetland birds has long dominated state T&E lists. While emergent wetland obligates may have been locally abundant, regional populations were vulnerable to disruption to these island habitats (Brooks et al. 1989).

Many programs are in place to restore wetland communities. Federal and state regulations offer considerable protection for wetlands habitat since the 1960s (e.g., Clean Water Act of 1977). Within the Mid-Atlantic states, the Partners for Wildlife program of the U.S. Fish and Wildlife Service has actively restored wetland habitats, the Wetlands Reserve Program of NRCS provides incentives to protect and restore wetlands, federal and state law requires mitigation for wetland losses, and private organizations (e.g. Ducks Unlimited) join with these programs to promote wetland creation and management. With this focus on wetland habitats, the loss of wetland habitats has been arrested and in some cases reversed (DEP 2008). But while this provides T&E birds requiring wetland habitats the greatest promise for protection, these protections have been inadequate to affect a recovery in these species. A third of wetland species continue to decline. In fact, no species in Table 2 (or 83% of these species) for which wetland habitat loss is the primary cause of decline, has been downlisted.

A number of factors contribute to the failure of wetland restoration efforts to recover obligate species. Considerable attention to the management of wetland habitats has focused on waterfowl. The emergent habitats associated with most listed wetland birds sometimes result inadvertently from waterfowl management, but generally are not the primary habitat objective. Wetland habitat management may restore lost wetlands, enhance the capacity to manage impounded wetlands, or generally enhance wetland features in an area, but many sites are small, in inappropriate locations, or managed for open water not conducive to listed species. Considerable debate continues over wildlife's benefit from wetland creation, mitigation, and enhancement (Turner et al. 2001). Mitigation sites are often along roadways, resulting in ecological traps that will not serve rare wetland species. Exceptions remain, where larger restoration projects have resulted in extensive wetland habitats which, at least for a period of time, support a diversity of wetland birds. So, while wetland loss has been arrested in Pennsylvania, no emergent wetland bird species has experienced substantial recovery.

The Case for Hope

While the condition of most T&E species remains grim, three species of birds, referenced above, demonstrate the potential for recovery: bald eagle, osprey and peregrine falcon. Not only in Pennsylvania, but also across their range, these species have recovered from severe declines and, in the case of the eagle and falcon, federal listing. While they serve as symbols of hope and provide a sense that the listing process is reversible, they also share many features in common in their life history, causes for decline, and methods of recovery. A brief summary follows.

Bald eagle, osprey and the peregrine falcon are birds of prey, foraging high in the food chain, and widely persecuted in the past. Osprey and bald eagles are closest in their ecological niche and often are sympatric. The official explanation for recovery of the eagle is stated by the USFWS: "The two main factors that led to the recovery of the bald eagle were the banning of the pesticide DDT and habitat protection afforded by the Endangered Species Act for nesting sites and important feeding and roost sites. This recovery could not have been accomplished without the support and cooperation of many private and public landowners" (USFWS 2008b). That cooperation reflects a shift in public perception of these birds since the 1970s that may be as much a factor in their decline and recovery as any direct biological factor. But all of the predispositions referenced above played into the collapse of these and many other birds of prey. Each experienced declines through the 20th Century. The tipping point for each of these species was the widespread use of DDT (EPA 1975). The inclusion of the bald eagle and peregrine falcon in the U.S. Fish and Wildlife Services' Endangered Species Act is also seen as a major factor in their recovery.

While never a common species, the osprey was extirpated from Pennsylvania by 1935 (Poole 1964). The declines were clearly not a result of DDT, which did not come into widespread use until after 1945 (EPA 1975). Both osprey and peregrine falcons were listed as extirpated from Pennsylvania in 1979 (Gill 1985) and eagles were reduced to two nesting pairs (Leberman 1990).

The common features in the decline of these charismatic raptors are matched by similarities in their recoveries. Each was reintroduced in Pennsylvania and neighboring states through a method known as "hacking" (Cade and Temple 1995), and each responded with successful recoveries. At the simplest level, the primary cause of these declines was addressed; DDT was banned in the United States in 1972, eagles received substantial protection in the 1940 Bald and Golden Eagle Protection Act, and then, most notably, bald eagles and peregrine falcons were listed in the ESA in 1973. Habitat improvements, primarily in the form of improved water quality and inadvertent expansion of habitat through construction of dams and reservoirs, played significant roles in osprey and eagle recovery.

Since the establishment of the Wildlife Diversity program by the Game Commission, a commitment to monitoring came with listing and recovery of high-priority species. Assessment of annual productivity has been the focus of monitoring federally listed eagle and peregrine falcon (McWilliams and Brauning 2000), and has continued since their federal delisting. These efforts documented the growth of nesting eagle populations to 132 pairs in 2006, sustaining an average annual population growth of at least 14% (Gross 2008). The state's nesting peregrine population tripled over 10 years, reaching 24 nesting pairs in 2007 (McMorris and Brauning 2008). Osprey monitoring has not been sustained at the level of the other two large raptors, but the recent breeding bird atlas reported 85 atlas 'blocks' with confirmed breeding osprey, reflecting the continued strong recovery and population expansion (BBA 2008). The restoration of these dramatic species to Pennsylvania, as across the country, are monumental achievements for conservation.

The example of raptor recoveries serves to demonstrate that interrupting a population trajectory heading to extinction is possible where the mechanisms are understood and the will and resources can be raised to initiate aggressive restoration. These were not easy cases, but dealt with factors including policy, public perception, regulations, research, and received considerable conservation action by many groups.

LITERATURE CITED

Bean, M. J. 1977. The Evolution of National Wildlife Law. Prepared for Council on Environmental Quality, Washington, D.C. 485pp.

Bishop, J. A. 2008. Temporal dynamics of forest patch size distribution and fragmentation of habitat types in Pennsylvania. PhD Dissertation in Ecology, The Pennsylvania State University, University Park, PA 140pp.

Brauning, D. W., ed. 1992. Atlas of Breeding Birds in Pennsylvania. University of Pittsburgh Press, Pittsburgh, PA. 484pp.

Brauning, D. M., M. Brittingham, D. Gross, R. C. Leberman, T. L. Master, and R. S. Mulvihill. 1994. Pennsylvania breeding birds of special concern: a listing rationale and status update. J. PA Acad. Sci. 68 (1):3–28.

Breeding Bird Survey Data (BBS) 2007. North American Breeding Bird Survey. U.S. Geological Survey, Patuxent Wildlife Research Center, Laurel, MD. Accessed online on September 30, 2008 at http://www.pwrc.usgs.gov/bbs/

Breeding Bird Atlas. 2008. Osprey, preliminary results from Second Pennsylvania Breeding Bird Atlas. Accessed online on at http://bird.atlasing.org/Atlas/PA/.

Brooks, R. P., K. D. Smith and D. A. Devlin. 1989. Wetland protection, regulation, and management. Pages 21–38. in Wetlands Ecology and Conservation: Emphasis in Pennsylvania. Edited by S. K. Majumdar, R. P. Brooks, F. J. Brenner and R. W. Tiner Jr. 1989. The Pennsylvania Academy of Science.

Cade, T. J. and S. A. Temple. 1995. Management of threatened bird species: evaluation of the hands-on approach. Ibis 137(1): 161–172.

Clark, R.J. and D.Klem, Jr. 1986. An overview of endangered and declining birds of Pennsylvania and adjacent states. Pages 211–33, In Endangered and Threatened species programs in Pennsylvania and other states: Causes, issues, and management. Eds., S.K. Majumdar, F.J. Brenner, and A.F.R. Rhoads, Pennsylvania Academy of Science, Easton, PA.

Cuperus, R., K. J. Canters, A. Helias, Udo de Haes and D. S. Friedman. 1999. Guidelines for ecological compensation associated with highways. Biological Conservation 90: 41–51.

Department of Environmental Protection, PA (DEP) 2008. Wetland Net Gain Strategy. Accessed online on September 30, 2008 at: http://www.dep.state.pa.us/dep/deputate/watermgt/wc/subjects/wwec/general/wetlands/NetGain.htm

Dunstan, F., 1985. Introduction, Page 4. in Genoways, H. H., Brenner, F. J. (Editors). Species of Special Concern in Pennsylvania. Special Publication of Carnegie Museum of Natural History, No. 11, Pittsburgh, 430 pp.

Endangered Species Act (ESA) 2008. Delisting a Species: *Section 4 of the Endangered Species Act.* Accessed online on September 30, 2008 at http://training.fws.gov/Library/Pubs9/delisting.pdf

Environmental Protection Agency, U. S. (EPA) 1975. *DDT, A Review of Scientific and Economic Aspects of the Decision To Ban Its Use as a Pesticide*, prepared for the Committee on Appropriations of the U.S. House of Representatives by EPA, July 1975, EPA-540/1-75-022.

French, J. C. 1919. "The Passenger Pigeon in Pennsylvania: Its remarkable history, habits and extinction." Altoona Tribune Company, Altoona, Pa.

Genoways, H.H. and F.J. Brenner 1985. Species of Special Concern in Pennsylvania. Carnegie Museum of Natural History, Special Pub. No. 11, Pittsburgh, PA. 430 pp.

Goodrich, L. J., M. Brittingham, J. A. Bishop, and P. Barber. 2002. Wildlife Habitat in Pennsylvania: Past, Present, and Future. Pennsylvania Department of Conservation and Natural Resources, PA Game Commission, PA Fish and Boat Commission, Harrisburg, PA. 236 pp.

_____, _____, _____, _____. 2006. An interagency-led effort: biodiversity conservation in Pennsylvania: a summary of the status of wildlife habitat and habitat threats statewide, Pages. 559–567 in R.B. McKinstry Jr., C.M. Ripp, and E. Lisy editors. Biodiversity Conservation Handbook: State, Local & Private Protection of Biological Diversity. The Environmental Law Institute, Washington, D.C.

Gill, F. B., editor. 1985 Chapter 5 – Birds. Pages. 299–351. in Genoways, H. H., Brenner, F. J. (Editors). Species of Special Concern in Pennsylvania. Special Publication of Carnegie Museum of Natural History, No. 11, Pittsburgh, 430 pp.

Gross, D. A. 1998. Birds: A review of status in Pennsylvania, Pages. 137–170. in Inventory and Monitoring of Biotic Resources in Pennsylvania (Technical Coordinators: J. D. Hassinger, R. J. Hill, G. L. Storm and R. H. Yahner), Pennsylvania Biological Survey.

Gross, D.A. 2008. Bald eagle breeding and wintering surveys. PA Game Commission, Harrisburg, PA. Access online on September 30, 2008 at http://www.pgc.state.pa.us/pgc/lib/pgc/reports/2008_wildlife/71101-07z.pdf

Hassinger, J., R. Hill, G. Storm, and R. Yahner. 1998. Inventory and Monitoring of Biotic Resources in Pennsylvania, Pennsylvania Biological Survey, 221 pp.

Kirkland, G. L. and P. M. Krim. 1990. Survey of the statuses of the mammals of Pennsylvania. J. of the Pennsylvania Acad. of Science 64(1):33–45.

Kosack, J. 1995. The Pennsylvania Game Commission, 1895–1995, 100 Years of Wildlife Conservation. PA Game Commission, Harrisburg, PA. 233pp.

Leberman, R.C. 1990. Bald Eagle. Page 92–93, In Atlas of Breeding Birds in Pennsylvania. Edited by D.W. Brauning. U. Pittsburgh Press. Majumdar, S.K. F.J. Brenner, and A.F. Rhoads, eds. 1986. Endangered & Threatened Species Programs in Pennsylvania and Other States: Causes, Issues & Management. Pennsylvania Academy of Science, Easton, PA. 519pp.

McMorris, F.A. and D. W. Brauning 2008. Peregrine falcon investigations. PA Game Commission, Harrisburg, PA. Accessed online at http://www.pgc.state.pa.us/pgc/lib/pgc/reports/2008_wildlife/71501-07z.pdf.

McWilliams, G.M. and D.W. Brauning 2000. The Birds of Pennsylvania. Cornell University Press, Ithaca, NY. 479pp.

Myers, W. L., and J. A. Bishop. 1999. Stratified land-use/land-cover for Pennsylvania. Pennsylvania Gap Analysis Program. Environmental Resources Research Institute, The Pennsylvania State University. University Park, PA.

National Marine Fisheries Service. 2006. Interim endangered and threatened species recovery planning guidance. National Marine Fisheries Service, Washington, D.C. Accessed on line at http://www.nmfs.noaa.gov/pr/recovery.

O'Grady, Michael 2002. Environmental Statutes Outline: A Guide to Federal Environmental Laws. Environmental Law Institute. 96pp.

Partners in Flight (PIF) 2008. Partners in Flight – U.S. Accessed on line at http://www.partnersinflight.org/description.cfm

Pennsylvania Game Commission (PGC) 2007. Pennsylvania Game Commission Annual Report, 2005–06. Pennsylvania Game News 78(1):2–28.

_____. 2008. Pennsylvania Game Commission Annual Report, 2006–07. Pennsylvania Game News 79(1):2–28.

Poole, E.L. 1964. Pennsylvania Birds: An annotated list. Delaware Valley Ornithology Club. Livingston Publishing Co., Narberth, PA. 94 pp.

Roe, C. 2006. Standard Operating Procedure No. 40.5. Changes in the Legal Status of Birds and Mammals. Pennsylvania Game Commission, Harrisburg, PA.

Tiner, R. W. 1989. Current status and recent trends in Pennsylvania's wetlands. Pages. 368–78. in Wetlands Ecology and Conservation: Emphasis in Pennsylvania. Edited by S. K. Majumdar, R. P. Brooks, F. J. Brenner and R. w. Tiner Jr. 1989. The Pennsylvania Academy of Sciences.

Turner, R.E., A.M. Redmond, and J.B. Zedler. 2001. Count it by acre or function – mitigation adds up to net loss of wetlands. National Wetlands Newsletter 26:6. Access online on September 30, 2008 at: http://d2d.ali-aba.org/_files/client/course_materials/sk081-ch18.pdf

U. S. Fish and Wildlife Service (USFWS) 2008a. Endangered Species Program; Cooperative Endangered Species Conservation Fund (Section 6). Accessed on line on October 1, 2008 at: http://www.fws.gov/endangered/grants/section6/index.html

_____. 2008b. Bald Eagle. Accessed 17 July 2008 at http://www.fws.gov/midwest/eagle/

U. S. Department of Agriculture (USDA) 2008. USDA Forest Service Northeastern Forest Inventory. Accessed September 30, 2008 http://www.fs.fed.us/ne/fia/about/index.html.

Warren, B. H. 1890. Report on the birds of Pennsylvania. 2nd ed. revised and augmented. State Board of Agriculture, Harrisburg. [The first edition was published in 1888.]

Warner, E.D., W.L. Myers, J.A. Bishop, and D. Miller. 2007. Land cover classification for Pennsylvania. Digital map data. Penn State Institutes of Energy and the Environment, Pennsylvania State University, University Park, Pennsylvania. In cooperation with the Pennsylvania Department of Conservation of Natural Resources, Harrisburg, Pennsylvania.

Avian Ecology and Conservation: A Pennsylvania Focus with National Implications. Edited by S. K. Majumdar, T. L. Master, M. C. Brittingham, R. M. Ross, R. S. Mulvihill and J. E. Huffman. © 2010. The Pennsylvania Academy of Science.

Chapter 15

Habitat Fragmentation: A Threat to Pennsylvania's Forest Birds

Margaret C. Brittingham[1] and Laurie J. Goodrich[2]
[1]The School of Forest Resources, The Pennsylvania State University, 409 Forest Resources Building, University Park, PA 16802
mxb21@psu.edu

[2]Acopian Center for Conservation Learning, Hawk Mountain Sanctuary, 410 Summer Valley Road, Orwigsburg, PA 17961

Habitat fragmentation occurs when large contiguous blocks of habitat are broken up into smaller patches of habitat by other land uses. In some cases, these habitat patches become islands separated from other like habitat patches. Fragmentation also occurs when contiguous blocks of habitat are penetrated by roads, transmission lines, or other corridors which do not necessarily isolate patches of habitat but do compromise the integrity of the habitat interior. Loss of habitat integrity may occur by increasing the amount of edge and introducing foreign or invasive species into the core. Habitat fragmentation can have negative effects on birds through direct habitat loss or indirectly through changes that occur as a result of the adjacent habitat type and the particular land use associated with it.

In this chapter, we review the causes and extent of fragmentation of Pennsylvania forests and the consequences to Pennsylvania's breeding birds. The chapter is divided into three broad sections. The first reviews what is known about the effects of habitat fragmentation on breeding forest birds with an emphasis on Pennsylvania and the Northeast. The second section focuses specifically on Pennsylvania forests and their status in terms of fragmentation and forest patch size. The third section looks at historic, current, and future impacts of habitat fragmentation on Pennsylvania's forest birds.

EFFECTS OF FOREST FRAGMENTATION

The effects of forest fragmentation on birds have been an issue of interest for over 30 years, and a number of reviews have been written on this topic (Faaborg et al. 1995, Walters 1998). Fragmentation results in both a quantitative and qualitative loss of habitat and can affect birds in a number of ways. As forests are converted to non-forest habitat, there is a direct loss of habitat for the birds which depend on that habitat type and the remaining habitat is often isolated from similar habitat patches. In addition, there is a decrease in forest interior (forest away from an edge or opening) and there is an increase in forest "edge" habitat. This change in edge-to-interior ratio results in physical changes to the microhabitat and changes in biotic interactions as species associated with the non-forest habitat come in contact with forest-dwelling species. Fragmentation caused by roads or other openings within a forest matrix creates additional edge habitat.

Area-sensitive and Forest-interior Species

As forests are fragmented and patch or woodlot size becomes smaller and more isolated, a specific group of species decline in number or are absent from the forest tract (Ambuel and Temple 1983, Robbins et al. 1989). These species are often categorized as "area-sensitive" or "forest-interior" species. A species is considered sensitive to fragmentation if density or fitness of individuals within the remaining habitat patches changes as fragmentation of the surrounding landscape increases (Walters 1998). An area-sensitive species has lower abundance and/or lower reproductive success in small woodlots. Similarly, forest-interior species tend to be less abundant near edges or have lower reproductive success near edges. Because smaller habitat patches have relatively more edge than larger ones, the two terms "area-sensitive" and "forest-interior" have often been used interchangeably. It should be noted that those species associated with forest gaps or patches of early successional forest habitat can also be considered "area-sensitive" if they require large blocks of forest habitat in order to prosper.

Area-sensitive species tend to be neotropical migrants (Faaborg 1995). Most nest in open cup nests on or near the ground and generally raise one brood per year. These birds are often absent from small woodlots including ones that well exceed the size of their home range and provide apparently suitable habitat. These species appear to be negatively impacted by the increase in edge-to-interior ratio. The consequence is that the breeding bird community within large contiguous tracts of forest is very different from the breeding bird community within small woodlots of the same forest type. The bird community within large forested areas is dominated by neotropical migrants such as warblers, vireos, thrushes, and tanagers. Smaller woodlots are dominated by year-round residents and short-distance migrants. Typical species would include chickadees, white-breasted nuthatches (*Sitta carolinensis*), woodpeckers, common grackles (*Quiscalus quiscula*), and corvids like American crows (*Corvus brachyrhynchos*) and blue jays (*Cyanocitta cristata*). Below we review how habitat loss and an increase in edge-to-interior ratio result in these changes.

Habitat Loss

The most noticeable effect of forest fragmentation is the outright loss of habitat. Species negatively impacted include those such as northern goshawk (*Accipiter gentilis*) and broad-winged hawk (*Buteo platypterus*) that have large home ranges, avoid areas of human activities and require a mostly closed canopy for nesting (Goodrich et al. 1996, Squires and Reynolds 1997). Other species have smaller home ranges but may rely on a specific microhabitat that is no longer present in the remaining habitat patch.

For example, worm-eating warblers (*Helmitheros vermivorum*) are considered area-sensitive. These warblers have small home ranges, but they prefer moderate to steep hillsides for breeding. If this habitat is absent, they will generally not be present within the woodlot (Hanners and Patton 1998). Robbins et al. (1989) found the probability of nesting worm-eating warblers was reduced by 50% in mid-Atlantic region woodlots less than 150 ha. Other specialized forest birds may find their microhabitat hard to find even in large woodlots. For example, the occurrence of cerulean warblers (*Dendroica cerulea*) was reduced by 50% in forests smaller than 700 ha (Robbins et al. 1989).

Increase in Edge Habitat and Negative Edge Effects

Historically, edge habitat was considered to be beneficial for wildlife as many of our game species use a mosaic of habitat patches or reach their highest abundance near edges, and there is often a greater diversity of wildlife near edges (Leopold 1933, Yahner 1988). However, there is a downside to this increase in diversity as many species of mammalian and avian nest predators such as gray squirrels (*Sciurus carolinensis*), raccoons (*Procyon lotor*), blue jays, and common grackles are also more abundant near edges or concentrate their hunting near edges. These predators tend to be generalists that thrive in habitats close to human habitation. Thus edges created by agriculture and residential development are often associated with high numbers of nest predators and as a consequence, high levels of nest predation. Brown-headed cowbirds (*Molothrus ater*) are obligate brood parasites that lay their eggs in the nests of other species. Cowbirds feed in open habitat but will travel into the forest to search for host nests. Consequently, their abundance and rates of parasitism are often higher near forest edges where they are in close proximity to both feeding and nest searching habitat (Brittingham and Temple 1983, Hoover et al. 2006).

The consequence of high rates of nest predation and in some cases nest parasitism is that nest success tends to be lower near edges, in small woodlots, and in more fragmented forests (Yahner and Scott 1988, Donovan et al. 1995, Hoover et al. 1995). For example, in southeast Pennsylvania, Hoover et al. (1995) found that wood thrush nest success was related to forest patch size with success ranging from a low of 0.12 in a small woodlot to over 0.70 in large woodlots and contiguous forest (Figure 1). The primary cause of nest failure was predation, and activity by nest predators was greater in small forest patches and near edges than in large areas of contiguous forest (Hoover et al. 1995).

In small woodlots, reproductive success may not be high enough to balance expected mortality. To get a rough estimate of woodlot size needed in southeast Pennsylvania to support a viable population of wood thrush, we estimated the nest success rate that would be needed to balance expected mortality rates. We used an estimated annual adult survival rate of 0.60 and an estimated annual juvenile survival rate of 0.30 (Temple and Cary 1988). We measured nest success, number of young per successful nest, and the number of nests per season in the field. Using these values, we determined that a nest success rate of at least 0.54 was needed to balance mortality and that level of success occurred on woodlots that were at least 100 ha (256 acres) in size (Table 1). Although there are many estimated val-

Table 1. Demographic parameters[a] used to calculate woodlot size needed by nesting wood thrush to balance annual mortality rates, Berks County, PA, 1990–1991. (Data from Hoover et al. 1995).

Parameter	Value
Annual adult survival	60%
Annual juvenile survival	30%
Fledglings/successful nest	3.3
Nests/season	1.5
Nest success	0.2-0.8

[a]Annual adult and juvenile survival rates were estimated from Temple and Cary (1988). Nest success and nests per season were measured in the field (Hoover et al. 1995).

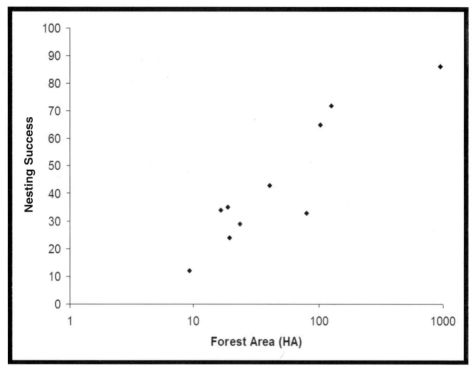

Figure 1: Nest success of wood thrush increases as forest patch size increases on 10 study sites in Berks County, Pennsylvania (1990–1991). (Figure from Hoover et al. 1995).

ues in the equation, it suggests that the reproductive success of wood thrush in many woodlots is not high enough to balance mortality rates. Porneluzi et al. (1993) found that nesting success and density of ovenbirds (*Seiurus aurocapilla*) in Pennsylvania was significantly reduced in woodlots as large as 183 ha compared to continuous forest habitat suggesting that woodlots may need to be larger than 183 ha to provide suitable habitat for many birds. Robbins et al. (1989) has shown that effects of fragmentation on density and site occupancy varies across species.

Types of Edges and Openings

As studies on fragmentation have progressed and occurred in a variety of habitat types, it has become evident that all edges and openings are not alike. The relative impact of fragmentation on an ecosystem depends on both the persistence of the change (e.g., how permanent or long-lasting) and the similarity of the disturbance to the native habitat (Marzluff and Ewing 2001). An urban area has high persistence and low similarity with the surrounding native cover and thus is expected to have the greatest fragmentation effects (Figure 2). Timber harvesting with adequate natural regeneration would have a much lower effect since persistence would be lower (e.g., the cut area will grow back to mature forest) and similarity would be high if the complement of species present before harvesting regenerates. Effects from agriculture would be intermediate.

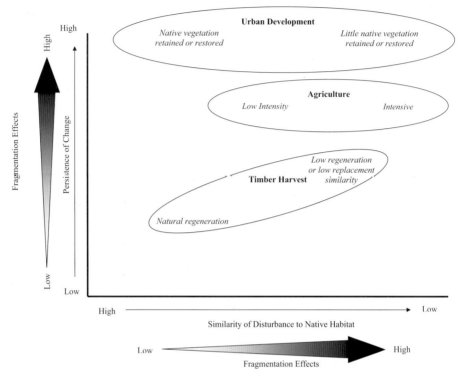

Figure 2:   The relative impact of fragmentation on an ecosystem depends on both the persistence (e.g. how permanent) of the disturbance and the similarity to the native habitat being replaced. (Figure modified from Figure 1 Marzluff and Ewing 2001).

Rodewald and Yahner (2001) working in Central Pennsylvania looked at nest success within forested landscapes with openings created by either agricultural or silvicultural practices. Nest success was lower within forests disturbed by agriculture than by silviculture, and this difference was attributed to an increased abundance of avian and mammalian nest predators in the landscape disturbed by agriculture. Although studies have shown some negative edge effects associated with timber harvesting (e.g. King et al. 1996, Yahner and Mahan 1997), the general conclusion is that openings and edges created by timber harvesting do not create the extent of negative fragmentation effects typically associated with agricultural and residential development (Rudnicky and Hunter 1993, Hanski et al. 1996, Donovan et al. 1997).

The creation of permanent edges within large areas of contiguous forest by roads and utility rights-of-way is a potentially more serious problem (Askins 1994). These permanent openings introduce species associated with open habitat into the forest interior by serving as travel corridors for nest predators and cowbirds moving from the open habitat to the forest (Askins 1994). Researchers have found higher rates of predation in forest habitat adjacent to these corridors (Chasko and Gates 1982, Askins et al. 1987, Small and Hunter 1988). In addition, declines in species richness and abundance of neotropical migrants also occur (Askin et al. 1987).

Other Effects of Fragmentation

Some neotropical migrants have lower pairing success in small woodlots and near edges than in large contiguous forest habitat (Gibbs and Faaborg 1990, Villard et al. 1993, Porneluzi et al. 1993, Goodrich unpublished data). For ovenbirds, small woodlots tend to have a lower abundance of individuals and a lower abundance of mated males (Goodrich unpublished data). In addition to reduced reproductive success in small woodlots and near edges, changes in the microclimate may result in a lower quantity and quality of food making these areas less preferred by females (Burke and Nol 1998). Fragmentation also affects extraterritorial movements of birds within the forest and surrounding landscape (Belisle et al. 2001, Norris and Stutchbury 2001).

Model to Predict Regional Fragmentation Effects

Thompson et al. (2002) developed a hierarchical model to explain how fragmentation effects vary regionally. Effects appear to operate in a top-down manner with factors occurring at an upper level constraining effects at a lower level. At the top level is the biogeographical scale. Bird species abundance and distribution vary geographically and the relative abundance of potential nest predators and nest parasites will ultimately influence the effects that openings or edges might have on reproductive success. For example, brown-headed cowbirds are most abundant in the midsection of the country close to their historical range, and their abundance declines as one moves farther away from this area (Hoover and Brittingham 1993). Consequently, rates of parasitism and effects of habitat fragmentation are greater towards the center of the cowbird's range than at farther distances.

The biogeographical scale in turn constrains effects at the landscape scale. The landscape scale encompasses the predominant land use and land cover in an area. This scale appears to be the most important in determining fragmentation effects. The landscape matrix and forest patch size influence rates of predation and brood parasitism. It appears that edge effects associated with fragmentation are most pronounced in landscapes where forest cover makes up 45–55% of the landscape (Thompson et al. 2002). In this case, predation rates tend to be high near edges and decline as one moves into the forest interior. At this level of forest cover, the open habitat is providing feeding sites, and nest predators that are using those feeding areas are penetrating into the forest adjacent to those areas.

In landscapes where the forest is less than 15% forested, as occurs in much of southern Pennsylvania, predation rates tend to be high in both the edge and the interior of the habitat. In this situation there is so much habitat available for feeding that these nest predators are ubiquitous in the environment. At the other extreme are landscapes that are more than 90% forested. This would be similar to some areas in northern Pennsylvania. In this case, predation rates tend to be low in both forest interior and forest edge because there is so little feeding habitat available for generalist nest predators.

The next level influencing fragmentation effect is the local or habitat scale. This refers to the patch size where the bird is nesting, the structure of the vegetation, and the distance of the nest from the edge. By far the majority of studies on effects of fragmentation on birds in Pennsylvania and other parts of the country have looked at this smallest scale (e.g. Yahner and Wright 1985, Porneluzi et al. 1993, Hoover et al. 1995, Hoover et al. 2006).

PENNSYLVANIA FORESTS – PATCH SIZE AND CORE AREAS

Historically, Pennsylvania and most of the northeastern United States were forested. During the eighteenth and nineteenth centuries massive deforestation occurred as a result of logging, agricultural development, and fires associated with expanding human population (e.g. MacCleery 1992). Since the early 1900's, the amount of forest cover in Pennsylvania and other eastern states has increased, but it is a different type of forest in both species composition and landscape pattern than what was here historically. Today Pennsylvania is over 60% forested, but most of that forest is fragmented or edge habitat with less than half of remaining forested land in "core" or interior forest habitat, away from edge (over 100 m from road or edge) (Goodrich et al. 2002). Forty-two percent of forest habitat in Pennsylvania is considered core habitat while 58% is considered edge (Figure 3). Of the core forest, 70% is found in patches of 5,000 acres (2,023 ha) or less, suggesting that large forests are increasingly rare statewide. Core forest varies regionally with the lowest proportion (less than 20%) in southeast and southwestern regions and the greatest amounts in the Ridge and Valley and Allegheny Plateau.

Southern Pennsylvania eco-regions and areas near the Great Lakes show less than 30% of remaining forest in core forest habitat for wildlife. Northern Pennsylvania show a higher proportion of core forest. In the Ridge and Valley eco-region and other southern eco-regions, the greatest amount of remaining core forest over 5,000 acres (2,023 ha) in size is on ridgetops (Goodrich et al. 2002).

CURRENT AND FUTURE CAUSES OF FRAGMENTATION

Today Pennsylvania is almost 60% forested but threats of fragmentation still continue. Below we review some of the causes of fragmentation with an emphasis on more recent threats.

Suburban Sprawl

In the past, agriculture was an important cause of fragmentation as forests were cleared for farms. Today, there is very little new land going into agricultural production. Instead, we see much of the agricultural land being converted to residential and suburban areas while the remaining farmland is being farmed more intensively. The loss of farmland and intensification of farming has detrimental effects on farmland wildlife while the conversion of farmland to suburban area has resulted in increasingly negative fragmentation effects (Figure 2). In general, urbanization causes more severe and long-lasting fragmentation effects because of the extent of changes to the vegetation, the persistence of those changes, and additional hazards associated with disturbance from people and pets (Marzluff and Ewing 2001).

The increase in sprawl development across the state has also encroached into forested habitats and reduced forest quality, particularly in eastern counties. For example, in Monroe county, the number of homes has grown by 23% since 1990 (US Census). Housing unit growth exceeded 15% from 1990 to 2000 in Butler, Chester, Juniata, Lancaster, Monroe, Centre, and York counties. State-wide the number of housing units has grown by 6.31% (Goodrich et al. 2002).

Increasing fragmentation of forest habitats by urban development brings greater accumulation of risk and mortality for wildlife. Simply the structures alone can be deadly to

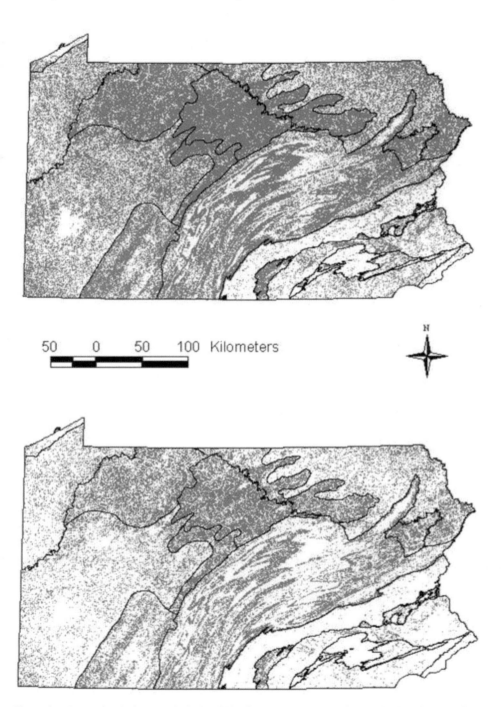

Figure 3: Pennsylvania images depicting 2001 forest cover as recorded by the LandSat satellite. The top image depicts total forest including both core forest and edge forest. The bottom image shows core forest. Core forest lands provide the highest quality breeding habitat for area-sensitive species. (Figure provided by J. Bishop).

wildlife (D. Klem, this volume, Chapter 20). In addition, bird populations can be reduced by the increase in predators around human dwellings, e.g. cats and dogs.

Roads

Roads are associated with almost all human activity and can have a major impact on the quality of forest habitat particularly when introduced into formerly roadless areas. Road density varies across Pennsylvania with greatest concentrations in the urbanized Southeast and Southwest (Goodrich et al. 2002). Roads are associated with habitat loss and fragmentation, increase in mortality, changes in behavior and productivity, and chronic disturbance (Trombulak and Frissell 2000, Saunders et al. 2002).

When roads are built there is a direct loss of habitat, but the extent can be much greater when edge effects and fragmentation effects are taken into account. Edge effects resulting in reduced densities of birds may extend up to 600 m within the forest (Reijnen et al. 1995, Forman and Deblinger 2000). Studies in Oregon found that productivity of bald eagles (*Haliaeetus leucocephalus*) declined with proximity to roads and that eagles preferentially nested away from roads (Anthony and Issacs 1989). As with other fragmentation effects, the extent of the effect varies with the size of the disturbance, the species of interest, the landscape matrix, and region. For example, King and DeGraaf (2002) found no effect on ovenbird productivity of unsurfaced forest roads within an extensive forest area in New England.

Roads can also be a significant source of mortality for birds. For example, a 10-year study of road mortality in Cape May, New Jersey recorded 250 raptors of 12 species over 145 km (90 miles) of road (Loos and Kerlinger 1993). Owls were the most numerous making up 88% of the dead raptors collected. Raptors may be attracted to roadsides because of the grassy habitat that attracts rodents; unfortunately, the road-side habitat has heightened risks. Finally, roads facilitate the use of an area by humans which in itself brings higher levels of disturbance, introduction of invasive plants, higher predation levels, and other more subtle degradation to the overall habitat for nesting birds.

Wind Power

Wind energy provides a renewable energy source but may also have negative impacts on birds depending on the number, size, lighting, and in particular the location of the wind turbines. Most of the research on impacts of wind farms on wildlife have focused specifically on quantifying collision mortality (Kuvlesky et al 2007, T. Katzner, this volume), but habitat loss and fragmentation associated with wind farm development may be equally important. Habitat loss and fragmentation is a consequence of the total area impacted by construction of the wind farm and the ancillary infrastructure associated with it. In addition to the individual turbines, each of which directly impacts from 0.08 ha (0.2 acres) to 0.2 ha (0.5 acres) (Kuvlesky et al. 2007), there is also the construction of roads to allow access to the turbines and electrical transmission lines to transport electricity. Direct habitat loss and fragmentation will be a function of the number of turbines, but road networks and transmission line corridors also cause extensive fragmentation as they may extend for long distances often traversing through extensive blocks of forest habitat. Leddy et al. (1999) found that grassland bird densities were higher on grasslands without wind turbines and in areas ≥80 m from any wind turbines. There has been virtually no research conducted on fragmentation effects of wind turbines on forest birds. In Pennsylvania, many of

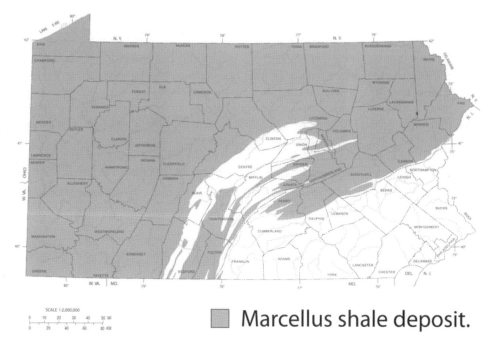

Marcellus shale deposit.

Figure 4:   The shaded area depicts the Marcellus Shale deposit where natural gas exploration and
development is targeted. (Original map prepared by Bureau of Topographic and Geological Survey, Third Edition, 1990. Modified by Penn State College of Agricultural Sciences, 2008).

the wind farms are placed on our forested ridges causing not only a direct hazard to
migrants using the ridge (see Chapter 22) but also fragmenting the areas in Pennsylvania
with the greatest extent of contiguous forest habitat (Goodrich et al. 2002).

Natural Gas Development

A new challenge to forest integrity is the accelerating pace of natural gas exploration and
development in Pennsylvania. Higher energy prices and improving technology have made
it easier and more attractive to drill for natural gas in Pennsylvania. Much of the new
drilling activity is targeted at natural gas found in the Marcellus Shale Formation (Figure
4). In 2006, Pennsylvania natural gas producers drilled approximately 3,900 wells in the
state, and that rate is not expected to decline in the foreseeable future. The footprint of an
individual well site includes the well pad site (generally 1.2–2.0 ha [3–5 acres]) plus associated pipelines and roads to service the wells.

Habitat fragmentation concerns include direct loss of habitat but more importantly fragmentation resulting from the pipelines, roads, and openings associated with the well site.
This is of particular concern because the Marcellus Shale Formation covers much of the
Allegheny Plateau region which encompasses our largest block of contiguous forest and is
the stronghold for many of our forest dwelling neotropical migrants. It is also the location
of much of our public lands which have played an important role in providing habitat for
our area-sensitive forest species.

OUTLOOK FOR PENNSYLVANIA FOREST BIRDS

Pennsylvania currently has stewardship responsibility for many forest-interior and area-sensitive forest songbirds. Responsibility species are ones for which a large proportion of the species population resides within the state (Rosenberg and Wells 1995). For example, 17% of the world population of scarlet tanagers (*Piranga olivacea*), 10% of worm-eating warblers (*Helmitheros vermivorus*), and 9% of the wood thrush (*Hylocichla mustelina*) population breed within Pennsylvania forests (Rosenberg and Wells 1995). From a regional and global perspective, Pennsylvania plays an important role in maintaining populations of these and other forest dwelling species. We have provided an overview of how fragmentation changes the quantity and quality of forest habitat and the far-reaching effects it can have on forest birds. Although we have focused on birds, it should also be noted that fragmentation affects entire communities with no taxonomic group unaffected.

As we look towards the future, we need to minimize future habitat fragmentation and maintain our remaining core forests and large blocks of contiguous forests in order to retain viable and abundant populations of the diversity of forest birds currently breeding within Pennsylvania forests. In the southeastern and southwestern regions of the state where core forest habitat is rare, efforts should be made to reduce isolation among woodlots and to restore ecological function within woodlots to enhance their suitability for area-sensitive species (Marzluff and Ewing 2001).

ACKNOWLEDGMENTS

We thank Joe Bishop for producing the Pennsylvania Forest Cover Maps and Andrea Lego for producing Figure 2. Jerry Hassinger and Robert Ross provided helpful comments on an earlier draft of this manuscript. This manuscript is Hawk Mountain Sanctuary contribution number 175.

LITERATURE CITED

Ambuel, B. and S. A. Temple. 1983. Area-dependent changes in bird communities and vegetation of southern Wisconsin forests. Ecology 64:1057–1068.

Anthony, R. G., and F. B. Isaacs. 1989. Characteristics of bald eagle nest sites in Oregon. Journal of Wildlife Management 53:148–159.

Askins, R. A., M. J. Philbrick, and D. S. Sugeno. 1987. Relationship between the regional abundance of forest and the composition of forest bird communities. Biological Conservation 39:129–152.

Askins, R. A. 1994. Open corridors in a heavily forested landscape: impact on shrubland and forest-interior birds. Wildlife Society Bulletin 22:339–347.

Belisle, M., A. Desrochers, and M. J. Fortin. 2001. Influence of forest cover on the movements of forest birds: a homing experiment. Ecology 82:1893–1904.

Brittingham, M. C., and S. A. Temple. 1983. Have cowbirds caused forest songbirds to decline. Bioscience 33:31–35.

Burke, D. M., and E. Nol. 1998. Influence of food abundance, nest-site habitat, and forest fragmentation on breeding ovenbirds. Auk 115:96–104.

Chasko, G. G. and J. E. Gates. 1982. Avian habitat suitability along a transmission-line corridor in an oak-hickory forest region. Wildlife Monographs 82:1–41.

Donovan, T. M., F. R. Thompson III, J. Faaborg, and J. R. Probst. 1995. Reproductive success of migratory birds in habitat sources and sinks. Conservation Biology 9:1380–1395.

Donovan, T. M., P. W. Jones, E. M. Annand, and F. R. Thompson. 1997. Variation in local-scale edge effects: mechanisms and landscape context. Ecology 78:2064–2075.

Faaborg, J., M. Brittingham, T. Donovan, and J. Blake. 1995. Habitat fragmentation in the temperate zone. Pp. 357–380 in Ecology and Management of Neotropical Migratory Birds. (T. E. Martin and D. M. Finch, eds.). Oxford University Press, New York.

Forman, R. T. T., and R. D. Deblinger. 2000. The ecological road-effect zone of a Massachusetts (USA) suburban highway. Conservation Biology 14:36–46.

Gibbs, J. P., and J. Faaborg. 1990. Estimating the viability of ovenbird and Kentucky warbler populations in forest fragments. Conservation Biology 4:193–196.

Goodrich, L. J., M. Brittingham, J. A. Bishop, P. Barber. 2002. Wildlife habitat in Pennsylvania: past, present, and future. Report to state agencies, 236 pp. Available at http://www.dcnr.state.pa.us/WLhabitat/.

Goodrich, L. J., S. T. Crocoll, and S. E. Senner. 1996. Broad-winged hawk (*Bureo platypterus*). The Birds of North America Online (A. Poole, Ed.). Ithaca: Cornel lab or Ornithology: retrieved from the Birds of North America Online: http://bna.birds.cornell.edu/bna/species/218.

Hanners, Lise A. and Stephen R. Patton. 1998. Worm-eating Warbler (*Helmitheros vermivorum*), The Birds of North America Online (A. Poole, Ed.). Ithaca: Cornell Lab of Ornithology; Retrieved from the Birds of North America Online: http://bna.birds.cornell.edu/bna/species/367.

Hanski, I. K., T. J. Fenske, and G. J. Niemi. 1996. Lack of edge effect in nesting success of breeding birds in managed forest landscapes. Auk 113:578–585.

Hoover, J. P. and M.C. Brittingham. 1993. Regional variation in cowbird parasitism of wood thrushes. Wilson Bulletin 105:228–238.

Hoover, J. P., M. C. Brittingham and L. J. Goodrich. 1995. Effects of forest patch size on nesting success of wood thrushes. Auk 112:146–155.

Hoover, J. P., T. H. Tear, and M. E. Baltz. 2006. Edge effects reduce the nesting success of Acadian Flycatchers in a moderately fragmented forest. Journal of Field Ornithology 77:425–436.

King, D. I., C. R. Griffin, and R. M. DeGraff. 1996. Effects of clearcutting on habitat use and reproductive success of the ovenbird in forested landscapes. Conservation Biology 10:1380–1386.

King, D. I., and R. M. DeGraaf. 2002. The effect of forest roads on the reproductive success of forest-dwelling passerine birds. Forest Science 48:391–396.

Kuvlesky, W. P., L. A. Brennan, M. L. Morrison, K. K. Boydston, B. M. Ballard, and F. C. Bryant. 2007. Wind energy development and wildlife conservation: Challenges and opportunities. Journal of Wildlife Management 71:2487–2498.

Leddy, K. L., K. F. Higgins, and D. E. Naugle. 1999. Effects of wind turbines on upland nesting birds in Conservation Reserve Program grasslands. Wilson Bulletin 111:100–104.

Leopold, A. 1933. Game Management. Charles Scribner Sons, New York.

Loos, G. and P. Kerlinger. 1993. Road mortality of saw-whet and screech-owls on the Cape May peninsula. Journal of Raptor Research 27: 210–213.

MacCleery, D.W. 1992. American forest – A history of resiliency and recovery. USDA Forest Service FS-540.

Marzluff, J. M., and K. Ewing. 2001. Restoration of fragmented landscapes for the conservation of birds: A general framework and specific recommendations for urbanizing landscapes. Restoration Ecology 9:280–292.

Norris, D. R., and B. J. M. Stutchbury. 2001. Extraterritorial movements of a forest songbird in a fragmented landscape. Conservation Biology 15:729–736.

Porneluzi, P., J. C. Bednarz, L. J. Goodrich, N. Zawada, and J. Hoover. 1993. Reproductive-performance of territorial ovenbirds occupying forest fragments and a contiguous forest in Pennsylvania. Conservation Biology 7:618–622.

Reijnen, R., R. Foppen, C. Terbraak, and J. Thissen. 1995. The effects of car traffic on breeding bird populations in woodland .3. Reduction of density in relation to the proximity of main roads. Journal of Applied Ecology 32:187–202.

Robbins, C. S., D. K. Dawson, and B. A. Dowell. 1989. Habitat area requirements of breeding forest birds of the middle Atlantic States. Wildlife Monographs 103:1–34.

Rodewald, A. D., and R. H. Yahner. 2001. Avian nesting success in forested landscapes: Influence of landscape composition, stand and nest-patch microhabitat, and biotic interactions. Auk 118:1018–1028.

Rosenberg, K.V. and J.V. Wells. 1995. Importance of geographic areas to neotropical migrant birds in the Northeast. Report to U.S. Fish and Wildlife Service, Cornell Lab. of Ornith. 120 pp.

Rudnicky, T. C., and M. L. Hunter. 1993. Avian nest predation in clearcuts, forests, and edges in a forest-dominated landscape. Journal of Wildlife Management 57:358–364.

Saunders, S. C., M. R. Mislivets, J. Q. Chen, and D. T. Cleland. 2002. Effects of roads on landscape structure within nested ecological units of the northern Great Lakes region, USA. Biological Conservation 103:209–225.

Small, M. F. and M. L. Hunter. 1988. Forest fragmentation and avian predation in forested landscapes. Oecologia 76:62–67.

Squires, J. R. and R. T. Reynolds. 1997. Northern goshawk (*Accipiter gentilis*). The Birds of North America Online (A. Poole, Ed.). Ithaca: Cornell Lab of Ornithology: retrieved from the Birds of North America Online: http://bna.birds.cornell.edu/bna/species/298.

Temple, S. A., and J. R. Cary. 1988. Modeling dynamics of habitat-interior bird populations in fragmented landscapes. Conservation Biology 2:340–347.

Thompson, F. R., T. M. Donovan, R. M. DeGraaf, J. Faaborg, S. K. Robinson. 2002. A multi-scale perspective of the effects of forest fragmentation on birds in eastern forests. Studies in Avian Biology 25:8–19.

Trombulak, S. C., and C. A. Frissell. 2000. Review of ecological effects of roads on terrestrial and aquatic communities. Conservation Biology 14:18–30.

Villard, M. A., P. R. Martin, and C. G. Drummond. 1993. Habitat fragmentation and pairing success in the ovenbird (*Seiurus aurocapillus*). Auk 110:759–768.

Walters, J. R. 1998. The ecological basis of avian sensitivity to habitat fragmentation. Pages 181–192 in J. M. Marzlaff and R. Sallabanks, editors. Avian Conservation – Research and Management. Island Press, Washington, DC.

Yahner, R. H. 1988. Changes in wildlife communities near edges. Conservation Biology 2: 333–339.

Yahner, R. H., and C. G. Mahan. 1997. Effects of logging roads on depredation of artificial ground nests in a forested landscape. Wildlife Society Bulletin 25:158–162.

Yahner, R. H., and D. P. Scott. 1988. Effects of forest fragmentation on depredation of artificial nests. Journal of Wildlife Management 52:158–161.

Yahner, R. H., and A. L. Wright. 1985. Depredation on artificial ground nests: effects of edge and plot age. Journal of Wildlife Management 49:508–513.

Avian Ecology and Conservation: A Pennsylvania Focus with National Implications. Edited by S. K. Majumdar, T. L. Master, M. C. Brittingham, R. M. Ross, R. S. Mulvihill and J. E. Huffman. © 2010. The Pennsylvania Academy of Science.

Chapter 16

The Status and Conservation of Farmland Birds in Pennsylvania

Andrew M. Wilson
School of Forest Resources
The Pennsylvania State University
University Park, Pennsylvania 16802
email: amw328@psu.edu

INTRODUCTION

Grassland-obligate bird populations have been in steady decline across North America for the past four decades or more (Vickery 2001, Sauer et al. 2008). The declines are of such magnitude that they have been predicted to become a "prominent wildlife conservation crisis of the 21st Century" (Brennan and Kuvlesky 2005). Declines have been particularly steep in the eastern United States, which due to bird distributional shifts following the large-scale destruction of native tall-grass prairies, supports significant populations of some grassland bird species (Sauer et al. 2008, Norment 2002). However, the declines in species often associated with grasslands are by no means restricted to native grassland habitats; in certain parts of their breeding range these species are largely dependent on agricultural grasslands and croplands. Further, these declines in farmland birds are not unique to North America: population decreases of similar timing and magnitude in a range of farmland bird species in Europe have received a great deal of attention from conservation biologists and policy makers alike (Donald et al. 2001, Gregory et al. 2005, Mattison and Norris 2005).

Changes in bird populations associated with farmland and grassland habitats are, of course, not new—the fortunes of these birds have long been inextricably linked with agriculture. Prior to European settlement, the birds that we now associate with these habitats in North America would have been abundant in the vast swathe of native grassland that stretched from Texas north into Canada, and from the Rockies east to The Mississippi. Some species quickly adapted to the new openings created by the agriculture of early settlers in the forested east of North America (Askins 1999). These were boom times for some species of open country, although at a continental scale this may have been very short-lived as by the mid 19th Century the vast tall-grass prairies were rapidly going under the plow. Within little more than a century, 99% of the tall grass prairie had disappeared (Noss et al. 1995).

In Pennsylvania, farmland birds would likely have been rare or absent prior to European settlement; in the words of Todd (1940) "There could have been few if any birds such as Bob-white, Prairie Horned Lark, Bobolink, Meadowlark, Vesper Sparrow, Savannah Sparrow and Grasshopper Sparrow". Although there were some natural grasslands in the state, estimated at around 230 square miles in extent (Latham and Thorne 2007), and natural disturbance events could have maintained a patchwork of early successional habitats; there can be no doubt that grassland bird species were restricted in range until the forests were cleared. By the time the first comprehensive accounts of Pennsylvania's avifauna were published late in the mid to late 19th Century, many of these species were described as common, if not abundant (Stone 1894, Todd 1940, McWilliams & Brauning 2000). Other species colonized rather later; for example the Henslow's sparrow *Ammodramus henslowii* was not confirmed to nest in the state until 1913 (Todd 1940) while the Savannah sparrow *Passerculus sandwichensis* appears to have been a scarce bird until the early decades of the 20th Century (McWilliams & Brauning 2000). Thus, the presence of these species in appreciable numbers in Pennsylvania is largely attributable to the clearing of forests for agriculture and coal-mining, and it is therefore not surprising that their numbers have continued to be driven by changes in our anthropogenically altered landscapes.

Farmland extent peaked at almost 20 million acres (8,093,713 ha), around 70% of Pennsylvania, in the late 19th Century (PA DEP 2008). During the first half of the 20th Century many farmed areas in PA were abandoned as farmers headed west to more fertile lands, leaving huge areas of land to regenerate as forest. Today around 25% of the state is open habitat, the majority of which is farmland (Myers et al. 2000). During recent decades, development has been the main cause of farmland loss, particularly in the southeast of the state. Between 1969 and 1992, for example, 27% of farmland was lost in the Lehigh Valley while around Philadelphia losses were 37% (Goodrich et al. 2002). Losses of pasture have been particularly dramatic with less than 50% of the 1978 acreage now remaining (PFBC & PGC 2005).

Although there has been steady decline in the area of grassland and farmland in Pennsylvania since the peak in late 19th Century, the rate of decline of birds associated with these habitats cannot be explained fully by loss of habitat extent. The main driver behind the more recent population losses is changes in the management and ownership of farmland, leading to fewer, larger farms that are more intensively managed. The drive to improve agricultural efficiency has led to increased use of herbicides and pesticides, which has removed important seed and invertebrate food sources. Increased use of fertilizer has resulted in a much more rapid growth of hay crops, which allows them to be cut frequently and early, thereby excluding grassland nesting birds that no longer have a suitable time-window in which to reproduce (Fawley and Best 1991). In 1950, the mean first cutting date for timothy and clover hay was July 5; by 1990 the mean first cutting was a full month earlier (Klinger 2008), a date which coincides with the peak of first nesting attempts for many grassland bird species. In addition, there has been a change in the hay crops planted -during the past 25 years alfalfa hay has increased by 45% while other hays have declined by 17% (Klinger 2008).

Of course, some of these changes are not new. Todd remarked in 1940, "This custom of early mowing is good economy for the farmer and secures better quality of hay, but it is disastrous for the Bobolink". However, it was during the 1970s and 1980s that the rate of "intensification" of farming practices reached its peak. During those decades, even species that had previously shown great adaptability in colonizing arable farmland, such as vesper sparrow *Pooecetes gramineus* and red-winged blackbird *Agelaius phoeniceus*, went into rapid decline. This period also coincided with a discontinuity in Federal set-aside programs. During 1956 to 1973 between 500,000 and 600,000 acres (200,000–240,000 ha) of farmland in Pennsylvania were idled through The Soil Bank and latterly the Feed Grain Programs. These large areas of set-aside are suggested to have provided important refuges for farmland and grasslands birds at that time but when these federal programs were discontinued, farmland was put back into production.

In this paper we review recent population trends of common farmland birds in Pennsylvania and compare trends for guilds of species that nest within grassland and cropland with those found non-cropped habitats in the farmland landscape, such as farmyards, hedges, small woodlots and scrub. The conservation implications of the recent trends in the light of both the current and potential future agricultural landscape of Pennsylvania are discussed.

FARMLAND BIRD POPULATION TRENDS

Population trends of farmland and other common birds in Pennsylvania were estimated using USGS BBS data for 1970 to 2007 (Sauer et al. 2008). During that period, 135 different BBS routes were surveyed in Pennsylvania, with a mean of 78 per year (range 52 to 99). Routes are distributed evenly across the state. BBS population trends for 1970–2007 were estimated using program TRIM (TRends and Indices for Monitoring data). TRIM is a statistical software to analyze time-series of counts with missing observations, using Poisson regression (Pannekoek and van Strien 2001). See Appendix for more details of the analysis.

Redundancy analysis was used to assign species to guilds using BBS data and remotely sensed land cover data around each survey route (see Appendix). Population trends across species guilds were estimated by averaging trends of species within that guild. This average can be considered to be an indicator index for a group of birds that share broadly similar ecological requirements (Gregory et al. 2005). The bi-plot resulting from the redundancy analysis shows the relationships between each of the 110 species and the land cover types (Fig 1a). Species located close to the land cover gradients are most associated with that habitat, while those close to the center of the plot tend to be associated to some extent with several habitats, and are therefore be considered habitat generalists. Those towards the left of the plot are most associated with the farmland land cover gradients (hay and arable) and those on the right most associated with forested land cover types. The species associated with farmland (hay & arable) were then divided into those that nest within fields: 10 species ("Field nesters"), and those associated with non-cropped habitats—17 species ("Farmland generalists"). A further 19 species that are common within the farmed landscape but also found in other habitats were grouped into a "Generalists/developed" guild and the remaining 64 were not associated with farmland (Fig 1b).

The "Farmland generalists" guild includes species that predominantly hunt or feed in open areas, e.g. red-tailed hawk *Buteo jamaicensis*, American kestrel *Falco sparverius*, eastern bluebird *Siala sialis*, eastern kingbird *Tyrannus tyrannus* and barn swallow *Hirundo rustica*; species associated with woodlots, shrubby areas and scattered trees in open country, e.g. yellow warbler *Dendroica petechia* and orchard oriole *Icterus spurious*; and species that are associated with human dwellings, e.g. Common Grackle *Quiscalus quiscula* and the non-native rock pigeon *Columba livia*, European starling *Sturnus vulgaris* and house sparrow *Passer domesticus*. While many of these farmland generalists are by no means restricted to farmland, our results suggest that their highest BBS counts in Penn-

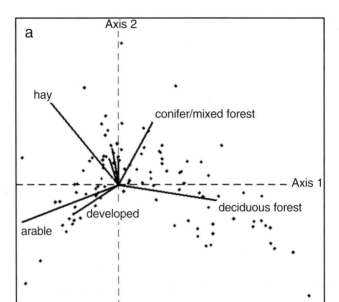

water, wetland and transitional gradients are above origin, between hay and conifer/mixed gradients

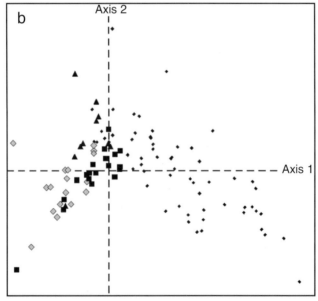

▲ Field nesters
◆ Farmland generalists
■ Generalists & developed
• Forest, transitional & wetland

Figure 1:   Redundancy Analysis bi-plots of species scores (diamonds) and land cover gradients (a), and species guilds (b) from USGS Breeding Bird Survey counts of common birds in Pennsylvania between 1998 and 2002. See Appendix for methods.

sylvania are found in farmed landscapes. Most of these species are characteristic birds of farmed areas in Pennsylvania and are often much more numerous than the "Field nesters", which could be considered to be farmland/grassland obligates. Further, many of the species in the "Generalists/developed" guild are also numerous in farmland landscapes, but these species often reach their highest densities in suburban and forest edge settings.

Killdeer *Charadrius vociferus* and bobolink *Dolichonyx oryzivorus* were the only species in the "Field nesters" guild whose populations increased during the period 1970 to 2007 (Table 1). Savannah sparrow populations were stable, while populations of the other species declined significantly. It is interesting to note that both Bobolink and Savannah Sparrow are more widespread in northern Pennsylvania than in the south (Brauning 1992). Ring-necked pheasant *Phasianus colchicus* was the most rapidly declining species, declining by an average of 7.36% per year, representing a loss of 94% of the population. It should be noted though that this species is not native to North America and population trends are clouded by changes in patterns of releasing captive-bred birds for hunting (Diefenbach et al. 2000). Among the other field nesters, estimated population losses between 1970 and 2007 were 77% for horned lark *Eremophila alpestris*, 55% for field sparrow *Spizella pusilla*, 81% for vesper sparrow, 63% for grasshopper sparrow *Ammodramus savannarum*, 56% for red-winged blackbird and 74% for eastern meadowlark *Sturnella magna*.

Among the "Farmland generalists", only four species showed statistically significant declines: purple martin *Progne subis* (70%), European starling *Sturnus vulgaris* (13%), common grackle *Quiscalus quiscula* (47%) and house sparrow *Passer domesticus* (40%). Ten of the farmland generalists increased significantly, though it should be noted among these are four species whose ranges have expanded northwards through Pennsylvania in recent decades: red-bellied woodpecker *Melanerpes carolinus*, fish crow *Corvus ossifragus*, northern mockingbird *Mimus polyglottas* and orchard oriole *Icterus spurius* (Brauning 1992).

The trend for the "Field nesters" species guild is strongly divergent from that of the other guilds (Figure 2). The "Farmland generalists" guild fared much better on average, increasing steadily through the 1970s, 1980s and 1990s, followed by a small decrease during the current decade. The "Generalists/developed" guild showed a similar pattern, with a steady increase in numbers until 2001. The sharp drop in the indices for the "Farmland generalists" and "Generalists/developed" guilds between 2002 and 2003 are considered to be caused by increased mortality of certain species due to West Nile Virus, which arrived in Pennsylvania in 2000 and has been shown to have caused rapid but short-term population declines of vulnerable species across North America, including American crow *Corvus brachyrhynchos*, blue jay *Cyanocitta cristata*, tufted titmouse *Baeolophus bicolor*, house wren *Troglodytes aedon* and eastern bluebird (LaDeau et al. 2007).

The contrasting fortunes of field nesting species and habitat generalists within Pennsylvania have resulted in a significant change in the assemblage of farmland birds. While some species have increased, perhaps due to the increase in non-farmed habitats associated with developments, the overwhelming pattern of decrease for species that nest within agricultural fields is compelling evidence that changes in agricultural practices are the principle drivers of these declines. The decline slowed between the mid 1980s and mid 1990s but has since continued at the same rate noted during the 1970s and early 1980s, with little evidence of a slowing or reversal in that trend in recent years. The period of rapid decline during the mid 1970s through mid 1980s coincides with the period when

Table 1.   Population trends of common bird species for three guilds associated with farmland in Pennsylvania for 1970 to 2007. Data from the USGS Breeding Bird Survey.

Guild and species name	annual population change mean	SE	trend and significance	% population change 1970 to 2007
Field nesters				
ring-necked pheasant *Phasianus colchicus*	−7.36	0.27	Steep decline (p<0.01)	−93.6
Killdeer *Charadrius vociferus*	0.64	0.16	Moderate increase (p<0.01)	25.8
horned lark *Eremophila alpestris*	−3.97	0.45	Moderate decline (p<0.01)	−76.7
field sparrow *Spizella pusilla*	−2.21	0.12	Moderate decline (p<0.01)	−55.3
vesper sparrow *Pooecetes gramineus*	−4.59	0.34	Moderate decline (p<0.01)	−81.6
Savannah sparrow *Passerculus sandwichensis*	−0.02	0.20	Stable	−0.7
grasshopper sparrow *Ammodramus savannarum*	−2.75	0.28	Moderate decline (p<0.01)	−63.4
bobolink *Dolichonyx oryzivorus*	0.80	0.20	Moderate increase (p<0.01)	33.2
red-winged blackbird *Agelaius phoeniceus*	−2.26	0.11	Moderate decline (p<0.01)	−56.1
eastern meadowlark *Sturnella magna*	−3.68	0.15	Moderate decline (p<0.01)	−74.1
Farmland generalists				
red-tailed hawk *Buteo jamaicensis*	4.88	0.41	Moderate increase (p<0.01)	455.8
American kestrel *Falco sparverius*	0.69	0.31	Moderate increase (p<0.05)	28.1
turkey vulture *Cathartes aura*	3.90	0.37	Moderate increase (p<0.01)	296.4
rock pigeon *Columba livia*	−0.17	0.19	Stable	−5.9
red-bellied woodpecker *Melanerpes carolinus*	8.96	0.42	Strong increase (p<0.01)	2095.9
eastern kingbird *Tyrannus tyrannus*	0.01	0.20	Stable	0.4
white-eyed vireo *Vireo griseus*	3.16	0.61	Moderate increase (p<0.01)	206.5
fish crow *Corvus ossifragus*	2.89	0.60	Moderate increase (p<0.01)	178.9
purple martin *Progne subis*	−3.26	0.42	Moderate decline (p<0.01)	−69.7
barn swallow *Hirundo rustica*	−0.09	0.14	Stable	−3.2
eastern bluebird *Sialia sialis*	3.94	0.26	Moderate increase (p<0.01)	302.0
northern mockingbird *Mimus polyglottos*	1.14	0.18	Moderate increase (p<0.01)	50.4
European starling *Sturnus vulgaris*	−0.38	0.13	Moderate decline (p<0.01)	−12.8
yellow warbler *Dendroica petechia*	2.28	0.14	Moderate increase (p<0.01)	125.1
common grackle *Quiscalus quiscula*	−1.77	0.12	Moderate decline (p<0.01)	−47.4
orchard oriole *Icterus spurius*	3.78	0.43	Moderate increase (p<0.01)	280.3
house sparrow *Passer domesticus*	−1.39	0.10	Moderate decline (p<0.01)	−39.6
Generalists/developed				
Canada goose *Branta canadensis*	3.15	1.06	Moderate increase (p<0.01)	205.4
wood duck *Aix sponsa*	4.62	0.73	Moderate increase (p<0.01)	408.3
mourning dove *Zenaida macroura*	2.40	0.12	Moderate increase (p<0.01)	134.9
chimney swift *Chaetura pelagica*	0.44	0.15	Moderate increase (p<0.01)	17.1
belted kingfisher *Ceryle alcyon*	−0.39	0.27	Stable	−13.1
downy woodpecker *Picoides pubescens*	1.30	0.18	Moderate increase (p<0.01)	59.2
northern flicker *Colaptes auratus*	−2.09	0.12	Moderate decline (p<0.01)	−53.3
blue jay *Cyanocitta cristata*	0.96	0.12	Moderate increase (p<0.01)	41.1
American crow *Corvus brachyrhynchos*	1.13	0.09	Moderate increase (p<0.01)	49.9
Carolina chickadee *Poecile carolinensis*	6.10	0.77	Moderate increase (p<0.01)	742.9
tufted titmouse *Baeolophus bicolor*	3.44	0.15	Moderate increase (p<0.01)	237.9
Carolina wren *Thryothorus ludovicianus*	6.40	0.36	Strong increase (p<0.01)	833.0
house wren *Troglodytes aedon*	−0.05	0.11	Stable	−1.8
American robin *Turdus migratorius*	0.11	0.08	Stable	4.0
gray catbird *Dumetella carolinensis*	1.22	0.11	Moderate increase (p<0.01)	54.7
song sparrow *Melospiza melodia*	0.40	0.09	Moderate increase (p<0.01)	15.5
northern cardinal *Cardinalis cardinalis*	1.77	0.10	Moderate increase (p<0.01)	88.1
brown-headed cowbird *Molothrus ater*	−1.03	0.18	Moderate decline (p<0.01)	−31.1
house finch *Carpodacus mexicanus*	10.31	0.61	Strong increase (p<0.01)	3320.0

Federal set-aside programs were discontinued. It should be noted that the species included in this guild of declining birds include some that are more often associated with tilled land than grassland in Pennsylvania, notably horned larks and vesper sparrows, species which may have been particularly well-suited to the idled fields during the set-aside period from the 1950s through to 1970s.

Although our analysis is restricted to population trends of common species, it is important to note that several scarce species of farmland and grassland habitats have also declined. One such species, which is now too scarce to be monitored by the BBS at the state level, is the Henslow's sparrow. According to PIF estimates, the Pennsylvania population of 1,900 birds is 2.4% of the global population. However, intensive surveys of reclaimed surface mines in western Pennsylvania found the population of Henslow's sparrows to be higher than previously thought, with an estimated population of 4,884 singing males in 2001 on reclaimed surface mines in a nine county study area, which encompasses the core of this species' range in The Commonwealth (Mattice et al. 2005). The populations on agricultural grasslands are thought to be modest, but further research is needed to ascertain how important farmland habitats in Pennsylvania are for this species, which is awarded the highest priority for grassland bird conservation in eastern and midwestern North America by *Partners In Flight* (PIF) (Blancher et al. 2007). Another formerly common nesting bird in agricultural areas of Pennsylvania is the upland sandpiper. This species is now rare, almost certainly numbering less than 100 pairs statewide. In neighboring states such of New Jersey and Ohio the small populations of this species are largely restricted to non-farmed sites, such as military areas. In Pennsylvania however, very small numbers of this species can still be found on farmland, but populations are so small and scattered that this species is considered vulnerable to extirpation.

The decline in field nesting birds in Pennsylvania is of conservation concern as is the case across North America. Population estimates derived from *Partners In Flight* (PIF) data (Blancher et al. 2007) suggest that Pennsylvania supports rather modest populations of these species, with the exception of Red-winged Blackbird for which the statewide population estimate is 1.5 million birds (Table 2). Although Pennsylvania supports relatively small proportions of the continental populations of these species, it is imperative that The

Table 2. Population estimates for field nesting birds in Pennsylvania and estimated percentage of the global population forum in the state. Source: Partners in Flight (Blancher et al. 2004)

	Pennsylvania population estimate	% of global population
ring-necked pheasant	20,000	0
killdeer	n.a.	n.a.
horned lark	15,000	0.1
field sparrow	50,000	0.4
vesper sparrow	20,000	0.2
Savannah sparrow	30,000	0.1
grasshopper sparrow	90,000	0.1
Henslow's sparrow	1,900	2.4
bobolink	70,000	0.4
red-winged blackbird	1,500,000	0.7
eastern meadowlark	46,000	0.5

n.a. not available.

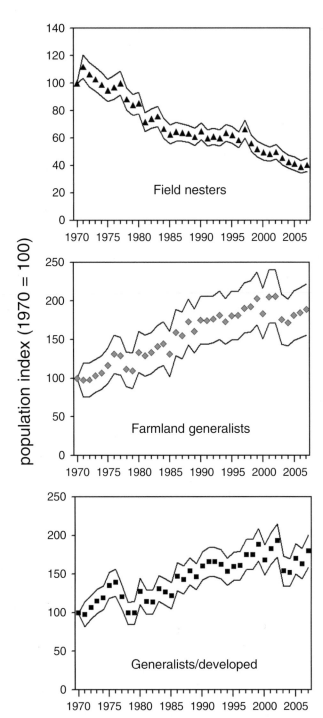

Figure 2: Population indices and 95% confidence intervals of three common bird species guilds in Pennsylvania for 1970 to 2007. See Appendix for methods.

Commonwealth plays its part in their conservation. Grassland bird species in particular are likely to face continued threats throughout their range but especially in the agriculturally intensive Midwest, which could result in peripheral states such as Pennsylvania playing an increasingly important role. During recent years, for example, the rapid expansion of corn production in the Midwest for biofuel production has resulted in concern being expressed for grassland bird populations there (Bies 2006), whereas changes in cropping patterns in the east have been rather modest (Matuszeski 2007). The conservation of the suite of declining common and rare species associated with farmland and grasslands will require species-specific management strategies delivered through a range of programs and initiatives. Some of these initiatives are now discussed.

FARMLAND BIRD CONSERVATION STRATEGIES

Conservation of declining grassland birds and farmland wildlife in general has received a great deal of attention in the last twenty years or so from scientists, conservationists, and policy makers. In order to prevent further declines in farmland wildlife, billions of dollars have been spent preserving remnant grasslands and planting of conservation grasslands through federal programs. Loss of farmland to development has spurred a concerted effort to permanently protect farmland from development and non-agricultural use, protecting and preserving millions of acres of farmland across the USA. However, despite these considerable efforts, farmland bird populations have continued to decline both in Pennsylvania and elsewhere. Stemming and reversing these declines require that farmland conservation efforts are ramped up. This will require an increased commitment to conservation through future farm bills, maintenance and enhancement of partnerships between government and non-government organizations, and a further commitment to research, such that management is adaptive and based on the best evidence for ways of combining agricultural and wildlife needs.

As there is very little natural grassland in Pennsylvania, conservation efforts for grassland obligate bird species have primarily focused on preserving and improving farmland habitats. It should be noted though that a considerable population of grassland obligate birds is found in reclaimed surface mines (see Chapter 6, this publication), and that conservation of primary surface mine grasslands, hand-in-hand with farmland conservation, should be a priority.

While native grassland preservation is a primary conservation focus in some states, preservation of farmland in the face of development is a priority in Pennsylvania, which leads the nation in the number of farms and acres preserved. During the last twenty years almost 400,000 acres on over 3,500 farms have been protected through the Pennsylvania Agricultural Conservation Easement Purchase Program, many of these in the southeast of the state, where development pressure is greatest (PDA 2008). Such measures are commendable for a broad range of conservation and socio-economic reasons; however, declining farmland birds will only benefit if those preserved acres are managed sympathetically for the species concerned.

Managing farmland for wildlife typically involves one of two approaches: 1) land retirement and planting of conservation cover, and 2) adjustment of crop management, for example by restricting mowing during the bird nesting season. The primary means of delivering these measures has been through farm bill programs. The most notable of these is the Conservation Reserve Program (CRP), which was introduced in the 1985 Food Security Act, with key aims of curtailing excess agricultural production and reducing soil erosion (Isaacs and Howell 1988). The CRP requires that farmers take erodible land out of arable production and sow grass, for contract periods of 10–15 years, in return for a rental income. Millions of acres of grassland have been created across agricultural areas of the United States through CRP. Numerous studies have shown that the new habitat created by CRP has benefited grassland bird species (e.g. Johnson and Igle 1995, Ryan et al. 1998, Swanson et al. 1999), but most grassland bird species have continued to decline since the introduction of CRP (Norment 2002), suggesting that it has not been sufficient to compensate for continuing population losses across the farmed landscape.

In some states CRP enrollment has idled huge areas of farmland but enrollment of agricultural land in Pennsylvania was modest through the late 1980s and 1990s (Lubowski et al. 2006). Further, the original aims of CRP were focused on reducing soil erosion and improving water quality. The program was not specifically designed with bird conservation in mind and hence mowing was allowed during the bird breeding season, which may have reduced the value of this new habitat for some grassland birds (Horn and Koford 2000). The potential of CRP lands for birds was widely recognized during the 1990s however, and the with the aims of expanding coverage specifically targeting grassland bird conservation, the Conservation Reserve Enhancement Program (CREP) was introduced in Pennsylvania 2000. By 2006, more than 163,000 acres of grassland and 30,000 of acres of other wildlife habitat had been created in Pennsylvania (USDA 2007). Research has shown that grassland birds are utilizing this habitat in PA but in rather modest numbers (Wentworth et al. in prep). Even so, by 2005 there was already evidence of some population level responses to these new habitats in the 20 counties of south-central Pennsylvania where CREP was rolled-out in 2000. For example, there were significant increases in eastern meadowlark populations in areas where the highest proportion of farmland was enrolled in CREP (Wilson and Brittingham 2007). However, BBS data for Pennsylvania do not indicate that CREP has, as yet, been sufficient to stem long-term declines in grassland bird populations at the state level. Further monitoring is needed to assess potential usage of CREP by grassland birds in other parts of the state. It should also be noted that while CREP fields provide suitable habitat for some ground-nesting species, such as grasshopper sparrow and eastern meadowlark, the dense vegetation typical of these fields (Wentworth et al in prep) is not suitable for other rapidly declining species that prefer sparse or short ground cover, including horned lark and vesper sparrow.

In addition to CRP and CREP, there are other farm bill programs that aim to increase the wildlife value of farmland. These include the Environmental Quality Incentives Program (EQIP) and Wildlife Habitat Incentive Program (WHIP). EQIP aims to support environmentally friendly pest management and conservation projects on working agricultural lands. While the primary aims of the program are to reduce soil erosion and improve water quality, there are also financial incentives to manage hay and small grain crops with the aims of providing bird nesting habitat. More than 53,000 acres of working farmland were enrolled in EQIP in Pennsylvania in 2007 alone (NRCS 2008), and while the proportion of these acres that are managed for birds may be small, the potential for this program to improve the value of farmland for wildlife is considerable due to its scale. Conversely, although WHIP is focused solely on developing and improving wildlife habitat, it is a much smaller program, and while local benefits for wildlife might be considerable, it is unlikely that without major expansion, it will be sufficient to contribute significantly to farmland bird population at the state scale. However, WHIP could potentially allow for very targeted conservation measures for rare species, such as the upland sandpiper. EQIP and WHIP have the potential to provide considerable benefits to farmland birds in Pennsylvania, but as yet there has been no assessment of their impacts on bird populations.

Maintaining populations of ground nesting farmland birds in Pennsylvania will require a multipronged approach. For Henslow's sparrow, the maintenance of grassland habitat on reclaimed surface mines is of utmost importance – populations of this species within agricultural areas are very low, and, as suggested by the fact that this species is now rarely found away from areas with surface mine grasslands, may not be viable. Such actions will benefit several other bird species that maintain substantial population in these non-agricultural grasslands. Bobolinks, eastern meadowlarks, grasshopper sparrows are still to be found in appreciable numbers within agricultural grasslands and as such will be vulnerable to future changes in grassland management practices. Subsidizing farmers to maintain grassland in a suitable condition, principally by delaying harvesting, could potentially benefit these species. Such schemes could be targeted to areas in which these species are concentrated. Other ground nesters, including horned lark, vesper sparrow, and savannah sparrow, are vulnerable to changes in agricultural practices on both grassland and tilled land. All these species reach their highest densities in very open mixed farmland (pers. obs.) in Pennsylvania, but our knowledge of the causes of their declines and possible methods of ameliorating them is scant.

Conservation efforts for farmland birds in Pennsylvania should be based on sound science. Often, conservation management practices are guided by studies of these species in their core ranges further west but the habitat requirements of these species may be very different in Pennsylvania. It is recommended that a continuing program of research of the ecology of these species and trialing methods of incorporating conservation practices into the conventional farming system would provide the best way of ensuring that these species are maintained as widespread breeding species in Pennsylvania. Such efforts should be coupled with targeted conservation and management of key areas, including agricultural lands and reclaimed surface mines, such that viable source populations are secured. Federal conservation programs provide the platform for such efforts, but it is vital that management is adapted and informed by future monitoring, such that the best outcomes and best value from public funds are achieved. Non-government organizations, universities, and other research groups should be involved wherever possible, to provide the scientific knowledge and conservation impetus that will be needed to prevent the agricultural fields of Pennsylvania from becoming deserted of wildlife value.

FUTURE CONSERVATION ISSUES

Agriculture in Pennsylvania will almost certainly continue to change and adapt to the demands for food and fiber for human consumption. Whether large-scale biomass production, climate change, and other causes of changing cropping patterns become major issues in Pennsylvania is still open for debate. However, projected future human population growth both globally and in the United States (United Nations 2004) and increased affluence will require a tripling of agricultural output in the current century (Avery 2007);

with increasingly globalized commodity markets, it's almost certain that agricultural lands within Pennsylvania will be required to contribute to this increased demand. This is a daunting prospect, but during the last 50 years we have constantly risen to the challenge of increasing agricultural yields—a considerable feat that should be applauded. However, we are increasingly aware that the environmental costs within agro-ecosystems have been considerable (Tilman 1999). The loss of farmland birds has been one of the most obvious consequences of these changes and has also been an important impetus to re-evaluate agricultural practices. Farmland conservation programs will need to adapt to changes in global agricultural commodity markets. The success of these programs is wholly dependent on the willingness of private landowners to engage in them, and the willingness of taxpayer to foot most of the bill. Increased demand for agricultural land could drive a shift of conservation programs from conservation reserve/set-aside, to increasing the wildlife potential of working lands through programs such as EQIP. The consequences of such potential shifts need to be carefully assessed; currently we are not in a good position to do so, due to a lack of long-term monitoring efforts.

The future of field-nesting bird species is far from secure, and while most of these species are not imminently threatened with extirpation from the state, without continued conservation efforts they could continue to disappear from large swathes of the state. Although specific changes in agriculture are difficult to predict and are sometimes rapid, we must continue to ensure that wildlife needs are considered alongside those of agricultural producers and consumers. Ecologists and conservationists need to be proactive in working alongside the agriculture industry to find pragmatic solutions for maintaining these birds on our working lands. Now, more than ever, farmland wildlife is dependent upon us finding ways to ensure that food production and providing wildlife habitat are compatible goals.

LITERATURE CITED

Askins, R. A. 1999. History of grassland birds in eastern North America. In: P. D. Vickery and J. R. Herkert, editors. Studies in Avian Biology, No 19. Lawrence, KS: Cooper Ornithological Society; 60–71.

Avery, D. T. 2007. How high yield farming saves nature. Society 44:137–143.

Bies, L. 2006. The Biofuels Explosion: Is Green Energy Good for Wildlife? Wildlife Society Bulletin 34:1203–1205.

Blancher, P. J. , K. V. Rosenberg, A. O. Panjabi, B. Altman, J. Bart, C. J. Beardmore, G. S. Butcher, D. Demarest, R. Dettmers, E. H. Dunn, W. Easton, W. C. Hunter, E. E. Iñigo-Elias, D. N. Pashley, C. J. Ralph, T. D. Rich, C. M. Rustay, J. M. Ruth, and T. C. Will. 2007. Guide to the Partners in Flight Population Estimates Database. Version: North American Landbird Conservation Plan 2004. Partners in Flight Technical Series No 5.

Brauning, D. W. 1992. Atlas of breeding birds in Pennsylvania. University of Pittsburgh Press, Pittsburgh, Pennsylvania.

Brennan, L. A., and W. P. Kuvlesky. 2005. North American grassland birds: An unfolding conservation crisis? Journal of Wildlife Management 69:1–13.

Diefenbach, D. R., C. F. Riegner, and S. Hardisky. 2000. Harvest and reporting-rates of game-farm ring-necked pheasants. Wildlife Society Bulletin 28:1050–1059.

Donald P. F., R.E. Green, and M. F. Heath. 2001. Agricultural intensification and the collapse of Europe's farmland bird populations. Proceedings of the Royal Society of London (B) 268:25–29.

Fawley, B. J., and L. B. Best. 1991. Effects of mowing on breeding bird abundance and species composition in alfalfa fields. Wildlife Society Bulletin 19:135–142.

Goodrich, L., M. Brittingham, J. Bishop, and P. Barber. 2002. Wildlife habitat in Pennsylvania: past, present future. Unpublished report to DCNR. http://www.dcnr.state.pa.us/wlhabitat/. Last accessed 7/8/2008.

Gregory, R. D., A. van Strien, P. Vorisek, A. W. Gmelig Meyling, D. G. Noble, R. P. B. Foppen, and D. W. Gibbons. 2005. Developing indicators for European birds. Philosophic Transactions of the Royal Society (B) 360:269–288.

Horn, D. T., and R. R. Koford. 2000. Relation of Grassland Bird Abundance to Mowing of Conservation Reserve Program Fields in North Dakota. Wildlife Society Bulletin 28:653–659.

Isaacs, B. and D. Howell. 1988. Opportunities for enhancing wildlife benefits through the Conservation Reserve Program. Transactions of the North American Wildlife and Natural Resources Conference 53:222–231.

Johnson, D. H., and L. D. Igl. 1995. Contributions of the Conservation Reserve Program to populations of breeding birds in North Dakota. Wilson Bulletin 107:709–718.

Klinger, S. 2008. Ring-necked Pheasant Management Plan for Pennsylvania 2008–2017. Draft report. The Pennsylvania Game Commission, Harrisburg, Pennsylvania.

LaDeau, S. L., A. M. Kilpatrick, and P. P. Marra. 2007. West Nile virus emergence and large-scale declines of North American bird populations. Nature 447:710–714.

Latham, R., and J. F. Thorne. 2007. Keystone Grasslands: Restoration and Reclamation of Native Grasslands, Meadows, and Savannas in Pennsylvania State Parks and State Game Lands. For the Wild Resource Conservation Program, Pennsylvania Department of Conservation and Natural Resources, Harrisburg, Pennsylvania. 100pp.

Lubowski, R. N., S. Bucholtz, R. Claassen, M. J. Roberts, J. C. Cooper, A. Gueorguieva, and R. Johansson. 2006. Environmental Effects of Agricultural Land-Use Change: The Role of Economics and Policy. Economic Research Report No. 25. United States Department of Agriculture, Economic Research Service. Washington, DC.

Mattice, J. A., D. W. Brauning, and D. R. Diefenbach. 2005. Abundance of Grassland Sparrows on Reclaimed Surface Mines in Western Pennsylvania. United States Department of Agriculture Forest Service Gen. Tech. Rep. PSW-GTR-191.

Mattison, E. H. A., and K. Norris. 2005. Bridging the gaps between agricultural policy, land-use and biodiversity. Trends in Ecology and Evolution 20:610–616.

Matuszeski, B. (ed). 2007. Biofuels And the Bay: Getting It Right To Benefit Farms, Forests and the Chesapeake. A report of The Chesapeake Bay Commission. Annapolis, Maryland.

McWilliams, G. M., and D. W. Brauning. 2000. The Birds of Pennsylvania. Cornell University Press, Ithaca, New York.

Myers, W., J. Bishop, R. Brooks, T. O'Connell, D. Argent, G. Storm, J. Stauffer, and R. Carline. 2000. Pennsylvania Gap Analysis Project: Leading Landscapes for Collaborative Conservation. School of Forest Resources & Cooperative Fish and Wildlife Research Unit and Environmental Resources Research Institute, The Pennsylvania State University, University Park, Pennsylvania.

Natural Resource Conservation Service (NRCS). 2008. Pennsylvania NRCS Programs. http://www.pa.nrcs.usda.gov/programs. Last accessed 7/8/2008.

Norment, C. 2002. On grassland bird conservation in the Northeast. Auk 119:271–279.

Noss, R. F., E. T. La Roe, and J. M. Scott. 1995. Endangered Ecosystems of the United States: A Preliminary Assessment of Loss and Degradation. USGS National Biological Resources Division. Biological Report 28, National Biological Service, Washington, D.C.

Ormsby, T., E. Napolean, R. Burke, C. Groessl, and L. Feaster. 2004. Getting to know ArcGIS desktop: basics of ArcView, ArcEditor, and ArcInfo. ESRI Press, Redlands, California.

Pannekoek, J., and A. J. van Strien. 2001. TRIM 3 Manual. Trends and Indices for Monitoring data Research paper no. 0102. Voorburg, The Netherlands.

Pennsylvania Department of Agriculture (PDA). 2008. Pennsylvania Farmland Protected by Preservation Board. www.agriculture.state.pa.us/agriculture/cwp/view.asp?Q=149320&A=390. Last accessed 7/8/2008.

Pennsylvania Department of Environmental Protection (PA DEP). 2008. Pennsylvania's Environmental Heritage Timeline. http://www.depweb.state.pa.us/heritage/cwp/view.asp?a=3&q=442704#1800. Last accessed 7/8/2008.

Pennsylvania Fish and Boat Commission and Pennsylvania Game Commission (PFBC and PGC). 2005. Pennsylvania Comprehensive Wildlife Conservation Strategy. The Pennsylvania Game Commission and Pennsylvania Fish and Boat Commission, Harrisburg, Pennsylvania.

Ryan, M. R., L. W. Burger, and E. W. Kurzejeski. 1998. The impact of CRP on avian wildlife: a review. Journal of Production Agriculture 11:61–66.

Sauer, J. R., J. E. Hines, and J. Fallon. 2008. The North American Breeding Bird Survey, Results and Analysis 1966–2007. Version 6.2.2008. USGS Patuxent Wildlife Research Center, Laurel, Maryland.

Stone, W. 1894. Birds of eastern Pennsylvania and New Jersey. Delaware Valley Ornithological Club, Philadelphia, Pennsylvania.

Swanson, D. A., D. P. Scott, and D. L. Risley. 1999. Wildlife benefits of the Conservation Reserve Program in Ohio. Journal of Soil and Water Conservation 54:390–394.

ter Braak, C. J. F., and P. Šmilaur. 2002. Canoco 4.5. Biometris, Wageningen University, Netherlands.

Tilman, D. 1999. Global environmental impacts of agricultural expansion: the need for sustainable and efficient practices. Proceedings of the National Academy of Sciences of the United States of America 96:5995–6000.

Todd, W. E. C. 1940. Birds of western Pennsylvania. University of Pittsburgh Press, Pittsburgh, Pennsylvania.

United Nations. 2004. World Population to 2300. United Nations, New York.

United States Department of Agriculture (USDA). 2007. Conservation Reserve Program – Monthly Contract Report, November 2007. USDA, Farm Service Agency.

Vickery, P. 2001. The recent advances in grassland bird research: where do we go from here? Auk 118:1–7.

Wentworth, K., M. Brittingham, and A. Wilson (in prep). Conservation Reserve Enhancement Program Fields: Benefits for Grassland, Scrub and Edge Species.

Wilson, A., and M. Brittingham. 2007. Impacts of the Conservation Reserve Enhancement Program on the Regional Trends in Bird and Eastern Cottontail Populations. Final Job Report 01004B. Pennsylvania Game Commission, Harrisburg, Pennsylvania.

APPENDIX. Analytical methods

Breeding Bird Survey population trends for 1970–2007 were estimated using program TRIM (TRends and Indices for Monitoring data). TRIM is statistical software to analyze time-series of counts with missing observations, using Poisson regression (Pannekoek and van Strien 2001). Analysis was restricted to 110 species for which there was sufficient data to calculate population indices. The linear population trend for the period 1970 to 2007 was estimated from the modeled slope parameter. The direction and significance of the trend is classified according to the overall slope as well as its 95% confidence interval (= slope +/– 1.96 times the standard error of the slope).

- Strong increase – increase significantly more than 5% per year.
- Moderate increase – significant increase, but not significantly more than 5% per year.
- Stable – no significant increase or decline, and it is certain that trends are less than 5% per year.
- Uncertain – no significant increase or decline, but not certain if trends are less than 5% per year.
- Moderate decline – significant decline, but not significantly more than 5% per year.
- Steep decline – decline significantly more than 5% per year

Redundancy Analysis (RDA) was used to relate bird community composition to land cover data, with the aim of defining guilds of bird species that are characteristic of farmland in Pennsylvania. Program CANOCO (ter Braak and Šmilaur 2002) was used to produce an ordination bi-plot which shows linear relationships between BBS counts and land cover (year 2000) types for each survey route (n=101). To ensure temporal compatibility between bird counts and land cover data, the mean BBS counts for each route for the years 1998–2002, within 2 years of land cover data, were used. Land cover data were derived from Landsat 7 satellite imagery as part of a cooperative project between the U.S. Geological Survey (USGS) and the U.S. Environmental Protection Agency (USEPA). ArcGIS (Ormsby et al. 2004) was used to extract the land cover information for 400m buffers around each BBS routes. Land cover types were grouped into eight categories: water, developed, hay, arable, coniferous/mixed forest, deciduous forest, wetland, and transitional/other. Species closest to the origin of the bi-plot are those which show the least specialization (are found in most habitats) and are considered habitat generalists. They were combined with species associated with the "developed" land cover gradient into a "Generalists/developed" bird species guild. Species associated with "arable" and "hay" were considered farmland species. These species were further divided into two guilds: those that nest within grass and arable fields – the "Field nesters" species guild, and other species – the "Farmland generalists" guild. All other species were associated primarily with forested, transitional, and wetlands and are not therefore considered in this analysis.

Population trends across species guilds were estimated by averaging trends of species within that guild. This average can be considered to be an indicator index for a group of birds that share broadly similar ecological requirements (Gregory et al. 2005). The geometric mean was used as the average measure of population change. Note that this is not weighted by population size; therefore, the relative population change of a scarce species has the same effect on the index as that for a common species. The variance for each index (I) was calculated as follows:

$$\mathrm{var}(I) \approx \left(\frac{I}{T}\right)^2 \sum_t \left(\frac{\mathrm{var}(I_t)}{I_t^2}\right)$$

where there are T indices to be averaged and the index for each species is denoted I_t. Standard errors (SE) and 95% confidence intervals (1.96 * SE) could then be calculated (Gregory et al. 2005).

Avian Ecology and Conservation: A Pennsylvania Focus with National Implications. Edited by S. K. Majumdar, T. L. Master, M. C. Brittingham, R. M. Ross, R. S. Mulvihill and J. E. Huffman. © 2010. The Pennsylvania Academy of Science.

Chapter 17

Eastern Hemlock Decline and Its Effect on Pennsylvania's Birds

Michael C. Allen[1] and James Sheehan, Jr.[2]

[1]Department of Biological Sciences, East Stroudsburg University, 200 Prospect St., East Stroudsburg, Pennsylvania, USA 18301-2999
michaelcobballen@yahoo.com

[2]Division of Forestry & Natural Resources, West Virginia University, Morgantown, WV 26506-6125

HEMLOCK IMPORTANCE AND HISTORICAL OVERVIEW

Eastern hemlock (*Tsuga canadensis* [L.] Carr.), in addition to being the state tree, is of special historic, aesthetic, and ecological value to Pennsylvania. As recently as the 1890's, Pennsylvania contained the largest source of hemlock timber in the world (the Allegheny High Plateau), and was home to a massive hemlock-based tanning and lumber industry (Whitney 1990). Though these activities considerably diminished its pre-colonial abundance (Whitney 1990, Bürgi et al. 2000), hemlock still dominates roughly 166,000 ha of forest in the state, including over a thousand hectares of old growth (Bjorkbom and Larson 1977, Alerich 1993). Our most shade-tolerant conifer, hemlock typically occurs in nearly pure stands along shady ravines or on moist slopes, and is most common in the northern counties and south along the Appalachian ridges (Fig. 2; Hough and Forbes 1943, Prasad and Iverson 2003).

In addition to its historic and aesthetic significance, eastern hemlock provides important wildlife habitat and enhances regional biodiversity. The unique microclimate created by shade-tolerant lower branches, acidic leaf litter, and a sparse shrub layer supports distinctive bird communities, as well as other dependent fauna (Yamasaki et al. 2000, Snyder et al. 2002, Ross et al. 2003, Ross et al. 2004). As a result, hemlock has been described as a foundation species, whose presence disproportionately influences ecosystem properties and community composition (Ellison et al. 2005). Birds typical of hemlock forests in Pennsylvania include the Blackburnian warbler (*Dendroica fusca*), black-throated green warbler (*D. virens*), blue-headed vireo (*Vireo solitarius*), and Acadian flycatcher (*Empidonax virescens*), among others (McWilliams and Brauning 2000, Ross et al. 2004, Swartzentruber 2004, Becker et al. 2008).

HEMLOCK WOOLLY ADELGID
Origins and Current Extent

The most serious current threat to eastern hemlock is the hemlock woolly adelgid (HWA; *Adelges tsugae* Annand), an aphid-like insect native to Japan. Introduced to the western United States in the 1920s, it reached Virginia by the 1950s and southeastern

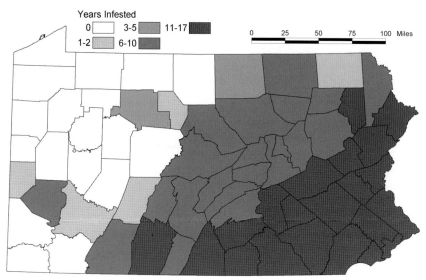

Figure 1: Pennsylvania counties - years infested with the hemlock wooly adelgid: 1991-2007 (Source: U.S. Forest Service 2008).

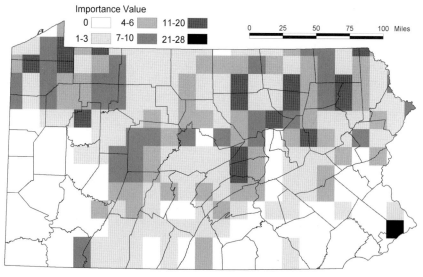

Figure 2: Eastern hemlock importance values in Pennsylvania based on the U.S. Forest Service's Forest Inventory and Analysis program (Source: Prasad and Iverson 2003).

Pennsylvania by the late 1960s (Gouger 1971, Loope 2004). Hemlock woolly adelgid was generally regarded as a pest of ornamental trees until the 1980s when reports of widespread defoliation and mortality in natural stands began to appear (Loope 2004).

From the southeast corner of the state, HWA spread north and west at about 20–30 km/year (Fig. 1). It arrived in northeastern Pennsylvania by 1989, Harrisburg by ca. 1995, and the Pittsburgh area by 2002 (Evans 2004, U.S. Forest Service 2008). Currently, HWA occupies roughly the eastern 2/3 of the state, including 49 of 67 counties (U.S. Forest Service 2008). Given this rate of spread, HWA could affect all Pennsylvania counties by as early as 2013 (Souto et al. 1996). Though recent estimates suggest advances of only 8 km/year in the colder northern counties, chances that these areas will remain adelgid-free are not hopeful (Evans and Gregoire 2007). Nationally, the range of HWA now stretches from Maine to Georgia, and continues to expand on all fronts (U.S. Forest Service 2008).

Life Cycle and Dispersal

The lifecycle of the hemlock woolly adelgid (as with most aphid-like insects) is complicated and multi-generational. Most relevant to hemlock decline are the two asexual wingless generations: "sistens" and "progrediens." The lifecycle begins in early spring when eggs laid by overwintering sistens hatch into tiny "crawlers" (the progrediens generation). These move about on the foliage until they find a suitable hemlock needle. Here, they insert their needle-like mouthparts into the vascular tissue of the needle, and remain for the rest of their lives (ca. 3 months). With maturity, they develop a white, waxy covering (the "wool"), which ultimately conceals the eggs laid before their death in early summer (Fig. 3). These eggs hatch into more crawlers (the sistens generation), which again settle on vacant hemlock needles and spend the summer in a dormant state. In the fall (and during

Figure 3: Hemlock woolly adelgid ovisacs on eastern hemlock twigs. The covering of waxy "wool" secreted by adult adelgids protects adults, eggs, and young from predation and desiccation (Photo: Terry Master).

winter warm spells) they resume growth, and by spring, are mature enough to lay eggs and continue the cycle (McClure 1996). Dispersal occurs during the crawler stage of either generation by wind or phoresy on the fur/feathers of mammals or birds (McClure 1990).

MECHANISMS OF HEMLOCK DECLINE

Impacts on Individual Trees

While a single adelgid represents a minute stress to a hemlock tree, the combined effect of high populations (i.e., thousands per m of branch) deprives the tree of water and nutrients (Fig. 3; McClure 1991, Wallace and Hain 2000). The result is needle loss, branch mortality, and ultimately death, typically within 4 to 10 years (Fig. 4; McClure 1991). Unfor-

Figure 4:   Eastern hemlock branch killed by hemlock woolly adelgid. Lower branches such as this one are often the first to die (Photo: Terry Master).

tunately, HWA also acts synergistically with other native and exotic insect pests (see Blumenthal and Werner 2005). Notably, the elongate hemlock scale (*Fiorinia externa* Ferris) often co-occurs with HWA, and alone can cause death within 10 years (McClure 2002).

Environmental factors, such as cold and drought, also play a role in hemlock mortality. Cold is beneficial to hemlocks as it kills overwintering HWA nymphs, while drought is detrimental as it exacerbates water shortages created by the thirsty adelgids (McClure 1991, Shields and Cheah 2005). The lack of cold-hardiness in HWA is somewhat hopeful, as the coldest areas of the state—the northeast corner and the Allegheny High Plateau— are also home to the greatest concentrations of hemlocks and hemlock birds (Brauning 1992a, Prasad and Iverson 2003). Similarly, hemlocks growing in moister situations (e.g., close to streams) may be less prone to drought stress, and have been found to survive better than those in drier situations (e.g., Becker et al. 2008).

Impacts at the Stand Level

Branch mortality due to HWA generally proceeds from the bottom branches upward, resulting initially in a more open forest (Evans 2003). Ultimately, crown death allows light to penetrate areas of former deep shade, and shrubs and hardwood saplings proliferate (Kizlinski et al. 2002, Small et al. 2005). The altered vegetation profile and increased snag density in heavily infested stands allow birds typical of deciduous/shrubby habitats, as well as woodpeckers, to increase in abundance (Tingley et al. 2002, Becker et al. 2008). Other species decrease as preferred foraging and/or nest sites disappear (Tingley et al. 2002). Ground- and stream-foraging birds may also be affected, as significant, if less obvious, changes also occur in soil (increased pH, nitrogen) and stream properties (increased temperature, decreased flow; Kizlinski et al. 2002, Evans 2004).

MONITORING AND SURVEY TECHNIQUES

Remote Sensing and Geographic Information Systems (GIS)

Compared with historical forest pathogen outbreaks (e.g., chestnut blight), we are far more prepared today to monitor the spread of HWA, evaluate its impacts, and to prioritize areas in need of management. This is largely a result of advances in remote sensing and geographic information system (GIS) technologies. In Pennsylvania, hemlock forests are currently being mapped by several state and federal agencies using digital aerial photos and GIS (Williams et al. 2002, Evans 2003, Blumenthal and Werner 2005). Methods have also been developed to remotely quantify hemlock defoliation with satellite imagery by measuring changes in reflectance (Royle and Lathrop 2002). These techniques have allowed ecologists to track the spread of HWA, locate ecologically important stands, and organize monitoring efforts for at-risk species (Evans 2003, Ross et al. 2004, Evans and Gregoire 2007).

Ground-based Survey Protocols

Numerous ground-based HWA monitoring techniques have also been developed (e.g., Costa and Onken 2006). These measurements may be classified into three categories: (1) adelgid abundance; (2) tree/branch health; and (3) hemlock mortality. Measurement of adelgid abundance usually involves recording the presence/absence or density of HWA on twigs (Wallace and Hain 2000, Evans 2003). The proportion of twigs on a branch that are sprouting new growth provides a measure of branch/tree health that is correlated with HWA abundance (Evans 2003). Whole branches or tree crowns can also be classified into ordinal categories based on health (Evans 2003, Sheehan 2003). Hemlock mortality (the percentage of dead hemlocks) has also been used as a measure of HWA impact (Tingley et al. 2002, Becker et al. 2008). All measurements mentioned are generally collected as a random sample throughout the study site, and then averaged to provide an index of infestation, tree health, and/or mortality (Costa and Onken 2006).

HEMLOCK ECOLOGY

It is largely through hemlock's unique structure that the tree exerts its influence on the physical and biological functioning of the communities it inhabits and often dominates. Mature individuals are characterized by a pyramidal crown, the apex of which is often drooping, and a conical form supported by a straight central trunk. The rather slender, flexible branches containing soft, short (1/2 inch), and flat deep-green needles are often gently arching lower on the trunk and can originate nearly to the ground in an open environment (Gilman and Watson 1994). Due to the tree's extreme shade tolerance, even in deep forest the hemlock's canopy may extend well down into the midstory (Ward et al. 2004). This increases the heterogeneity of the forest's vertical structure with important consequences for avian habitat selection (Benzinger 1994, Yamasaki et al. 2000). Fully-stocked stands are moreover characterized by a dense canopy, dense shading, and a deep duff layer which can result in a practically non-existent understory (Burns and Honkala 1990). In Pennsylvania, some shade-tolerant shrubs (e.g. *Rhododendron spp.*) can become abundant, as is often the case in the southern part of the hemlock's range (Ellison et al. 2005).

Other structural characteristics are apt to strongly influence avian as well as other hemlock-associated biodiversity. Hemlock stands are generally warmer in winter and cooler in summer than hardwood-dominated ones (Ellison et al. 2005) and in riparian situations reduce the likelihood of stream-drying (Snyder et al. 2002). Hemlock's year-round retention of dense foliage functions to block wind and absorb solar radiation, which contributes to favorable microclimatic conditions in winter (Evans 2004). This provides protected roost sites and abundant winter cover for many species of wildlife including long-eared owls and ruffed grouse (Benzinger 1994, Yamasaki et al. 2000). In contrast, the cool, moist habitat in summer relative to hardwood-dominated stands may favor some nesting species (Benzinger 1994). The abundant vertical layering of hemlock branches throughout a stand provide many nesting opportunities for species associated with the low, mid, or upper canopy. For birds that prefer to nest in its branches, the abundance of hemlock throughout the nesting territory may also suggest other apparently suitable nest sites that must be searched by a predator, thus increasing the probability of survival (Martin and Roper 1988). While hemlock may not provide greater opportunity for cavity nesters than hardwoods (reviewed in Benzinger 1994), the tendency for the tree to be long-lived may favor development of cavities important to some species (Yamasaki et al. 2000).

In addition to cover, hemlock is directly important as a food resource. The seeds of the small 3/4 inch cones, which mature from September to October and are available well into the winter months (Burns and Honkala 1990), support granivores such as winter-irruptive finches (e.g., siskins, grosbeaks, crossbills), chickadees, and goldfinches (Yamasaki et al.

2000). While insect abundance and diversity is generally lower in hemlocks than in hardwoods (Futuyma and Gould 1979), its foliage is likely an important year-round resource for gleaning insectivores. The wide ridges and furrows of the trunks of mature trees, as well as retained and fallen dead wood, supply prey for bark foragers and woodpeckers. Indirectly, food resources for insectivores are likely a function of the hemlock's influence on microclimate conditions (e.g., temperature and moisture). In riparian areas, hemlock appears to enhance aquatic biodiversity (Snyder et al. 2002), a factor likely to cascade up through the avian food chain via emergent aquatic macroinvertebrates.

HEMLOCK BIRDS

"High up in the hemlocks the drowsy sounds of the Black-throated Green Warbler are heard, and the lively chatter of the Blackburnian Warbler catches the ear. Is not this a bit of northern Maine?"—Dwight (1892:132)

Largely as a consequence of its structural uniqueness, hemlock habitat attracts distinctive breeding bird communities. While no species is found exclusively in hemlock forests, several are either regionally restricted or more abundant there; thus, hemlock habitat supports a significant proportion of their populations. In Pennsylvania, this applies to several species, which vary in the strength and geographic extent of their hemlock association, and therefore in their vulnerability to hemlock decline. A common denominator among many (but not all) hemlock birds in the state is a northern distribution (see above quotation) and an affinity for conifers. Here we discuss several possible at-risk species in the state in order of their suspected vulnerability.

Blackburnian Warbler

Perhaps the most hemlock-dependent songbird in the state, the blackburnian warbler prefers hemlock to other conifers, and rarely inhabits hardwood-dominated stands (Todd 1940, Mulvihill 1992a, McWilliams and Brauning 2000). Early Pennsylvania ornithologists invariably noted this preference (Dwight 1892, Todd 1893, Baily 1896, Cope 1898, Harlow 1912), and Alexander Wilson, while collecting in Pennsylvania, even mistakenly dubbed the female a new species, the hemlock warbler (Bent 1953). More recently, comparisons of hemlock and hardwood sites in eastern (Ross et al. 2004, Swartzentruber 2004), central (Becker et al. 2008), and western Pennsylvania (M. A., unpublished data) found them to be present only in hemlock stands. Extremely high populations (> 200 territories per 100 ha) are reported from old growth hemlock forests on the Allegheny Plateau (Haney 1999). In Connecticut, Tingley et al. (2002) found Blackburnian warblers only at their least-infested hemlock sites.

Black-throated Green Warbler

This warbler is less restricted to coniferous habitat than the preceding, and can even be found in pure hardwood forests at higher elevations (> 300 m; Todd 1893, Santner 1992). Nevertheless, most authors consider it a characteristic bird of hemlock stands (Baily 1896, Cope 1898, Harlow 1912, McWilliams and Brauning 2000), and it is generally much more abundant in hemlock versus nearby hardwoods (e.g., Haney 1999, Ross et al. 2004, Swartzentruber 2004, Becker et al. 2008). These warblers may be especially sensitive to hemlock decline, as one study found them to be 15 times more abundant in healthy versus infested stands in Connecticut (Tingley et al. 2002).

Blue-headed Vireo

The blue-headed vireo can be found breeding in deciduous, coniferous, or mixed forests in the higher elevations of the state, though hemlock is often considered its characteristic habitat (Baily 1896, Cope 1898, McWilliams and Brauning 2000). Indeed, at least in northern Pennsylvania, they can be far more abundant in hemlock stands versus surrounding hardwoods (Haney 1999, Ross et al. 2004, Swartzentruber 2004). Territory densities in Pennsylvania hemlock forests average 44 per 100 ha (n = 3 studies), relative to 3 and 8 per 100 ha in hardwood and "young, managed" forest, respectively (Haney and Schaadt 1996, Ross et al. 2004, Becker et al. 2008). In Connecticut, populations were about 2.5 times higher in healthy versus heavily infested stands (Tingley et al. 2002).

Acadian Flycatcher

Acadian flycatchers differ from the preceding species in that they approach their northern (rather than southern) breeding range limit in Pennsylvania. While commonly associated with hardwoods in the South, hemlock-lined streams form the primary habitat for this species in the Northeast (Benzinger 1994, Lyons and Livingston 1997, Tingley et al. 2002, Ross et al. 2004). In Pennsylvania, the association is most pronounced in the northern counties and elsewhere in the Appalachians, where several studies have found considerably higher populations in hemlock relative to nearby hardwoods (Haney 1999, Ross et al. 2004, Becker et al. 2008). Possible reasons for this association are a preference for an open understory (Wilson and Cooper 1998), and a proclivity for nesting in low hemlock branches (Fig. 5). In hemlock dominated habitat, typically 80 to 100% of nests are placed in hemlocks (Lyons and Livingston 1997, Sheehan 2003, Allen et al. 2006, Becker et al. 2008). Loss of these preferred nest sites due to HWA may contribute to the lower populations observed in infested hemlock stands (Tingley et al. 2002, Sheehan 2003).

Other Species

All Pennsylvania birds that typically associate with northern conifers, likely also inhabit eastern hemlock as it is a major evergreen in the state. This includes, in part, magnolia warbler (*Dendroica magnolia*), golden-crowned kinglet (*Regulus satrapa*), red-breasted nuthatch (*Sitta canadensis*), Swainson's thrush (*Catharus ustulatus*), and northern goshawk (*Accipiter gentiles*). Cope (1898) and others (Todd 1893, Harlow 1912) considered magnolia warbler to be a hemlock associate; however, their tolerance for dense, young conifer stands may make them more resilient to hemlock decline (Mulvihill 1992b). Golden-crowned kinglet and red-breasted nuthatch frequently inhabit native hemlock groves, which likely provide valuable habitat in landscapes with few evergreen plantations (M. A., personal observation). Both Swainson's thrush and northern goshawk are relatively rare breeders found mainly in northern Pennsylvania, and frequently associate with eastern hemlock (Brauning 1992b, Benzinger 1994).

Other potentially vulnerable species include those dependent on habitats that frequently co-occur with hemlock (e.g., *Rhododendron* thickets, ravines). Among these are Canada

Figure 5:   Acadian Flycatcher incubating nest in Eastern Hemlock with thinning foliage resulting
from adelgid infestation (Photo: Terry Master)

warbler (*Wilsonia canadensis*), winter wren (*Troglodytes troglodytes*), and Louisiana
waterthrush (*Seiurus motacilla*). Degradation of hemlock canopies and subsequent
changes in shrub growth and stream properties could prove unfavorable for these species
(Evans 2004).

SPATIO-TEMPORAL PATTERNS OF HEMLOCK DECLINE

The impacts of HWA on hemlock forests are not uniform across the landscape. Remote
sensing analysis of hemlock health over time (1984–1998) in northern New Jersey indicated that decline occurred at differential rates across the region, and that temporal patterns
were clustered spatially (Royal and Lathrop 2002). This analysis identified four general
patterns of decline over the 14-year period: 1) little to moderate apparent decline; 2) severe
decline followed by improvement; 3) severe decline, improvement, and then severe
decline once more; and 4) steady decline to a severe condition. The different spatial patterns and the varying lengths of time over which hemlock habitat is eventually degraded
or disappears entirely will likely have crucial implications for populations of associated
and dependent birds. Factoring in the management decisions (see below) and other potential anthropogenic and stochastic environmental influences affecting hemlock decline will
further complicate predictions of avian abundance and occurrence. For instance, aggressive efforts to control HWA through biological means in areas of the Delaware Water Gap

National Recreation Area appear to have resulted in extended hemlock persistence in a relatively healthy condition despite significant past HWA-induced mortality (Evans 2003, J. Sheehan, personal observation).

MANAGEMENT—PROS AND CONS

Given the grim trajectory of hemlock ecosystems in the region, the question arises as to whether we must be passive observers of hemlock's disappearance, or active participants in an effort to stem the tide? Effective management of HWA at the landscape scale has proven extremely difficult (Ellison et al. 2005). In Pennsylvania, an extensive cooperative management effort has been implemented by the Department of Conservation and Natural Resources (DCNR) hinging around biological control, the most promising (albeit potentially risky) current strategy (Blumenthal and Werner 2005, Ellison et al. 2005). From 1999 to 2004, DCNR released nearly 180,000 adelgid-consuming non-native beetles (mainly the tiny lady beetle, *Sasajiscymnus tsugae* Sasaji and McClure) at 50 locations throughout the state. These beetles have overwintered successfully (Evans 2003, Blumenthal and Werner 2005), but to date have shown only tentative signs of effectively reducing adelgid populations at the landscape level (Cheah et al. 2005). In addition to biological control, DCNR has mapped and prioritized 146 "high value" hemlock stands to receive chemical control by trunk or soil injections of Imidacloprid (DCNR 2008). While this can be costly (ca. $1 per inch of diameter; Blumenthal and Werner 2005) and injurious to native insects, it is the only reliable method of maintaining at least a few representative "pristine" hemlock stands into the future (Putz 2005).

Other potential methods of HWA control and/or remediation have thus far been of limited utility. These include hybridization and the planting of ecological surrogates. Hybridization attempts with resistant hemlocks from Asia and the western U.S. have proven unsuccessful (Blumenthal and Werner 2005). Moreover, it is unknown to what degree the product of such attempts would ecologically resemble eastern hemlock. Replanting efforts with evergreens such as white pine have been undertaken by DCNR (2008); however, from an avian perspective, it is not known whether these shade-intolerant species will be adequate substitutes. Somewhat encouragingly, in New Jersey and parts of New England, black-throated green and blackburnian warblers are known to inhabit spruce plantations, though in lower numbers (Benzinger 1994, Tingley et al. 2002). The logging of eastern hemlocks in anticipation of death by HWA (known as "preemptive logging") is sometimes touted as a remediation practice for HWA (Foster and Orwig 2006). This practice is becoming widespread in New England, where more than 2400 ha were cut in Connecticut in the late 1990's alone (Foster and Orwig 2006). Preemptive logging is likely detrimental to hemlock birds, as it causes more drastic vegetation changes, soil scarification, and greater increases in invasive species than HWA alone (Kizlinski et al. 2002, Foster and Orwig 2006).

In the absence of the discovery of a highly effective biological control agent, the greatest hope for the persistence of eastern hemlock ecosystems in eastern North America is likely to be natural genetic resistance. As discussed above, the severity of HWA infestation across the landscape is often patchy, with some stands appearing to be less affected than others. These stands, if persistent, may become important sources of breeding stock for future replanting or resistance-breeding efforts.

Eastern hemlock survived a similar population bottleneck around 5000 years ago, also likely caused by an herbivorous insect (the hemlock looper; Foster 2000). It is evident that at least some hemlock-associated birds persisted as well. However, human beings have introduced new challenges including forest fragmentation, deer overpopulation, and a warming climate. It is to be hoped that today's hemlock forests and their associated birdlife—either despite us or with our help—will prove their resilience once again.

LITERATURE CITED

Alerich, C. 1993. Forest statistics for Pennsylvania—1978 and 1989. U.S. Forest Service, Resource Bulletin NE-126.
Allen, M. C., J. Sheehan, Jr., T. L. Master, and R. S. Mulvihill. 2006. Breeding biology, natural history, and habitat selection of the Acadian flycatcher (*Empidonax virescens*) in the Ligonier Valley, southwestern Pennsylvania. Powdermill Avian Research Center, Carnegie Museum of Natural History, Rector, Pennsylvania, USA.
Baily, W. L. 1896. Summer birds of northern Elk County, PA. The Auk 13:289–297.
Becker, D. A., M. C. Brittingham, and C. B. Goguen. 2008. Effects of hemlock woolly adelgid on breeding birds at Fort Indiantown Gap, PA. Northeastern Naturalist: in press.
Bent, A. C. 1953. Life histories of North American wood warblers. U.S. National Museum Bulletin Number 203. Washington, D.C.
Benzinger, J. 1994. Hemlock decline and breeding birds. II. Effects of habitat change. Records of New Jersey Birds 20:34–51.
Bjorkbom, J. C., and R. G. Larson. 1977. The Tionesta Scenic and Research Natural Areas. U.S. Forest Service General Technical Report NE-31.
Blumenthal, E. M., and S. M. Werner. 2005. An overview of hemlock woolly adelgid IPM in Pennsylvania: 1999–2004. Pages 220–231 in B.P. Onken and R.C. Reardon, editors. Third symposium on hemlock woolly adelgid in the eastern United States. U.S. Forest Service, FHTET-2005-01.
Brauning, D. (editor) 1992a. Atlas of breeding birds in Pennsylvania. University of Pittsburgh Press, Pittsburgh, Pennsylvania, USA.
_____. 1992b. Swainson's thrush *Catharus ustulatus*. Pages 268–269 in D. Brauning, editor. Atlas of breeding birds in Pennsylvania. University of Pittsburgh Press, Pittsburgh, Pennsylvania, USA.
Bürgi, M., E. W. B. Russell, and G. Motzkin. 2000. Effects of postsettlement human activities on forest composition in the north-eastern United States: a comparative approach. Journal of Biogeography 27:1123–1138.
Burns, R. M., and B. H. Honkala. 1990. Silvics of North America. Volume 1. Conifers. U.S. Forest Service, Agriculture Handbook 654, Washington, D.C.
Cheah, C., M. A. Mayer, D. Palmer, T. Scudder, and R. Chianese. 2005. Assessments of biological control of hemlock woolly adelgid with *Sasajiscymnus tsugae* in Connecticut and New Jersey. Pages 116–130 in B.P. Onken and R.C. Reardon, editors. Third symposium on hemlock woolly adelgid in the eastern United States. U.S. Forest Service, FHTET-2005-01.
Cope, Jr., F. R. 1898. The summer birds of Susquehanna County, Pennsylvania. Proceedings of the Academy of Natural Sciences of Philadelphia 50:76–88.
Costa, S., and B. Onken. 2006. Standardized sampling for detection and monitoring of hemlock woolly adelgid in eastern hemlock forests. U.S. Forest Service, FHTET-2006-16.
DCNR (Pennsylvania Department of Conservation and Natural Resources). 2008. DCNR management of hemlock woolly adelgid. DCNR website, URL: http://www.dcnr.state.pa.us/forestry/woollyadelgid/pestmanagement.aspx (accessed March 2008).
Dwight, Jr., D. 1892. Summer birds of the crest of the Pennsylvania Alleghanies. The Auk 9:129–141.
Ellison, A. M., M. S. Bank, B. D. Clinton, E. A. Colburn, K. Elliott, C. R. Ford, D. R. Foster, B.D. Kloeppel, J. D. Knoepp, G. M. Lovett, J. Mohan, D. A. Orwig, N. L. Rodenhouse, W. V. Sobczak, K. A. Stinson, J. K. Stone, C. M. Swan, J. Thompson, B. von Holle, and J. R. Webster. 2005. Loss of foundation species: consequences for the structure and dynamics of forested ecosystems. Frontiers in Ecology and the Environment 9:479–486.

Evans, A. M., and T. G. Gregoire. 2007. A geographically variable model of hemlock woolly adelgid spread. Biological Invasions 9:369–382.

Evans, R. A. 2003. Hemlock ecosystems and hemlock woolly adelgid at Delaware Water Gap National Recreation Area. National Park Service, Bushkill, Pennsylvania, USA.

_____. 2004. Hemlock woolly adelgid and the disintegration of eastern hemlock ecosystems. Park Science 22:53–56.

Foster, D. R. 2000. Hemlock's future in the context of its history: an ecological perspective. Pages 1–4 in K.A. McManus, K.S. Shields, and D.R. Souto, editors. Proceedings: symposium on sustainable management of hemlock ecosystems in eastern North America. U.S. Forest Service, GTR-NE-267.

Foster, D. R., and D.A. Orwig. 2006. Preemptive and salvage harvesting of New England forests: when doing nothing is a viable alternative. Conservation Biology 20:959–970.

Futuyma, D. J., and F. Gould. 1979. Associations of plants and insects in a deciduous forest. Ecological Monographs. 49:33–50.

Gilman, E. F., and D. G. Watson. 1994. *Tsuga canadensis* Canadian Hemlock. Fact Sheet ST-646, Florida Cooperative Extension Service, Institute of Food and Agricultural Sciences, University of Florida, Gainesville, Florida, USA.

Gouger, R. J. 1971. Control of *Adelges tsugae* on hemlock in Pennsylvania. Scientific Tree Topics 3:1–9.

Haney, J. C. 1999. Hierarchical comparisons of breeding birds in old-growth conifer-hardwood forest on the Appalachian Plateau. Wilson Bulletin 111:89–99.

Haney, J. C., and C. D. Schaadt. 1996. Functional roles of eastern old growth in promoting forest bird diversity. Pages 76–88 in M.B. Davis, editor. Eastern old-growth forests. Island Press, Washington, D.C.

Harlow, R. C. 1912. The breeding birds of southern Center County, Pennsylvania. The Auk 29: 465–478.

Hough, A. F., and R. D. Forbes. 1943. The ecology and silvics of forests in the High Plateau of Pennsylvania. Ecological Monographs 13:299–320.

Kizlinski, M. L., D. A. Orwig, R. C. Cobb, and D. R. Foster. 2002. Direct and indirect ecosystem consequences of an invasive pest on forests dominated by eastern hemlock. Journal of Biogeography 29:1489–1503.

Loope, L. 2004. The challenge of effectively addressing the threat of invasive species to the National Park System. Park Science 22:14–20.

Lyons, P. J., and J. E. Livingston. 1997. Identification and characterization of Acadian flycatcher breeding habitat on Quabbin reservation. Silvio O. Conte National Fish and Wildlife Refuge, Department of Conservation and Recreation, Belchertown, Massachusetts, USA.

Martin, T. E., and J. J. Roper. 1988. Nest predation and nest-site selection of a western population of the Hermit Thrush. Condor 90:51–57.

McClure, M. S. 1990. Role of wind, birds, deer, and humans in the dispersal of hemlock woolly adelgid (Homoptera: Adelgidae). Environmental Entomology 19:36–43.

_____. 1991. Density-dependent feedback and population cycles in *Adelges tsugae* (Homoptera: Adelgidae) on *Tsuga canadensis.* Environmental Entomology 20:258–264.

_____. 1996. Biology of Adelges tsugae and its potential for spread in the northeastern United States. Pages 16–25 in S.M. Salome, T.C. Tigner, and R.C. Reardon, editors. Proceedings of the first hemlock woolly adelgid review. U.S. Forest Service, FHTET 96-10.

_____. 2002. The elongate hemlock scale, *Fiorinia externa* Ferris (Homoptera: Diaspididae): a new look at an old nemesis. Pages 248–253 in R. C. Reardon, B. P. Onken, and J. Lashcomb, editors. Symposium on the hemlock woolly adelgid in eastern North America. New Jersey Agricultural Experiment Station, New Brunswick, New Jersey, USA.

McWilliams, G. M., and D. W. Brauning. 2000. The birds of Pennsylvania. Cornell University Press, Ithaca, New York, USA.

Mulvihill, R. S. 1992a. Blackburnian Warbler *Dendroica fusca.* Pages 320–321 in D. Brauning, editor. Atlas of breeding birds in Pennsylvania. University of Pittsburgh Press, Pittsburgh, Pennsylvania, USA.

_____. 1992b. Magnolia warbler *Dendroica magnolia*. Pages 312–313 in D. Brauning, editor. Atlas of breeding birds in Pennsylvania. University of Pittsburgh Press, Pittsburgh, Pennsylvania, USA.

Prasad, A. M., and L. R. Iverson. 2003. Little's range and FIA importance value database for 135 eastern U. S. tree species. U.S. Forest Service, Northeastern Research Station, Delaware, OH.

Putz, F. E. 2005. Stopping hemlock from going chestnut: saving representative hemlock stands. Harvard Forest Publication, Petersham, Massachusetts, USA.

Ross, R. M., R. M. Bennett, C. D. Snyder, J. A. Young, D. R. Smith, and D. P. Lemarie. 2003. Influence of eastern hemlock (*Tsuga canadensis* L.) on fish community structure and function in headwater streams of the Delaware River basin. Ecology of Freshwater Fish 12:60–65.

Ross, R. M., L. A. Redell, R. M. Bennett, and J. A. Young. 2004. Mesohabitat use of threatened hemlock forests by breeding birds of the Delaware River Basin in northeastern United States. Natural Areas Journal 24:307–315.

Royle, D. D., and R. G. Lathrop. 2002. Using landsat imagery to quantify temporal and spatial patterns in hemlock decline. Pages 67–72 in R. C. Reardon, B. P. Onken, and J. Lashcomb, editors. Symposium on the hemlock woolly adelgid in eastern North America. New Jersey Agricultural Experiment Station, New Brunswick, New Jersey, USA.

Santner, S. 1992. Black-throated greed warbler *Dendroica virens*. Pages 318–319 in D. Brauning, editor. Atlas of breeding birds in Pennsylvania. University of Pittsburgh Press, Pittsburgh, Pennsylvania, USA.

Sheehan, Jr., J. 2003. Habitat selection in the Acadian flycatcher: the potential impact of hemlock woolly adelgid infestations and other anthropogenic stressors. Thesis. East Stroudsburg University, East Stroudsburg, Pennsylvania, USA.

Shields, K. S., and C. A. Cheah 2005. Winter mortality in *Adelges tsugae* in 2003 and 2004. Pages 354–356 in B. P. Onken and R. C. Reardon, editors. Third symposium on hemlock woolly adelgid in the eastern United States. U.S. Forest Service, FHTET-2005-01.

Small, M. J., C. J. Small, and G. D. Dreyer. 2005. Changes in a hemlock-dominated forest following woolly adelgid infestation in southern New England. Journal of the Torrey Botanical Society 132:458–470.

Snyder, C. D., J. A. Young, D. P. Lemarie, and D. R. Smith. 2002. Influence of eastern hemlock (*Tsuga canadensis*) forests on aquatic invertebrate assemblages in headwater streams. Canadian Journal of Fisheries and Aquatic Sciences 59:262–275.

Souto, D., T. Luther, and B. Chianese. 1996. Past and current status of HWA in eastern and Carolina hemlock stands. Pages 9–15 in S.M. Salom, T.C. Tignor, and R.C. Reardon, editors. Proceedings of the first hemlock woolly adelgid review. U.S. Forest Service, FHTET 96-10.

Swartzentruber, B. 2004. The effects of hemlock woolly adelgid on breeding populations of three species of eastern hemlock dependent songbirds. Thesis, East Stroudsburg University, East Stroudsburg, Pennsylvania, USA.

Tingley, M. W., D. A. Orwig, R. Field, and G. Motzkin. 2002. Avian response to removal of a forest dominant: consequences of hemlock woolly adelgid infestations. Journal of Biogeography 29:1505–1516.

Todd, W. E. C. 1893. Summer birds of Indiana and Clearfield Counties, Pennsylvania. The Auk 10:35–46.

_____. 1940. Birds of western Pennsylvania. University of Pittsburgh Press, Pittsburgh, Pennsylvania, USA.

U.S. Forest Service. 2008. Hemlock woolly adelgid website. U.S. Forest Service, URL: http://www.na.fs.fed.us/fhp/hwa/ (accessed March 2008).

Ward, J. S., M. E. Montgomery, C. A. S.-J. Cheah, B. P. Onken, and R. S. Cowles. 2004. Eastern hemlock forests: guidelines to minimize the impacts of hemlock woolly adelgid. U.S. Forest Service, NA-TP-03-04.

Wallace, M. S., and F. P. Hain. 2000. Field surveys and evaluation of native and established predators of the hemlock woolly adelgid (Homoptera: Adelgidae) in the southeastern United States. Environmental Entomology 29:638–644.

Whitney, G. G. 1990. The history and status of hemlock-hardwood forests of the Allegheny Plateau. Journal of Ecology 78:443–458.

Williams, D. W., M. E. Montgomery, and K. S. Shields. 2002. Monitoring hemlock woolly adelgid and assessing its impacts in the Delaware River Basin. Pages 360–363 in R. C. Reardon, B. P. Onken, and J. Lashcomb, editors. Symposium on the hemlock woolly adelgid in eastern North America. New Jersey Agricultural Experiment Station, New Brunswick, New Jersey, USA.

Wilson, R. R., and R. J. Cooper. 1998. Breeding biology of Acadian flycatchers in a bottomland hardwood forest. Wilson Bulletin 110:226–232.

Yamasaki, M., W. B. DeGraaf, and J. W. Lanier. 2000. Wildlife habitat associations in eastern hemlock—birds, smaller mammals and forest carnivores. Pages 135–143 in K. A. McManus, K. S. Shields, and D. R. Souto, editors. Proceedings of the symposium on sustainable management of hemlock ecosystems in eastern North America. U.S. Forest Service, GTR-NE-267.

Avian Ecology and Conservation: A Pennsylvania Focus with National Implications. Edited by S. K. Majumdar, T. L. Master, M. C. Brittingham, R. M. Ross, R. S. Mulvihill and J. E. Huffman. © 2010. The Pennsylvania Academy of Science.

Chapter 18

The Louisiana Waterthrush as an Indicator of Headwater Stream Quality in Pennsylvania

Steven C. Latta[1] and Robert S. Mulvihill[2]

[1]Department of Conservation and Field Research, National Aviary, 700 Arch St., Allegheny Commons West, Pittsburgh, PA 15212
steve.latta@aviary.org

[2]Carnegie Museum of Natural History, Powdermill Avian Research Center, 1847 Route 381, Rector, PA 15677
mulvihill@pabirdatlas.org

INTRODUCTION

Terrestrial bird population declines have often been attributed to fragmentation of forest habitats and conversion of native habitats for agricultural or urban land uses. The probable causes of declines of riparian bird species are varied, but are likely linked to sedimentation, acidification and other stream contaminants, and the loss of surrounding vegetative cover in the riparian corridor. Degraded streams have been implicated in reduced reproductive success in the northern hemisphere for several bird species (Vickery 1992, Feck and Hall 2004). In particular, acid deposition from a variety of sources resulting in soil calcium depletion is thought to affect some riparian birds by limiting the quality and quantity of arthropod prey, thereby reducing the calcium needed for reproduction and the growth of nestlings (Hames et al. 2002). This may be a particularly important factor in songbird population declines in montane streams at higher elevations (Hames et al. 2002), but other causes of mortality and reduced reproductive success are also suspected (Robinson 1995).

A Neotropical migratory bird, the Louisiana waterthrush (*Seiurus motacilla*) breeds in forested headwater riparian habitats in Pennsylvania and eastern North America. The waterthrush is a Pennsylvania Species of Concern (Wildlife Action Plan), listed as a Partner's in Flight (PIF) Stewardship Species (Rich et al. 2004), a Priority Species of the Central Hardwoods Bird Conservation Region (BCR 24), and a Species of Conservation Concern in several other BCRs in the Appalachian region. The waterthrush has been proposed as an indicator of environmental change in riparian habitats on its breeding (O'Connell et al. 2003, Mattson and Cooper 2006) and over-wintering (Master et al. 2005) grounds, and has been adopted by the National Park Service as one of a few "vital signs" for the Eastern Rivers and Mountains Network (ERMN).

The use of birds as indicators of ecosystem condition has been of growing importance in conservation, but population dynamics of riparian passerines have only rarely been used to assess stream health. Our ongoing studies of the ecology of the Louisiana waterthrush in Pennsylvania in relation to environmental stressors such as acid deposition, acidic abandoned mine drainage, and land use issues were begun by Mulvihill in 1996. Long-term studies such as this enable us to test hypotheses about various cause and effect relationships that may impact the population viability of the species. Here we summarize Pennsylvania studies which have revealed impacts of stream acidification and land use on waterthrush breeding density, reproductive success and productivity, foraging patterns, and population dynamics. We also present new avenues of research that will lead us to a more complete understanding of waterthrush ecology and how breeding ground events interact with events in the non-breeding season to determine population size. Results have particular significance for direct management of headwater riparian habitats to support viable populations of this species.

BACKGROUND

Acidification of freshwater ecosystems from anthropogenic causes is a major ecological problem world-wide. Reduced pH in streams occurs from several causes, including abandoned mine drainage (Herlihy et al. 1990, Earle and Callaghan 1998) and acidic precipitation (Schindler 1988, Herlihy et al. 1993). Drainage from mines is a direct and localized contaminant, but acid precipitation from rain and snowfall impacts entire regions. The acidity of a stream may be affected by local differences in soils and bedrock which can neutralize some acid inputs, but streams can also be impacted by past acid precipitation events because continued leeching of acidic compounds from the soil can and do affect forest and stream ecosystems for many years (Likens et al. 1996, Hames et al. 2002, Kowalik et al. 2007). Estimates suggest that approximately 5% of Pennsylvania's streams are chronically acidified and about 35% are episodically acidified (EPA 2006). One-fifth of streams in the northern Appalachian region of the United States are acidic, with about half of these due to abandoned mine drainage and half from acid precipitation (Herlihy et al. 1990, Herlihy et al. 1993). Acid precipitation and acidic drainage from mines have affected more than 5,000 miles of streams within the breeding range of the waterthrush (EPA 2006).

Headwater streams comprise about two-thirds of the linear reach of most major catchments and, therefore, are critically important to their ecological integrity (Freeman et al. 2007). Effects of water acidification on wildlife have been found to occur through shifts in trophic relationships (Schreiber and Newman 1988). In particular, many aquatic macroinvertebrate species are acid-intolerant, and changes in species composition with acidification are well documented. Increased acidity shifts the macroinvertebrate community to a comparatively few acid-tolerant taxa with a corresponding loss of a large number of acid-sensitive taxa, including most mayfly (Ephemeroptera) species (e.g. Rutt et al. 1990, Courtney and Clement 1998, Guerold et al. 2000). Insectivorous birds, which feed at higher trophic levels, can be negatively affected by changes in prey quality and quantity arising from effects of acid waters on macroinvertebrates (Graveland 1998). Not only prey abundance, but the availability of key, calcium-rich macroinvertebrates required for formation of eggs by birds may also be affected (Ormerod et al. 1991). For example, acidification has been found to affect White-throated Dipper (*Cinclus cinclus*) breeding ecology, including laying dates, clutch size, territory size and reproductive success in Great

Britain (Ormerod et al. 1988, O'Halloran et al. 1990, Ormerod et al. 1991, Ormerod and Tyler 1991, Vickery 1992).

The Louisiana waterthrush is a stream-dependent, forest-interior, migratory songbird that occupies linear territories along streams where it depends primarily on aquatic macroinvertebrates for food (Robinson 1995). It breeds throughout the eastern United States and winters in Mexico, Central America, and the Caribbean islands. Both sexes help build an open-cup nest on banks, slopes, or in upturned tree roots along streams. Typically only one clutch of five (range: 3–6) eggs is laid, but most birds re-nest if the first attempt fails. Incubation begins upon the laying of the last egg. Only the female incubates, and eggs hatch after a mean of 13 days (Robinson 1995, Mulvihill et al. 2008). Nestlings are fed by both parents until ready to fledge at a mean 10 days of age. Parents then divide the brood for another 3–4 weeks of post-fledging care (Robinson 1995, Quattrini et al. 2000).

The waterthrush is considered a Pennsylvania Species of Conservation Concern and is listed as a priority species for several Bird Conservation Regions because of its dependence on this specialized habitat threatened by a number of environmental stressors (Rich et al. 2004). As a member of a suite of riparian-oriented species, the waterthrush co-occurs along cobble-strewn streams and forested headwaters in Pennsylvania with Acadian flycatcher (*Empidonax virescens*), winter wren (*Troglodytes troglodytes*), Kentucky warbler (*Oporornis formosus*), American redstart (*Setophaga ruticilla*), and Swainson's thrush (*Catharus ustulatus*). We are currently working to understand population dynamics by determining factors that are associated with changes in habitat quality at a variety of scales. We are identifying landscape-level factors, characteristics of waterthrush territories, and specific stream quality measures associated with reproductive success and survival on both the breeding and wintering grounds, and we seek to determine whether the Louisiana waterthrush can be used to economically and efficiently evaluate the health of stream systems. Our approach is especially unique because ours is the first study to identify factors affecting population size of a riparian songbird on both its breeding and wintering grounds. Previous research on terrestrial species has shown this to be the most promising avenue to identify key conservation threats to migratory species (Faaborg et al. 2009).

RECENT RESEARCH

Our studies of Louisiana waterthrush population and breeding biology have focused on both acidified (pH range 4.5–5.5) and relatively pristine, circumneutral (pH ~7) streams in western Pennsylvania, but some data have also been generated by collaborations in broader studies of the ecological health of forested headwater streams throughout the state (O'Connell et al. 2003, Mulvihill et al. 2008). In western Pennsylvania we monitor 2–3 km reaches of first and second order streams in the Ohio River Drainage in the Laurel Highlands. On two streams we have studied the effects of acidification over more than a ten-year period (since 1996), while on other streams we have gathered data in 2–5 year intervals. Our study streams are generally in close proximity (2–30 km apart) to one another. Circumneutral streams include Loyalhanna Creek and Powdermill, Phoebe, and Camp runs in Westmoreland County, Roaring and Tressler runs in Somerset County, and Blackberry and Rock runs in Fayette County. Increased acidity was recorded on Laurel, Linn, and Penrod runs in Westmoreland County, Gary's Run in Somerset County, and Jonathan Run in Fayette County. We monitored Laurel Run and Powdermill Run from 1996 to 2008;

Linn, Loyalhanna, and Camp runs for five years, 1998–2000 and 2007–2008; Tressler, Mill, Jonathan, and Blackberry for three years, 1998–2000; Rock Run for two years, 1999–2000; and Penrod and Phoebe runs for two years, 2007–2008.

All streams are located in contiguous forest with >80% forest cover in a 1 km radius. Mixed deciduous forest surrounding our study streams is characterized by American beech (*Fagus grandifolia*), red maple (*Acer rubrum*), and yellow poplar (*Liriodendron tulipifera*); some sites also have Eastern hemlock (*Tsuga canadensis*), black birch (*Betula lenta*), and yellow birch (*Betula alleghaniensis*). Typical forest understory species present at our sites include common spicebush (*Lindera benzoin*), witch hazel (*Hamamelis virginiana*), and striped maple (*Acer pensylvanicum*). The groundcover is largely dominated by fern species and a diversity of vernal woodland wildflowers.

Diet and Foraging Behavior

Louisiana waterthrush have been found to occupy streams with a prey biomass containing a higher proportion of mayflies (Ephemeroptera), stoneflies (Plecoptera), and caddisflies (Trichoptera) (Mattson and Cooper 2006, Mulvihill et al. 2008), which are together commonly measured as the "%EPT" or the proportion of these orders among all aquatic macroinvertebrates found in the stream. Waterthrush are largely dependent upon these stream macroinvertebrates, but these insects are sensitive to sedimentation, acidification, and inputs of other pollutants.

To understand how changes in stream macroinvertebrates impact Louisiana waterthrush reproduction, we observed nestling provisioning of waterthrushes at our study sites (Mulvihill and Latta, unpubl. data). We collected data during 234 nest watches, each lasting a minimum of 0.5 hours and a maximum of 4.0 hours for a total of 437 hours of observation. Nest watches were conducted at three times of day (early morning: 0600–1000; midday: 1000–1400; afternoon: 1400–1800) during each of three nestling stages (0–3 days old, 4–7 days old, 8–10 days old). During nest watches, we recorded feeding frequency by noting all provisioning by the adult male or female. Although most common food items were small or otherwise unidentifiable, we specifically recorded whenever waterthrush brought conspicuous, novel prey to feed the nestlings. As an indicator of food volume brought to the nest, we also recorded fecal sac removal rates, and assumed that fecal sac production is affected both by feeding frequency and food volume, and that fecal sacs are a uniform mass.

Effects of Brood Size

Brood size in our study ranged from 2–6, with a median of four. For analysis, we grouped nests into three brood size categories (<4, =4, >4) and tested for differences in overall feeding rate and feeding rate per nestling. Similar to many other studies, our research shows that waterthrush do not make significantly more feeding trips to nests with larger broods. Although feeding rate tended to increase with brood size, the difference was neither statistically significant nor large enough to keep feeding rates from decreasing significantly on a per nestling basis with increasing brood size. This pattern, observed in a variety of passerines (Breitwisch et al. 1986), usually is interpreted as evidence of lower per nestling energetic demand with increasing brood size due to the thermoregulatory benefits associated with huddling of many nestlings (Clark 1985). Importantly, however, waterthrush also may be providing more food on average during feeding trips to larger broods. Although not measured directly, and subject to several assumptions noted above, fecal sac removal rates per nestling were significantly higher for larger broods, suggesting that adults were compensating for the decreased rate of feeding individual nestlings in larger broods by bringing more food per trip.

Age and Sex Differences

Through color banding and plumage differences waterthrush can be reliably aged as first-time breeders (SY) or more experienced breeders (ASY) (Mulvihill 1993, Pyle 1997). Provisioning rates by both adult males and females increased significantly across nestling stages (nestling age), but *post hoc* pair-wise comparisons showed that the difference was attributable to significantly lower feeding rates for the early stage (0–3 days old) nestlings. More complex is the pattern of provisioning by adult males and females of different age classes. Males feed nestlings at higher rates than females, and there is a non-significant trend for ASY males to feed nestlings at higher rates than SY males. This results in ASY males providing a higher proportion of the overall feedings to nestlings. But among females there is no difference in provisioning rates between adult age classes.

While male waterthrush fed nestlings at a higher rate than females and contributed a higher percentage of feedings to overall provisioning, these differences were driven most-ly by differences occurring in the earliest nestling stage (0–3 days old). Sex differences in provisioning in this early nestling stage may be the result of the female spending consid-erable time brooding the young at the nest, while the male often feeds the nestlings. The male also was observed feeding the female directly, and providing food to her to give to the nestlings.

Land use and stream condition had some impact on food provisioning, likely as a result of changes in the aquatic macroinvertebrate prey base. In regions with significant home development along streams, an increase in nutrient loading to the streams resulted in high-er abundances of aquatic macroinvertebrates compared to non-impacted sites, but no loss of diversity. We found no significant difference in overall feeding rate associated with this modest increase in vacation homes. But with the increased acidic abandoned mine drainage and acid deposition that typically reduces both the abundance and diversity of macroinver-tebrate prey (Fig. 1; Mulvihill 1999), provisioning rates to waterthrush nestlings were reduced on acidic streams, although the differences were not statistically significant. We have suggested that perhaps in response to reduced aquatic macroinvertebrate prey, waterthrush which nested along acid-impacted streams supplemented their nestlings' diet with novel prey much more often than did waterthrush nesting along non-impacted streams (Mulvihill et al. 2008). Differences in the rate of inclusion of novel prey in the diet of nestlings on acid-impacted streams points to an effect of water quality in nestling provi-sioning behavior of waterthrush occupying these streams. As an example, the number and frequency of salamanders fed to nestlings is much greater on acid-impacted streams. A sim-ilar pattern was observed for inclusion of conspicuous terrestrial prey, such as caterpillars.

Supporting this hypothesis are data from more than 300 observations of foraging behav-ior of the waterthrush. Louisiana waterthrush commonly pick, glean, sally-glean, or hawk insects from pools, leafy or woody debris, bare or mossy rocks, or soil occurring in-stream, along the stream bank, or off-stream. Foraging rates and size classes of insects taken by waterthrush did not vary much among streams of varying quality, but the location of for-

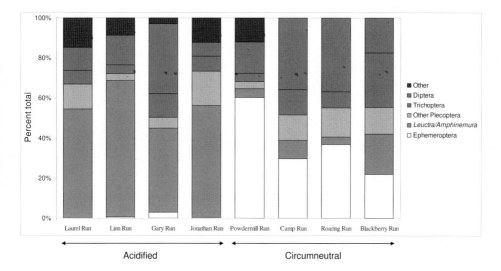

Figure 1: With moderate levels of stream acidification (4.5–5.5) acid-intolerant mayflies were replaced by two acid-tolerant stonefly genera, *Leuctra* and *Amphinemura*. (From Mulvihill et al. 2008)

aging waterthrushes did vary with stream acidity. We found that as water acidity increased in the mainstream, waterthrush territories shifted to include more small tributaries or off-stream sites. As such, the ratio of offstream territory length to mainstream territory length increased, and waterthrushes significantly increased use of these peripheral sites for foraging (Fig. 2). These peripheral sites and tributaries were most often tributaries that were less acidic than the mainstream, suggesting that they may contain prey items that were a higher %EPT, but they may have also hosted larger numbers of the novel prey that these birds were more likely to utilize. Some more work needs to be done, however, to assess how these peripheral sites are used by the waterthrush.

Breeding biology

We studied breeding phenology and reproductive success by locating and monitoring Louisiana waterthrushes soon after their arrival in Pennsylvania in late-March and early-April. Males were usually captured and banded before they paired by means of territorial-song playback, while most females were caught and banded when feeding young at the nest, and nestlings were banded a few days prior to fledging (~8 days old). In our population most males, females, and nestlings were color-banded on study streams each year.

We followed behavior to determine when pairs were nesting and searched for every nest attempt at each site. In monitored territories >90% of nests were found, usually with eggs. Nests were checked at 3- to 4-day intervals for survival of eggs and nestlings. In cases where the clutch-initiation date was not known, it was back-calculated from observed hatching and/or fledging dates on the basis of an average 13-day incubation (beginning with the last egg laid) and 10-day nestling period (Robinson 1995, Mulvihill et al. 2008). A nesting attempt was considered successful if at least one young was known to have

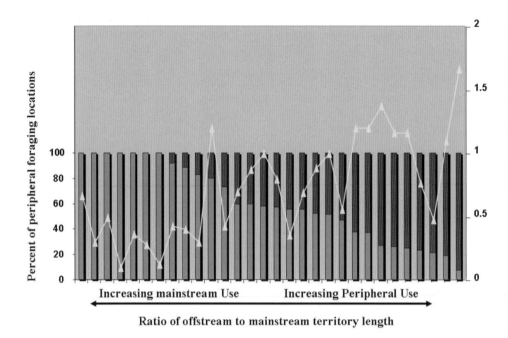

Figure 2:   Louisiana waterthrush increasingly foraged in peripheral locations away from the main stream when territories were formed in more acidic streams. At these sites territories shifted to include more small tributaries or offstream sites.

fledged. If fledging was not observed directly, observations of banded fledglings or adults carrying food were used to confirm nesting success.

We compared breeding ecology of the Louisiana waterthrush on acidified and circumneutral streams. Waterthrush breeding density on acidified streams was ~1 territory km^{-1} and was significantly reduced compared to circumneutral streams where breeding density was >2 territories km^{-1} (Fig. 3). Territories on acidified streams were disjunct and almost twice as long as on circumneutral streams, while on circumneutral streams territories were generally contiguous.

Clutch initiation was significantly delayed on acidified streams, on average by nine days in comparison to circumneutral streams. Birds nesting along acidified streams laid smaller clutches, and nestlings were smaller. Stream acidity had no effect on nest success or annual fecundity (fledglings/female). However, the number of young fledged km^{-1} was nearly twice as high on circumneutral streams as on acidified streams because of the differences in breeding densities.

Waterthrush apparently recognize stream quality by environmental or behavioral cues which are as yet not well understood. Acidified streams were characterized by a younger, less site-faithful breeding population, and a lower pairing success. Individual birds were also less likely to return multiple years to breed on acidified streams, allowing inexperienced breeders to settle on these streams. In contrast, circumneutral streams tended towards having older birds, few if any of which were unpaired, and a high rate of annual return to territories.

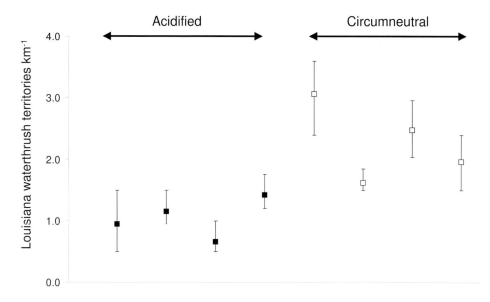

Figure 3:   Mean (± SE) breeding density of Louisiana waterthrush on acidified (solid squares) and circumneutral streams (open squares) in southwestern Pennsylvania. (From Mulvihill et al. 2008)

We conclude that acidified headwaters constitute lower quality habitat for breeding Louisiana waterthrush. However, breeding birds can raise young on these acidified streams, and apparently compensate for reduced prey resources to fledge young by increasing territory size, foraging in peripheral non-acidified areas, and by provisioning young with novel prey.

Over-Winter Ecology

In addition to breeding ground events, there is also a critical need for understanding the effects of riparian habitat degradation on over-wintering birds in the Neotropics. Migratory bird populations can be regulated by factors occurring on the breeding grounds, the over-wintering grounds, or during migration between these sites (Sherry and Holmes 1996), so modern approaches to the conservation of migratory birds recognize that population limitation can occur on a variety of spatial and temporal scales, and that understanding the complexity of habitat usage is necessary for management of wide-ranging species (Faaborg et al. 2009). Unfortunately, most research on migrant birds on their wintering grounds has focused on a few forest and scrub species, and almost no work has focused on riparian species.

Little is known of Louisiana waterthrush population dynamics and its potential use as an indicator of stream condition on the wintering grounds. Waterthrush winter throughout Central America and the Caribbean, often on highly threatened mountain streams where it is associated with torrent tyrannulet (*Serpophaga cinera*), American dipper (*Cinclus mexicanus*), buff-rumped warbler (*Phaeothlypis fulvicauda*), black phoebe (*Sayornis nigricans*), and spotted sandpiper (*Actitis macularia*) in Costa Rica (Master et al. 2005), and with Bicknell's thrush (*Catharus bicknelli*), ovenbird (*Seiurus auricapillus*), American redstart (*Setophaga ruticilla*), black-throated blue warbler (*Dendroica caerulescens*), ruddy quail-dove (*Geotrygon montana*), broad-billed tody (*Todus subulatus*) and narrow-billed tody (*Todus angustirostris*) along forested streams of Hispaniola (Latta, pers. obs). In two years of field work we have developed study sites in over-wintering habitat along 6 streams in the Dominican Republic, and determined territory size, density, site fidelity, and return rates of >75 individuals. We have also begun to relate measures of forest cover, landscape-level land use, territory characteristics, and stream quality to waterthrush abundance, demographic indices (sex and age ratios), density and territory size, body condition, site fidelity, and survival. We will then evaluate the relative importance of landscape, site, and territory characteristics in affecting population dynamics of waterthrush on wintering grounds.

We are also beginning to use genetic markers to potentially identify distinct subpopulations of Louisiana waterthrush across its range, assess the connectivity of wintering and breeding populations, and provide the basis for studies of carryover effects of habitat conditions. Two types of high-resolution molecular markers, mitochondrial DNA (mtDNA) and microsatellites, are being used to quantify genetic diversity and examine population structure of waterthrush. The hypervariable mtDNA control region and six microsatellite loci are being amplified by means of the polymerase chain reaction (PCR). The amplified mtDNA fragments are then sequenced and aligned to identify variable sites, and each microsatellite locus is genotyped in all individuals. The genetic variation identified by each molecular marker is then quantified statistically. These analyses will provide information on how healthy the waterthrush population is in terms of genetic diversity, and on whether to manage the population as a single genetic unit, or as multiple, genetically-discrete breeding and wintering subpopulations. If the population is significantly structured, it may also be possible to connect specific over-wintering sites with particular North American breeding subpopulations. Ideally, we would like to know where birds nesting in Pennsylvania, for example, spend the over-wintering period.

CONSERVATION CONCERNS

Our studies are developing the empirical framework necessary to use a migratory songbird, the Louisiana waterthrush, as an indicator of environmental impacts on stream quality. Because recreation, tourism, resource extraction, and industry are major drivers of economic development in Pennsylvania, and are often focused on streams, it is incumbent on governments and the community to protect waters and stream-side habitats from contamination and loss of economic and ecological value. To aid in the accomplishment of this goal in an economically feasible manner, our studies focus on how a key component of stream ecosystems is impacted by stream degradation, and we are developing the conceptual and empirical framework for using waterthrush as indicators of habitat conditions on a variety of geographic scales.

Our continuing studies of waterthrush in Pennsylvania suggest that territory density and size, mating success, and productivity vary between acidic streams and circumneutral streams (Fig. 3; Mulvihill et al. 2008). Because ecology is closely linked to resource availability, and given the known negative impact of acid pollution on aquatic macroinvertebrates (Fig. 1), streams with reduced pH constitute comparatively low quality habitat for breeding Louisiana waterthrush. Waterthrush do, however, appear to be able to compensate for reduced prey resources to fledge young on acidified streams by increasing territory size, foraging in peripheral non-acidified areas (Fig. 2), and provisioning young with novel prey. But the number of young produced per kilometer of stream will still be much reduced. Clearly, stream remediation is a high priority for the conservation of this species.

Beyond stream water quality, however, we have very few data on habitat characteristics that may drive waterthrush population dynamics. Currently we are conducting studies for a broader habitat assessment to determine the impact of habitat change on waterthrush. At each territory and each nest, physical measures of the stream and surrounding landscape are quantified and mapped on Geographic Information System (GIS) layers. GIS is then used to quantify a broad array of territory attributes, as well as forest cover on a landscape scale. Reproductive success and survival rates are then related to these biotic measures of riparian habitat quality. Potential factors include land use across the landscape, forest cover, tree and vegetation diversity, abundance of seeps and other wet areas, stream morphology and depth regimes, the presence of particular microhabitats, and other physical variables.

We are also now beginning to look beyond the physical characteristics of streams and territories and how they affect nesting success. Specifically, our work will, for the first time, focus on the survival of waterthrush fledglings once they leave the nest. Using radiotelemetry, we will begin to identify how waterthrush use habitat during the critical period when the chicks have left the nest but before they have left on migration to the wintering grounds. Very few studies have looked at how fledglings of any species survive in this period, but it is suspected that there is a high level of mortality that is affected by habitat conditions that the birds encounter. This period of time may be of extreme importance to the waterthrush because of their dependence on stream-side habitats that are often impacted by forestry, road-building, housing, agriculture and other concerns.

Finally, by combining this work with companion studies from the breeding and the wintering grounds, we are also evaluating the relative importance of habitat conditions throughout the annual cycle in affecting population dynamics of the Louisiana waterthrush.

CONCLUSIONS

Protecting our migratory bird populations, as well as maintaining and restoring streams and riparian habitat, is important to our well being and to protecting our natural heritage. Like many states, the Commonwealth of Pennsylvania is facing complex problems in determining how changing habitat conditions, such as the loss of forest cover, increased runoff from mines and other sources of contaminants, and acid deposition from precipitation, are impacting birds and other game and non-game wildlife. This is particularly detrimental to Pennsylvania's economy, since hunting and fishing are key components of the state's tourism and recreation complex. Determining the impact of habitat change on every species of plant and animal is not possible or practical, and would be enormously expensive. Our goal is to provide the Commonwealth, and land and wildlife managers, with a validated tool to use as a cost-effective indicator of conservation and remediation efforts. Indicator taxa, like birds, which are easily observed and predictably responsive, are needed as proxy measures of ecosystem health and as early warning signals for changes in habitat conditions. Demonstrating the value of one bird species as a bio-indicator for one widespread habitat may result in the use of other bio-indicators in other habitats.

Because Pennsylvania lies in the center of the breeding range of this Species of Conservation Concern, we also hold a special responsibility, as well as a unique opportunity, to develop conservation recommendations for this species. Thus, another goal of our research is to provide guidance for the evaluation, management, and conservation of stream habitats, and to improve and enhance habitat vital to the long-term conservation of a species that the Commonwealth of Pennsylvania has designated as a Species of Concern and that also has national protected status. We expect results to lead to management guidelines that will emphasize a broad array of in-stream, riparian, and landscape-scale habitat conditions, including guidelines for land use characteristics, stream sedimentation, acidification and contamination, and specific habitat features necessary for healthy populations of this species. The data generated through these activities will provide the scientific foundation for specific conservation actions, and will provide local residents and land managers with critical information needed to conserve highly threatened habitats. Furthermore, results can be used to guide management efforts within the Important Bird Areas, Bird Conservation Regions, and Pennsylvania State Parks, State Forests, and Wildlife Management Areas.

LITERATURE CITED

Breitwisch, R., Merritt, P. G. and G. H. Whitesides. 1986. Parental investment by the Northern Mockingbird: male and female roles in feeding nestlings. Auk 103:152–159

Clark, L. 1985. Consequences of homeothermic capacity of nestlings on parental care in the European Starling. Oecologia 65:387–393.

Courtney, L. A., and W. H. Clements. 1998. Effects of acidic pH on benthic macroinvertebrate communities in stream microcosms. Hydrobiologia 379:133–145.

Earle, J., and T. Callagan. 1998. Impacts of mine drainage on aquatic life, water uses, and man-made structures. Pp. 4.1–4.10. in: *Coal Mine Drainage Prediction and Pollution Prevention in Pennsylvania*. B.C. Brady, T. Kania, W. M Smith and R. J. Hornberger (Eds.). PA Department of Environmental Protection, Harrisburg. Pennsylvania, U.S.A.

Environmental Protection Agency. 2006. Areas impacted by acidification: Acid mine drainage and acid deposition remain significant problems in Region III. http://www.epa.gov/region03/acidification/r3_acidifcation.htm

Faaborg, J., Anders, A. D., Bildstein, K. L., Dugger, K. D., Gauthreaux, S. A., Heglund, P. J., Hobson, K. A., Holmes, R. T., Jahn, A., Johnson, D. H., Latta, S. C., Levey, D. J, Marra, P. P., Merkord, C. L., Nol, E., Rothstein, S. I. , Sillett, S. T., Sherry, T. W., Thompson III, F. R. and N. Warnock. *In press*. Recent advances in understanding migration systems of New World landbirds. Ecological Monographs.

Feck, J., and R. O. Hall, Jr. 2004. Response of American Dippers (*Cinclus mexicanus*) to variation in stream water quality. Freshwater Biology 49:1123–1137.

Freeman, M.C., Pringle, C. M. and C. R. Jackson. 2007. Hydrologic connectivity and the contribution of stream headwaters to ecological integrity at regional scales. Journal of the America Water Resources Association 43: 5–14.

Graveland, J. 1998. Effects of acid rain on bird populations. Environmental Review 6: 41–54.

Guerold, F., Boudot, J., Jacquemin, G., Vein, D., Merlet, D. and J. Rouiller. 2000. Macroinvertebrate community loss as a result of headwater stream acidification in the Vosges mountains (N-E France). Biodiversity and Conservation 9:767–783.

Hames, R. S., Rosenberg, K. V., Lowe, J. D., Barker, S. E. and A. A. Dhondt. 2002. Adverse effects of acid rain on the distribution of the Wood Thrush *Hylocichla mustelina* in North America. PNAS 99:11235–11240.

Herlihy, A. T., Kaufmann, P. R., Mitch, M. E. and D. D. Brown. 1990. Regional estimates of acid mine drainage impact on streams in the Mid-Atlantic and Southeastern United States. Water, Air and Soil Pollution 50:91–107.

_____, _____, Church, M. R., Wigington, P. J. and J. R. Webb. 1993. The effect of acidic deposition on streams in the Appalachian Mountain and Piedmont Region of the Mid-Atlantic United States. Water Resources Research 29:2687–2703.

Kowalik, R. A., Cooper, D. M., Evans, C. M. and S. J. Ormerod. 2007. Acid episodes retard the biological recovery of upland British streams from acidification. Global Change Biology 13:2439–2452.

Likens, G. E., Driscoll, C. T. and D. C. Buso. 1996. Long-term effects of acid rain: Response and recovery of a forest ecosystem. Science 272:244–246.

Master, T. L., Mulvihill, R. S., Leberman, R. C. and J. Sánchez. 2005. A preliminary study of riparian songbirds in Costa Rica, with emphasis on wintering Louisiana waterthrushes. In (C. J. Ralph, ed.) Bird conservation, implementation, and integration, Proc. 3rd International Partners In-Flight Conference, Vol. 1. Gen. Tech. Rep. PSW-GTR-191. Albany, CA.

Mattsson, B. J., and R. J. Cooper. 2006. Louisiana waterthrushes (*Seiurus motacilla*) and habitat assessments as cost-effective indicators of instream biotic integrity. Freshwater Biology 51:1941–1958.

Mulvihill, R. S. 1993. Using wing molt to age passerines. North American Bird Bander 18:1–10.

_____. 1999. Effects of stream acidification on the breeding biology of an obligate riparian songbird, the Louisiana waterthrush (*Seiurus motacilla*). Pp. 51–61 in The effects of acidic deposition on aquatic ecosystems in Pennsylvania. (W. E. Sharpe and J. R. Drohan, eds.) Proceedings of the 1998 PA Acidic Deposition Conference, Vol. 2, Environmental Resources Research Institute, University Park, PA.

_____, and S. C. Latta. *In prep.* A comparison of Louisiana waterthrush (*Seiurus motacilla*) foraging behavior on pristine, fragmented, and acidified streams across Pennsylvania.

_____, Newell, F. L. and S. C. Latta. 2008. Effects of acidification on the breeding ecology of a stream-dependent songbird, the Louisiana waterthrush (*Seiurus motacilla*). Freshwater Biology 53: 2158–2169

O'Connell, T.R., Brooks, R. P., Laubscher, S. E., Mulvihill, R. S. and T. L. Master. 2003. *Using Bioindicators to Develop a Calibrated Index of Regional Ecological Integrity for Forested Headwater Ecosystems.* Final Report to U.S. Environmental Protection Agency, STAR Grants Program. Report No. 2003-01, Penn State Cooperative Wetlands Center, Penn State University, University Park, Pennsylvania, U.S.A.

O'Halloran, J., Gribbin, S. D., Tyler, S. J. and S. J. Ormerod. 1990. The ecology of dippers *Cinclus cinclus* (L.) in relation to stream acidity in upland Wales: time-activity budgets and energy expenditure. Oecologia 85:271–280.

Ormerod, S. J. and S. J. Tyler. 1991. Exploitation of prey by a river bird, the dipper *Cinclus cinclus* (L.) along acidic and circumneutral streams in upland Wales. Freshwater Biology 25:105–116.

_____, Bull, K. R., Cummins, C. P., Tyler, S. J. and J. A. Vickery. 1988. Egg mass and shell thickness in dippers (*Cinclus cinclus*) in relation to stream acidity in Wales and Scotland. Environmental Pollution 55:107–121.

_____, O'Halloran, J., Gribbin, S. D. and S. J. Taylor. 1991. The ecology of dippers *Cinclus cinclus* in relation to stream acidity in upland Wales: breeding performance, calcium physiology, and nestling growth. Journal of Applied Ecology 28:419–433.

Pyle, P. 1997. *Identification Guide to North American Birds, Part 1.* Slate Creek Press, Bolinas, California, U.S.A.

Quattrini, L. Cunkelman, A. A. and R. S. Mulvihill. 2000. Brood division and fledgling behavior in Louisiana waterthrushes. Abstract 198 in Abstracts of the 118th Stated Meeting of the American Ornithologists' Union, Memorial University of Newfoundland, St. John's, NF, Canada, August 14–19.

Rich, T. D., Beardmore, C. J., Berlanga, H., Blancher, P. J., Bradstreet, M. S. W., Butcher, G. S., Demarest, D. W., Dunn, E. H., Hunter, W. C., Inigo-Elias, E. E., Kennedy, J. A., Martell, A. M., Panjabi, A. O., Pashley, D. N., Rosenberg, K. V., Rustay, C. M., Wendt, J. S. and T. C. Will. 2004. *Partners in Flight North American Landbird Conservation Plan.* Cornell Lab of Ornithology, Ithaca, New York, U.S.A.

Robinson, D. W. 1995. Louisiana waterthrush (*Seiurus motacilla*). Pp. 1–18 in (A Poole and F. Gill, eds.) The Birds of North America, No.151. The Academy of Natural Sciences, Philadelphia, PA and the American Ornithologists' Union, Washington D. C., U.S.A.

Rutt, G. P., Weatherley, N. S. and S. J. Ormerod. 1990. Relationships between the physicochemistry and macroinvertebrates of British upland streams: the development of modeling and indicator systems for predicting fauna and detecting acidity. Freshwater Biology 24:463–480.

Schindler, D. W. 1988. Effects of acid rain on freshwater ecosystems. Science 239:149–157.

Schreiber, R. K. and J. R. Newman. 1988. Acid precipitation effects on forest habitats: implications for wildlife. Conservation Biology 3:249–259.

Sherry, T. W., and R. T. Holmes. 1996. Winter habitat quality, population limitation, and conservation of Neotropical-Nearctic migrant birds. Ecology 77:36–48.

Vickery, J. 1992. The reproductive success of the dipper (*Cinclus cinclus*) in relation to the acidity of streams in south-west Scotland. Freshwater Biology 28:195–205.

Avian Ecology and Conservation: A Pennsylvania Focus with National Implications. Edited by S. K. Majumdar, T. L. Master, M. C. Brittingham, R. M. Ross, R. S. Mulvihill and J. E. Huffman. © 2010. The Pennsylvania Academy of Science.

Chapter 19

Colonially Nesting Waders

ROBERT M. ROSS[1]

United States Geological Survey (retired)
Northern Appalachian Research Laboratory
176 Straight Run Road
Wellsboro, Pennsylvania 16901, USA
rmross@chilitech.net

INTRODUCTION

Scope and Taxa Treated

Wading birds, or waders, are not a taxonomically uniform group, being chiefly defined by their foraging habitat (shallow, open waters or wetland) and relatively long legs. Thus defined, waders typically include the Ciconiiformes: Ardeidae (bitterns, herons, and egrets), Ciconiidae (storks), Threskiornithidae (ibises and spoonbills), as well as Phoenicopteriformes Phoenicopteridae (flamingos) (del Hoyo et al. 1992, Sibley 2000). Some consider cranes (Gruiformes: Gruidae) as well as Charadriiformes such as avocets and stilts (Recurvirostridae), curlews, and godwits (Scolopacidae) among waders, or even shorebirds (Charadriiformes) in general (Curry-Lindahl 1978, Terres 1980). Because only herons and their allies (Ardeidae) and historically one ibis (Threskiornithidae), among all waders (however defined), breed colonially in Pennsylvania, this discussion focuses on only seven of these species: great blue heron (*Ardea herodias*), great egret (*Ardea alba*), snowy egret (*Egretta thula*), cattle egret (*Bubulcus ibis*), black-crowned night-heron (*Nycticorax nycticorax*), yellow-crowned night-heron (*Nyctanassa violacea*) and glossy ibis (*Plegadis falcinellus*). Since the double-crested cormorant (*Phalacrocorax auritus*), an unrelated waterbird (Pelicaniformes: Phalacrocoracidae), now nests colonially with other wading species in Pennsylvania, I include this species in the review as well. Though green heron (*Butorides virescens*) occasionally nests in colonies (Davis and Kushlan 1994), the species is largely a solitary nester in Pennsylvania. Another solitary-nesting wader, sandhill crane (*Grus canadensis*), only recently began breeding in western Pennsylvania (Wilhelm 1992).

Significance of Pennsylvania's Colonial Waders

The significance of wading birds in Pennsylvania differs by species and its history. Pennsylvania is largely a forested state whose aquatic habitats are dominated by rivers, steams, and freshwater wetlands. With the exception of a small section of Lake Erie, there are no

---

[1] Present address: 146 Cattail Lane, Wellsboro, PA 16901, USA

coastal habitats, large embayments, or offshore islands where populations of many wading species reach their greatest densities. The great blue heron, which breeds in monospecific colonies throughout much of Pennsylvania, was considered vulnerable to significant population decline by loss of breeding colonies and habitat only a quarter century ago (Gill 1985). Since then positive population trends have been observed and the species seems more secure in Pennsylvania (Ross in press). Great and snowy egrets began nesting in Pennsylvania in the latter half of the 20th century, as part of a general expansion from their principally southeastern United States range (Brauning 1992). Only the great egret continues to breed in Pennsylvania, at a single mixed-species colony on a lower Susquehanna River island, in addition to a few nests (<10) at a mixed colony in Kiwanis Park, York, Pennsylvania. The cattle egret arrived in Pennsylvania as a breeding colonial species as part of a late 20th century North American invasion. First documented nesting in the 1970s, it was gone less than two decades later as a breeder (Schutsky 1992b). Glossy ibis exhibited a similar colonization pattern but nested for only 2 years (Fingerhood 1992).

Black-crowned and yellow-crowned night-herons have been a part of Pennsylvania's indigenous breeding avifauna as long as anyone has documented that fauna, with records dating back a century or more (Brauning 1992). The more careful records of the past quarter century suggest highly variable, small, breeding-pair numbers (D. W. Brauning and D. Siefken, Pennsylvania Game Commission, unpublished data). Few colonies are now known to exist, with the yellow-crowned night-heron breeding often singly at fewer than half a dozen sites. By contrast, the double-crested cormorant has only recently (1996) taken up resident status in Pennsylvania, invading a mixed colony of waders on a lower Susquehanna River island (Master 2004). It shows signs of a population explosion similar to that of cattle egret late last century. Taken as a whole, Pennsylvania's wading species have demonstrated varying importance, in terms of both contributions to their global populations as well as a challenge to resource managers in conserving their breeding status.

HISTORICAL PRESENCE AND HABITAT USE

Pennsylvania's colonial wading species vary considerably in terms of the importance of the state to each species' global, North American, and eastern USA breeding population. Furthermore breeding ranges have expanded or contracted, sometimes dramatically, since historic records have been available (Hatch and Weseloh 1999, Telfair 2006). By far the most widespread and abundant of Pennsylvania's colonial waders is the great blue heron. This species reaches its greatest densities in the (historic) glaciated northern tier of Pennsylvania, where topography and soils favor formation of wetlands and natural ponds or lakes (Schwalbe and Ross 1992). This population (1,654 nests in 1993) represents a significant portion of the heron's core inland breeding range (Ross in press), though perhaps less important when considering the large coastal breeding population of this essentially North and Central American species (Butler 1992). Historically the species underwent a severe decline in the state (first half of the 20th Century) before rebounding to its current secure, though vulnerable, breeding status (Schwalbe and Ross 1992, Ross in press).

At the opposite end of the spectrum are three waders that were recently extirpated from the state: snowy egret, cattle egret, and glossy ibis. The snowy egret is a new-world species breeding in North (primarily southeastern U.S.A.), Central, and South America (AOU 1998, Parsons and Master 2000). Only a few nests of the snowy egret have even been documented in Pennsylvania, at only two locations, between 1975 and 1987 (Schutsky 1992c, McWilliams and Brauning 2000). The cattle egret is now a circumequitorial species, having originated in Africa and invaded all continents, except Antarctica, in a mere half century (Telfair 2006). It's peek breeding population of some 7,500 nesting pairs in Pennsylvania at a single site in 1981 rapidly diminished to zero by 1989 (Schutsky 1992b). Glossy ibis is a cosmopolitan species breeding in eastern North America, Central America, and Venezuela, as well as other European, African, Asian and Australian locales (Davis and Kricher 2000). In Pennsylvania it nested at the same site as cattle egret, producing only eight nests in 1975 and 1976 (Fingerhood 1992).

Colonial waders currently breeding in Pennsylvania, though in low numbers and at few sites, include great egret and the two indigenous night-herons. The great egret is a global species with breeding populations concentrated in temperate and subtropical zones (McCrimmon et al. 2001). In Pennsylvania, breeding appears to have occurred as part of the rebound associated with legal protection from plume hunting circa 1900 and was first documented in 1957 (Brauning 1992, McCrimmon et al. 2001). Black-crowned night-heron is also a New and Old World species but does not breed in Australia (Davis 1993). Historically, this heron bred throughout the state, with greatest numbers in the Piedmont region of the southeast (McWilliams and Brauning 2000). Numbers have declined over the past century, however, with only a handful of sites and less than 100 nests now known (Schutsky 1992a, T.L. Master, unpublished data). The yellow-crowned night-heron, a neotemperate and neotropical species, underwent a range retraction from the northeastern and midwestern United States in the late 1800s and a reoccupation of that breeding range in the early to mid 1900s (Watts 1995). In recent decades it appears to be retracting again from the northern limits of its range (Watts 1995). Pennsylvania nests are few in number at scattered Piedmont and Coastal Plain sites in the southeastern corner.

The double-crested cormorant, a non-wading colonial waterbird, represents a species closely associated with Pennsylvania's colonial waders and a new breeder to the state as well. There is no evidence that this species ever bred in Pennsylvania (McWilliams and Brauning 2000). A North American species, its well known post-DDT-era range and population expansion in the eastern U.S. has expressed itself in many states, Pennsylvania included (Hatch 1995, Weseloh et al. 1995, McWilliams and Brauning 2000). Its breeding population in Pennsylvania, despite management action to protect endangered herons at an important riverine colony through depredation, continues to rise, currently nearing 100 pairs (T.L. Master, unpublished data).

Habitats Available to and Used by Pennsylvania's Waders

Habitats required by Pennsylvania's colonial waders to complete their life cycles include both terrestrial (primarily for nesting) and aquatic (feeding) components. These habitats may be further categorized by numerous classification schemes (eg. Cowardin et al. 1979, Tiner 1984, PNHP 2008) but broadly include forests at various states of maturity, wetlands, rivers, and lakes or other open waters. Often islands in rivers, lakes, or embayments are utilized as nesting sites. Foraging habitats of some of these waders also include marine coastal shallows, which do not occur in Pennsylvania.

The occurrence and availability of these habitat types in Pennsylvania have also changed since European settlement. Historically a heavily forested state (>90%), all but an insignificant (<1%) portion of the original forest was cut or burned by the early 20th Century (Davis 1996, Goodrich et al. 2002). Currently 62% of the state is covered by forest. Of the eight species included in this discussion, only great blue heron and yellow-crowned night-heron require forest habitats, other than small stands of trees on islands or near water, for any part of their life cycle. Though they may nest near water, great blue heron often nest in mature forest tracts considerable distances from water (Butler 1992, Schwalbe and Ross 1992). Yellow-crowned night-herons may also nest in forest habitat some distance from water, apparently seeking low-light conditions but open understory (Watts 1995). In Pennsylvania, small colonies or single nests have occurred mostly in riparian habitats where the birds feed (often in sycamore trees along creeks) or in urban parks (Schutsky 1992d). Cattle egret may use upland forests for nesting but use a variety of habitat types near water as well (Telfair 2006). Though there is a history of abandonment of heronries in Pennsylvania due to logging (Gill 1985, Schwalbe and Ross 1992), lack of forested habitat in the state does not appear to have limited populations of either species in the past or present.

The remaining available habitats, wetlands, rivers, lakes, and open water, are used by Pennsylvania's waders for either nesting or feeding purposes. Wetlands and rivers currently constitute 2.5% of Pennsylvania's landscape (Myers et al. 2000). Despite some 83,000 miles of streams and rivers in Pennsylvania, these aquatic habitats are the rarest and most threatened in the state (Goodrich et al. 2002). Half the state's wetlands have been lost since European settlement (Tiner 1984). Remaining aquatic habitats are degraded by pollution, urban sprawl, and invasive species. Open-water habitat, once rare and present primarily in a few scattered lakes across the former glaciated northern plateaus, has increased substantially throughout the state in the past half century due to the damming of rivers and streams for flood-control and recreational purposes. Increased shallow-water foraging opportunities from such artificial lakes and reservoirs come at the expense of flooded wetlands and riverine environs, however, with dubious benefit to great blue heron, great egret, and snowy egret. Migrating double-crested cormorants, however, have certainly benefited from these changes. Probably the greatest threat to Pennsylvania's wading-bird habitat is the potential for further loss of riverine breeding habitat from artificial dam construction on large rivers.

BREEDING COLONIES

Species Composition and Location

Most of the eight subject species typically nest in multi-species colonies; however, great blue heron, cattle egret, and yellow-crowned night-heron more frequently nest monospecifically (Brauning et al. 1988–2006, Scharf 1989, Watts 1995, Telfair 2006). They may nest with other ardeids or waterbirds, an apparent adaptation to provide added vigilance or protection from predators (Davis 1993). Historically most breeding colonies populated by Pennsylvania's waders have been and continue to be monospecific great blue heron colonies (Brauning et al. 1988–2003, McWilliams and Brauning 2000). All great blue heron colonies in Pennsylvania, furthermore, are monospecific (Ross in press). Five of the subject species have almost exclusively nested with other ardeids in Pennsylvania to the extent they have been documented: great egret, snowy egret, cattle egret, glossy ibis, and double-crested cormorant (Brauning et al. 1988–2003, Brauning 1992, McWilliams and Brauning 2000). Black-crowned night-heron nest both monospecifically and in mixed-

Table 1. Recent censuses at 5-year intervals of great blue heron breeding colonies in Pennsylvania. Data (PGC 1987–2007) are based on a network of volunteers as well as state wildlife management employees.

Year	No. colonies observed	Colony size (no. active nests)		
		$\bar{x}$	s	Range
1987	28	40.8	44	1–150
1992	27	42.6	56	2–213
1997	75	20.5	25	1–147
2002	60	27.6	52	1–383
2007	35	26.0	21	1–80[1]

[1]The large Barrows Heronry in Mercer County is still active but was not counted this year.

species colonies in Pennsylvania (Brauning et al. 1988–2003, Schutsky 1992a). Yellow-crowned night-heron are principally found in small monospecific colonies, though some interspecific groups also occur (Brauning et al. 1988–2003, Schutsky 1992d).

Great blue heron breeding colonies are located throughout the state, but principally in the glaciated Appalachian Plateau physiographic province (Schwalbe and Ross 1992, McWilliams and Brauning 2000, Ross in press). All of the known multi-species colonies of waders in Pennsylvania, historical and current, are limited to three locations: (1) John R. Heinz National Wildlife Refuge (formerly the Tinicum National Environmental Center) and the lower Delaware River basin, (2) river islands of the lower Susquehanna River in Lancaster and Dauphin counties, and (3) tributaries and urban parks of the lower Susquehanna River basin (Appendix 1).

Colony Size

Great blue heron rookeries in Pennsylvania are quite variable in size, with coefficients of variation near or greater than 100% (Table 1). They range in size from simple isolated nests to colonies of several hundred nests. In Mercer County's Barrows colony 441 nests were counted in 1999 (Brauning 2000), making it the 2nd largest wading bird breeding colony ever recorded in the state. Mean colony sizes of 20–43 over a 15 year period in Pennsylvania (Table 1) compare to 36 (n = 32, s = 31) for great blue heronries in or near Michigan Great Lakes in 1987 (Scharf 1989) and 67 (n = 17, s = 71) in nearby northeastern Ohio in 1993 (Carlson 1995).

Most of the other colonial breeders typically occupy mixed-species colonies; therefore, the single-species nest counts (Appendix 1) are only an indication of colony size. Rookery Island remains the largest recorded heronry in the state, with over 1,000 active nests of cattle egret and black-crowned night-heron counted in 1985 (Appendix 1). In 1981 over 7,500 cattle egret associated with the island were counted, but active nests were not counted (Schutsky 1992b). These numbers attest to the scale and pace of the 1970–80s cattle egret invasion of Pennsylvania. Data for the more typical monospecific nesting habitat of yellow-crowned night-heron demonstrate its preference for small colonies ($\bar{x}$ = 3.4 nests per colony) and even solitary sites in Pennsylvania (Table 2). It's use of urban parks and residential nesting trees suggest a highly adaptive species with potential to increase its population in the state, despite low numbers at present. Double-crested cormorant colony

Table 2. Colony size by species for all documented colonially breeding waders (plus double-crested cormorant) of Pennsylvania. Data based on Appendix 1.

Species	No. colony counts[a]	Colony size (no. nests)		
		$\bar{x}$	s	Range
Great egret (*Ardea alba*)	32	95.6	67	3–193
Snowy egret (*Egretta thula*)	3	2.7	1	2–3
Cattle egret (*Bubulcus ibis*)	6	429.3	220	160–772
Black-crowned night-heron (*Nycticorax nycticorax*)	81	88.9	91	3–456
Yellow-crowned night-heron (*Nyctanassa violacea*)	25	3.4	3	1–10
Glossy ibis (*Plegadis falcinellus*)	2	4.0	3	2–6
Double-crested cormorant (*Phalacrocorax auritus*)	12	26.1	26	1–72

[a]Excludes pre-1975 colonies.

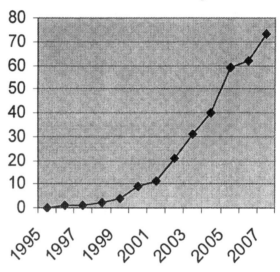

Figure 1:   Wade Island double-crested cormorant colony size (number of active nests) by year. Data courtesy of the Pennsylvania Game Commission.

size is still relatively small, but the single colony has exhibited an exponential increase in size over its 12-year history (Figure 1).

Longevity and Turnover

Brauning and Siefken (Brauning et al. 2003) tracked all known individual great blue heron nesting colonies (81 total) over a 5-year period (1997–2002) and found a 4% per year net loss of colonies (as well as a 3% per year net loss of nests). Observed rates of abandonment were higher for smaller colonies (1–5 nests) than large colonies (>20 nests). By comparison, Scharf (1989) noted a colony turnover rate of +5% per year for coastal and insular great blue heron colonies in Michigan. Graham et al. (1996) reported a 6% per year net colony increase from a decade span (1981–1991) in Ontario (n = 1, 613 colonies). The average colony longevity was 9 years, and the oldest colony was 93 years. Other large colonies have survived 71 years in British Columbia, 37 years in Minnesota, and over 70 years in Pennsylvania (Butler 1992, E. Brucker, personal communication).

Trophic Considerations

Pennsylvania's colonial breeders are carnivores with diets consisting largely of aquatic organisms (both invertebrates and vertebrates). Principally piscivorous, both great blue heron and great egret also prey on amphibians, reptiles, rarely birds, small mammals, and invertebrates such as crustaceans and insects (Butler 1992, McCrimmon et al. 2001). Snowy egret exhibits a broader diet that includes annelid worms, mollusks, and arthropods such as crabs (Parsons and Master 2000). Cattle egret has perhaps the broadest diet of terrestrial prey, including many kinds of arthropods, depending on habitat and season (Telfair 2006) The most diverse diet of all Pennsylvania's waders is that of black-crowned night-heron, which may consume all the above items, plus plant materials, carrion, and garbage (Davis 2003). Adult individuals at the Wade Island colony were observed scurrying along established trails through the undergrowth to grab fish dropped or regurgitated by the island's nesting cormorants (see below) in 2007, thus displaying their opportunistic nature (B. Romano and D. Detwiler, personal communication). Yellow-crowned night-heron, by contrast, is a crustacean specialist, preferring crabs and crayfish in freshwater habitats (Watts 1995). Double-crested cormorant are almost exclusively piscivorous, with insects, crustaceans, and amphibians occasionally taken (Johnson et al. 1997, Hatch and Weseloh 1999).

Due to colonially breeding waders' known propensity to drop food items from their nests (whether by accident or in response to human disturbance), specific information is available on nestling diets at some Pennsylvania breeding colonies. At two large inland heronries in Pennsylvania, I found 19 species of fish dropped from nests to the forest floor, including common carp (*Cyprinus carpio*) as large as 36 cm total length (Table 3). Two of these prey species, black bullhead (*Ameiurus melas*) and warmouth (*Lepomis gulosus*), are endangered in Pennsylvania (PFBC 2008). The majority (64%) of the fish dropped, however, were nonindigenous invasive species (common carp and gizzard shad, *Dorosoma cepedianum*), while panfish comprised 28% and sport fish (bass; walleye, *Sander vitreus*; and pickerel) only 3%.

Diet information from the large multi-species breeding colony at Wade Island in Pennsylvania's Susquehanna River is beginning to emerge (Master et al. 2007). In 2006 nesting adult great egrets consumed primarily fish, crayfish, and tadpoles near their island colony in proportions varying by water depth and nestling developmental stage. Fledged young birds diversified from exclusively fish to fish, amphibians, and invertebrates with age.

Diet information on nesting double-crested cormorants at Wade Island was recently obtained as a result of efforts to control cormorant expansion at the nesting colony and prevent the loss of state-endangered great egrets and black-crowned night-herons. From 37 cormorant stomachs (birds shot on or near the breeding colony) examined for prey items,

Table 3. Number, size, and species of fish dropped and sampled from tree nests of great blue heron at two large colonies (Brucker and Barrows) in Mercer County, Pennsylvania, 1986–1993.

	Brucker		Barrows		Both colonies	
	No. found	Total length (cm)	No. found	Total length (cm)	No. found	Total length (cm)
Species	$\bar{x}$	s	$\bar{x}$	s	$\bar{x}$	s
Gizzard shad (*Dorosoma cepedianum*)	134	19.1	3.3	9	16.8	5.1	143	19.1	3.6
Common carp (*Cyprinus carpio*)	50	29.5	4.3	3	25.9	2.5	53	29.7	4.6
Golden shiner (*Notemigonus crysoleucas*)	0			1	7.0		1	7.0	
White sucker (*Catostomus commersoni*)	0			4	10.2	3.0	4	10.2	3.0
Black bullhead (*Ameiurus melas*)	2	25.7	4.3	6	21.1	3.0	8	22.1	3.8
Yellow bullhead (*Ameiurus natalis*)	1	?	?	0			1	?	?
Brown bullhead (*Ameiurus nebulosus*)	2	21.6	1.8	1	18.4		3	20.6	2.3
Channel catfish (*Ictalurus punctatus*)	1	?	?	0			1	?	?
Stonecat (*Noturus flavus*)	1	14.2		0			1	14.2	
Grass pickerel (*Esox americanus vermiculatus*)	0			6	10.9	4.6	6	13.5	5.1
Central mudminnow (*Umbra limi*)	0			8	9.1	1.3	8	9.1	1.3
Green sunfish (*Lepomis cyanellus*)	2	11.4		0			2	11.4	
Pumpkinseed (*Lepomis gibbosus*)	2	14.5	1.5	4	9.4	2.0	6	10.9	3.3
Warmouth (*Lepomis gulosus*)	3	10.9	0.8	5	14.0	2.0	8	13.0	2.3
Bluegill (*Lepomis macrochirus*)	19	11.7	4.3	17	10.7	3.3	36	11.7	3.8
Largemouth bass (*Micropterus salmoides*)	0			4	18.3	6.1	4	18.3	6.1
White crappie (*Pomoxis annularis*)	16	17.3	4.3	0			16	17.3	4.3
Black crappie (*Pomoxis nigromaculatus*)	2	21.6	5.3	1	17.8		3	20.3	4.3
Walleye (*Sander vitreus*)	1	36.1		2	12.4	2.0	3	20.3	13.7

? = Identity confirmed but length not determinable.

remains from 137 individual fish of nine taxa were found and identified (Table 4). The majority of these prey fish were centrarchid panfish (58%), while only 5% were sportfish (smallmouth bass, *Micropterus dolomieu*, and pike, Esocidae sp.). Though cormorants may drop prey fish from their nests, digestive pellets are also regurgitated daily by parent birds in the colony, contributing to nutrient enrichment of colonial nest sites (Hatch and Weseloh 1999). This process typically results in the death of tree and shrub vegetation at such colonies and abandonment by ardeid nesters (Hatch and Weseloh 1999). Breeding colonies limited to ardeids rarely kill nesting trees, however, and provide a rich understory source of food for scavengers as well as the terrestrial community as a whole (Ross 1990).

THREATS TO COLONIAL NESTERS

Current Conservation Status

All eight colonial waders discussed here are considered to be secure globally (G5), but their ranking and status in Pennsylvania varies considerably (Table 5; PNHP 2008, Steele

Table 4. Number and identity of fish species found in stomachs of double-crested cormorants (*Phalacrocorax auritus*) taken at Wade Island, Susquehanna River, in May and July of 2006. In all, 102 identifiable fish or fish parts were found in sample.

Species or taxon	No. individuals	Percent of total
Cyprinidae spp.	15	15
White sucker (*Catostomus commersoni*)	12	12
Bullhead (*Ameiurus* spp.)	8	8
Esocidae spp.	2	2
White perch (*Morone americana*)	3	3
Rock bass (*Ambloplites rupestris*)	50	49
Pumpkinseed (*Lepomis gibbosus*)	1	1
Smallmouth bass (*Micropterus dolomieu*)	3	3
Largemouth bass (*Micropterus salmoides*)	5	5

Table 5. Global and state rank and state conservation status (PNHP 2008) of the seven species of colonial waders (plus double-crested cormorant) covered by this review. None of the eight species have federal conservation status.

Species	Global rank	State rank[a]	State status[b]
Great blue heron	G5	S3S4B, S4N	
Great egret	G5	S1B	PE
Snowy egret	G5		
Cattle egret	G5		
Black-crowned night-heron	G5	S2S3B	PE
Yellow-crowned night-heron	G5	S1B	PE
Glossy ibis	G5		
Double-crested cormorant	G5		

[a]B = breeding, N = non-breeding.
[b]P = Pennsylvania, E = endangered, T = threatened.

et al. in press). In Pennsylvania, only great blue heron is considered "apparently secure" to "vulnerable", while black-crowned night-heron ranks "vulnerable" to "imperiled" (Table 5). Both great egret and yellow-crowned night heron are currently ranked as "critically imperiled" for breeding, and the remaining three waders have been "extirpated" for 2–3 decades (Tables 5 and Appendix 1). Double-crested cormorant has no rank or status in Pennsylvania because it is considered an invasive species with no historic presence. Since the state agency with management jurisdiction for birds (Pennsylvania Game Commission) recognizes only two status categories (Pennsylvania threatened or endangered), only the three species with imperiled or critically imperiled state ranking are considered state endangered (Table 5).

Populations Trends

Population trends for three of the four species currently breeding in Pennsylvania are either stable or increasing in North America and the eastern United States. Breeding Bird Survey (BBS) data show significant positive trends for great blue heron in both the eastern U.S. (+2.96, P < 0.0001, 1365 routes) and Pennsylvania (+2.58%, P < 0.001, 82 routes;

BBS 2008). BBS data for great egret show a positive trend in the eastern U.S. (+2.30, P = 0.05, n = 319) with insufficient data for Pennsylvania (BBS 2008). Yellow-crowned night-heron may be increasing in eastern U.S. and is not generally of management concern (Watts 1995). BBS data for black-crowned night-heron, however, show a negative trend in eastern U.S. (–6.09, P < 0.001, n = 115), though Davis (1993) describes the eastern population as stabilized or increasing.

Among the currently extirpated waders of Pennsylvania, snowy egret shows a positive eastern-central U.S. population BBS trend (+4.10, P < 0.05, n = 167) but is probably declining along the Atlantic coast (Parsons and Master 2000). Cattle egret in eastern U.S. have largely stable populations, though BBS data for the past quarter century show negative trends (Telfair 2006). Glossy ibis populations north of Virginia have generally declined in the last quarter century after an earlier period of expansion (BBS 2008, Davis and Kricher 2000). The non-wading double-crested cormorant continues its population expansion in the eastern U.S., with a positive BBS trend of 5.00 (P = 0.01, n = 252).

Fishery Conflicts

Conflicts between man and waterbirds as predators on fish in the wild and at fish-rearing facilities have existed for centuries (Pitt and Conover 1996, Hatch and Weseloh 1999). Much has been written on how to reduce such conflicts at fish hatcheries (McAtee and Piper 1936, Mott 1978, Andelt and Hopper 1996). The consensus is that, other than lethal methods, complete screening or netting of raceways is the most effective and reliable method of preventing losses to avian predators (McAtee and Piper 1936, Mott 1978, Pitt and Conover 1996). Though state hatcheries in Pennsylvania are often outfitted with netting to protect trout in raceways where needed, many private aquaculture facilities are not and continue to incur losses or employ lethal methods, sometimes without the necessary permits. For this reason, black-crowned night-heron, a notorious hatchery visitor (Andelt and Hopper 1996, Pitt and Conover 1996) and state endangered species (Table 5), is potentially the most vulnerable of our breeding waders to hatchery-related mortality, depending on the location of fish rearing facilities. Great blue heron is a more common predator at many hatcheries (Parkhurst et al. 1992), but its status is more secure in the state and therefore less at risk overall. Recent downgrading of black-crowned night-heron's status by the PGC to endangered may afford it greater protection in environmental reviews for the siting of fish-rearing facilities or depredation permitting. Though capable of causing significant economic losses at aquaculture facilities (e.g. see Glahn and Brugger 1995), double crested cormorants are not generally a problem at the relatively small aquaculture facilities of Pennsylvania.

Fishery conflicts in the natural environment are well known for the double-crested cormorant. However, demonstration of non-compensatory prey losses in open waters is rare, owing partly to the difficulty and expense of conducting such studies. An exception is the work done at Lake Oneida, New York, where breeding and migrant cormorants have been shown to significantly reduce yellow perch and walleye (important sport fisheries) recruitment at the lake (Rudstam et al. 2004). Strong cases for similar impacts in the much larger Great Lakes have also emerged in recent years (Schneider et al. 1998, Ross and Johnson 1999, Johnson et al. 2002, Lantry et al. 2002). These studies have generally shown that sport or commercially important fish species make up only small portions of the opportunistic cormorant's diet, but where large breeding colonies exist, even these small percentages can amount to large numbers of fish consumed. Predation rates by nesting cormorants sometimes equal or exceed those of piscivorous fishes or sport and commercial fisheries. In the case of Pennsylvania's fledgling cormorant breeding population (<100 active nests), this problem has not yet occurred. The potential for conflict over a smallmouth bass sport fishery in the Susquehanna River exists, however, with unchecked cormorant breeding population expansion.

Breeding Habitat Loss

Despite extensive forest habitat in the state, the greatest threat to nesting great blue herons continues to be logging of forests without regard to the presence of heron colonies, especially on private lands where most colonies occur (Ross in press). Disturbance of colonies may also cause abandonment. Many of these displaced pairs will establish new colonies or merge with existing ones in subsequent years, partially mitigating the impact.

Two of the remaining colonial nesters, great egret and black-crowned night-heron, typically nest in large mixed colonies on river islands. Many of those islands are in public ownership and thus not threatened by deforestation or development. Loss of large nesting trees due to flood events is a risk for some of these islands, however. Other factors, such as invasive plant species or the killing of large nesting trees by accumulated cormorant guano and nest-building activity could alter tree composition unfavorably for these now endangered waders. The threat of fabric-dam construction to provide recreational opportunities in rivers remains for some areas, including the Sheetz Islands Archipelago, approximately 1 km downstream of the Wade Island heronry.

Due to its propensity to nest in small colonies in residential neighborhoods or urban parks, yellow-crowned night-heron nesting habitat does not appear to be at risk of loss. Human disturbance is more likely to affect such colonies. Factors affecting their choice of nesting sites are not well understood, and thus little can be done to manage this endangered species, short of local public education.

Because double-crested cormorant is considered a recent invasive species in Pennsylvania, potentially impacting two endangered species at a shared breeding colony (Wade Island, Susquehanna River), it makes little sense to discuss threats to its breeding habitat. Human disturbance clearly is the most likely threat it faces in the long run, though, despite possible agency depredation culling to protect endangered herons at Wade Island.

Loss or Alteration of Food Resources

The risk of altered food resources affecting Pennsylvania's waders depends on the nature and degree of changes in prey base as well as the degree of specialization in prey requirements for each wading species. An important factor in the loss of aquatic ecosystem integrity in Pennsylvania is the alarming increase of invasive species in lakes, rivers, and wetlands. For both fish and crayfish, non-indigenous species introduction is the principal or second-most important factor in their imperilment (Williams et al. 1989, Taylor et al. 2007). Pennsylvania's ichthyofauna and aquatic invertebrate communities have not escaped the effects of many of these harmful introductions, including invasion and potential displacement of native species by the invasive rusty crayfish (*Cercopagis pengoi*) in the Susquehanna River (Gunderson 2002). For our currently breeding generalist waders (great blue heron, great egret, and black-crowned night-heron), changes in the abundance of prey species may not pose a problem. In fact, their opportunistic feeding habits may help to control invasive species population explosions. Yellow-crowned night-heron, however, which specializes on crustaceans (Watts 1995), is more likely to be affected by the rusty crayfish invasion, in ways we may not yet understand. It could even benefit, during an initial crayfish invasion, from a more abundant or accessible food supply.

SUMMARY

Historically, seven species of colonial waders (Ciconiiformes: Ardeidae and Threskiornithidae) plus one associated non-wader (Pelicaniformes: Phalacrocoracidae) have been documented to breed in Pennsylvania. Five of these currently breed in the state: great blue heron, great egret, black-crowned night-heron, yellow-crowned night-heron, and double-crested cormorant. Three of these breeders (great egret and both night-herons) are state endangered species with only a single large (great egret) or handful (both night-herons) of breeding colonies known in the state. Ironically, the colonially nesting double-crested cormorant recently began to nest in Pennsylvania and threatens the only sizeable (great egret) or principle (black-crowned night-heron) breeding colony for those endangered species by co-nesting with them. Great blue heron is the only secure but vulnerable colonial wader currently nesting in the state.

Several of Pennsylvania's colonial waders (great egret, snowy egret, cattle egret, yellow-crowned night-heron, and glossy ibis) are near the northeastern limit of their present breeding range where they nest principally along coastal plains, estuaries, and river mouths. Consequently, Pennsylvania's populations are not critical to these species' viability on a global, or even continental, basis. Pennsylvania's great blue heron breeding population, however, is significantly large enough to constitute an important component of its core inland continental population. A fledgeling double-crested cormorant breeding population (<100 nests) is demonstrating its classical exponential growth pattern, despite a substantial culling effort by management agencies to protect endangered nesting herons.

Habitat required by nesting and foraging waders in Pennsylvania is generally abundant and of sufficient quality to allow expansion of all eight historically breeding species. Intrinsic population and range-periphery factors are probably more important in determining the size of their respective breeding populations in Pennsylvania. Human persecution or disturbance is probably only a minor and local factor in colony selection, longevity, and success. Urban sprawl and development are a concern, but most of these wading species appear to be adaptive and resilient (great blue heron), even attracted (black-crowned and yellow-crowned night-herons), to human habitation, parks, and buildings. Because there are so few colonies of several of the species in Pennsylvania, however, even natural catastrophes (e.g., 100-year flood destroying Wade Island in the Susquehanna River) are a risk for their loss. Other long-term risk factors or threats include (1) competition for nest trees from double-crested cormorants, (2) invasive plants (affecting nest trees on river islands) or aquatic organisms (affecting native crayfish prey), (3) fishery conflicts at hatcheries or in natural habitats, and (4) locally contaminated environments (e.g. riverine or lacustrine sediment loads affecting food sources).

LITERATURE CITED

American Ornithologists' Union (AOU). 1998. Check-list of North American Birds. 7th edition. American Ornithologists' Union, Washington, D.C.

Andelt, W. F., and S. N. Hopper. 1996. Effectiveness of alarm-distress calls for frightening herons from a fish rearing facility. The Progressive Fish-Culturist 58:258–262.

Brauning, D. W., editor. 1992. Atlas of Breeding Birds in Pennsylvania. University of Pittsburgh Press, Pittsburgh.

Brauning, D. W., J. P. Dunn, and J. Siefken. 1988–2006. Colonial Nesting Bird Studies, Pennsylvania Game Commission, Harrisburg, Pennsylvania, USA.

Butler, Robert W. 1992. Great blue heron (*Ardea herodias*), The Birds of North America Online (A. Poole, editor). Cornell Lab of Ornithology, Ithaca, New York; retrieved from the Birds of North America Online: http://bna.birds.cornell.edu.bnaproxy.birds.cornell.edu/bna/species/025.

Carlson, B. A. 1995. Nest site characterisitics of great blue herons (*Ardea herodias*) in northeast Ohio. Ohio Journal of Science 95(5):312–315.

Cowardin, L. M., V. Carter, F. C. Golet, and E. T. LaRoe. 1979. Classification of wetlands and deep-water habitats of the United States. U. S. Department of the Interior, FWS/OBS 79/81.

Curry-Lindahl, K. 1978. Conservation and management problems of wading birds and their habitats: a global overview. Pages 83–97 in A. Sprunt IV, J. C. Ogden, and S. Winckler, editors. Wading Birds. National Audubon Society, New York, New York, USA.

Davis, M. B. 1996. Eastern Old-Growth Forests: Prospects for Rediscovery and Recovery. Island Press, Washington DC, USA,

Davis, Jr., W. E. 1993. Black-crowned night-heron (*Nycticorax nycticorax*), The Birds of North America Online (A. Poole, editor). Cornell Lab of Ornithology, Ithaca, New York; retrieved from the Birds of North America Online: http://bna.birds.cornell.edu.bnaproxy.birds.cornell.edu/bna/species/074. doi:bna.74.

Davis, Jr., W. E., and J. Kricher. 2000. Glossy ibis (*Plegadis falcinellus*), The Birds of North America Online (A. Poole, editor). Cornell Lab of Ornithology, Ithaca, New York; retrieved from the Birds of North America Online: http://bna.birds.cornell.edu.bnaproxy.birds.cornell.edu/bna/species/545. doi:bna.545.

Davis, W. E., Jr., and J. A. Kushlan. 1994. Green heron (*Butorides virescens*). In The Birds of North America, No. 129 (A. Poole and F. Gill, Eds.). Philadelphia: The Academy of Natural Sciences; Washington, D.C.: The American Ornithologists' Union.

del Hoyo, J., A. Elliot, and J. Sargatal (eds). 1992. Handbook of the Birds of the World, Vol. 1. Lynx Edicions, Barcelona.

Fingerhood, E. D. 1992. Glossy ibis. Pp. 426–427 in Atlas of Breeding Birds in Pennsylvania (D. W. Brauning, ed.). Univ. of Pittsburgh Press, Pittsburgh, PA.

Gill, F. B. 1985. Birds. Pages 299–351 in H. H. Genoways and F. J. Brenner (editors). Species of Special Concern in Pennsylvania. Carnegie Museum of Natural History Special Publication No. 11, Pittsburgh, Pennsylvania.

Glahn, J. F. and K. E. Brugger. 1995. The impact of double-crested cormorants on the Mississippi delta catfish industry: a bioenergetics model. Colonial Waterbirds 18 (Spec. Publ. 1): 168–175.

Goodrich, L. J., M. Brittingham, J. A. Bishop, and P. Barber. 2002. Wildlife habitat in Pennsylvania: past, present, and future. Report to state agencies, 236 pages. Available at http://www.dcnr.state.pa.us/wlhabitat/.

Graham, K., B. Collier, M. Bradstreet, and B. Collins. 1996. Great blue heron (*Ardea herodias*) populations in Ontario: data from and insights on the use of volunteers. Colonial Waterbirds 19(1):39–44.

Gunderson, J. 2002. Rusty crayfish: a nasty invader. Minnesota Sea Grant. Retrieved online at http://www.seagrant.umn.edu/ais/rustycrayfish_invader.

Hatch, J. J. 1995. Changing populations of double-crested cormorants. Colonial Waterbirds 18 (Spec. Publ. 1): 8–24.

Hatch, J. J., and D. V. Weseloh. 1999. Double-crested cormorant (*Phalacrocorax auritus*), The Birds of North America Online (A. Poole, editor). Cornell Lab of Ornithology, Ithaca, New York; retrieved from the Birds of North America Online: http://bna.birds.cornell.edu.bnaproxy.birds.cornell.edu/bna/species/441 doi:bna.441.

Johnson, J. H., R. M. Ross, and D. R. Smith. 1997. Evidence of secondary consumption of invertebrate prey by double-crested cormorants. Colonial Waterbirds 20(3):547–551.

Johnson, J. H., R. M. Ross, and R. D. McCullough. 2002. Little Galloo Island, Lake Ontario: a review of nine years of double-crested cormorant diet and fish consumption information. Journal of Great Lakes Research 28(2):182–192.

Lantry, B. F., T. H. Eckert, C. P. Schneider, and J. R. Chrisman. 2002. The relationship between abundance of smallmouth bass and double-crested cormorants in the eastern basin of Lake Ontario. Journal of Great Lakes Research 28(2):193–201.

Master, T. L. 2004. Current status and management options for double-crested cormorants in Wade Island. East Stroudsburg University, East Stroudsburg, Pennsylvania.

Master, T. L., D. L. Detwiler IV, and W. Romano. 2007. Foraging success and habitat use by a population of great egrets (*Ardea alba*) on the Susquehanna River in Harrisburg, Pennsylvania. IV North American Ornithological Conference, Veracruz, Mexico, October 2007.

McAtee, W. L., and S. E. Piper. 1936. Excluding birds from reservoirs and fishponds. U. S. Department of Agriculture Leaflet 120.

McCrimmon, Jr., D. A., J. C. Ogden, and G. T. Bancroft. 2001 . Great egret (*Ardea alba*), The Birds of North America Online (A. Poole, editor). Cornell Lab of Ornithology, Ithaca, New York; retrieved from the Birds of North America Online: http://bna.birds.cornell.edu.bnaproxy.birds. cornell.edu/bna/species/570 doi:bna.570.

McWilliams, G. M., and D. W. Brauning. 2000. The Birds of Pennsylvania. Cornell University Press, Ithaca, New York.

Mott, D. F. 1978. Control of wading bird predation at fish-rearing facilities. Pages 131–132 in A. Sprunt IV, J. C. Ogden, and S. Winckler, editors. Wading Birds. National Audubon Society Research Report No. 7, New York, New York, USA.

Myers, W.L., et al. 2000. Pennsylvania Gap Analysis Project: Leading landscapes for collaborative conservation. Final Rep. U.S. Geol. Survey-Gap Analysis Program. 142pp.+appendices.

Parkhurst, J. A., R. P. Brooks, and D. E. Arnold. 1992. Assessment of predation at trout hatcheries in central Pennsylvania. Wildlife Society Bulletin 20:411–419.

Parsons, K. C., and T. L. Master. 2000. Snowy egret (*Egretta thula*), The Birds of North America Online (A. Poole, editor). Cornell Lab of Ornithology, Ithaca, New York; retrieved from the Birds of North America Online: http://bna.birds.cornell.edu.bnaproxy.birds.cornell.edu/bna/species/ 489. doi:bna.489.

Pennsylvania Natural Heritage Program (PNHP). 2008. Retrieved online at http://www.naturalheritage. state.pa.us.

Pennsylvania Fish and Boat Commission (PFBC). 2008. Retrieved online at http://www.fish.state. pa.us/endang1.htm.

Pitt, W. C., and M. R. Conover. 1996. Predation at intermountain west fish hatcheries. Journal of Wildlife Management 60(3):616–624.

Ross, R. M. 1990. Saving a heron rookery. Bird Watcher's Digest 12(6):62–67.

Ross, R. M. Great blue heron. In: Terrestrial Vertebrates of Pennsylvania: a case study in conservation. (In press). Steele, M. A., M. C. Brittingham, T. J. Maret, and J. F. Merrit (eds). Johns Hopkins University Press, Baltimore.

Ross, R. M., and J. H. Johnson. 1999. Fish losses to double-crested cormorant predation in eastern Lake Ontario, 1992–1997. Pp. 61–70 in M. E. Tobin (Tech. Ed.). Symposium on double-crested cormorants: population status and management issues in the Midwest (9 December 1997, Milwaukee, WI). U.S. Department of Agriculture Technical Bulletin No. 1879.

Rudstam, L. G., A. J. VanDeValk, C. M. Adams, J. T. Coleman, J. L. Forney, and M. E. Richmond. 2004. Cormorant predation and the population dynamics of walleye and yellow perch in Oneida Lake. Ecological Applications 14(1):149–163.

Scharf, W. C. 1989. Coastal great blue heron and great egret colonies of the Michigan Great Lakes. Jack-Pine Warbler 67(2):52–65.

Schneider, C. P., Schiavone, A., Jr., Eckert, T. H., McCullough, R. D., Lantry, B. F., Einhouse, D. W., Chrisman, J. R., Adams, C. M., Johnson, J. H., and R. M. Ross. 1998. Double-crested cormorant predation on smallmouth bass and other warm water fishes of the eastern basin of Lake Ontario:

overview and summary. New York Department of Environmental Conservation Special Report. December 15, 1998.

Schutsky, R. M. 1992a. Black-crowned night-heron. Pages 60–61 in D. W. Brauning (editor). Atlas of Breeding Birds in Pennsylvania. University of Pittsburgh Press, Pittsburgh.

Schutsky, R. M. 1992b. Cattle egret. Pp. 56–57 in D. W. Brauning (editor). Atlas of Breeding Birds in Pennsylvania. University of Pittsburgh Press, Pittsburgh.

Schutsky, R. M. 1992c. Snowy egret. Pages 54–55 in D. W. Brauning (editor). Atlas of Breeding Birds in Pennsylvania. University of Pittsburgh Press, Pittsburgh.

Schutsky, R. M. 1992d. Yellow-crowned night-heron. Pages 62–63 in D. W. Brauning (editor). Atlas of Breeding Birds in Pennsylvania. University of Pittsburgh Press, Pittsburgh.

Schwalbe, P. W., and R. M. Ross. 1992. Great blue heron, *Ardea herodias.* Pages 50–51 in D. W. Brauning (editor). Atlas of Breeding Birds in Pennsylvania. University of Pittsburgh Press, Pittsburgh.

Sibley, D. A. 2000. National Audubon Society the Sibley Guide to Birds. Alfred A. Knopf, New York.

Steele, M. A., M. C. Brittingham, T. J. Maret, and J. F. Merrit (eds). Terrestrial Vertebrates of Pennsylvania: a case study in conservation. (In press). Johns Hopkins University Press, Baltimore.

Taylor, C. A., and 9 others. 2007. A reassessment of the conservation status of crayfishes of the United States and Canada after 10+ years of increased awareness. Fisheries 32(8):372–389.

Telfair II, R. C. 2006. Cattle egret (*Bubulcus ibis*), The Birds of North America Online (A. Poole, editor). Cornell Lab of Ornithology, Ithaca, New York; retrieved from the Birds of North America Online: http://bna.birds.cornell.edu.bnaproxy.birds.cornell.edu/bna/species/113. doi:bna.113.

Terres, J. K. 1980. The Audubon Society Encyclopedia of North American Birds. Alfred A. Knopf, New York.

Tiner, R. W. 1984. Wetlands of the United States: current status and recent trends. U. S. Fish and Wildlife Service, Washington DC, USA.

Watts, Bryan D. 1995. Yellow-crowned Night-Heron (*Nyctanassa violacea*), The Birds of North America Online (A. Poole, Ed.). Ithaca: Cornell Lab of Ornithology; Retrieved from the Birds of North America Online: http://bna.birds.cornell.edu.bnaproxy.birds.cornell.edu/bna/species/161.doi:bna.161.

Weseloh, D. V., P. J. Ewins, J. Struger, P. Mineau, and C. A. Bishop. 1995. Double-crested cormorants of the Great Lakes: changes in population size, breeding distribution and reproductive output between 1913 and 1991. Colonial Waterbirds 18 (Spec. Publ. 1): 48–59.

Wilhelm, G. 1992. Sandhill cranes in Mercer County. Pennsylvania Birds 6(3):105–106.

Williams, J. E., and 7 others. 1989. Fishes of North America endangered, threatened, or of special concern: 1989. Fisheries 14(6):2–20.

APPENDIX 1

Number of active nests in all known breeding colonies, historic and current by year since 1975, of six species of wading birds plus double-crested cormorant in Pennsylvania. Data from Brauning et al. (1988–2006), Brauning (1992), McWilliams and Brauning (2000); and Pennsylvania Birds 21:2007.

River Basin	Rookery Location	Species	Pre-1975 (largest)	1975	1976	1978	1983	1984	1985	1986	1987	1988	1989	1990	1991	1992	1993
Delaware	Tinicum Township (Delaware Co.)	GREG	1														
	Heinz (Tinicum) NWR (Philadelphia Co.)	GREG				3											
		SNEG				3											
		BCNH										75	8	75+	75	50	
	Mud Island (Philadelphia Co.)	GREG									6		18				
		BCNH				12					30						
	Chester Co.	YCNH	1														
	Montgomery Co.	YCNH	1														
	West Lawn/Reading (Berks Co.)	BCNH															7
Susquehanna	Rookery Island (Lancaster Co.)	GREG										3					
		SNEG		2							3						
		CAEG		772			261	392	578	413	160						
		BCNH					106	272	456	257	235						
		GLIB		6	2												
	Pinetown et al. (Lancaster Co.)	YCNH		1						1	1						
	Creek Road et al. (Lancaster Co.)	BCNH											71	85	35		
	Codorus Creek (York Co.)	BCNH													12		
	Kiwanis Lake (York Co.)	GREG														3	3
		BCNH															3
		YCNH															
	Lake William (York Co.)	BCNH									10	8	8	4	7		
	Governor's Island (Dauphin Co.)	YCNH															
	Bellevue Park (Dauphin Co.)	YCNH															
	Camp Hill (Cumberland Co.)	YCNH	2														
	Wade Island (Dauphin Co.)	GREG	1 (+?)				20		30	90	48	74	78	92	81	161	
		BCNH					150		150	130	191	180	268	344	276	252	
		YCNH											2				
	Rockville Bridge (Dauphin co.)	DCCO													1		
		BCNH															
	Total nests			780	2	18	537	664	1214	891	687	340	453	600	487	466	23
	Total colonies reported			1	1	2	2	2	3	3	5	5	5	4	6	4	3
	Total species			3	1	2	3	2	3	4	5	3	3	3	3	2	2

APPENDIX 1 continued.

Number of active nests in all known breeding colonies, historic and current by year since 1975, of six species of wading birds plus double-crested cormorant in Pennsylvania. Data from Brauning et al. (1988–2006), Brauning (1992), McWilliams and Brauning (2000); and Pennsylvania Birds 21:2007.

River Basin	Rookery Location	Species	1994	1995	1996	1997	1998	1999	2000	2001	2002	2003	2004	2005	2006	2007
Delaware	Tinicum Township (Delaware Co.)	GREG														
	Heinz (Tinicum) NWR (Philadelphia Co.)	GREG														
		SNEG														
	Mud Island (Philadelphia Co.)	BCNH	75+		24											
		GREG						12								
	Chester Co.	BCNH														
		YCNH														
	Montgomery Co.	YCNH														
	West Lawn/Reading (Berks Co.)	BCNH				15		12	16	9			15		12	10
Susquehanna	Rookery Island (Lancaster Co.)	GREG														
		SNEG														
		CAEG														
		BCNH														
		GLIB														
	Pinetown et al. (Lancaster Co.)	YCNH	2	3	1	1		1	2							
	Creek Road et al. (Lancaster Co.)	BCNH	90+	100		80	109	92	92	88	79	50	55		31	18
	Codorus Creek (York Co.)	BCNH														
	Kiwanis Lake (York Co.)	GREG												3	4	4
		BCNH	8	21	10	10		20	19	23	23	20	40	35	97	26
		YCNH											1	2	0	
	Lake William (York Co.)	BCNH							21							
	Governor's Island (Dauphin Co.)	YCNH														
	Bellevue Park (Dauphin Co.)	YCNH														3
	Camp Hill (Cumberland Co.)	YCNH		5		4					4				5	
	Wade Island (Dauphin Co.)	GREG	133	136	155	131	144	159	148	166	142	193	171	162	145	173
		BCNH	238	230	200	99	181	120	134	93	107	99	128	63	77	62
		YCNH														
	Rockville Bridge (Dauphin co.)	DCCO			1	1	2	4	9	11	21	31	40	59	62	72
		BCNH														
Total nests			**546**	**495**	**391**	**341**	**436**	**408**	**441**	**390**	**376**	**393**	**450**	**324**	**433**	**368**
Total colonies reported			**5**	**5**	**4**	**6**	**3**	**5**	**8**	**4**	**4**	**3**	**4**	**2**	**5**	**6**
Total species			**3**	**3**	**4**	**4**	**3**	**4**	**4**	**3**	**4**	**3**	**4**	**4**	**4**	**4**

Avian Ecology and Conservation: A Pennsylvania Focus with National Implications. Edited by S. K. Majumdar, T. L. Master, M. C. Brittingham, R. M. Ross, R. S. Mulvihill and J. E. Huffman. © 2010. The Pennsylvania Academy of Science.

Chapter 20

Sheet Glass as a Principal Human-Associated Avian Mortality Factor

Daniel Klem, Jr.
Acopian Center for Ornithology
Department of Biology
Muhlenberg College
Allentown, Pennsylvania 18104-5586
klem@muhlenberg.edu

INTRODUCTION

Perhaps without reasonable dispute, major habitat modification and outright destruction are the leading human-associated threats to free living wild birds. Disturb an ecosystem by markedly altering or destroying habitat and you eliminate any chance for the survival of species that rely on that space for food, shelter, and reproduction. Among the most vulnerable to habitat changes are birds that typically occupy the higher trophic levels of ecosystems, and as a result are often meaningful indicators of overall environmental health. Even considering the devastating effects of pesticides, oil spills and pollution in general, cat predation, and the victims of power lines and the higher image effects of communication towers and wind turbines, a growing amount of evidence overwhelmingly supports the claim that clear and reflective sheet glass is the next leading universal human-associated cause of bird attrition worldwide (American Ornithologists' Union 1975, Banks 1979, Klem 1990b, 1991, 2006, 2007, Graham 1997, Erickson et al. 2001, Harden 2002); sheet glass that is present in most human dwellings that are being built in ever increasing numbers on avian breeding and non-breeding grounds and across their migratory routes. Here I provide evidence for this claim by first describing why birds collide with sheet glass, the details or characteristics of these types of collisions, the known and potential magnitude of the kill, and lastly how this universal threat can be addressed as an important conservation issue for birds and people.

SUMMARY OF CONSERVATION POLICY ISSUES ADDRESSING THE GLASS THREAT FOR BIRDS

1. Sheet glass is a proven killer of wild birds, but its attrition on specific species or its part in explaining the decrease in bird populations in general is in need of further study.

Figure 1: Clear glass corridor showing see-through effect in the downtown area of the city of Toronto, Ontario, Canada.

2. Education programs are needed to inform the general public, the government and non-profit conservation community, and the building industry, to include glass manufacturers, architects, developers, and landscape architects and planners. Current evidence indicates that with the exception of habitat destruction, the lethal toll attributable to sheet glass is equal to or far greater than any other human-associated avian mortality factor.

3. Individual birds that are killed striking glass, from a few to hundreds at any one site, go unnoticed or are ignored at countless residential and commercial buildings the world over. Regulation requiring the incorporation of preventive measures in existing, remodeled, or new buildings will save millions of lives while preserving our birds as a unique natural resource. In the U.S., under the Migratory Bird Treaty Act (MBTA) and the Endangered Species Act (ESC), the enforcement of avian protection at buildings where birds are predictably and repeatedly killed will aide in initiating preventive measures. Minimally, regulations are recommended to require warning labels be attached to sheet glass to alert building industry professionals that this product is a proven lethal hazard for birds.

AN OVERVIEW OF THE FACTS AND THEIR INTERPRETATIONS

To be sure glass has enriched human life for at least 16 centuries (Klem 1979, 1989), permitting a view, often spectacular, of the outside world from the indoor protection of dwellings. The clarity of contemporary low-iron sheet glass is unrivaled in history. Since we are not birds we cannot be certain about their motives or actions, but in general birds behave as if glass is invisible to them by injuring or killing themselves flying into clear and reflective panes (Figures 1, 2). Extensive observations and experimentation support the interpretation that birds simply do not see clear or reflective glass as a barrier to be avoided (Klem 1989, 1990b, Klem et al. 2004, Ogden 1996, O'Connell 2001). Since its use in human structures, sheet glass as a source of bird mortality is predicted to have increased as the size, clarity, and number of panes have increased with time.

The repeated strikes of individual birds at a window can be of deep concern and even extreme annoyance to some homeowners or workplace observers. These harmless collisions are the result of combatants interpreting their reflected images as territorial rivals, and as a result of their fighting they can appear exhausted, disheveled and even bloody. Although related in that the birds are deceived by glass, these types of collisions are not the same type of strikes resulting in serious injury or death considered here. To eliminate these repeated defending strikes the mirrored image of the offending bird must be eliminated at the pane it is hitting, but the nature of these attacks make it possible that destroying a reflection on one offending window may simply result in the territorial bird moving its aggression to another rival reflected in another pane in the same structure whose location is still in the space it seeks to defend. These harmless but troubling attacks typically will stop when the breeding season is over, but some species such as the northern cardinal (*Cardinalis cardinalis*) can defend areas and fight their reflections throughout the year.

From harmful collisions the dead and dying victims of sheet glass are most often hidden from view in vegetation surrounding human dwellings. They are either killed outright,

Figure 2:   Tinted panes showing the reflective effect in a multistory commercial building away from the downtown area of the city of Toronto, Ontario, Canada.

injured and struggling to recover at or away from the strike site, or are quickly taken by predators and scavengers (Klem 1990b, Klem et al. 2004). Continuous monitoring of single homes and the results of field experiments document that one out of every two strikes results in a fatality (Klem 1990a). Fatal or injurious collisions occur when flying birds attempt to reach habitat visible on the other side of clear panes (Figure 1), or by attempting to reach illusions of habitat and sky reflected in the glass surface (Figure 2; Klem 1979, 1989). The cause of death is often mistakenly thought to be a broken neck because of neck flexibility in freshly killed specimens; such flexibility is the result of special articulating surfaces of the avian cervical vertebrae (heterocoelous). Detailed external and internal studies of glass collision victims, to include hundreds of radiographs (x-rays), reveal that lethal strikes result from head trauma: intracranial pressure, breaking of the blood-brain barrier, and brain swelling and cranial herniation (Klem 1990a, Veltri and Klem 2005).

Lethal collisions are possible wherever birds and glass mutually occur. Glass casualties have been recorded the world over at panes of all sizes in residential homes and single or multistory buildings (Klem 1979, 1989). The sex, age, or resident status of birds in any locale has little influence on their vulnerability to windows. There is no season or time of day, and almost no weather conditions during which birds elude glass. Collections of glass-killed specimens beneath tinted panes indicate that transparent or reflective panes of various colors appear to be equally lethal to birds. Strikes occur at sheet glass of various sizes, heights, and orientation in urban, suburban, and rural environments, but birds are more vulnerable to large (> 2 m^2) panes near ground level and at heights above 3 m in suburban and rural areas. At least in the northern latitudes of North America, strikes are more frequent during the non-breeding season when birds are attracted to feeders (feeding tables in the United Kingdom) in large numbers than at any other time of the year, including migratory periods when glass casualties typically attract the most human attention because they are often more visible in urban areas on sidewalks or around workplaces. As noted, birds act as if clear and reflective glass is invisible to them; consequently, the best predictor of the number of strikes at any one location is the density of birds in the vicinity of the invisible hazard. Artificial and natural foods, watering areas, vegetation, weather conditions that affect visibility, and overall landscape structures that influence flight paths can account for increased densities of birds near windows (Klem 1989, 1990b, Klem et al. 2004, Gelb and Delacretaz 2006).

Interestingly, there is the impression from some observers that birds of prey and scavengers such as gulls and crows use glass panes as tools to obtain food. They speculate that by frightening smaller birds from feeders and fruit-laden and other vegetation will result in strikes at nearby windows where the dead and injured become easy prey for the hunters. Although this is an intriguing possibility there is no convincing evidence supporting this interpretation. Alternatively, it is more likely that active predators and scavengers become conditioned over time and learn that a particular site offers vulnerable prey for the taking. That this latter explanation is more reasonable is supported by the frequency with which raptors, especially *Accipiter* hawks, become strike victims, and a study documenting a sharp-shinned hawk (*Accipiter striatus*) and loggerhead shrike (*Lanius ludovicianus*) that repeatedly patrolled the windows of a residence to collect prey until, at least, the hawk became a casualty at the same location (Klem 1981).

A North American survey of museums and select individuals on documented bird-glass strikes in 1975-76 recognized 225 or 25% of the 917 species occurring in the continental

U.S. and Canada (American Ornithologists' Union 1983). Since then 42 additional species have increased this total to 267 or 28% of the 947 species currently recognized as occurring in North America north of Mexico (American Birding Association 2007). Intermittent survey requests and lists of glass casualties in several publications document 759 species representing 8% of the approximately 10,000 bird species worldwide. The species recorded most often striking glass in order of documented frequency from the 1975-76 survey for North America are: American robin (*Turdus migratorius*), dark-eyed junco (*Junco hyemalis*), cedar waxwing (*Bombycilla cedrorum*), ovenbird (*Seiurus aurocapilla*), Swainson's thrush (*Catharus ustulatus*), northern flicker (*Colaptes auratus*), hermit thrush (*Catharus guttatus*), yellow-rumped warbler (*Dendroica coronata*), northern cardinal, and evening grosbeak (*Coccothraustes vespertinus*); and for a comparable area in Europe: blackcap (*Sylvia atricapilla*), garden warbler (*Sylvia borin*), European greenfinch (*Carduelis chloris*), chaffinch (*Fringilla coelebs*), European pied flycatcher (*Ficedula hypoleuca*), great tit (*Parus major*), Eurasian blackbird (*Turdus merula*), Eurasian sparrowhawk (*Accipiter nisus*), song thrush (*Turdus philomelos*), Eurasian bullfinch (*Pyrrhula pyrrhula*), common goldcrest (*Regulus regulus*), European robin (*Erithacus rubecula*), Eurasian woodcock (*Scolopax rusticola*), and willow warbler (*Phylloscopus trochilus*). The species not recorded colliding with glass belong to major groups such as tubenoses, waterfowl, waders and shorebirds, several gulls, terns and auks, almost all soaring raptors, and many terrestrial species of galliforms, columbiforms, and passeriforms that occur in sparsely human-populated desert, grassland, and forest habitat. One striking exception is a documented account of a band-rumped storm-petrel (*Thalssidroma castro*) that hit the window of a stationary vessel in the waters around the Hawaiian Islands.

Species often assumed to be immune to glass strikes are those commonly found around human dwellings, especially in cities; they include the rock pigeon (*Columba livia*), European starling (*Sturnus vulgaris*), and house or English sparrow (*Passer domesticus*). Each of these species is a documented window-kill, but they are thought to be disproportionately represented as glass kills given their seemingly lower overall frequency as casualties and their higher densities in the vicinity of windows. One explanation is that they may gain protection from their behavior of flying to perches such as sills and ivy or other vegetation that are near glass surfaces where, like feeders close to windows, if they strike the glass they do so with a force below which is needed to injure or kill themselves, but perhaps with enough to learn that an invisible barrier exists and the space it occupies should be avoided thereafter. At one known location where one of these species seem especially vulnerable to glass, R. F. Johnston (University of Kansas, personal communication) described to me how the windows of the museum at the University of Kansas are recessed and the site of relatively frequent strikes by rock pigeons; he speculated that this species' habit of entering cave opening or cave-like depressions of cliffs may make them vulnerable to this type of framing that mimic caves and where glass blocks access a short distance beyond the entrance.

Among species of special concern the swift parrot (*Lathamus discolor*) of Australia is noteworthy as a listed member of the threatened birds of the world with 1.5% of the 1,000 breeding pair population annually documented as window-kills (BirdLife International 2000, Klem 2006, 2007). Other species of global conservation concern that are known victims of glass strikes are listed by BirdLife International (2000) in various threat categories: Critically Endangered are those facing extreme high risk for extinction in the wild in the immediate future; Endangered are facing a high risk of extinction in the wild in the near future; Vulnerable are facing a high risk of extinction in the wild in the medium-term future; Conservation Dependent are species with ongoing specific attention or habitat-specific programs without which they would be classified within a more threatened category; Near Threatened are species that do not qualify for Conservation Dependent status, but are close to qualifying as Vulnerable. Known and globally threatened glass casualties are: Critically Endangered – Townsend's shearwater (*Puffinus auricularis*) and yellow-crested cockatoo (*Cacatua suphurea*); Endangered – swift parrot described above and eastern bristlebird (*Dasyornis brachypterus*); Vulnerable – Gould's petrel (*Pterodroma leucoptera*), cape gannet (*Morus capensis*), superb parrot (*Polytelis swainsonii*), cerulean warbler (*Dendroica cerulea*), marsh grassbird (*Megalurus pryeri*); Near Threatened – northern bobwhite (*Colinus virginianus*), copper pheasant (*Syrmaticus soemmerringii*), oriental darter (*Anhinga melanogaster*), black rail (*Laterallus jamaicensis*), bush thick-knee (*Burhinus grallarius*), plain pigeon (*Patagioenas inornata*), whistling green-pigeon (*Treron formosae*), New Zealand pigeon (*Hemiphaga novaseelandiae*), red-headed woodpecker (*Melanerpes erythrocephalus*), olive-sided flycatcher (*Contopus cooperi*), Bell's vireo (*Vireo bellii*), flame robin (*Petroica phoenicea*), diamond firetail (*Stagonopleura guttata*), golden-winged warbler (*Vermivora chrysoptera*), Kirtland's warbler (*Dendroica kirtlandii*), Brewer's sparrow (*Spizella breweri*), and painted bunting (*Passerina ciris*). Kirtland's warbler and the plain [Puerto Rican] pigeon are known window victims that also appear on the U.S. Endangered Species List. Glass casualties that are species of conservation concern highlighted by the National Audubon Society 2007 WatchList for the USA are 6 or 9% of the 67 species on their Red List, and 24 or 26% of the 94 species on their Yellow List (Butcher et al. 2007, National Audubon Society 2007). Red List birds are declining rapidly, have very small populations or limited ranges, and face major conservation threats; they are species of global conservation concern. Yellow List birds are also declining but at a slower rate than those on the Red List; they are species of national conservation concern (Table 1).

With the exception of currently threatened species where every unintended loss can be critical, such as the attrition of swift parrots from window collisions, the toll that glass exacts on most individual species and bird populations overall is unknown. Because the avian eye, like other vertebrates, seems incapable of recognizing clear and reflective panes as barriers to avoid, this unintended human-associated avian mortality factor is an especially deceptive and important conservation problem. The shear diversity of victims and their individual traits suggests that sheet glass is an indiscriminate killer where the fittest individual members of a species are as vulnerable as the less fit. Most natural population mortality factors are compensatory with disproportionate attrition resulting from starvation or predation one year while disease or unseasonable weather claim more the following year. By contrast the attrition attributable to glass is an additive mortality factor, one acting unrelentingly all year round every year, an ever present and growing invisible source of killing of which these losses are added to other sources, which in turn increase the survival burden for individual species and bird populations in general.

Before much was known, annual deaths attributable to windows were hypothesized to be 3.5 million in the 1970s (Banks 1979). Since then extensive studies for more than three decades permit a more informed estimate of an annual toll attributable to sheet glass in the USA alone to be between approximately 100 million and 1 billion (Klem 1990b). The wide-

Table 1. National Audubon Society WatchList species that are documented as sheet glass
casualties in the United States (Butcher 2007, National Audubon Society 2007).

Common Name	Scientific Name
Red List	
black rail	*Laterallus jamaicensis*
Bell's vireo	*Vireo bellii*
Bicknell's thrush	*Catharus bicknelli*
golden-winged warbler	*Vermivora chrysoptera*
Kirtland's warbler	*Dendroica kirtlandii*
cerulean warbler	*Dendroica cerulea*
Nelson's sharp-tailed sparrow	*Ammodramus nelsoni*
Yellow List	
mountain quail	*Oreotyx pictus*
yellow rail	*Coturnicops noveboracensis*
American woodcock	*Scolopax minor*
short-eared owl	*Asio flammeus*
buff-bellied hummingbird	*Amazilia yucatanensis*
Costa's hummingbird	*Calypte costae*
calliope hummingbird	*Stellula calliope*
rufous hummingbird	*Selasphorus rufus*
Allen's hummingbird	*Selasphorus sasin*
red-headed woodpecker	*Melanerpes erythrocephalus*
olive-sided flycatcher	*Contopus cooperi*
willow flycatcher	*Empidonax traillii*
oak titmouse	*Baeolophus inomatus*
wood thrush	*Hylocichla mustelina*
blue-winged warbler	*Vermivora pinus*
Virginia's warbler	*Vermivora virginiae*
prairie warbler	*Dendroica discolor*
bay-breasted warbler	*Dendroica castanea*
prothonotary warbler	*Protonotaria citrea*
worm-eating warbler	*Helmitheros vermivorum*
Kentucky warbler	*Oporornis formosus*
Canada warbler	*Wilsonia canadensis*
Brewer's sparrow	*Spizella breweri*
rusty blackbird	*Euphagus carolinus*

ranging difference among these figures attests to the complexity of attempting to determine
accurate amounts from a source in which every individual bird is a potential victim and
sheet glass of every size is a potential killing site in the environment. This 100 million to 1
billion glass-related kills is based on the assumption that 1 to 10 birds are killed at one
building in the U.S. each year using 1970s census data to estimate numbers of buildings in
the USA (Klem 1990b). A supporting study that evaluated the lower 100 million kills as reasonable relied on 5,500 volunteers who optionally recorded bird strikes at windows while
counting visitors to feeding stations at their homes (Dunn 1993). To put these numbers in
perspective, annual USA bird populations are estimated to be 20 billion individuals in the
fall, and annual glass kills are estimated to be 0.5 to 5.0% of this figure. Other annual
sources of human-associated bird mortality are: 120 million from hunting, 60 million from
vehicular collisions, 10,000 to 40,000 from wind power turbine strikes, and hundreds of

millions to as many as a billion by domestic cats (American Ornithologists' Union 1975, Banks 1979, Klem 1990b, Klem 1991, Erickson et al. 2001, Harden 2002). Common sense suggests that even the remarkable upper estimate of 1 billion kills attributable to domestic cats is likely to be far less than the annual kill at sheet glass, reasoning that cats are active predators that most often capture vulnerable prey, while sheet glass is an indiscriminate killer that takes the strong as well as the weak and is astronomically more abundant than cats in the environment. Consequently, the 1 billion toll attributable to glass in the USA alone is most likely highly conservative; the figure is surely in the billions worldwide.

Although accounts of bird-glass collisions appear relatively early in formal ornitholog-ical literature (Baird et al. 1874a, b, Townsend 1931), comprehensive studies document-ing the details about this source of avian mortality and its potential consequences for avian conservation date from the last three decades of the 20th Century to the present (Banks 1976, Banks 1979, Klem 1979, 1989, 2006, 2007, Ogden 1996, Graham 1997). However, even with detailed accounts published in peer-reviewed scientific literature, the glass threat to birds was almost universally overlooked and ignored by those who were most suited to educate and address means of preventing these unintended kills, among them pro-fessionals such as conservation and ornithological scientists in academe, conservation groups, government agencies, and members of the building industry such as architects, glass manufacturers, and landscape architects and planners. Past and present encyclopedic works on birds either completely ignore (Terres 1980, Podulka et al. 2004) or meagerly mention (Gill 2007) the attrition of birds at sheet glass. With more than meager irony, countless professional ornithologists and avian conservationists have work space in build-ings that kill the very organisms they are charged and dedicated to study and protect. In general and to date most members of the building industry tend to view this issue as uncomplimentary, one that associates their work or products with injury and death. Even informed scientists and other members of the conservation community including federal, state, and regional governments charged with, or at least party to, protecting birds have focused their attention on higher profile bird kills by domestic cats, pesticides, power lines, communication towers, and wind power turbines, primarily because of resource lim-itations and the intractable and universal problem that glass poses for birds and the chal-lenges for humans attempting to address it. Although educational efforts remain para-mount for all interested constituencies at all levels, public and professional attention to this issue was markedly increased beginning in spring 2003. From this time to the present, pre-viously sporadic and sparse media attention, mostly during migratory periods, has dra-matically increased, alerting and educating a growing number of people about the seri-ousness of the glass hazard for birds at local, regional, national, and to some degree inter-national levels (Yakutchik 2003, Malakoff 2004, Nielsen 2006). From this exposure select glass and window-film manufacturers, architects, and conservation groups have shown an increased interest in saving birds from glass.

An extraordinary amount of natural history information is available from bird-glass col-lision casualties. From two single homes where the occupants worked and were present and monitoring their windows daily over an entire year, 61 strikes (54.1% outright fatali-ties) occurred at a single level residence in the rural Midwest USA, and 47 strikes (55.3% outright fatalities) occurred at a suburban home in the Northeast USA (Klem 1990a). An enormously rich source of data is obtainable from window victims considering that every piece of sheet glass in any human structure the year round in rural, suburban, and urban environments the world over is a potential killing site. Since 1978 the Field Museum in Chicago annually has added about 1,000 local window-killed and salvaged specimens to its bird collection (Lowther 1995). The freezers of the museum at the University of Nebraska-Lincoln are filled and staff have pleaded that donors no longer donate window-kills because they are overwhelmed (Labedz 1997). Window casualties are especially useful in contributing information on migratory movements and distribution, breeding and non-breeding ranges and their expansions and contractions, first records of the geographic occurrence of a species, in addition to obvious whole specimen-related studies of species-specific form and function (Klem 1979, 1990b). It is more than likely Kirtland's warblers were being killed and available for discovery at glass panes along their migratory route between Michigan and the Bahamas before their non-breeding location was known and a window-killed specimen was collected while in passage in Ohio (Walkinshaw 1976). Talpin (1991) described the value of glass casualties to migration studies of several Australian birds. The first record of a white-bellied emerald (*Amazilia candida*) for El Salvador was a window-kill in downtown San Salvador on 3 November 2004 (Jones 2005). Detailed gross anatomy and histology of the alimentary tracts of house sparrow and American robin were obtained from window victims (Klem et al. 1982, 1983, 1984). For their extraordinary scientific value systematic searches and use of window-killed specimens are encouraged year round and worldwide.

SUMMARY OF CURRENT AND FUTURE SOLUTIONS

There are currently many solutions that effectively reduce or eliminate bird strikes, but none that is universally applicable for all human structures. Protective measures range from physical barriers that keep birds from striking to visual cues that protect by transforming the area occupied by glass into uninviting space or a recognizable obstacle to be avoided. Covering panes with garden netting or insect screening protect birds by keeping them from striking the unyielding glass surface; a commercial screen is available for residential windows (see www.birdscreen.com). The application of decals to windows is a common practice to alert birds to the glass hazard. The use of popular single objects on an offending window such as falcon silhouettes or ultraviolet (UV)-reflecting maple leaves are mostly ineffective. Controlled experiments have revealed that a single falcon silhouette applied to a window resulted in nine deaths over a 54-day period compared to 12 deaths at an unaltered control window. Other experiments reveal that it is the visibility and number, not the shape of decals that contribute to strike prevention (Klem 1990b); the more decals, the fewer strikes and the fewer deaths. Apply enough decals to uniformly cover the entire glass surface such that they are separated by 5 to 10 cm (2-4 in) and you eliminate strikes altogether; thus, fewer decals offer less protection for birds. Strung beads or bamboo sections, Mylar strips, and feathers on monofilament line are also effective if applied in an amount that uniformly covers the glass surface, and spaced 10 cm (4 in) apart when oriented vertically, and 5 cm (2 in) apart when oriented horizontally. It is important to apply decals and other window coverings to the outside surface of reflective panes so the deterrent is visible to birds. Even a perfectly clear window acts like a perfect mirror if no light is visible from indoors, so these clear panes and typically reflective tinted panes must have preventive applications on the outside surface to be effective. One-way window films that present an opaque or translucent image when viewed from the outside, but only weakly diminish the view from the inside are effective strike prevention coverings (see CollidEscape film at www.flap.org). The long-term solution to saving bird lives from glass strikes is a new sheet glass that through coatings or internal structures provides an outside view of patterning that birds will recognize and avoid, and an inside view that is unobstructed for humans. One type of film or glass coating that has promise for effective prevention is one that incorporates UV signals, patterns that absorb and reflect wavelengths between 300 to 400 nm; most see UV signals as an elegant solution since birds theoretically see it and we humans do not. However, birds may be incapable of interpreting UV signals as an alert to danger since lower wavelengths of UV, blue, and purple colors are most often associated with attraction behaviors, sexual selection and finding food (Burkhardt 1982, Bennett and Cuthill 1994, Vitala et al. 1995, Bennett et al. 1996, Hunt et al. 1998). Colored signals used by many animals, including birds, as warnings or an alert to danger (e.g., aposematic coloration) are most often in the upper visual wavelengths of the electromagnetic spectrum, the yellows, oranges, and reds. Although design flaws limit interpretation, there was no statistically significant differences in the overall strike rate of all birds at wind turbines painted with UV-reflecting paint compared to those with non-UV-reflecting paint; however, whereas raptors showed no difference in strike rate at the two painted types, passerine fatalities were actually twice as high at the UV-reflecting painted turbines compared to the non-UV-reflecting painted controls, but were thought to be primarily due to higher numbers of horned larks (*Eremophila alpestris*) in the area (Young et al. 2003). Notwithstanding their function to attract, it is reasonable to suspect that UV signals could also be used to alert birds to danger, and our ongoing research continues to address the effectiveness of UV signals to alert birds to the glass hazard; some preliminary experiments are promising. Supporting this view, a German glass manufacturer has a current product that claims to use UV-signals to effectively prevent bird strikes (see ORNILUX glass at www.birdsandbuildings.org). Where acceptable, architectural designs that angle sheet glass by 20 and 40 degrees from the vertical offer protection by reducing the force with which birds hit the clear or reflecting surfaces (Klem et al. 2004).

For the millions of humans that enjoy feeding birds a relatively easy way to protect those that visit feeders is to place the feeder within 1 m (a bit over 3 ft) from the glass surface. Experiments that tested the vulnerability of birds visiting feeders placed 1 to 10 m from a window document higher kill rates the more distant a feeder is placed from the glass surface (Klem et al. 2004). Birds gain protection from feeders that are close to glass because they come and go from the feeder, and if after leaving they strike or glance off a nearby window they do not build up enough momentum to injure themselves. Alternatively, a bird can be killed outright from striking a window after leaving a perch from just over a meter from a window. Concerned citizens should demand that all feeders be placed within one meter of windows at our local, state, and national park visitor centers where the visiting public enjoys such exhibits.

CONCLUSION

Notwithstanding the relatively recent media coverage, and its positive influence in educating a few professionals in the building industry and conservation community, bird kills at sheet glass continues to be an under-appreciated source of human-associated mortality for select species and bird populations in general. Among other responsibilities, the charge of the Division of Migratory Bird Management within US Fish and Wildlife Service is the mandate to address the unintentional killing of a single individual of a protected species within the borders of the United States of America. Treaties and legislation exists to justify this protection for all but a few introduced wild bird species under, as amended, the Migratory Bird Treaty Act (MBTA) of 1918 and the Endangered Species Act (ESA) of 1973. These documents have been used in legal proceedings to address the unintended killing of birds from pesticides and power lines, but legal opinion views the enforcement of unintended bird kills at sheet glass to be impractical (Corcoran 1999). No reasonable person would advocate requesting law enforcement officers to go house to house searching for evidence of window-kills and charging homeowners with the unintentional killing at their windows, but it is reasonable to expect government agencies to monitor and address unintentional killing at structures at which hundreds of birds are killed at glass, in several well-known cases, in a single day. The annual bird attrition at such kill sites is, in legal parlance, substantial, foreseeable, and avoidable, and birds do merit protection from sheet glass at these locations under the purview of the MBTA and ESA. At the least, we should expect the MBTA and ESA to be consistently enforced, no matter what the source of unintended mortality.

The US Green Building Council (USGBC) has established a voluntary rating system called Leadership in Energy and Environmental Design (LEED) to promote the construction of environmentally friendly structures, so-called "green buildings." There is currently no specific LEED evaluation point for preventing bird kills at glass in new or remodeled structures. However, Swarthmore College near the city of Philadelphia installed ceramic frit glass with translucent dots in portions of a new science building that all but eliminates bird collisions at these special panes, and they applied for and received a LEED point under a rating category for innovative design. No matter how many LEED criteria are met, to include a compliance level high enough to earn their highest Platinum certification, no building is green to me if birds are being killed and injured flying into its glass panes. It is hoped and the USGBC is encouraged to incorporate bird-safe design that includes the lethal glass hazard for birds in future versions of their LEED evaluation system. Until that time, New York City Audubon and the City of Toronto have prepared and published building guidelines in an attempt to inform architects and other building professionals about how to make human structures safe for birds (Brown and Caputo 2007, City of Toronto Green Development Standard 2007).

To repeat what I have written elsewhere (Klem 2006), 10,000 plus birds that are killed on one foggy night at a communication tower is a horrific but rare event. By contrast, more than that number are almost certainly killed daily at residential and commercial buildings in North America alone, and tens of thousands more are likely killed each day elsewhere around the world. Addressing this unintended carnage is imperative to protect our current and future bird populations struggling to survive in the global environment that must increasingly be shared with more and more humans, an environment experiencing a growing use of glass in a growing construction industry.

Arguably, except for habitat destruction and alteration, the amount of human-associated avian mortality at sheet glass is a scale above any other source, to include those capturing the attention of influential conservation agencies and organizations. From an ethical and moral perspective, any unintended and unnatural killing related to human presence and activity in the environment should be addressed and reduced if not eliminated. Guilt and anxiety are reasonable feelings among those who admire and respect life. These emotions and the vast and growing amount of documented evidence justify human action to protect bird life from a lethal hazard that they cannot protect themselves. Not so comforting is to acknowledge that given that birds act as if clear and reflective glass is invisible to them, casualties from sheet glass will continue to occur whether or not the magnitude of these unintended tragedies continue to be mostly ignored. More than a few dedicated humans are needed to effectively address this important and intractable conservation problem for birds and people.

ACKNOWLEDGMENTS

I dedicate this chapter to the late Dr. William G. George who in the early 1970s introduced and encouraged me to investigate the prospect and determine if bird kills at windows are a relevant conservation issue for birds and people. He liked to refer to glass kills as "window predation," and would colorfully describe such events as "...birds dashing themselves to death against glass panes..." I am as grateful to his wife Marian and their daughter Sarah for tolerating my presence on so many occasions when I attended, and eventually abandoned, my field experiments on their lovely farm among the hills of beautiful southern Illinois. I am especially grateful to Peter G. Saenger in the Acopian Center for Ornithology, Department of Biology, Muhlenberg College for his professional assistance in gathering valuable reference materials, and for reviewing earlier drafts of this manuscript. I thank the Baird Ornithological Club, the Lancaster County Bird Club, and especially the late Sarkis Acopian, Detroit Audubon Society, and the Safari Club at the Philadelphia Zoo for encouragement and financial support of our ongoing studies on the bird-glass issue at Muhlenberg College.

LITERATURE CITED

American Birding Association. 2007. ABA Checklist. Available from http://.americanbirding.org/checklist/index.html (accessed November 2007).

American Ornithologists' Union. 1975. Report of the ad hoc committee on scientific educational use of wild birds. Auk 92 (Suppl.): 1A–27A.

American Ornithologists' Union. 1983. Check-list of North American birds, 6th Edition. American Ornithologists' Union, Baltimore, Maryland, USA.

Baird, S. F., T. M. Brewer, and R. Ridgway. 1874a. A history of North American birds: land birds, Volume I. Little, Brown and Company, Boston, USA.

Baird, S. F., T. M. Brewer, and R. Ridgway. 1874b. A history of North American birds: land birds, Volume III. Little, Brown and Company, Boston, USA.

Banks, R. C. 1976. Reflective plate—hazard to migrating birds. Bioscience 26: 414.

Banks, R. C. 1979. Human related mortality of birds in the United States. U.S. Fish and Wildlife Service Special Report 215: 1–16.

Bennett, A. T. D. and I. C. Cuthill. 1994. Ultraviolet vision in birds: what is its function? Vision Research 34: 1471–1478.

Bennett, A. T., I. C. Cuthill, J. C. Partridge, and E. J. Maier. 1996. Ultraviolet vision and mate choice in zebra finches. Nature 380: 433–435.

BirdLife International. 2000. Threatened birds of the world. Lynx Edicions and BirdLife International, Barcelona, Spain, and Cambridge, UK. Updates available from http://www.birdlife.org/action/science/species/global_species_programme/whats_new.html (accessed December 2007).

Brown, H. and S. Caputo. 2007. Bird-safe building guidelines. New York City Audubon Society, New York, New York, USA.

Burkhardt, D. 1982. Birds, berries and UV. Naturwissenschaften 69: 153–157.

Butcher, G. S., D. K. Niven, A. O. Panjabi, D. N. Pashley, and K. V. Rosenberg. 2007. The 2007 WatchList for United States Birds. American Birds 61: 18–25.

City of Toronto Green Development Standard. 2007. Bird-friendly development Guidelines. City Planning, Toronto, CANADA.

Corcoran, L. M. 1999. Migratory Bird Treaty Act: strict criminal liability for non-hunting caused bird deaths. Denver University Law Review 77: 315–358.

Dunn, E. H. 1993. Bird mortality from striking residential windows in winter. Journal of Field Ornithology 64(3): 302–309.

Erickson, W. P., G. D. Johnson, M. D. Strickland, D. P. Young, Jr., K. J. Sernka, and R. E. Good. 2001. Avian collisions with wind turbines: a summary of existing studies and comparisons to other sources of avian collision mortality in the United States. National Wind Coordinating Committee, Washington, D. C.

Gelb, Y. and N. Delacretaz. 2006. Avian window strike mortality at an urban office building. The Kingbird 56: 190–198.

Gill, F. B. 2007. Ornithology, 3rd Edition. W. H. Freeman and Company, New York, New York, USA.

Graham, D. L. 1997. Spider webs and windows as potentially important sources of hummingbird mortality. Journal of Field Ornithology 68(1): 98–101.

Harden, J. 2002. An overview of anthropogenic causes of avian mortality. Journal of Wildlife Rehabilitation 25: 4–11.

Hunt, S., A. T. D. Bennett, I. C. Cuthill, and R. Griffith. 1998. Blue tits are ultraviolet tits. Proceedings of Royal Society 265: 451–455.

Jones, H. L. 2005. Central America. North American Birds 59: 162–165.

Klem, D. Jr. 1979. Biology of collisions between birds and windows. Ph.D. Dissertation, Southern Illinois University at Carbondale, Illinois.

Klem, D. Jr. 1981. Avian predators hunting birds near windows. Proceedings of the Pennsylvania Academy of Science 55: 90–92.

Klem, D. Jr. 1989. Bird-window collisions. Wilson Bulletin 101(4): 606–620.

Klem, D. Jr. 1990a. Bird injuries, cause of death, and recuperation from collisions with windows. Journal of Field Ornithology 61(1): 115–119.

Klem, D. Jr. 1990b. Collisions between birds and windows: mortality and prevention. Journal of Field Ornithology 61(1): 120–128.

Klem, D. Jr. 1991. Glass and bird kills: an overview and suggested planning and design methods of preventing a fatal hazard. Pages 99–104 *in* L. W. Adams and D. L. Leedy, editors.Wildlife Conservation in Metropolitan Environments NIUW Symposium Series 2, National Institute for Urban Wildlife, Maryland, USA.

Klem, D., Jr. 2006. Glass: a deadly conservation issue for birds. Bird Observer 34: 73–81.

Klem, D., Jr. 2007. Windows: an unintended fatal hazard for birds. Pages 7–12 in Connecticut State of the Birds 2007. Connecticut Audubon Society, Fairfield, Connecticut, USA.

Klem, D., Jr., C. R. Brancato, J. F. Catalano, and F. L. Kuzmin. 1982. Gross morphology and general histology of the esophagus, ingluvies and proventriculus of the House Sparrow (*Passer domesticus*). Proceedings of the Pennsylvania Academy of Science 56: 141–146.

Klem, D., Jr., S. A. Finn, and J. H. Nave, Jr. 1983. Gross morphology and general histology of the ventriculus, intestinum, caeca and cloaca of the House Sparrow (*Passer domesticus*). Proceedings of the Pennsylvania Academy of Science 57: 27–32.

Klem, D., Jr., M. A. Parker, W. L. Sprague, S. A. Tafuri, C. J. Veltri, and M. J. Walker. 1984. Gross morphology and general histology of the alimentary tract of the American Robin (*Turdus migratorius*). Proceedings of the Pennsylvania Academy of Science 58: 151–158.

Klem, D., Jr., D. C. Keck, L. Marty, A. J. Miller Ball, E. E. Niciu, and C. T. Platt. 2004. Effects of window angling, feeder placement, and scavengers on avian mortality at plate glass. Wilson Bulletin 116: 69–73.

Labedz, T. E. 1997. Windows of death: a look at bird strikes. University of Nebraska State Museum, Museum Notes 95: 1–4.

Lowther, P. E. 1995. Ornithology at the Field Museum. Pages 145–161 in W. E. Davis, Jr. and J. A. Jackson, editors. Contributions to the history of North American Ornithology. Memoirs of the Nuttall Ornithological Club, No. 12, Cambridge, Massachusetts, USA.

Malakoff, D. 2004. Clear & present danger. Audubon 106(1): 65–68.

National Audubon Society. 2007. The 2007 Audubon WatchList. Available from http://web1. audubon.org/science/watchlist/browseWatchlist.php (accessed November 2007).

Nielsen, J. 2006. Windows: a clear danger to birds. Morning Edition, National Public Radio, 3 January (Available online at <http://www.npr.org/templates/story/story.php?storyId=5076012).

O'Connell, T. J. 2001. Avian window strike mortality at a suburban office park. The Raven 72(2): 141–149.

Ogden, L. J. E. 1996. Collision course: the hazards of lighted structures and windows to migrating birds. World Wildlife Fund Canada and the Fatal Light Awareness Program.

Podulka, S., R. W. Rohrbaugh, Jr., R. Bonney, editors. 2004. Handbook of bird biology, 2nd Edition. Cornell Laboratory of Ornithology, Ithaca, New York, USA.

Talpin, A. 1991. A little used source of data on migrant birds. Corella 15: 24–26.

Terres, J. K. 1980. The Audubon Society encyclopedia of North American birds. Alfred A. Knopf, New York, New York, USA.

Townsend, C. W. 1931, Tragedies among Yellow-billed Cuckoos. Auk 48: 602.

Veltri, C. J. and D. Klem, Jr. 2005. Comparison of fatal bird injuries from collisions with towers and windows. Journal of Field Ornithology 76: 127–133.

Vitala, J., E. Korpimaki, P. Palokangas, and M. Koivula. 1995. Attraction of kestrels to vole scent marks in ultraviolet light. Nature 373: 425–427.

Walkinshaw, L. R. 1976. A Kirtland's Warbler life history. American Birds 30: 773.

Yakutchik, M. 2003. Philadelphia Inquirer Magazine (11 May): 12–17.

Young, D. P., Jr., W. P. Erickson, M. D. Strickland, R. E. Good, and K. J. Sernka. 2003. Comparison of avian responses to UV-light-reflective paint on wind turbines. Subcontract Report July 1999 – 2000. National Renewable Energy Laboratory, Golden, Colorado USA.

Avian Ecology and Conservation: A Pennsylvania Focus with National Implications. Edited by S. K. Majumdar, T. L. Master, M. C. Brittingham, R. M. Ross, R. S. Mulvihill and J. E. Huffman. © 2010. The Pennsylvania Academy of Science.

SECTION IV

Emerging Issues and their Impacts on Birds

Section Overview

Shyamal K. Majumdar and Ioana A. Marin
Department of Biology
Lafayette College
Easton, PA 18042
majumdas@lafayette.edu

The purpose of this section is to identify and describe several important emerging issues and their impacts on birds' ecosystems. Additionally, the ways birds from diverse ecosystems respond to these changes and the preventive methods that should be taken to minimize the impacts are discussed.

Global climate change has long been known to exert stresses in living organisms, including birds. In chapter 21, Root and Goldsmith illustrate with specific examples the relationship between the increase in global temperature and the distribution and migration patterns of certain North American bird species. The authors project extinction possibilities of certain birds that are endemic in mountainous areas and advocate drastic reduction of industrial gas emissions into the atmosphere and utilization of alternative energy sources in order to reduce the process of extinction of vulnerable birds species.

Brandes et al. (chapter 22) survey direct and indirect mortality risks of birds to wind power turbines in Pennsylvania, California, and several countries in Europe. Based on two cases of high wind turbines mortality – one in California and the other in Norway, the chapter focuses on how the lack of scientific pre- and post- construction studies of the wind power turbines could have negatively impacted the development of other wind turbines. The authors' survey identified raptors as the most vulnerable to turbine collisions, compared to other avian species. In order to minimize habitat loss and avian mortality due to collisions with turbines, the writers provide a set of guidelines for selecting appropriate sites and building "bird-friendly" wind turbines.

Approximately 60% of all infectious diseases induced by fungi, bacteria, and viruses in animals are transmitted directly or indirectly to humans. In recent years, several viruses have been identified as emerging pathogens in many species of wild birds and other mammals. Because of their pathogenecity and subsequent avian-mediated transmission to certain mammals, including humans, the overall perspectives of two zoonotic viral pathogens – namely, West Nile Virus (WNV) and avian flu virus (H5N1) – have been discussed in respective chapters (23, 24, and 25).

Chapters 23 and 24 focus on WNV. Chapter 23, authored by Owen and Garvin includes a comprehensive overview on WNV, emphasizing its geographical distribution and impacts on wild bird populations in North America. The authors also provide information on WNV transmission via certain mosquito vectors, serological prevalence in WNV-inflicted captured birds, and clinical symptoms, as well as pathological signs, following WNV infections, mainly in raptors. Huffman and Roscoe (chapter 24) describe the effects of WNV in raptors. The authors include a list of WNV detection assays with important details, such as specificity or target species. A detailed discussion on WNV vectors and their control, as well as an epizootiology of WNV are covered in this chapter. Also, the authors briefly discuss the clinical signs and pathology of WNV infections in raptors along with vaccine availability and use. The authors from both chapters emphasize the need for further research on several aspects of WNV biology.

In chapter 25, Goel et al. describe the modes of transmission and the impact of avian flu virus (H5N1) on human health and society. The chapter begins with a history of the virus and chronolizes a list of H5N1 virus outbreaks around the world. The role of migratory waterfowl in the spread of the avian flu virus and its impact on human society is analyzed. A detailed response plan to pandemic avian influenza is also included in the chapter.

With the advent of industrial revolution many harmful gases, metals, organic compounds, pesticides etc. began to accumulate in the air, land and aquatic ecosystems. It has soon become evident that many mammals, birds, and other organisms are affected directly and indirectly, while their ecosystems are at risk. The last two chapters in this section survey the overall impact of different anthropogenic and environmental contaminants on birds' diverse ecosystems.

In chapter 26, Waters presents an overview of the global impact of environmental contaminants. The author begins with general considerations about ecosystem functionality, focusing in on wildlife depletion, and ultimately on birds. The chapter then continues with an assessment of the worldwide avian biodiversity status and with two detailed sections on contaminants categories: metals and organophosphates. Delivery systems of selected varieties of contaminants are also discussed.

Stratford, in chapter 27, provides a detailed review of environmental contaminants that affect avian species specifically in Pennsylvania. The chapter addresses two classes of contaminants – metals and organic compounds, with detailed subsections, focusing on specific substances or categories of substances (e.g., lead, mercury, petroleum, organochloride insecticides, etc). For each subsection the author presents information in a logical fashion, starting with general details about the contaminants, continuing with case histories of contaminations, and finally analyzing the direct and indirect effects on different bird species.

Avian Ecology and Conservation: A Pennsylvania Focus with National Implications. Edited by S. K. Majumdar, T. L. Master, M. C. Brittingham, R. M. Ross, R. S. Mulvihill and J. E. Huffman. © 2010. The Pennsylvania Academy of Science.

Chapter 21

Global Climate Change: Conservation Challenges and Impacts on Birds

Terry L. Root[1] and Elizabeth S. Goldsmith[2]

[1]Woods Institute for the Environment, 473 Via Ortega Drive, Stanford University, Stanford, CA 94305

[2]Stanford University School of Medicine, 300 Pasteur Drive, MSOB X3C01, Stanford, CA 94304-5404

troot@stanford.edu

INTRODUCTION

On evolutionary timescales, climate has always varied substantially, and species have responded to changing temperatures and the resulting consequences either by adapting or by becoming extinct. Over the last few hundred years, however, human activities have contributed to distinctly accelerating temperature changes on global and local scales. The Northern Hemisphere surface temperature has increased more during the twentieth century than during any other century over the last 1000 years, and research has shown that hot days and nights on land are very likely warmer and more frequent now than they were a century ago (IPCC 2007a). The frequency of 100- and 500-year floods has increased over most land areas, and more intense and longer droughts have been observed over wider areas since the 1970s, particularly in the tropics and subtropics (IPCC 2007a). Since approximately the beginning of the Industrial Revolution, carbon dioxide levels in the atmosphere have increased by 35% and methane levels by 150% (IPCC 2001a), and the average global temperature has increased by approximately 0.8°C over the last 100 years, with a change of 0.4°C over the last 30 years of the 20th century (IPCC 2007a).

In response to this temperature increase over the last 100 years, wild plants and animals already exhibit significant changes on all continents. For example, the National Audubon Society's recent analysis of Christmas Bird Count data found that the medians of abundance for 58% (of observed species of North American early winter birds have moved northward over the last 40 years, with an average northward movement—including all species that did not move northward—of 35 miles (Niven et al. 2009). Such changes are certainly understandable, as all living species are affected by temperature. Two types of changes are particularly common in species throughout a wide variety of taxonomic groups and over broad geographical areas; (1) shifts in range boundaries (e.g., moving north in the Northern Hemisphere) and/or shifts in the density of individuals from one portion of their range to another (e.g., the center of the abundance pattern moving up in elevation), and (2), shifts in the timing (i.e., phenology) of events primarily occurring in spring and/or autumn. Based on the physiology of species, these types of changes tend to be consistent with those expected with increasing ambient temperatures.

The adaptive responses to climate change exhibited in species around the globe are often further hampered by other changes to species' living conditions, such as habitat modifications, introduction of invasive species, pollution, and over-harvesting of plant or animal resources. For example, the National Audubon Society Christmas Bird Count analyses found that while most North American early winter birds had shifted northward, only 10 of 26 (38%) observed grassland bird species moved significantly north, and 9 moved south (Niven et al. 2009). The authors postulate that despite many grassland birds' need for moderate temperatures, they may be unable to shift northward due to ongoing rapid reduction in grassland habitat areas, largely through conversion to intensive human uses including pastures, hayfields and row crops. The synergistic impact of global warming and other human-induced changes on the planet's fauna and flora is greater than any single disturbance could be, and the pressure to tolerate broader and quicker changes is pushing birds and other species toward extinction.

As the global temperature continues to increase, the magnitude of the impact on birds and other global biota can be expected to increase as well. Warming is expected to continue escalating over the 21st century, by a minimum of 1.1°C and possibly by up to 6.4°C or more (IPCC 2007a). Given the observed responses of animals and plants to ongoing temperature change, we can expect that habitat and lifestyle changes required for species' survival will likely increase along with temperature, as will the potential for extinction.

TYPES OF ECOLOGICAL RESPONSES TO CLIMATIC CHANGE

As the globe warms, all species will have to adapt to some extent to the escalating rise in global average temperature. Given the constraints of species, the different types of adaptation include moving in space, shifting in time, modifying behavior such as becoming active at night rather than during the day (Pendlebury et al. 2004), exhibiting phenotypic plasticity (Coppack 2007, Gienapp et al. 2008), undergoing microevolutionary response change (Bradshaw and Holzapfel 2001), or the most irreversible of all: extinction. We will discuss the most common—or at least, the most studied—of these: range changes and phenological shifts. Additionally, the irreversibility of extinctions demands attention.

Distribution Shifts

Ambient temperature is one of the primary factors shaping the ranges of birds (Root 1988a,b). For example, the northern range edge of many birds wintering in North America is directly related to their metabolism. Species with higher basal metabolic rates (BMR: the metabolic rate of an individual while sleeping and not digesting, growing, etc.) are able to winter farther north than those with lower BMRs. All species have a range of ambient temperatures within which they must live. Limits also exist for other environmental factors, such as precipitation thresholds. How much the globe warms will determine the number of species needing to move to avoid being subjected to temperatures beyond their threshold of survival (Walther et al. 2002). The same can be said for precipitation. Indeed, species across a wide variety of taxonomic groups and geographical areas have moved poleward and up in elevation during the last century (McCarty 2001, Root and Schneider

2002, Walther et al. 2002, Parmesan 2006). The type and extent of these shifts appear to be species-specific. The National Audubon Society's (NAS) recent analysis of Christmas Bird Count (CBC) data found that the medians of abundance for 58% (177 / 305) of observed species of North American early winter birds have moved northward over the last 40 years, with an average northward movement, including all species that did not move northward, of 35 miles (Niven et al. 2009).

Many studies have found that the ranges of birds have been shifting and undoubtedly will continue to shift in association with temperature changes. These types of changes are quite common and discussed frequently in the literature. As species move, various biotic interactions, such as predator-prey relationships (blackburian warbler (*Dendroica fusca*) and spruce budworm caterpillars (*Choristoneura occidentalis*)) become disconnected. As species shift separately from one other, some species will assemble together with species they are not grouped with presently. Consequently, these new communities of species will form what have been called "no analogue communities". Pollen cores have shown that in prehistoric times species occurred together in communities that we do not see together today (Whitlock et al. 2000). We are already seeing evidence of species shifting differentially and finding species together today that were not together just a decade or two ago. For example, some species of dragonflies are shifting their ranges north due to climate change, causing species of dragonflies not previously together to co-occur. Concern is being raised because competition and predation by the newly expanding species may be detrimental to the long-time resident dragonfly species (Flenner and Sahlen 2008). These types of differential changing by species could have quite an effect on ecosystem services, many of which we have come to rely on largely without knowing it. One obvious service that could break down is that of wild pollinators, as animals and the plants they pollinate shift at different speeds and in different directions (Brosi et al. 2008).

Phenology Shifts

The phenology of many birds, that is, the timing of their seasonal activities, is also changing in response to climate change. A consistent pattern of phenological change strongly associated with regional warming is occurring in the vast majority of species in the northern hemisphere (IPCC 2007b, 2001b, Parmesan and Yohe 2003, Root and Schneider 2002, Root et al. 2003). For example, in the Upper Peninsula of Michigan, spring migrants were arriving an average of about 15 days earlier in the spring of 1996 than they had in the spring of 1965. Of the 45 species for which records were sufficiently complete, four had shifted the timing of arrival so early (to January 1) that they became resident species in the area rather than migrants (Figure 1), 15 were arriving earlier, and one species [hermit thrush (*Catharus guttatus*)], was arriving later (Figure 2). The species wintering closer to the Upper Peninsula arrived earlier than those wintering farther south. From the mid 1960s to the mid 1990s the *difference between* the arrival times of these two types of migrants did not change, even though the actual arrival times of both groups shifted earlier over time.

For all Northern Hemisphere plants and animals showing phenological changes in the spring, the average number of days changed over the last 30 years of the 20th century was roughly 15.5 days, or about 5 days per decade (Root et al. 2003). The increase in global average temperatures over that time period was around 0.4°C (IPCC 2007a). Given that the predicted global-average-temperature increase for the 21st century is between about

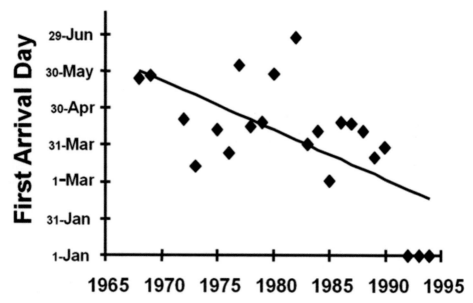

Figure 1:   The day of the year when the first mourning dove (*Zenaida macroura*) was seen
(arrived) from 1965 to 1996. Note that in 1993 this dove was no longer a migrant to the
Upper Peninsula of Michigan, but instead a resident, due to range expansion.

1.1°C and approximately 6.4°C or higher (IPCC 2007a), more extreme shifts in phenology can likely be expected. Warming, however, varies by scale, meaning regional changes
differ from global changes, and temperatures vary from region to region and also within a
region over time. This all makes it more difficult to understand how species are reacting.
Saunders' (1959) investigation of the timing of migration from 1914 to 1949 found that for
those 36 years, birds arrived earlier in warm years and later in colder ones. Marra and co-
authors' (2005) examination of 40 years of banding data from three banding stations in the
eastern US found little evidence for a trend in migration timing, which, as the authors
explained, "makes sense" because no significant trend in increasing spring temperatures
was found in eastern North America over the specific time period. The variability in passage time of Nearctic-Neotropical migrants banded on the Louisiana Gulf Coast and at
Powdermill Nature Reserve or Long Point Bird Observatory could be due to the migrants
having faster or slower passage times depending on annual variations in ambient temperatures (Marra et al. 2005).

    Data from Powdermill Nature Reserve was again used in an investigation, this time with
46 years of data collected on 78 migrating songbirds (van Buskirt et al. 2009). Although
the first forty years of these data overlapped with the Marra et al. study (2005), van
Buskirk and colleagues (2009) indicate that spring migration was significantly earlier from
1961 to 2006. They, however, detrended the data in order to eliminate possible spurious
correlations, and showed that the timing of spring migration was strongly related to spring
temperatures; migration occurs faster in warmer spring and slower when colder. Authors
of both of these studies point out that the rate of warming in the eastern United States has

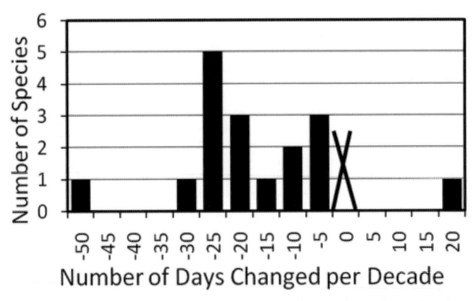

Figure 2: The number of days per decade species arrived earlier (negative numbers) or later (positive numbers) in 1996 compared to 1965 in the Upper Peninsula of Michigan. Only birds showing a significant change in arrival time are included, which is the reason for the "X" at zero days changed per decade.

been quite gradual, which both studies indicate is the probable reason for the lack of obvious trends in spring migration. Both of these studies indicate that species in these areas may be somewhat buffered from the rapid changes that species in other regions of the U.S. and world are experiencing.

Around the globe, species are not faring quite as well as birds in the eastern U.S. are reported to be. In a global study looking at all 8,750 species of birds, Jetz and colleagues (2007) used methods from the Millennium Ecosystem Assessment to project land-cover changes along with possible warming scenarios to estimate that between ~10% and ~20% of the birds on this planet could be imperiled by 2100. That is around 950 to 1,800 species of birds. Most of these will be tropical species, as the diversity in the tropics is quite high and tropical species tend to have small ranges.

Extinction

Until we are able to develop and extensively implement new sources of energy, such as wind and solar and new technologies such as hybrid and electric cars, we will likely undergo a difficult and drawn-out process of lowering our levels of fossil-fuel use enough to greatly reduce our greenhouse gas emissions. We are currently on a carbon dioxide emissions trajectory that is higher than any of the scenarios projected by the IPCC (2007a). Consequently, the probability of the average global temperature increasing more than 2°C is uncomfortably possible. Around that temperature, the extinction rate of known species is expected to be around 20% of the known species around the planet, which works out to around 350,000 to 400,000 species (IPCC 2007b).

The species most likely to be included in those committed to extinction include endemic species entirely restricted to mountainous regions (Pounds et al. 1999, Williams et al. 2003). As the globe warms, there is no place for these species to go, except extinct. Another option would be for humans to capture, relocate and then manage the species, making sure they both survive and do not become invasive species. This, however, is not a very viable option, given the number of species involved and given our limited knowledge, personnel, political will, and funding. Because suitably high elevations for these species exist in spatial isolation, they are unable to colonize new areas as the climate warms (Grabherr et al., 1994, Pounds et al. 1999, Midgley et al. 2002, Klanderud and Birks 2003, Konvicka et al. 2003, Williams et al. 2003). Unless climate change and habitat loss can be slowed, widespread extinctions will likely follow (IPCC 2007b, Sekercioglu et al. 2008).

One of the most important aspects of a species that can telegraph extinction danger is the size of a species distribution. Those with larger ranges are assumed to be less in danger of extinction than those with smaller ranges. Shoo and colleagues (2005) found, however, that on an elevation gradient, three-fourths of endemic species were predicted to drop in population size more rapidly than their ranges will contract. Consequently, in mountainous regions, using range size as a proxy for identifying those species in danger of extinction does not appear to be reliable, at least when species are responding rapidly to a threat such as rapid warming.

Much can still be done to ensure the survival of species. Decreasing carbon footprints and designing new technology will help transition away from the use of carbon-based fuels. As far as species are concerned, much work is needed to help us understand the probable reactions of species to rapid climate change. Which species are likely to shift into cooler areas? Which species will become separated by moving in different directions due to rapid climate change, and what type of interactions will be stopped by the separation? How fast might species shift? What types of new interactions between species will occur? What species will need to be helped to reach locations that are suitable for their survival, and will we need to manage these species to ensure that relocation succeeds? How can we remove the non-climate-related stresses from species so that they have a better chance of surviving the stresses caused by climate change? The list can go on and on, but the bottom line is that each of us can help reduce the number of species facing extinctions.

LITERATURE CITED

Bradshaw, W. E. and C. M. Holzapfel. 2001. Genetic shift in photoperiodic response correlated with global warming. Proceedings of the National Academy of Sciences, USA 98:14509–14511.

Brosi, B. J., Daily, G.C., Shih, T. M., Oviedo, F. and G. Duran. 2008. The effects of forest fragmentation on bee communities in tropical countryside. Journal of Applied Ecology 45 (3): 773–783.

Coppack, T. 2007. Experimental determination of the photoperiodic basis for geographical variation in avian seasonality. Journal of Ornithology 148(2): 459–467.

Flenner, I. and G. Sahlen. 2008. Dragonfly community re-organisation in boreal forest lakes: rapid species turnover driven by climate change? Insect Conservation and Diversity 1: 169–179.

Gienapp, P. C., Teplitsky, J., Alho, S., Mills, J. A. and J. Merila. 2008. Climate change and evolution: Disentangling environmental and genetic responses. Molecular Ecology 17(1): 167–178.

Grabherr G., Gottfried, M. and H. Pauli. 1994. Climate effects on mountain plants. Nature 369: 448.

IPCC. 2007a. Climate Change 2007: The Physical Science Basis. Contribution of Working Group I to the Fourth Assessment Report of the Intergovernmental Panel on Climate Change, S. Solomon,

D. Qin, M. Manning, M. Marquis, K Averyt, M. M. B. Tignor, H. L. Miller, Jr., Z. and Chen, Eds. Cambridge University Press, Cambridge, UK, 996 pp.

IPCC. 2007b. Climate Change 2007: Impacts, Adaptation and Vulnerability. Contribution of Working group II to the Fourth Assessment Report of the Intergovernmental Panel on Climate Change, M.L. Parry, O.F. Canziani, J.P. Palutikof, P.J. van der Linden and C.E. Hanson, Eds. Cambridge University Press, Cambridge, UK, 976pp.

IPCC. 2001a. Climate Change 2001: The Scientific Basis. Contribution of Working Group I to the third Assessment Report of the Intergovernmental Panel on Climate Change. J.T. Houghton, Y. Ding, D.J. Griggs, M. Noguer, P.J. van der Linden, X. Da, K. Maskell, C.A. Johnson, Eds. Cambridge University Press, UK, 881pp.

IPCC. 2001b. Climate Change 2001: Impacts, Adaptation and Vulnerability. Contribution of Working Group II to the Third Assessment Report of the Intergovernmental Panel on Climate Change. James J. McCarthy, Osvaldo F. Canziani, Neil A. Leary, David J. Dokken and Kasey S. White, Eds. Cambridge University Press, UK.

Jetz, W., Wilcove, D. S. and A. P. Dobson. 2007. Projected impacts of climate and land-use change on the global diversity of birds. Public Library of Science, Biology 5(6): e157 doi:10.1371/journal.pbio.0050157

Klanderud, K. and H. J. Birks. 2003. Recent increases in species richness and shifts in altitudinal distributions of Norwegian mountain plants. Holocene 13(1): 1–6.

Konvicka M., Maradova, M., Benes J., Fric Z. and P. Kepka. 2003. Uphill shifts in distribution of butterflies in the Czech Republic: effects of changing climate detected on a regional scale. Global Ecology & Biogeography 12(5): 403.

Marra, P. P., Francis, C.F., Mulvihill, R. S. and F R. Moore. 2005. The influence of climate on the timing and rate of spring bird migration. Oecologia 142(2): 307–315.

McCarty, J. P. 2001. Ecological consequences of recent climate change. Conservation Biology 15(2): 320–331.

Midgley, G. F., Hannah, L., Millar, D., Rutherford, M. C. and L. W. Powrie. 2002. Assessing the vulnerability of species richness to anthropogenic climate change in a biodiversity hotspot. Global Ecology and Biogeography 11(6): 445.

Niven, D. K., Butcher, G. S. and G. T. Bancroft. 2009. Birds and Climate Change: Ecological Disruption in Motion. National Audubon Society Report issued February 2009. Accessed March 8, 2009 at http://www.audubon.org/bird/bacc/index.html.

Parmesan, C. 2006. Ecological and evolutionary responses to recent climate change. Annual Review of Ecology, Evolution and Systematics 37: 637–669.

_____, and G. Yohe. 2003. A globally coherent fingerprint of climate change impacts across natural systems. Nature 421: 37–42.

Pendlebury, C. J., MacLeod, M. G. and D. M. Bryant. 2004. Variation in temperature increases the cost of living in birds. Journal of Experimental Biology 207: 2065–2070.

Pounds, J. A., Fogden, M. P. and J. H. Campbell. 1999. Biological response to climate change on a tropical mountain. Nature 398: 611.

Root, T. 1988a. Energy constraints on avian distributions and abundances. Ecology 69: 330 – 339.

_____. 1988b. Environmental factors associated with avian distributional limits. Journal of Biogeography 15: 489–505.

_____, Price, J. T., Hall, K. R., Schneider, S. H., Rosenzweig, C. and J. A. Pounds. 2003. Fingerprints of global warming on animals and plants. Nature 421: 57–60.

_____, and S. H. Schneider. 2002. Overview and implications for wildlife. Wildlife Responses to Climate Change: North American Case Studies, Eds. S. H. Schneider and T. L. Root. Washington, D.C., Island Press: 1–56.

Saunders, A. A. 1959. Forty years of spring migration in southern Connecticut. Wilson Bulletin 71(3): 208 – 219.

Sekercioglu, C. H., Schneider, S. H., Fay, J. P. and S. R. Loarie. 2008. Climate change, elevational range shifts, and bird extinctions. Conservation Biology 22: 140–150.

Shoo, L. P., Williams, S. E. and J.-M. Hero. 2005. Potential decoupling of trends in distribution area and population size of species with climate change. Global Change Biology 11: 1469–1476.

van Buskirk, J., Mulvihill, R. S. and R. C. Leberman. 2009. Variable shifts in spring and autumn migration phenology in North American songbirds associated with climate change. Global Change Biology 15(3): 760–771.

Walther, G., Post, E., Convey, P., Menzel, A., Parmesan, C., Beebee, T. J. C., Fromentin, J.-M., Hoegh-Guldberg, O., and F. Bairlein. 2002. Ecological responses to recent climate change. Nature 416: 389 – 395.

Whitlock, C., Sarna-Wojcicki, A. M., Bartlein, P. J. and R. J. Nickman. 2000. Environmental history and tephrostratigraphy at Carp Lake, southwestern Columbia Basin, Washington, USA. Palaeogeography, Palaeoclimatology, Palaeoecology 155: 7 – 29.

Williams, S. E., Bolitho, E. E. and S. Fox. 2003. Climate change in Australian tropical rainforests: An impending environmental catastrophe. Proceedings: Biological Sciences 270: 1887–1892.

Avian Ecology and Conservation: A Pennsylvania Focus with National Implications. Edited by S. K. Majumdar, T. L. Master, M. C. Brittingham, R. M. Ross, R. S. Mulvihill and J. E. Huffman. © 2010. The Pennsylvania Academy of Science.

Chapter 22

Wind Power Mortality

D. Brandes[1], T.A. Miller[2], and T.E. Katzner[3]
[1]Dept of Civil & Environmental Engineering, Acopian Engineering Center,
Lafayette College, Easton, PA 18042
[2]Carnegie Museum of Natural History, Powdermill Nature Reserve,
1847 Route 381, Rector, PA 15677
[3]Department of Conservation and Field Research, National Aviary,
700 Arch St., Allegheny Commons West, Pittsburgh, PA 15212
todd.katzner@aviary.org

INTRODUCTION

Wind energy creates challenges and opportunities for Pennsylvania wildlife. This is especially true for volant birds and bats that can be directly impacted by turbines, but also for other species that are indirectly impacted. Of particular concern to avian ecologists are the potential lethal and sub-lethal effects of development of wind turbines on birds. Lethal direct effects involve birds striking (or being struck by) turbine blades or turbine support structures. Available data suggest that raptors are at higher risk of direct collisions than are other avian species (NWCC, 2004). Sub-lethal effects cover a wide range of indirect consequences, ranging from habitat loss to the energetic impacts of behavioral alteration. The goal of this section is to focus on direct and indirect mortality effects of wind turbines on birds, both outside and within Pennsylvania. We also identify gaps in knowledge as primary areas for future scientific investigation and suggest general best practices for establishment of wind power in as bird-friendly a manner as possible.

WIND POWER MORTALITY AT OTHER SITES

Wind power facilities have been vilified in the conservation and activist world, primarily for their impacts on diurnal flying animals, especially birds of prey. To some degree this perspective is justified, as some wind energy generating plants have been constructed at sites where a bit of foresight would have predicted serious environmental impacts. However, it is also true that most turbines do not kill large numbers of birds. Nonetheless, there has been little scientific study of impacts of turbines on birds (NRC, 2007) and much of the published research has focused on sites where bird kill problems had already been documented.

The classic example of a poorly-sited wind power facility is the Altamont Pass Wind Resource Area (APWRA) east of Livermore, California. The Altamont facility has been in place since 1982 and contains approximately 5,400 wind turbines of 27 types throughout its 160 km^2 area (Hunt 2002). What makes Altamont especially dangerous to birds of prey is that the area has traditionally supported large populations of California ground squirrels (*Spermophilus beecheyi*). Predatory birds from surrounding areas are drawn to the

APWRA in search of food, thereby increasing effective population density and putting far more individuals at risk than just breeding birds from the immediate area. The most recent peer-reviewed literature on Altamont suggests that annual mortality includes approximately 67 (80% CI = 25–109) golden eagles (*Aquila chrysaetos*), 188 (80% CI = 116–259) red-tailed hawks (*Buteo jamaicensis*), 348 (80% CI = –49 to 749) American kestrels (*Falco sparverius*), 440 (80% CI = –133 to 1,013) burrowing owls (*Athene cunicularia hypugaea*), 1,127 (80% CI = –23 to 2,277) raptors, and 2,710 (80% CI = –6,100 to 11,520) other birds (Smallwood and Thelander 2008). These numbers are dramatic and point out the importance to avian conservation and to wind energy facilities of pre-construction scientific evaluation and post-construction management.

Mortality rates at other wind energy facilities are not as dramatic as at Altamont, perhaps because they have not been as well studied or perhaps because they kill fewer birds. Another example of a poorly conceived (from an ornithological perspective) facility is the wind farm on the island of Smøla in Norway. There, turbines were erected throughout one of the world's highest-density breeding sites of White-tailed Sea Eagles (*Haliaeetus albicilla*). The density of nesting pairs on Smøla has been approximately cut in half and mortality of eagles has been high (E. Dahl, personal communication).

In spite of this seemingly gloomy backdrop, there are some studies that show either variable or relatively low mortality-related impacts of wind turbines on birds. In particular, one study in Spain (Barrios and Rodriguez 2004) showed that mortality of birds of prey was highly seasonal and spatially variable, such that birds were almost never struck by turbine blades at one site and only struck during specific seasons at a second site. A study in the Netherlands (Desholm and Kahlert 2005) showed that only a tiny fraction of ducks (<1%) engaged in daily movements were even exposed to risk at an offshore wind farm.

It seems obvious that to understand mortality risk to birds from development of wind turbines there is great value in careful pre-construction siting and post-construction monitoring. However, there have, to date, been no peer-reviewed studies of the impacts of wind turbines on migrating birds in the Appalachians. In Pennsylvania, annual migration of raptors and passerines along our ridges is a key component of our natural heritage. Pre- and post-construction studies at these sites are therefore critical to evaluate mortality impacts of turbines on birds.

WHAT IS KNOWN OF WIND POWER MORTALITY IN PENNSYLVANIA

Currently there are 12 utility-scale wind energy sites either operating or under construction in Pennsylvania (see Table 1). Unfortunately none of the pre- or post-construction avian monitoring data and/or reports that may exist for these facilities has been published (either in hard copy or on-line) in a readily-accessible form for review by independent scientists. Reports are typically done by consultants to wind energy developers and are filed with the local municipality as part of the project application. There are, to date, no recorded incidents of high numbers of avian collision fatalities with wind turbines in Pennsylvania, although some sites have experienced minor collision mortality events (D. Gross, PGC, personal communication). There is some evidence that passerine mortality events are related to specific weather conditions (D. Gross, personal communication).

As of January 2008, 15 developers have signed onto the 2007 Pennsylvania Game Commission (PGC) "Wind Energy Voluntary Cooperation Agreement" that specifies minimum avian monitoring requirements for all wind energy sites (http://www.dcnr.state.pa.us/wind/).

Table 1. Summary information on utility-scale wind energy sites in Pennsylvania (data from www.awea.org).

Site	County	Geography	Status	Turbines
Garrett	Somerset	Plateau	operating (2000)	8
Turnpike	Somerset	Plateau	operating (2001)	6
Mill Run	Fayette	Plateau	operating (2001)	10
Meyersdale	Somerset	Ridgetop	operating (2003)	20
Waymart	Wayne	Ridgetop	operating (2003)	43
Bear Creek	Luzerne	Plateau/Broad Ridge	operating (2006)	12
Locust Ridge	Schuylkill	Plateau/Broad Ridge	operating (2006)	13
Locust Ridge II	Schuylkill	Plateau/Broad Ridge	operating (2008)	51
Allegheny Ridge	Cambria/Blair	Plateau & Alleg Front	operating (2007)/expanding	40+
Casselman	Somerset	Plateau	operating (2007)	23
Lookout	Somerset	Ridgetop	operating (2008)	18
Forward Wind	Somerset	Plateau	operating (2008)	14

These requirements include pre-construction raptor migration monitoring and breeding bird surveys, as well as post-construction carcass searches, but do not include nocturnal bird migration surveys. Prior to this voluntary agreement, developers were under no regulatory obligation to PGC or USFWS to do avian monitoring at wind energy sites. Privacy agreements between wind energy developers and the PGC will prevent independent scientists from accessing monitoring information from wind energy sites for the foreseeable future. This is unfortunate since many proposed sites are located in regions of Pennsylvania with very limited data on migrating raptors or breeding birds.

KNOWLEDGE GAPS

It is apparent from existing data that in most cases wind turbines do not cause high levels of avian mortality (USGAO, 2005; NRC, 2007). However, the high rates of collision fatalities at facilities such as Altamont, California and Smøla, Norway that were sited within raptor concentration areas indicate the potential for significant avian mortality. Avoidance of raptor concentration areas remains the key to reducing avian collision risk; however, much remains to be learned about the behavioral responses of raptors to turbines. It is likely that the majority of collisions occur under particular conditions that can be avoided with micro-siting (i.e., adjustments in turbine location on the order of 100s of meters to a avoid migration pathway) and turbine operation schedules that avoid high-risk periods.

Currently there is a complete lack of data in the Appalachian region from scientifically rigorous studies using Before-After-Control-Impact (BACI) designs. Low collision rates based on carcass searches that have been reported for most facilities might simply be a result of low avian use, or could be the result of avoidance. In the latter case, the issue of cumulative impacts of dozens of wind power plants containing thousands of turbines becomes significant (the American Wind Energy Association estimates that Pennsylvania contains approximately 5000 MW of wind energy capacity, corresponding to some 3000 turbines). If by avoiding turbines, birds are forced out of preferred habitat and migration corridors into less suitable areas, indirect mortality is possible, although this will be difficult to measure. Therefore, in addition to better data on behavioral response of birds to turbines to better understand when and how collisions occur, a regional perspective that considers the connectivity of habitat and migration pathways will be necessary to fully understand the impact of large-scale wind power development in Pennsylvania.

Finally, relatively little research has been done on possible mitigation measures (USGAO, 2005) to reduce collisions with turbines. Several methods have been suggested, including paint schemes, ultraviolet coatings, and the use of noise as a deterrent, but the results of pilot testing have been inconclusive.

LIMITING AVIAN MORTALITY AT WIND POWER FACILITIES

Collision risk is proportional to numbers of birds exposed to turbines. To reduce risk, we recommend:

- Avoid placing turbines on raptor migration pathways such as narrow ridgetops or the edge of escarpments like the Allegheny Front:
  - ° If development of such areas is deemed necessary, employ setbacks from sloping terrain and flexible turbine operation schedules that avoid high-risk conditions (i.e., conditions when large numbers of raptors are moving through rotor-swept zone)
  - ° Avoid placing turbines in gaps in ridges, as some research shows that certain weather conditions promote "channeling" of passerine migration through such features
- Avoid placing turbines in or near sensitive habitats such as wetlands, contiguous forests, or other areas identified as ecologically significant (e.g., Important Bird Areas). Demographic impacts of habitat loss are, for many species, more consequential for survivorship (and hence mortality rates) than are direct effects of turbine strike.
- Engage in pre- and post-construction scientific evaluation and monitoring at all wind energy sites, particularly those that are believed to pose higher potential risk.
- A focused collaborative effort with independent scientists is essential to develop and implement the highest-quality research and therefore to produce the best possible management strategies to reduce impacts of wind turbines on birds.
- Transparency and peer-reviewed publication of all scientific studies is essential in order for the larger scientific community to understand and evaluate risk from development of wind turbines. Lack of transparency only injures and prolongs the current emotionally-driven discussion of this issue.

LITERATURE CITED

Barrios, L. and A. Rodriguez. 2004. Behavioural and environmental correlates of soaring-bird mortality at on-shore turbines. *Journal of Applied Ecology* 41: 72–81.

Desholm, M. and J. Kahlert. 2005. Avian collision risk at an offshore wind farm. *Biology Letters* 1:296–298.

Hunt, G., 2002. *Golden Eagles in a Perilous Landscape: Predicting the Effects of Mitigation for Wind Turbine Blade-Strike Mortality*. Cal. Energy Commission Consultant Report.

National Research Council (NRC), 2007. *Environmental Impacts of Wind-Energy Projects*. National Academies Press, Washington, DC. 394 pp.

National Wind Coordinating Committee (NWCC) 2004. Wind Turbine Interactions with Birds and Bats: A Summary of Research Results and Remaining Questions. Fact Sheet: Second Edition.

Smallwood, K.S. and C.G. Thelander. 2008. Bird mortality at the Altamont Pass Wind Resource Area, California. *Journal of Wildlife Management* 72:215–223.

United States Government Accountability Office (USGAO) 2005. *Wind Power Impacts on Wildlife and Government Responsibilities for Regulating Development and Protecting Wildlife*. GAO-05-906.

Avian Ecology and Conservation: A Pennsylvania Focus with National Implications. Edited by S. K. Majumdar, T. L. Master, M. C. Brittingham, R. M. Ross, R. S. Mulvihill and J. E. Huffman. © 2010. The Pennsylvania Academy of Science.

Chapter 23

Epizootiology of West Nile Virus in Wild Birds

Jennifer C. Owen[1,2] and Mary C. Garvin[3]
[1]Department of Fisheries and Wildlife, Michigan State University,
East Lansing, MI 48824
[2]Department of Large Animal Clinical Sciences, Michigan State University,
East Lansing, MI 48824
[3]Department of Biology, Oberlin College, Oberlin, OH, 44074
jcordesowen@gmail.com, mary.garvin@oberlin.edu

INTRODUCTION

West Nile virus (WNV) is a mosquito-borne virus in the family Flaviviridae, Japanese encephalitis virus serogroup, which also includes St. Louis encephalitis, yellow fever and dengue fever. First discovered in the West Nile region of Uganda, Africa in 1937, the virus has since been detected in Africa, the Middle East, Europe, and Asia (CDC 2008). WNV was first detected in North America in New York City in 1999 (Nash et al. 2001). Although the source and route of the introduction remain unclear, the North American strain appears most closely related to isolates from Israel in 1998 (Lanciotti et al. 2000).

Since it's detection in North America, WNV has received a great deal of attention from public health officials, as well as domestic livestock and wildlife health specialists and considerable effort has been devoted to understanding the basic ecology of the virus. This body of literature is summarized in reviews by Komar (2003), Marra et al. (2004), Weaver and Barrett (2004), Hayes et al. (2005), Kramer et al. (2007) and Kilpatrick et al. (2007). Here we focus on the impact of West Nile virus on wild bird populations in North America.

ECOLOGY

Mosquito Vectors

The WNV transmission includes an enzootic cycle and an epizootic cycle. The endemic cycle involves transmission within the bird population by ornithophilic species of mosquitoes, especially the *Culex pipiens and Culex restuans* complex (Hayes 1989, Campbell et al. 2002). Mosquitoes acquire the virus by feeding on an infected bird, although vertical transmission through eggs from infected females has also been reported (Nasci et al. 2001, Dohm et al. 2002, Goddard et al. 2003). The competence of a species of mosquitoes as a vector depends on a number of factors including the susceptibility of the particular species to the virus and the level of circulating virus in the source of the blood meal (Turell et al. 2002)

During the epizootic period of the cycle, mammals become infected with the virus when bitten by a bridge vector, a species of mosquito that feeds on both birds and mammals. Thus far in North America, virus has been detected in a total of 62 species of mosquitoes (CDC 2007), though only about 33 species are believed to be important vectors. Species of soft ticks are also capable of transmitting virus under laboratory conditions (Hutcheson et al. 2005) but their involvement in nature is likely less important (Lawrie et al. 2004). West Nile virus transmission in the absence of vectors also has been reported among laboratory birds via oral transmission (Komar et al. 2003).

Vertebrate Reservoir Hosts

WNV has been detected in over 300 species of birds in North America (CDC 2007). The importance of birds as amplification hosts and for maintaining the enzootic cycle (Hayes 1989), depends on the magnitude and duration of their viremia post-infection (Komar et al. 2003), typically 1–7 days post-inoculation (dpi), with most birds having cleared the virus by 4 dpi (Komar et al. 2003). Reservoir host competence is also influenced by a number of factors including the abundance of infected mosquitoes and behavioral and ecological factors that result in birds coming into close proximity to infected mosquitoes. Orders of birds considered competent reservoirs include songbirds (Order Passeriformes), shorebirds (Order Charadriiformes), owls, (Order Strigiformes), and hawks (Order Falconiformes) (Komar 2003, Komar et al. 2003). Whereas, doves and pigeons (Order Columbiformes), woodpeckers (Order Piciformes), and ducks and geese (Order Anaseriformes) are considered less likely amplification hosts (Komar et al. 2001a, Komar et al. 2003). Kilpatrick et al. (2007) created a model that calculated a competence index for the 53 species of wild vertebrates that have been experimentally infected and studied in the laboratory and concluded that eight species were most likely to be competent hosts: blue jay (*Cyanocitta cristata*), western scrub-jay (*Aphelocoma californica*), American crow (*Corvus brachyrhynchos*), black-billed magpie (*Pica hudsonia*), common grackle (*Quiscalus quiscula*), house finch (*Carpodacus mexicanus*), house sparrow (*Passer domesticus*), and ring-billed gull (*Larus delawarensis*). Of these, the blue jay, common grackle, American crow, and house sparrow may suffer high mortality (Komar 2003, Komar et al. 2003, Godsey et al. 2005). Interestingly, reptiles and mammals, including the American alligator (*Alligator mississippiensis*) and eastern chipmunk (*Tamias striatus*) may be more competent hosts than many species of birds, including suspected avian hosts such as the northern cardinal (*Cardinalis cardinalis*), gray catbird (*Dumetella carolinensis*), and northern mockingbird (*Mimus polyglottos*) (Kilpatrick et al. 2007).

During the epizootic cycle non-avian hosts, such as human, horses and other mammals become infected. While these dead-end hosts may experience morbidity and even mortality, particularly horses, they typically do not develop viremias capable of infecting a mosquito. Humans and mammals are more likely to become infected later in the summer and fall after significant amplification during the summer. In the Washington D.C. area in 2004 Kilpatrick et al. (2006b) found a shift in the feeding preference of *Culex pipiens* from American Robins to humans in the late summer after the robins migrate south. Because both robins and *Cx. pipiens* are abundant in areas of dense human populations, *Cx. pipiens* species becomes an ideal bridge vector between infected avian reservoir host populations and humans.

SEROLOGICAL SURVEILLANCE

Following the 1999 outbreak of WNV in New York City, antibody surveys of wild birds were conducted to determine which species would be the best natural sentinels for WNV activity. Monitoring antibody levels in wild birds is useful in that it allows for determination of the extent and pace of the geographic spread of the virus and reservoir host poten-

Table 1. Summary of WNV antibody data for birds captured in North America following the 1999 outbreak of West Nile virus in the United States. The table summarizes data from studies conducted in the Eastern United States from 1999–2004. We only included species for which more than 10 individuals were sampled.

Order	Family	Species	n^1	Proportion positive for WNV	WNV Ab prevalence
Anseriformes	Anatidae	Domestic goose, *Anser anser*	11	0.64	High
		Canada goose, *Branta canadensis*	1376	0.02	Low
		Wood duck, *Aix sponsa*	298	0.03	Low
		Mallard, *Anas platyrhynchos*	88	0.05	Low
		Ring-necked duck, *Aythya collaris*	19	0.05	Low
Galliformes	Meleagrididae	Wild turkey, *Meleagris gallopavo*	37	0.41	High
	Phasianidae	Domestic chicken, *Gallus gallus*	317	0.34	High
		Common peafowl, *Pavo cristatus*	25	0.08	Low
Charadriiformes	Haematopodidae	American oystercatcher, *Haematopus palliates*	28	0.00	Low
Columbiformes	Columbidae	Rock pigeon, *Columba livia*	728	0.27	High
		Mourning dove, *Zenaida macroura*	409	0.20	High
		Common ground dove, *Columbina passerine*	60	0.27	High
Piciformes	Picidae	Red-headed woodpecker, *Melanerpes erythrocephalus*	18	0.06	Low
		Red-bellied woodpecker, *Melanerpes carolinus*	237	0.06	Low
		Downy woodpecker, *Picoides pubescens*	41	0.00	Low
		Northern flicker, *Colaptes auratus*	21	0.05	Low
Passeriformes	Tyrannidae	Eastern wood pewee, *Contopus virens*	31	0.03	Low
		Eastern phoebe, *Sayornis phoebe*	18	0.00	Low
		Great-crested flycatcher, *Myiarchus crinitus*	50	0.02	Low
	Corvidae	Blue jay, *Cyanocitta cristata*	406	0.06	Low
		American crow, *Corvus brachyrhynchos*	31	0.10	Med
		Fish crow, *Corvus ossifragus*	12	0.25	High
	Paridae	Tufted titmouse, *Baeolephus bicolor*	466	0.01	Low
	Sittidae	White-breasted nuthatch, *Sitta carolinensis*	56	0.04	Low
	Troglodytidae	Carolina wren, *Thryothorus ludovicianus*	160	0.12	Med
	Turdidae	Eastern bluebird, *Sialia sialis*	153	0.04	Low
		Swainson's thrush, *Catharus ustulatus*	75	0.03	Low
		Wood thrush, *Hylocichla mustelina*	40	0.18	Med
		American robin, *Turdus migratorius*	492	0.13	Med

continued

Table 1. *continued.*

Order	Family	Species	n^1	Proportion positive for WNV	WNV Ab prevalence
	Mimidae	Gray catbird, *Dumetella carolinensis*	428	0.11	Med
		Northern mockingbird, *Mimus polyglottos*	351	0.14	Med
		Brown thrasher, *Toxostoma rufum*	354	0.05	Low
	Sturnidae	European starling, *Sturnus vulgaris*	169	0.01	Low
	Bombycillidae	Cedar waxwing, *Bombycilla cedrorum*	14	0.14	Med
	Parulidae	Yellow-rumped warbler, *Dendroica coronata*	74	0.01	Low
		Ovenbird, *Seiurus aurocapillus*	70	0.06	Low
		Northern waterthrush, *Seiurus noveboracensis*	22	0.05	Low
		Yellow-breasted chat, *Icteria virens*	48	0.13	Med
	Thraupidae	Summer tanager, *Piranga rubra*	68	0.09	Med
		Scarlet tanager, *Piranga olivacea*	71	0.03	Low
	Emberizidae	Eastern towhee, *Pipilo erythrophthalmus*	197	0.10	Med
		Chipping sparrow, *Spizella passerina*	27	0.04	Low
		Field sparrow, *Spizella pusilla*	33	0.03	Low
		Song sparrow, *Melospiza melodia*	115	0.01	Low
		White-throated sparrow, *Zonotrichia albicollis*	292	0.01	Low
	Cardinalidae	Northern cardinal, *Cardinalis cardinalis*	3376	0.18	Med
		Rose-breasted Grosbeak, *Pheucticus ludovicianus*	14	0.21	High
		Blue grosbeak, *Passerina caerulea*	45	0.00	Low
		Indigo bunting, *Passerina cyanea*	97	0.03	Low
	Icteridae	Red-winged blackbird, *Agelaius phoeniceus*	342	0.02	Low
		Common grackle, *Quiscalus quiscula*	596	0.04	Low
		Boat-tailed grackle, *Quiscalus major*	77	0.01	Low
		Brown-headed cowbird, *Molothrus ater*	865	0.03	Low
		Orchard oriole, *Icterus spurius*	76	0.04	Low
	Frigillidae	House finch, *Carpodacus mexicanus*	982	0.03	Low
		American goldfinch, *Carduelis tristis*	73	0.01	Low
	Passeridae	House sparrow, *Passer domesticus*	2748	0.09	Med

Summary based on the following studies: Komar et al. (2001a), Komar et al. (2001b), Ringia et al.(2004), Komar et al. (2005), Godsey et al. (2005), Gibbs et al. (2006), and Beveroth et al. (2006)
[1]Total number of individuals sampled from all studies in which data for the particular species was collected.

tial of the sentinel species. For instance, a species that demonstrates high prevalence of WNV neutralizing antibodies, is abundant in nature, and is able to maintain high viremias is likely to be important in maintaining the enzoonotic cycle (Gibbs et al. 2006). In Table 1 we summarize data from antibody prevalence studies conducted between 1999–2004 by rating overall prevalence as low, medium, and high. Notice that birds in the same family tend to have similar antibody prevalence. For instance, all 3 dove species had similar antibody prevalence of 20 – 27%, whereas, woodpeckers had very low prevalence of 0 – 6% of the individuals sampled. However, caution should be used in interpreting such data given that seroprevalence is influenced by a number of factors including (1) level of exposure, which varies with age, sex, environment, habitat, and behavior, (2) interspecific variation in immune response, such that some birds clear infection without developing antibodies or antibody titers may decline soon after infection (see below) and (3) pathological effect and probability of mortality. For instance, blue jays have low seroprevalence but exhibit high mortality.

Little is known about the persistence of antibodies post-WNV infection (but see Gibbs et al. 2005, Wilcox et al. 2007). Gibbs et al. (2005) found WNV antibodies in naturally infected rock pigeons (*Columba livia*) persisted for 15 months post capture. In a similar study, Wilcox et al. (2007) found antibody persistence in fish crows (*Corvus ossifragus*) for at least 12 months. However, neither study controlled for timing of infection or initial virus dose. In a study on gray catbirds (*Dumetella carolinensis*, n = 60) experimentally infected with WNV, only half of the individual remained positive for WNV neutralizing antibodies 5 months post-infection (Owen and Garvin unpub data). There is little known about the degree to which antibodies protect birds from reinfection, particularly at low titers (but see Fang and Reisen 2006). Maternal transfer of WNV antibodies to offspring has been documented in owls (Hahn et al. 2006), flamingos (Baitchman et al. 2007), and pigeons (Gibbs et al. 2005). The persistence of these maternal antibodies typically lasts for 3–4 weeks post-hatching. Whether these maternally-derived antibodies protect the young from infection during that several week period or beyond is unknown. However, high antibody titers are observed in juveniles (Hahn et al. 2006) and are likely to provide some protection post-hatching.

CLINICAL SIGNS OF DISEASE

West Nile virus is a neurotropic flavivirus which may cause encephalitis (inflammation of the brain), and meningitis (inflammation of the membranes surrounding the central nervous system). In birds, clinical signs of infection vary by species, with some birds exhibiting no symptoms and others experiencing severe neurological disorders. Much of what we know about the clinical disease comes from WNV-infected raptors in rehabilitation centers (Joyner et al. 2006). Raptors as a taxonomic group appear to be particularly susceptible to WNV and represent approximately 15% of the species listed on the CDC WNV avian mortality database (CDC 2008). Further information on clinical signs of WNV comes from experimental infection studies (see Steele et al. 2000, Weingartl et al. 2004, Nemeth et al. 2006). Visible symptoms of clinical disease vary greatly in specificity and severity and may include lethargy, fasting, lack of coordination, depression, emaciation, green urates, and catabolization of muscle stores (Weingartl et al. 2004, Nemeth et al. 2006), with more advanced signs of disease including severe neurological abnormalities such as head tremors, seizures, and blindness (see Marra et al. 2004).

Pathology of a WNV infection also varies among species and individuals. Upon necropsy, gross findings of WNV infection may include one or more of the following: enlarged spleen (splenomegaly); congestion (swelling due to increased blood flow) of the lung, heart, liver, cerebral cortex, proventriculus, testes, spleen, skeletal muscle, and kidneys; necrosis of pectoral muscle and cerebrum; histopathological lesions of the calvaria, meninges, heart, lung, kidney, spleen, and myocardium; hemorrhages in skeletal muscle, liver, esophagus, calvarium, brain, heart, gastrointestinal tract, spleen, pancreas, and lung; swelling of the spleen and kidney; and/or a pale mycardium (Steele et al. 2000, Weingartl et al. 2004, Nemeth et al. 2006). In addition, infection with the virus may make birds more susceptible to concomitant infections such as, Aspergillosis, condition caused by infection of fungi in the genus *Aspergillus* (Steele et al. 2000, Bertelsen et al. 2004 Owen and Williams unpub data). Though these pathological signs of WNV are associated with a variety of physiological effects, they do not necessarily lead to death (see Marra et al. 2004).

GEOGRAPHIC SPREAD

Since its introduction WNV has spread across the entire continental United States, into much of southern Canada, Mexico, Central America, and several South American countries (see Kilpatrick et al. 2007). The mechanisms by which the virus has spread across the continent remain unclear, though many have been suggested including migrating and dispersing birds, active or passive movements of mosquitoes, and the human transport of both (Rappole et al. 2000, Peterson et al. 2003, Rappole and Hubálek 2003, Kilpatrick et al. 2004, Reisen et al. 2004, Kilpatrick et al. 2006a, Owen et al. 2006). The role of migrating birds in this as well as other bird-borne pathogens has received much attention. In the case of WNV, the observed spread loosely coincides with the movement of migratory birds (Rappole et al. 2000, Peterson et al. 2003). While experimental studies (Owen et al. 2006) theoretical models (Peterson et al. 2003) and circumstantial evidence (Rappole et al. 2000, Rappole and Hubálek 2003) suggest migratory birds are capable of spreading the virus along their migratory routes, there is no direct evidence of a free-ranging birds migrating while infectious. Moreover, capture of infectious birds during migration reveals little or nothing about when and where birds became infected. Only by tracking a viremic bird during its entire migration can we confirm its role in movement of the virus. Unfortunately, tracking viremic birds is difficult due to the brevity of viremia in most species.

Likewise, the role of birds as long–term reservoirs of WNV and the mechanisms by which transmission is annually reinitiated in temperate climates are not understood. One hypothesis suggests that the virus overwinters in dormant mosquitoes which become active the following spring and infect a bird during a subsequent blood meal. Support for this hypothesis has been found by Nasci et al. (2001), Farajollahi et al. (2005), Bugbee and Forte (2004), and Anderson and Main (2006) all of whom detected WNV RNA in diapausing *Culex pipiens* mosquitoes in New York, New Jersey, Pennsylvania, and Connecticut, respectively. Moreover, both Nasci et al. (2001) and Anderson and Main (2006) found evidence of viable virus in overwintering mosquitoes.

A second hypothesis, first proposed by Crans et al. (1994) for eastern equine encephalitis virus, is based on recrudesence of overwintering latent virus in the avian host tissue. According to this hypothesis, the virus may temporarily return to the peripheral circulation each spring as the result of stressful situations such as breeding or migration which may suppress the bird's immune system (Greenman et al. 2005, Owen and Moore 2006, Owen and Moore 2008), thereby making the bird infectious to newly emerged mosquitoes. Because the presence of long-term, chronic arboviral infections in avian hosts is not well-documented, the feasibility of such a mechanism is difficult to evaluate. Reisen et al. (2003b) detected western equine encephalitis and St. Louis encephalitis RNA in the tissues of several avian species 6 weeks post-infection. Similarly, Reisen et al. (2006) found WNV RNA in tissues of 6 species of birds 6 weeks after infection. Still, in both studies infectious levels of virus were detected only in a small proportion of the positive birds. Moreover, in temperate climates, chronic infections would need to persist for much

longer than 6 weeks to serve as the basis of an overwintering mechanism. Several reported efforts to cause relapse of chronic infections through administration of an immunosuppressive agent have been unsuccessful (Reisen et al. 2001, Reisen et al. 2003a). In a
study of WNV in gray catbirds, Owen and Garvin (unpub data) did not detect WN viral
RNA (*Dumetella carolinensis*) after > 5 months post-infection, providing no support for
the recrudescence hypothesis. Given that avian species vary greatly in their response to
WNV, more studies are needed on other species to test this hypothesis.

POPULATION IMPACT

Nearly a decade after detection of WNV in North American, we still have little understanding of the impact on populations of wild birds. Unlike Old World species, North
American birds appear to be particular susceptible, especially corvids and raptors (Bernard
et al. 2001, McLean et al. 2001, Caffrey et al. 2003, 2005). In addition, greater sage grouse
(*Centrocercus urophasianus*), a species declining in the west, also experiences high mortality when infected with WNV (Naugle et al. 2004, Clark et al. 2006). Other species of
wild birds were likely impacted as well, but such effects may have gone undetected due to
relatively low visibility, more distant proximity of the their habitat to humans, and difficulty of sampling.

The causes of mortality in wild bird populations are often difficult to monitor. Even in
marked, well-studied populations, sick birds are quickly preyed upon and carcasses are
immediately scavenged. Even when carcasses are found, determination of the cause of
death can be difficult and often impossible. For these reasons, the direct, population-level
impacts of pathogens on wild birds in general are difficult to discern. Kilpatrick et al.
(2007) provide an excellent summary of the impact of West Nile virus on birds in the eastern hemisphere. Still they note that the population impact of WNV remains unclear despite
reports of high mortality in wild birds following detection of WNV in North America.
Efforts such as Audubon breeding bird counts provide opportunities to monitor bird populations for pre- and post- WNV comparison. Such surveys have documented declines in
a number of species, especially members of the family Corvidae, which includes blue jays
and crows. Moreover, laboratory studies have clearly demonstrated WNV-induced morbidity and mortality in these and other species, with the greatest mortality seen in American crow (100%), fish crow (50%), blue jay (75%), and greater sage grouse (100%)
(Komar et al. 2003, Clark et al. 2006).

In an effort to combine these field and laboratory observations to empirically demonstrate the population-level impact of WNV on North American birds, LaDeau et al. (2007)
developed a model based on 26 years of data from the United States Geological Survey
North American Breeding Bird Survey. They focused on 20 species of wild birds that are
abundant in sections of the eastern United States where WNV was first detected and for
which susceptibility to WNV was understood from laboratory studies. In addition, they
included 5 other species for which tolerance to the virus is not understood.

For all selected species they compared population levels before and after 2002–2003,
the period during which the greatest number of human cases of WNV was reported. The
most notable decline in abundance was reported in American crows which had in some
areas drop by 45% after a 20 year population high. Also notable is that for 8 of the target
species, post-WNV population levels were lower than any other time of the 26 year peri-

od. Moreover, after controlling for the effects of climate and habitat, factors that would normally influence population levels, 7 species reached population levels that were significantly lower than expected by chance. Especially notable were the American crow, American robin, chickadee and eastern bluebird populations, all of which had been increasing in abundance prior to 2002. To a lesser degree population declines were also observed in the blue jay, tufted titmouse and house wren. Declines in other species were more regional which may be explained by geographic variation in mosquito abundance due to variation in mosquito diversity (Turrell et al. 2002), feeding behavior (Kilpatrick et al. 2006b) and breeding habitat availability. In addition, Saito et al. (2007) reported increased mortality in raptors after 2002, though the causes of this mortality remain unclear. Ingestion of infected prey (Garmendia et al. 2000) has been demonstrated in the laboratory (Komar et al. 2003) and remains a possible route of infection that would make raptors a particularly susceptible species. In addition, heightened awareness of WNV among the general public may have resulted in enhanced reporting of mortality and submission of carcasses, particularly for species which are more visible and are abundant in urban areas, such as crows and jays.

CONCLUSION

West Nile virus has received a great deal of attention from the scientific community since its detection in North America nearly a decade ago, as evidenced by the volume of literature generated to date. However, we still understand little about its impact on wild bird populations. Kilpatrick et al. (2007) suggests specific areas of future research efforts such as the genetic basis for the interspecific differences in morbidity and mortality. We also suggest that understanding the effect of life history strategies and stress on probability of acquiring infection and ultimately, to disease warrants attention. Answers to these and many other questions are not only critical to our understanding of the impact of WNV on avian populations, but in a broader sense, to the role of all disease-causing agents in the ecology and evolution of birds.

ACKNOWLEDGEMENTS

The recrudescence work and JO were supported by a grant from the National Science Foundation [0418715].

LITERATURE CITED

Anderson, J. F., and A. J. Main. 2006. Importance of vertical and horizontal transmission of West Nile virus by *Culex pipiens* in the Northeastern United States. J Infect Dis 194:1577–1579.

Baitchman, E. J., M. F. Tlusty, and H. W. Murphy. 2007. Passive transfer of maternal antibodies to West Nile virus in flamingo chicks (*Phoenicopterus chilensis* and *Phoenicopterus ruber ruber*). J Zoo Wildl Med 38:337–340.

Bernard, K. A., J. G. Maffei, S. A. Jones, E. B. Kauffman, G. Ebel, A. P. Dupuis, 2nd, K. A. Ngo, D. C. Nicholas, D. M. Young, P. Y. Shi, V. L. Kulasekera, M. Eidson, D. J. White, W. B. Stone, and L. D. Kramer. 2001. West Nile virus infection in birds and mosquitoes, New York State, 2000. Emerg Infect Dis 7:679–685.

Bertelsen, M. F., R. A. Olberg, G. J. Crawshaw, A. Dibernardo, L. R. Lindsay, M. Drebot, and I. K. Barker. 2004. West Nile virus infection in the eastern loggerhead shrike (*Lanius ludovicianus migrans*): pathology, epidemiology, and immunization. J Wildl Dis 40:538–542.

Beveroth, T. A., M. P. Ward, R. L. Lampman, A. M. Ringia, and R. J. Novak. 2006. Changes in sero-prevalence of West Nile virus across Illinois in free-ranging birds from 2001 through 2004. Am. J. Trop. Med. Hyg. 74:174–179.

Bugbee, L. M., and L. R. Forte. 2004. The discovery of West Nile virus in overwintering *Culex pipiens* (Diptera: Culicidae) mosquitoes in Lehigh County, Pennsylvania. J Am Mosq Control Assoc 20:326–327.

Caffrey C., T. J. Weston, and S. C. R. Smith. 2003. High mortality among marked crows subsequent to the arrival of West Nile virus. Wild. Soc. Bull. 31:870–872.

Caffrey C., S. C. R. Smith, T. J. Weston. 2005. West Nile virus devastates an American crow population. The Condor 107:128–132.

Campbell, G. L., A. A. Marfin, R. S. Lanciotti, and D. J. Gubler. 2002. West Nile virus. The Lancet Infect. Dis. 2:519–529.

Centers for Disease Control and Prevention. 2007. West Nile virus entomology. Available from http://www.cdc.gov/ncidod/dvbid/westnile/mosquitoSpecies.htm Accessed March 2008.

Centers for Disease Control and Prevention. West Nile virus activity. Available from http://www.cdc.gov/ncidod/dvbid/westnile/background.htm. Accessed March 2008.

Clark, L, J. Hall, R. McLean, M. Dunbar, K. Klenk, R. Bowen, C. A. Smeraski. 2006. Susceptibility of greater sage-grouse to experimental infection with West Nile virus. J Wildl Dis 42: 14–22.

Crans, W. J., D. F. Caccamise, and J. R. McNelly. 1994. Eastern equine encephalomyelitis virus in relation to the avian community of a coastal cedar swamp. J Med Entomol 71:711–728.

Dohm, D. J., M. R. Sardelis, and M. J. Turell. 2002. Experimental vertical transmission of West Nile virus by *Culex pipiens* (Diptera: Culicidae). J Med Entomol 39:640–644.

Fang, Y., and W. K. Reisen. 2006. Previous infection with West Nile or St. Louis encephalitis viruses provides cross protection during reinfection in house finches. Am. J. Trop. Med. Hyg. 75:480–485.

Farajollahi, A., W. J. Crans, P. Bryant, B. Wolf, K. L. Burkhalter, M. S. Godsey, S. E. Aspen, and R. S. Nasci. 2005. Detection of West Nile viral RNA from an overwintering pool of *Culex pipiens pipiens* (Diptera: Culicidae) in New Jersey, 2003. J Med Entomol 42:490–494.

Garmendia, A. E., H. J. Van Kruiningen, R. A. French, J. F. Anderson, T. G. Andreadis, A. Kumar, and A. B. West. 2000. Recovery and identification of West Nile virus from a hawk in winter. J Clin Microbiol 38:3110–3111.

Gibbs, S. E., A. B. Allison, M. J. Yabsley, D. G. Mead, B. R. Wilcox, and D. E. Stallknecht. 2006. West Nile virus antibodies in avian species of Georgia, USA: 2000–2004. Vector Borne Zoonotic Dis 6:57–72.

Gibbs, S. E., D. M. Hoffman, L. M. Stark, N. L. Marlenee, B. J. Blitvich, B. J. Beaty, and D. E. Stallknecht. 2005. Persistence of antibodies to West Nile virus in naturally infected rock pigeons (*Columba livia*). Clin Diagn Lab Immunol 12:665–667.

Goddard, L. B., A. E. Roth, W. K. Reisen, and T. W. Scott. 2003. Vertical transmission of West Nile Virus by three California Culex (Diptera: Culicidae) species. J Med Entomol 40:743–746.

Godsey, M. S., Jr., M. S. Blackmore, N. A. Panella, K. Burkhalter, K. Gottfried, L. A. Halsey, R. Rutledge, S. A. Langevin, R. Gates, K. M. Lamonte, A. Lambert, R. S. Lanciotti, C. G. Blackmore, T. Loyless, L. Stark, R. Oliveri, L. Conti, and N. Komar. 2005. West Nile virus epizootiology in the southeastern United States, 2001. Vector Borne Zoonotic Dis 5:82–89.

Greenman, C. G., L. B. Martin, 2nd, and M. Hau. 2005. Reproductive state, but not testosterone, reduces immune function in male house sparrows (*Passer domesticus*). Physiol Biochem Zool 78:60–68.

Hahn, D. C., N. M. Nemeth, E. Edwards, P. R. Bright, and N. Komar. 2006. Passive West Nile virus antibody transfer from maternal Eastern screech-owls (*Megascops asio*) to progeny. Avian Dis 50:454–455.

Hayes, C. G. 1989. West Nile fever. Pages 59–88 in T. P. Monath, editor. The arboviruses: epidemiology and ecology. CRC Press,Boca Raton, Florida.

Hayes, E. B., N. Komar, R. S. Nasci, S. P. Montgomery, D. R. O'Leary, and G. L. Campbell. 2005. Epidemiology and transmission dynamics of West Nile virus disease. Emerg Infect Dis 11:1167–1173.

Hutcheson, H. J., C. H. Gorham, C. Machain-Williams, M. A. Lorono-Pino, A. M. James, N. L. Marlenee, B. Winn, B. J. Beaty, and C. D. Blair. 2005. Experimental transmission of West Nile virus

(Flaviviridae: Flavivirus) by Carios capensis ticks from North America. Vector Borne Zoonotic Dis 5:293–295.

Joyner, P. H., S. Kelly, A. A. Shreve, S. E. Snead, J. M. Sleeman, and D. A. Pettit. 2006. West Nile virus in raptors from Virginia during 2003: clinical, diagnostic, and epidemiologic findings. J Wildl Dis 42:335–344.

Kilpatrick, A. M., P. Daszak, M. J. Jones, P. P. Marra, and L. D. Kramer. 2006a. Host heterogeneity dominates West Nile virus transmission. Proc Biol Sci 273:2327–2333.

Kilpatrick, A. M., L. D. Kramer, M. J. Jones, P. P. Marra, and P. Daszak. 2006b. West Nile virus epidemics in North America are driven by shifts in mosquito feeding behavior. PLoS Biol 4:e82.

Kilpatrick, A. M., Y. Gluzberg, J. Burgett, and P. Daszak. 2004. Quantitative risk assessment of the pathways by which West Nile virus could reach Hawaii. Ecohealth 1:205–209.

Kilpatrick, A. M., S. L. LaDeau, and P. P. Marra. 2007. Ecology of West Nile virus transmission and its impact on birds in the Western Hemisphere. Auk 124:1121–1136.

Komar, N. 2003. West Nile virus: epidemiology and ecology in North America. Adv. Virus. Res. 61:185–234.

Komar, N., J. Burns, C. Dean, N. A. Panella, S. Dusza, and B. Cherry. 2001a. Serologic evidence for West Nile virus infection in birds in Staten Island, New York, after an outbreak in 2000. Vector Borne Zoonotic Dis 1:191–196.

Komar, N., N. A. Panella, J. E. Burns, S. W. Dusza, T. M. Mascarenhas, and T. O. Talbot. 2001b. Serologic evidence for West Nile virus infection in birds in the New York City vicinity during an outbreak in 1999. Emerg Infect Dis 7:621–625.

Komar, N., N. A. Panella, S. A. Langevin, A. C. Brault, M. Amador, E. Edwards, and J. C. Owen. 2005. Avian hosts for West Nile virus in St. Tammany Parish, Lousiana, 2002. Am. J. Trop. Med. and Hyg. 73:1031–1037.

Komar, N., L. S., S. Hinten, N. Nemeth, E. Edwards, D. Hettler, B. Davis, R. Bowen, and M. Bunning. 2003. Experimental infections of North American birds with the New York strain of West Nile virus. Emerg Infect Dis 9:311–322.

Kramer, L. D., J. Li, and P. Y. Shi. 2007. West Nile virus. Lancet Neurol 6:171–181.

LaDeau, S. L., A. M. Kilpatrick, and P. P. Marra. 2007. West Nile virus emergence and large-scale declines of North American bird populations. Nature 447:710–713.

Lanciotti, R. S., A. J. Kerst, R. S. Nasci, M. S. Godsey, C. J. Mitchell, H. M. Savage, N. Komar, N. A. Panella, B. C. Allen, K. E. Volpe, B. S. Davis, and J. T. Roehrig. 2000. Rapid detection of West Nile virus from human clinical specimens, field-collected mosquitoes, and avian samples by a TaqMan reverse transcriptase-PCR assay. J. Clin. Microbiol. 38:4066–4071.

Lawrie, C. H., N. Y. Uzcategui, E. A. Gould, and P. A. Nuttall. 2004. Ixodid and argasid tick species and West Nile virus. Emerg Infect Dis 10:653–657.

Marra, P. P., S. Griffing, C. Caffrey, A. M. Kilpatrick, and R. McLean. 2004. West Nile virus and Wildlife. Biosci. 54:393–402.

McLean, R. G., S. R. Ubico, D. E. Docherty, W. R. Hansen, L. Sileo, and T. S. McNamara. 2001. West Nile virus transmission and ecology in birds. Ann N Y Acad Sci 951:54–57.

Nasci, R. S., H. M. Savage, D. J. White, J. R. Miller, B. C. Cropp, M. S. Godsey, A. J. Kerst, P. Bennett, K. Gottfried, and R. S. Lanciotti. 2001. West Nile virus in overwintering Culex mosquitoes, New York City, 2000. Emerg Infect Dis 7:742–744.

Nash, D., F. Mostashari, A. Fine, J. Miller, D. O'Leary, K. Murray, A. Huang, A. Rosenberg, A. Greenberg, M. Sherman, S. Wong, and M. Layton. 2001. The outbreak of West Nile virus infection in the New York City area in 1999. N Engl J Med 344:1807–1814.

Naugle D. E., C. L. Aldridge, B. L. Walker, T. E. Cornish, B. J. Moynahan, M. J. Holloran, K. Brown, G. D. Johnson, E. T. Schmidtmann, R. T. Mayer, C. Y. Kato, M. R. Matchett, T. J. Christiansen, W. E. Cook, T. Creekmore, R. D. Falise, E. T. Rinkes, and M. S. Boyce. 2004. West Nile virus: pending crises for Greater Sage-Grouse. Ecology Letters. 7:704–713

Nemeth, N., D. Gould, R. Bowen, and N. Komar. 2006. Natural and experimental West Nile virus infection in five raptor species. J Wildl Dis 42:1–13.

Owen, J., F. Moore, N. Panella, E. Edwards, R. Bru, M. Hughes, and N. Komar. 2006. Migrating birds as dispersal vehicles for West Nile virus. Ecohealth 3:79–85.

Owen, J. C., and F. R. Moore. 2006. Seasonal differences in immunological condition of three species of thrushes. Condor 108:390–399.

Owen, J. C., and F. R. Moore. 2008. Swainson's thrushes in migratory disposition exhibit reduced immune function. Journal of Ethology 26:383–388.

Peterson, A. T., D. A. Vieglais, and J. K. Andreasen. 2003. Migratory birds modeled as critical transport agents for West Nile virus in North America. Vector Borne Zoonotic Dis. 3:27–37.

Rappole, J. H., S. R. Derrickson, and Z. Hubalek. 2000. Migratory birds and spread of West Nile virus in the Western Hemisphere. Emerg Infect Dis 6:319–328.

Rappole, J. H., and Z. Hubálek. 2003. Migratory birds and West Nile virus. J. Appl. Microbiol. 94:47S–58S.

Reisen, W. K., R. Chiles, V. Martinez, Y. Fang, E. Green, and S. Clark. 2004. Effect of dose on house finch infection with western equine encephalomyelitis and St. Louis encephalitis viruses. J Med Entomol 41:978–981.

Reisen, W. K., R. E. Chiles, E. N. Green, Y. Fang, F. Mahmood, V. M. Martinez, and T. Laver. 2003a. Effects of immunosuppression on encephalitis virus infection in the house finch, *Carpodacus mexicanus*. J Med Entomol 40:206–214.

Reisen, W. K., R. E. Chiles, V. M. Martinez, Y. Fang, and E. N. Green. 2003b. Experimental infection of California birds with western equine encephalomyelitis and St. Louis encephalitis viruses. J Med Entomol 40:968–982.

Reisen, W. K., Y. Fang, H. D. Lothrop, V. M. Martinez, J. Wilson, P. Oconnor, R. Carney, B. Cahoon-Young, M. Shafii, and A. C. Brault. 2006. Overwintering of West Nile virus in Southern California. J Med Entomol 43:344–355.

Reisen, W. K., L. D. Kramer, R. E. Chiles, E. G. Green, and V. M. Martinez. 2001. Encephalitis virus persistence in California birds: preliminary studies with house finches. J Med Entomol 38:393–399.

Ringia, A. M., B. J. Blitvich, H. Y. Koo, M. Van de Wyngaerde, J. D. Brawn, and R. J. Novak. 2004. Antibody prevalence of West Nile virus in birds, Illinois, 2002. Emerg Infect Dis 10:1120–1124.

Saito, E. K., L. Sileo, D. E. Green, C. U. Meteyer, G. S. McLaughlin, K. A. Converse, and D. E. Docherty. 2007. Raptor mortality due to West Nile virus in the United States, 2002. J Wildl Dis 43:206–213.

Steele, K. E., M. J. Linn, R. J. Schoepp, N. Komar, T. W. Geisbert, R. M. Manduca, P. P. Calle, B. L. Raphael, T. L. Clippinger, T. Larsen, J. Smith, R. S. Lanciotti, N. A. Panella, and T. S. McNamara. 2000. Pathology of fatal West Nile virus infections in native and exotic birds during the 1999 outbreak in New York City, New York. Vet Pathol 37:208–224.

Turell, M. J., M. O'Guinn, D. J. Dohm, J. Webb, J.P., and M. R. Sardelis. 2002. Vector competence of *Culex tarsalis* from Orange County, California, for West Nile virus. Vector Borne Zoonotic Dis. 2:193–196.

Weaver, S. C., and A. D. Barrett. 2004. Transmission cycles, host range, evolution and emergence of arboviral disease. Nat Rev Microbiol 2:789–801.

Weingartl, H. M., J. L. Neufeld, J. Copps, and P. Marszal. 2004. Experimental West Nile virus infection in blue jays (*Cyanocitta cristata*) and crows (*Corvus brachyrhynchos*). Vet Pathol 41:362–370.

Wilcox, B. R., M. J. Yabsley, A. E. Ellis, D. E. Stallknecht, and S. E. Gibbs. 2007. West Nile virus antibody prevalence in American crows (*Corvus brachyrhynchos*) and fish crows (*Corvus ossifragus*) in Georgia, USA. Avian Dis 51:125–128.

Avian Ecology and Conservation: A Pennsylvania Focus with National Implications. Edited by S. K. Majumdar, T. L. Master, M. C. Brittingham, R. M. Ross, R. S. Mulvihill and J. E. Huffman. © 2010. The Pennsylvania Academy of Science.

Chapter 24

West Nile Virus in Raptors

Jane E. Huffman

Department of Biological Sciences, Northeast Wildlife DNA Laboratory,
East Stroudsburg University of Pennsylvania, East Stroudsburg, PA 18301
jhuffman@po-box.esu.edu

Douglas E. Roscoe

NJ Division of Fish and Wildlife, Office of Fish and Wildlife Health and Forensics,
141 Van Syckels Road, Hampton, NJ 08827
roscoe@eclipse.net

HISTORY

West Nile virus (WNV; genus *Flavivirus*) is an arthropod borne virus (arbovirus). It is in a family (*Flaviviridae*) of RNA viruses, which possess a single-stranded positive-sense RNA genome. WNV is an emerging pathogen of public health and veterinary importance. It is known to affect birds, horses, and humans—and occasionally other mammals—and, in one case, alligators in Florida that had been fed WNV-infected horsemeat. The virus was discovered in Africa in 1937, and was first detected in North America in 1999 during an outbreak in New York (O'Donnell and Travis, 2007). The *genotype* of the WNV detected in North America is most similar to the virus found in an outbreak in Israel in 1998, and distinct from other strains of WNV found around the world, which do not kill birds. Since the summer of 1999, West Nile Virus infections have been confirmed throughout all of the United States. In North America, WNV has been associated with death in >198 species of birds, including ≥42 species of raptors (Komar, 2003). In 2002 WNV rapidly expanded its distribution across many previously unaffected states, sickening and killing many thousands of birds, including a much higher proportion of raptors than in earlier years. The cause of this huge expansion is not yet known, though it is hypothesized that a variant strain, environmental conditions favoring vectors, critical mass of susceptible species or factors of surveillance may have played a role.

CLINICAL SIGNS

Clinical signs of WNV in raptors vary and not all birds show all symptoms. Great Horned Owls for example can present with bobble head, while Red-tailed Hawks do not, most likely based on location of the infection and degree of brain swelling.

Clinical signs have been divided into three phases. Phase 1 consists of depression, anorexia, weight loss (in proportion to duration of starvation), sleeping, pinched off blood feathers, and elevated white blood cell count. In addition to the above, phase 2 presents with head tremors, green urates (indicating liver necrosis), mental dullness/central blindness and general lack of awareness of surroundings, ataxia (clumsiness or poor equilibrium), weakness in legs, exaggerated aggression, very high fever, polio-like flaccid paralysis, excessive sleeping, and detached retinas. In phase 3, more severe tremors, seizures, and death occur (Saito et al. 2007).

Some birds can get the disease and show no outward signs—blood tests reveal exposure (through the presence of antibodies) or current infection (virus in the blood). Experimentally infected raptors develop mosquito-infectious levels of virus in the blood (>10^5 WNV plaque forming units/ml serum) within 5 days of exposure and are likely to be infective for only a few days. These raptors also shed virus from the mouth and the cloaca (Nemeth et al. 2006). Infected birds that do not yet display obvious clinical signs may still be more prone to accidents, such as flying into windows, cars or fences.

PATHOLOGY

The most common histologic lesions associated with WNV infection in raptors are myocardial inflammation, necrosis, and fibrosis; skeletal muscle degeneration, inflammation, fibrosis, and lymphoplasmacytic encephalitis. Other lesions included hepatitis, lymphoid depletion in spleen and bursa, splenic and hepatic hemosiderosis, pancreatitis, and ganglioneuritis. Gross lesions included calvarial and leptomeningeal hemorrhage, myocardial pallor, and splenomegaly. Although many species tested were positive for WNV infection, severity of lesions varied among species (Ellis et al. 2007; Saito et al. 2007). Owls with WNV infection exhibit anemia and leukocytosis with heterophilia, eosinophilia, and monocytosis, which is characteristic of chronic inflammation (Fitzgerald et al. 2003). WNV infected Red-tailed hawks may be anemic with heterophilic leukocytosis and regenerative left shift (Joyner et al. 2006).

ASSAYS TO DETECT WNV IN BIRDS

The diagnostic assays used to detect WNV infections of raptors and other birds focus on either the detection of the virus or the antibodies generated in response to the virus. The identification of WNV virus antigen in birds includes the reverse –transcriptase polymerase chain reaction (RT-PCR) and immunochromatographic test strip technique with labeled antibodies to WNV. Among the antibody assays are the plaque reduction neutralization test (PRNT), the immunoflourescence assay for IgG and IgM, the blocking enzyme-linked immunosorbent assay (ELISA), microarray-based active immunoassay techniques and an immunochromatographic test for IgM.

Since the discovery of WNV in the United States, an integral part of monitoring has been testing dead bird tissue by using real-time and standard RT-PCR (Shi P-Y et al. 2001, Kauffman et al. 2003, Lanciotti, 2003). The detection limit for WNV by both methods is as low as 0.08 PFU (1.9 $\log_{10}$ PFU/mL), which indicates that RT-PCR is more sensitive than cell culture and more accurately indicates infection, since RNA is more stable than infectious virus in tissues (Kauffman et al. 2003).

Using oral swab samples to detect West Nile virus in dead birds, Stone et al. (2005) compared the Rapid Analyte Measurement Platform (Response Biomedical Corp, Burnaby, British Columbia, Canada, RAMP) assay with VecTest and real-time reverse-transcriptase–polymerase chain reaction. The sensitivities of RAMP and VecTest (Medical Analysis Systems Camarillo, CA, USA) for testing corvid species were 91.0% and 82.1%, respectively. Both tests incorporate immunochromatographic test strips by using labeled antibodies to detect antigen in samples. VecTest uses antibodies bound to gold sol particle labels, while the RAMP test uses antibodies bound to fluorescently labeled latex particles. Development of a visible reddish-purple line in both the test and control zones on the VecTest strip indicates a positive result. The RAMP test strip, enclosed within a cartridge, is inserted into a reader that calculates the ratio between the fluorescence emitted at the test and control zones and displays the results as RAMP units. Values above a background threshold are recorded as positive.

Gancz et al. (2004) evaluated a rapid antigen-capture assay (VecTest) for detection of West Nile virus in oropharyngeal and cloacal swabs, collected at necropsy from owls (N = 93) and raptors (N = 27). Sensitivity was 93.5%–95.2% for northern owl species but ≤42.9% for all other species. Specificity was 100% for owls and 85.7% for raptors

The PRNT is often referred to as the gold standard for WNV antibody detection. But, due to its complexity and long turnaround time, it is increasingly reserved as a confirmatory test or for establishing the presence of WNV infection in a geographic area.

The immunofluorescence assay measures both IgG and IgM antibodies to WNV (Beaty et al. 1995). Although historically considered insensitive, recent studies using commercially available slides have shown acceptable performance; the immunofluorescence assay is thus a cost-effective way to measure WNV antibodies in laboratories that routinely test small numbers of samples.

The enzyme-linked immunosorbent assay (ELISA) format is the most popular method currently used to detect WNV IgG and IgM. Both indirect and monoclonal antibody-mediated antigen capture formats of IgG ELISAs have been described, whereas nearly all IgM ELISAs utilize the IgM capture format. Before 2000, WNV antibody ELISAs employed native WNV antigens; since then, there has been a dramatic shift toward using recombinant WNV antigens, particularly subviral particles containing the envelope protein. Like in the other assays mentioned, however, antibodies induced by other flavivirus infections may crossreact with both native and recombinant WNV antigens, necessitating concurrent measurement of antibodies to flaviviruses endemic in a given geographic area. The new microsphere immunoassay shows great promise as a sensitive, specific, and cost-effective method for simultaneously measuring antibodies to multiple flaviviruses. This method has also been used to characterize antibodies to nonstructural WNV proteins; these antibodies appear to be highly specific for WNV, and their measurement may soon be the test of choice for diagnosing WNV infection.

To reduce the assay time for detecting virus-specific antibodies in serum, Groves et al. (2008) developed microarray-based active immunoassay techniques for detecting West Nile virus (WNV)-specific IgM molecules in chicken blood. The assay uses electrophoretic concentration of IgM molecules onto WNV antigens arrayed on a dialysis membrane followed by detection of bound IgM molecules with functionalized magnetic beads as active labels. This assay takes only 15 minutes and has the same sensitivity as a commercially available human WNV IgM antibody-capture enzyme-linked immunosorbent assay (commonly called a MAC-ELISA) modified for use with chicken sera.

Spectral's RapidWN™ West Nile Virus IgM Test is the first immunochromatographic test for West Nile virus IgM which can be used by public health laboratories, clinical diagnostic laboratories, research institutes and universities. It is a quick and sensitive pre-screening test used for detecting West Nile virus specific IgM in patients' serum and plasma, with results within 15 minutes. It has high sensitivity and specificity >95% correlation with acute infection (PRNT), 94% correlation with FOCUS WNV IgM ELISA. No instrument or calibration is required.

TREATMENT AND VACCINE

There is no prescribed treatment for the viral infection in raptors. Supportive care can be provided, and it is possible for birds to recover. In general, the likelihood of recovery depends on in what phase the bird is at the time of intervention. Phase 1 birds, characterized by anorexia respond reasonably well to supportive care. Once they reach Phase 2, characterized by mild neurologic signs, some birds respond to supportive care, but others do not and proceed to Phase 3. Complete recovery is uncertain. Birds suffering from the severe tremors and seizures characteristic of Phase 3 are close to death. Intervention is probably not going to alter the course.

An avian WNV vaccine has yet to be developed. There is a WNV vaccine for horses that when administered to 10 red-tailed hawks did not induce seroconversion (Nusbaum et al. 2003; Dauphin and Zientara 2007). Jarvi (2007) has led a collaborative project to test a WNV vaccine, developed for humans, by Hawaii Biotech Inc. on avian populations. The vaccine uses copies of a small fragment of protein found on the exterior shell of WNV to trick the immune system into responding and developing immunological protection. Jarvi (2007) tested the human WNV vaccine on dozens of 21-day-old domestic geese. Roughly half of the goslings were then injected at 90 days of age with live WNV at a biologically secure research facility in Madison, Wisconsin. The results showed that the vaccinated birds had higher antibody responses and lower virus counts than the non-vaccinated groups. Most importantly, none of the geese showed any adverse effects due to exposure to the vaccine. The vaccine appears to be safe and effective in domestic geese.

Turell et al. (2003) evaluated a DNA vaccine for West Nile Virus to determine whether its use could protect fish crows (*Corvus ossifragus*) from fatal WNV infection. Although oral administration of a single DNA vaccine dose failed to elicit an immune response or protect crows from WNV infection, IM administration of a single dose prevented death and was associated with reduced viremia.

VECTORS OF WNV AND THEIR CONTROL

A total of 11,898 mosquito pools (a pool is a sample of mosquitoes, usually no more than 50 of the same species and sex, collected within a defined sampling area and period) from 459 counties in 38 states and the District of Columbia tested positive for WNV. Among the WNV-positive pools, 8,665 (72.8%) were made up of *Culex* mosquitoes thought to be the principal vectors of WNV transmission (i.e., *Cx. pipiens*, *Cx. quinquefasciatus*, *Cx. restuans*, *Cx. salinarius*, and *Cx. tarsalis*) (MMWR, 2007). *Cx. pipiens*, an ornithophilic species, breeds in stagnant and polluted pools (i.e. rain gutters, untended drains, discarded tires). *Culex* mosquitoes remain the primary vector target for prevention of WNV disease in the United States.

Unidentified or other species of *Culex* mosquitoes made up 3,032 (25.5%) pools, and non-*Culex* species (i.e., *Aedes* spp., *Anopheles* spp., *Coquillettidia* spp., *Culiseta* spp., *Ochlerotatus* spp., and *Psorophora* spp.) made up 135 (1.1%) pools. Data from 2006 included the first report of WNV infection in *Culex apicalis*, which was collected in Arizona (MMWR, 2007). *Aedes vexans* is the fresh floodwater mosquito and is the primary biting pest for humans in New Jersey. WNV was cultured from a pool of *Ae. vexans*, which had been collected on September 9, 1999 at the start of the WNV outbreak in New Jersey. It is important, when control strategies are being formulated, to know that a "bridge vector" from birds to people is involved.

Mosquito control begins with an integrated program of surveillance through mosquito trapping, species identification, virus culturing and serologic monitoring of sentinel chicken flocks, trapped wild birds or spontaneous mortalities of sentinal species (crows or raptors). Once problem areas are identified control measures are focused on larvae, which may be controlled by a biological method of stocking mosquitofish (*Gambusia affinis*). Larvae and adult mosquitoes may also be controlled through physical methods involving drainage of stagnant water (i.e. tires, gutters, drains) or restoration of tidal flow in coastal marshes through open marsh water management. This latter method involves using a rotary ditcher to cut ditches in the tidal meadow to interconnect stagnant pools with tidal rivers. In the process the spoils are sprayed thinly to avoid mounds adjacent to the ditch. Mounded spoils cause growth of different plant species, which would disturb the uniformity of the meadow and disrupt the ecosystem. Some areas lend themselves to chemical control agents such as larvacides or adulticides. These may be applied from low volume truck mounted sprayers or in large open areas by aircraft. Adulticides consist primarily of malathion a low toxicity acetylcholinesterase inhibitor. They are viewed as a last resort to deal with residual mosquito populations not controlled by the other methods.

From July to September 2002, an outbreak of West Nile virus (WNV) caused a high number of deaths in captive owls at the Owl Foundation, Vineland, Ontario, Canada. Peak death rates occurred in mid-August. The outbreak occurred in the midst of a louse fly (*Icosta americana*, family *Hippoboscidae*) infestation. Of the flies tested, 16 (88.9 %) of 18 contained WNV RNA (Gancz et al. 2004). In New Jersey at the Mercer County Wildlife Rehabilitation Center between July 26, 2003 and November 6, 2003 12% of the pools of *Icosta sp.* flies collected from 25 red-tailed hawks exhibiting CNS signs, emaciation, unconsciousness, and lethargy were positive for WNV RNA. One pool (2%) of 46 collected from Great Horned Owls with similar signs during the same period at the Center were positive for WNV RNA (Diane Nickerson, unpublished data). It is not known if these louse flies actually vector the WNV.

EPIZOOTIOLOGY

Since the introduction of WNV into the New York Metropolitan area in 1999 the wildlife pathology units of New York (NY) and New Jersey (NJ) have been monitoring WNV mortalities in wild raptors. Surveillance findings for NY cover a period from 1999 to 2003 (Chu et.al., 2003), while those from NJ cover a period from 1999 to 2005. In New York 12% of dead hawks (N=359) tested positive. In New Jersey that figure was 5% (N=204), but that masked the disproportionate 11% of the Red-tailed Hawks (N=74), which were positive. Although the sample size for Merlins was small in both NY (N=15) and NJ

(N=13) the prevalence was relatively high at 33% and 31%, respectively. Similarly, 33% of American Kestrels from NY (N=33) and NJ (N=6) were infected. Great Horned Owls from NY (N=63) and NJ (N=20) tested positive for WNV with a frequency of 14% and 20%, respectively. None of the combined 22 Peregrine Falcons, 29 Bald Eagles, 21 Ospreys, 24 Barred Owls and 42 Eastern Screech Owls from NY and NJ tested positive for WNV.

Since 1999, WNV infection has been identified in approximately 300 avian species, including 11 species in which it was identified for the first time during 2006 (MMWR 2007). In 2006, a total of 4,106 dead WNV-infected birds were reported from 701 counties in 43 states, with peak numbers occurring during mid-August. Corvids accounted for 3,292 (80%) of the birds; the majority of states targeted corvids for surveillance (MMWR 2007). In contrast Red-tailed Hawks, which are representative of the temporal distribution of raptor mortalities from WNV in New Jersey (NJDFW, unpublished data), peaked in September (Figure 1). The earliest occurrence of WNV among raptors targeted for surveillance in New Jersey was in the third week of August (Coopers Hawk) and the last case (Red-tailed Hawk) in the third week of October.

Raptors infected with WNV that are admitted to rehabilitation facilities, either because of WNV-associated illness or injury or for other unrelated complications, may serve as an alternate source for early detection of WNV infection (Nemeth et al. 2007). Experimental infections of five species of raptors demonstrate that they become infected from mosquito bites or ingestion of virus by feeding on infected prey (Nemeth et al. 2006). Thus, raptors may be infected at a greater rate than nonraptors. Dead raptors and other birds (particularly corvids) have been used for early detection of WNV activity. However, once WNV activity is established in a location, birds that are highly susceptible to fatal infection are removed from the environment, and as a result, avian death rates should diminish

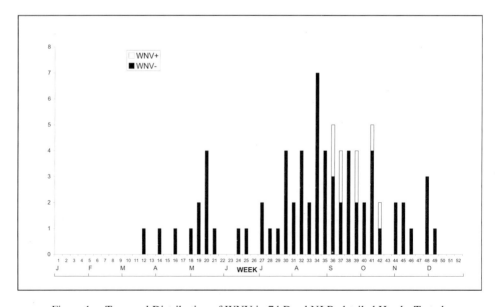

Figure 1:   Temporal Distribution of WNV in 74 Dead NJ Red-tailed Hawks Tested.

(Eidson 2001). In addition, many hawk and owl species are known to survive WNV infection (Komar et al., 2003; Stout et al., 2005; Nemeth et al., 2006).

REPORTING WNV

WNV data are reported to CDC through ArboNET, an Internet-based arbovirus surveillance system managed by state health departments and CDC. State and local health departments, wildlife agencies, veterinarians and mosquito control commissions collaborate to 1) collect reports from health-care providers and clinical laboratories regarding cases of WNV disease in humans; 2) collect and test dead birds, often focusing on corvids (e.g., crows, jays, and magpies), which have high mortality attributed to WNV infection; 3) collect reports of WNV infection in nonhuman mammals; and 4) collect mosquitoes to test for evidence of WNV infection.

Scientists from the US Geological Survey, the Centers for Disease Control and Prevention (CDC) and state wildlife agencies have worked together to learn more about the ecology of WNV. These collaborations have increased our understanding of the dynamics and impacts of WNV in wild birds, but much remains to be discovered.

REFERENCES

Beaty, B. J., C. H. Calisher, R. E. Shope. Arboviruses. In: Lennette, E. H., D. A. Lennette and E. T. Lennette, editors. Diagnostic procedures for viral, rickettsial, and chlamydial infections, 7th ed. Washington: American Public Health Association; 1995. p. 189–212.

Chu, M., W. Stone, K. J. McGowen, A. A. Dhondt, W. M. Hochachka and J. E. Therrien. 2003. West Nile File. Winter 2003 Birdscope p. 10–11.

Dauphin, G. and S. Zientara. 2007. West Nile virus: Recent trends in diagnosis and vaccine development. Vaccine 25: 5563–5576.

Eidson, M., N. Komar, F. Sorhage, R. Nelson, T. Talbot, F. Mostashari, R. McLean and West Nile Virus Avian Mortality Surveillance Group. 2001. Crow deaths as a sentinel surveillance system for West Nile virus in the north-eastern United States, 1999. Emerging Infectious Diseases 7: 615–620.

Ellis A. E., D. G. Mead, A. B. Allison, D. E. Stallknecht and E. W. Howerth. 2007. Pathology and epidemiology of natural West Nile viral infection of raptors in Georgia. Journal of Wildlife Diseases 43: 214–223.

Fitzgerald S. D. , J. S. Patterson, M. Kiupel, H. A. Simmons, S. D. Grimes, C. F. Sarver, R. M. Fulton, B. A. Steficek, T. M. Cooley J. P. Massey, and J. G. Sikarskie. 2003. Clinical and Pathologic Features of West Nile Virus Infection in Native North American Owls (Family Strigidae). Avian Diseases 602–610

Gancz,A. Y., D. G. Campbell, I. K. Barker, R. Lindsay, and B. Hunter. 2004. Detecting West Nile Virus in Owls and Raptors by an Antigen-capture Assay. Emerging Infectious Diseases 10: 2004–2006.

Gancz, A. Y., I. K. Barker, R. Lindsay, A. Dibernardo, K. McKeever, and B. Hunter. 2004. West Nile Virus Outbreak in North American Owls, Ontario, 2002. Emerging Infectious Disease 10:

Groves, S. S. M. J. Turell, C. L. Bailey, and V. N. Morozov. 2008. Rapid active assay for the detection of antibodies to West Nile Virus in chickens. American Journal of Tropical Medicine 78: 63–69.

Jarvi, S. 2007. Saving Hawaii's endangered birds. Kaunana Magazine. Winter 2007 Volume 1.

Joyner, P. H., S. Kelly, A. A. Shreve, S. E. Snead, J. M. Sleeman and Denise A. Pettit. 2006. West Nile virus in raptors from Virginia during 2003: Clinical, diagnostic, and epidemiologic findings. Journal of Wildlife Diseases 42: 335–344.

Kauffman, E. B., Jones, S. A., Dupuis, A. P., Ngo, K. A., Bernard, K. A., Kramer, L. D. 2003. Virus detection protocols for West Nile virus in vertebrate and mosquito specimens. Journal of Clinical Microbiology 41: 3661–3667.

Komar, S., S. Langerin, S. Hinten, N. Nemeth, E. Edwards, D. Hettler, E. Davis, R. Bowen and M. Bunning. 2003. Experimental infection of North American birds with the New York 1999 strain of West Nile virus. Emerging Infectious Diseases 9: 311–312.

Lanciotti, R. S. 2003. Molecular amplification assays for the detection of flaviviruses. Advances Virus Research 61: 67–99.

MMWR 2007 56: 556–559

Nemeth, N., D. Gould, R Bowen and N. Komar 2006. Natural and Experimental West Nile Virus Infection in Five Raptor Species. J. Wildlife Diseases 43(1): 1–13.

Nemeth, N., G. Kratz, E. Edwards, J. Scherpelz, R. Bowen,and N. Komar 2007. Surveillance for West Nile Virus in Clinic-admitted Raptors, Colorado. Emerging Infectious Disease 13:

Nusbaum, K. E.,J. C. Wright, W. B. Johnston, A. B. Allison, C. D. Hilton, L. A. Staggs, D. E. Stallknecht, and J. L. Shelnutt. 2003. Absence of Humoral Response in Flamingos and Red-Tailed Hawks to Experimental Vaccination with a Killed West Nile Virus Vaccine. Avian Diseases 47: 750–752.

O'Donnell, C. R. and D. A. Travis. 2007. West Nile Virus. International Zoo Yearbook 41: 75–84.

Saito, E. K., L. Sileo, D. E. Green, C. U. Meteyer, G. S. McLaughlin, K. A. Converse and D. E. Docherty. 2007. Raptor mortality due to West Nile Virus in the United States, 2002. Journal of Wildlife Diseases 43: 206–213.

Shi, P-Y, E. B. Kauffman, P. Ren, A. Felton, J. H. Tai, A. P. Dupuis II. 2001. High-throughput detection of West Nile virus RNA. Journal of Clinical Microbiology 39: 1264–1271.

Stone, W. B., J. E. Therrien, R. Benson, L. Kramer, E. B. Kauffman, M. Eidson, and S. Campbell. 2005. Assays to Detect West Nile Virus in Dead Birds. Emerging Infectious Diseases 11: 1770–1773.

Stout, W. E., A. G. Cassini, J. K. Meece, J. M. Papp, R. N. Rosenfield, and K. D. Reed . 2005. Serologic Evidence of West Nile Virus Infection in Three Wild Raptor Populations. Avian Diseases 49: 371–375.

Turell, M. J., M. Bunning, G. V. Ludwig, B. Ortman, J. Chang. 2003. DNA Vaccine for West Nile Virus Infection in Fish Crows (*Corvus ossifragus*). Army Medical Research Institute of Infectious Diseases Fort Detrick MD Virology Division. Defense Technical Information Service Accession Number ADA428582.

Avian Ecology and Conservation: A Pennsylvania Focus with National Implications. Edited by S. K. Majumdar, T. L. Master, M. C. Brittingham, R. M. Ross, R. S. Mulvihill and J. E. Huffman. © 2010. The Pennsylvania Academy of Science.

Chapter 25

Avian Influenza: Disease Transmission, Spread, and Economic Impacts

Aviva J. Goel, Michael T. Favara, and Shyamal K. Majumdar
Lafayette College
Easton, Pennsylvania 18042-1783
majumdas@lafayette.edu

INTRODUCTION

The influenza virus has been prevalent for over two thousand years. The virus has reached pandemic proportions in numerous instances, most notably the Spanish flu pandemic of 1918, in which the H1N1 strain of the influenza A virus was responsible for the deaths of 20 to 50 million people worldwide (U.S. Department of Health and Human Services 2005a). Since 1918, there have been various outbreaks of different strains of the influenza A virus, none of them reaching the same pandemic proportions as the 1918 outbreak.

Recently, there has been speculation that there is the possibility of a new pandemic in the near future—a pandemic that is caused by the H5N1 strain of the influenza A virus. Originating from Southeast Asia, this strain of the virus is transmitted through birds, and has come to be commonly known as "avian influenza" (Kolata 1999). While H5N1 has been classified as an epizootic (an epidemic in non-humans) and a panzootic (a disease affecting animals of many species, especially over a wide area) infection, there have been instances where the virus has jumped species and caused several human casualties (U.S. Department of Health and Human Services 2006).

Infections by the avian influenza A virus are separated into two different categories: highly pathogenic avian influenza (HPAI) and low pathogenic avian influenza (LPAI). Currently, there are several strains of both HPAI and LPAI that are circulating around the planet. According to the Centers for Disease Control, avian influenza viruses of the subtypes A5 and A7, including H5N1, H7N7, and H7N3 viruses have been associated with HPAI, and human infections with these viruses have ranged from mild (H7N3 and H7N7 strains) to severe and fatal disease (H7N7 and H5N1 strains). On the other hand, human illness due to infection with LPAI viruses has been observed having symptoms ranging in severity from very mild, such as conjunctivitis, to more serious influenza-like illnesses (U.S. Department of Health and Human Services 2005b).

According to the World Health Organization (WHO), there has been an increase in the number of cases of avian influenza as well as in the number of deaths reported in humans. This increase in incidence seemed to "correspond to winter and spring in the northern hemisphere. If this pattern continues, an upsurge in cases could be anticipated" (World Health Organization 2008). Already, there has been a huge impact of H5N1 on human society, specifically the financial, political, social and personal responses to both actual and predicted deaths in birds, humans, and other animals. Billions of U.S. dollars are being raised and spent for research on H5N1 and preparation for a potential avian influenza pandemic. Over ten billion dollars have been lost and over two hundred million birds have been killed to try to contain H5N1 (International Institute for Sustainable Development (IISD) 2006).

With the dire economic and social impact of this virus, there have been several measures discussed and implemented to contain it. The United States has collaborated with eighty-eight foreign governments as well as with eight prominent international health organizations, including the WHO, the Food and Agriculture Organization of the United Nations (FAO), and the World Organization for Animal Health, in order to increase the efficiency of monitoring, investigation, prevention, containment, and treatment of the disease (United States Agency for International Development 2006). Ongoing detailed and highly coordinated onsite surveillance and analysis of human and animal H5N1 avian flu outbreaks are being conducted and reported by the USGS National Wildlife Health Center, the Centers for Disease Control and Prevention, the World Health Organization, the European Commission, and others (United States Department of Health and Human Services 2002).

TRANSMISSION AND OUTBREAKS OF THE H5N1 VIRUS

Since 1996 alone, there have been various instances wherein avian influenza A viruses have jumped from birds to humans. One of the most notable examples of this occurred in August 1997, in which a breakout of H5N1, a strain of the HPAI, occurred in Hong Kong. After an initial scare in August when a three-year-old child died of respiratory complications related to infection by H5N1, there were eighteen reported cases and six fatalities in November 1997 (U.S. Department of Health and Human Services 2007). Prior to this, there had been no known transmissions of avian influenza A virus between birds and humans.

Scientists discovered that the mode of transmission of the virus had occurred in the chicken markets that were located throughout Hong Kong. Testing of the birds in specific markets showed that one out of every five chickens appeared to be infected with the H5N1 virus (Kolata 1999). Additionally, scientists learned that eighty percent of the birds were coming from the Guangdong Province in southern China—the exact location where the 1968 Hong Kong flu pandemic began. The most significant risk factor for human H5N1 illness was visiting a live poultry market in the week before the onset of illness (U.S. Department of Health and Human Services 2007). In order to prevent the continued transmission between infected birds and humans, authorities ordered the slaughtering of all poultry in Hong Kong—approximately 1.5 million birds. After this, the poultry markets were shut down for a month until 200,000 chickens were tested, with none of them possessing the H5N1 virus (U.S. Department of Health and Human Services 2007). Since the 1997 outbreak in Hong Kong, there have been various other instances of worldwide H5N1 infection, including an H5N1 outbreak in mainland China in February 2004 that resulted in the culling of 9 million birds as well as the onset of a government-subsidized vaccination program (World Health Organization 2007). In addition, several other southeast Asian nations have recently reported outbreaks of H5N1 infection, including Cambodia, Laos, Pakistan, South Korea, Thailand, and Vietnam (Tiensin 2006; Morris 2005; Wijeratne and Majumdar 2005).

Similarly, on February 1, 2008, it was reported that 26 individuals in India were placed under quarantine after culling poultry in the state of West Bengal, India (Majumdar 2008). Since the beginning of this outbreak, avian influenza has spread to 13 out of the 19 districts in West Bengal. Preliminary tests for bird flu in humans have produced negative results, but more tests are being conducted on the sick individuals. The effects on the egg and poultry industry were devastating, with egg exports dropping by about 50 percent in just two weeks, accounting for $20 million in losses. As a response, over 2.6 million birds have been culled in order to bring the bird flu situation under control. However, in the past four outbreaks in India since 2006, avian influenza has not been shown to spread from birds to humans (Majumdar 2008).

SPREAD OF H5N1 IN MIGRATORY WATERFOWL

The H5N1 strain is highly pathogenic, and according to Olsen et al. (2006), the ecological impacts and epidemiology of the pathogen cannot be fully understood without taking the vector or host into consideration. Therefore, it is highly important to note that although many birds act as a reservoir for the highly pathogenic form of the virus, it is most prevalent in wild birds. Initially, the spread of H5N1 among domestic poultry was thought to have taken place as a result of the transportation of infected poultry (Webster et al. 1992). Though the poultry industry is largely affected, recent studies have suggested that migratory waterfowl can act as long-distance vectors for the spread of H5N1 (Keawcharoen et al. 2008; Gilbert et al. 2006). This is possibly due to the fact that the areas that were affected had no previous record of the presence of the H5N1 virus, and this corresponded to the fall migration period (Teifke et al. 2007; Nagy et al. 2007; Bragstad et al. 2007). Additionally, in a study conducted by Kilpatrick et al. (2006), it was suggested through quantitative analysis that the global spread of H5N1 could be linked to the migration of waterfowl. Out of the 21 introductions of the H5N1 virus into countries in Asia, nine were most likely due to poultry, and three were through migratory birds. In contrast, most introductions (20 out of 23) in Europe were as a result of migratory fowl. In another study, it was reported that the introductions of the virus into North America followed similar patterns as those in Europe (Olsen et al., 2006). However, it was also suggested that the spread of the virus followed a cyclic pattern, with increased spread and pathogenicity noted during migratory periods and trade periods. This highlights the synergy between trade and wild animal movements in the pandemic spread of the pathogen (Kilpatrick et al., 2006).

Research on the type of aquatic bird species that is responsible for spread of avian influenza has been documented. In their study, Olsen et al. (2006) reported that the virus is most common among migratory birds of aquatic environments such as the Anseriformes (i.e. ducks, geese, swans) as well as the Charadriiformes (i.e. gulls, terns and waders). Gilbert et al. (2006) reported that in May 2005, a major H5N1 outbreak occurred in Lake Qinghai, China, an important breeding place for migratory bird species in eastern Asia. Soon after this outbreak, various species of geese, ducks, and swans were reported to be infected with the H5N1 virus in Mongolia, which further spread across Eurasia to Turkey, Romania, and Ukraine (Gilbert et al. 2006). Similar studies highlight the mute and whooping swans as vectors of H5N1, with reported outbreaks occurred in Denmark, the Czech Republic, and Germany (Bragstad et al. 2007; Nagy et al. 2006; Teifke et al. 2007). However, there is also conflicting evidence that suggests that wild waterbirds may not be linked to the spread of this disease. In 2006, Olsen et al. identified that most wild birds diseased with this virus were highly infected, and therefore unable to migrate and spread the disease. Thus, further studies are needed to determine the implications of migratory waterfowl in the H5N1 spread.

SPREAD OF THE H5N1 VIRUS TO HUMANS

Although the avian influenza A virus rarely spreads from birds to humans, it spreads very frequently among birds. In poultry, domesticated birds may become affected through direct contact with infected waterfowl or other diseased poultry, as well as through contact with surfaces including dirt or cages, and materials such as water or feed that have been contaminated with the virus (U.S. Department of Health and Human Services 2005c). In addition to these, people, vehicles and other inanimate objects can be carriers for the spread of the virus from one farm to another.

Avian influenza A viruses may be transmitted from animals to humans in two main ways: either through an intermediate host (such as a pig), or directly from birds or from avian virus-contaminated environments to people (U.S. Department of Health and Human Services 2005d). Because influenza A viruses have eight separate gene segments, this genome enables the viruses to mix and create new influenza A viruses, if viruses from two separate species infect the same person or animal. According to the Centers for Disease Control, if a pig were infected with a human influenza A virus and an avian influenza A virus at the same time, the new replicating viruses could undergo reassortment and produce a new virus combining features of both the human and avian forms, a process known as antigenic shift (U.S. Department of Health and Human Services 2005d). This new virus could potentially infect humans and spread from person to person, but have different features from previous human influenza A infections. The origin of H1N1 swine flu virus responsible for the recent swine flu pandemic might have originated through similar kind of genetic recombination (Cohen 2009). However, there are many instances that avian influenza A viruses could simply pass from birds to humans, as this was the mode of transmission for the 1997 outbreak of H5N1 in Hong Kong (U.S. Department of Health and Human Services 2005d).

ECONOMIC AND SOCIAL IMPACTS OF AVIAN INFLUENZA

H5N1 has incurred an immense impact on human society, specifically the financial, political, social, and personal responses to both actual and predicted deaths in birds, humans, and other animals (International Institute for Sustainable Development (IISD) 2006). People have reacted by buying less chicken causing poultry sales and prices to fall. Many individuals have stockpiled supplies for a possible flu pandemic. According to a recent report published in the *New York Times*, governments worldwide "have spent billions planning for a potential influenza pandemic: buying medicines, running disaster drills, [and] developing strategies for tighter border controls" (Rosenthal and Bradsher 2006). Investment strategies are changing in order to account for the effects of H5N1 (Cooper and Coxe 2005).

Most importantly, poultry farming practices have become altered due to H5N1. Farmers now kill all infected poultry, vaccinate poultry against bird flu, vaccinate poultry workers against human flu, limit their travel in areas where H5N1 is found, increase farm hygiene, limit contact between livestock and wild birds, reduce open-air wet markets, decrease purchases of live fowl, and have improved veterinary vaccine availability and cost.

The cost of poultry farming has increased, while the cost to consumers has gone down due to fears of H5N1, driving demand below supply, resulting in devastating losses for many poultry farmers. Poor poultry farmers cannot afford mandated measures keeping their bird livestock from contact with wild birds, thus risking losing their livelihood altogether. Multinational poultry farming has been incurring financial losses as H5N1 achieves status as endemic in wild birds worldwide (Poultry Sector Suffers 2007). Financial ruin for poor poultry farmers, being as severe as starvation, has caused some to commit suicide and many others to stop cooperating with efforts to deal with H5N1, further increasing human toll, spread of the disease, and chances for a pandemic mutation (Avian Flu Talk 2006).

If a pandemic occurs, a local response will be more important than a national or international response, as every community will have its own resources swamped dealing with its own problems. International groups, nations, local governments, corporations, schools, and groups of all kinds have made plans and run drills to prepare for a H5N1 pandemic. Online avian flu forums have received increasing attention. Self help groups have organized to provide news and information about resources, aid and relief efforts in preparation for avian flu (Avian Flu Talk 2006). With these overwhelming responses to an outbreak, countries have stressed the importance of caution, and not panic, specifically referring to the recent outbreak in Kolkata, India (Caution, not panic 2008). Consumption of poultry products has fallen to negligible levels in West Bengal, but chicken sales are recovering in the rest of India after an initial wobble when the latest outbreak was announced (Majumdar 2008). In response to the increased level of unnecessary panic caused amongst civilians as a result of the recent H5N1 outbreak in India, the government has issued several precautionary measures for handling poultry and fighting the disease. Instead of dismissing all poultry as being infectious, birds should be kept in enclosed or screened-off areas. In addition, only those handling birds should be allowed near cages; the cages should be washed and disinfected regularly. Birds bought from any fair or market should be kept in separate enclosures (Fighting Flu 2008). Finally, all poultry cooked at temperatures at or above 70°C cannot carry avian influenza (Chicken, well done 2008).

RESPONSE PLANS

In order to solidify the nation's movement towards preparation for a possible avian influenza pandemic, governmental response to the growing threat of the outbreak was required. Therefore, on October 5, 2005, U.S. Senators Harry Reid, Evan Bayh, Dick Durbin, Ted Kennedy, Barack Obama, and Tom Harkin introduced a bill entitled "The Pandemic Preparedness and Response Act" (Democrats Work to Protect Americans From Avian Flu 2005). This bill calls for:

- Preparing for a pandemic by finalizing, implementing and funding pandemic preparedness and response plans.

- Improving surveillance and international partnerships to monitor the spread of avian flu and detect the emergence of a flu strain with pandemic potential immediately.
- Protecting Americans through the development, production, and distribution of an effective vaccine.
- Planning ahead for a pandemic by stockpiling antivirals, vaccines and other essential medications and supplies.
- Strengthening the public health infrastructure.
- Increasing awareness and education about pandemic flu.
- Devoting adequate resources to pandemic preparedness.

Similarly, in September 2005, President George W. Bush announced the "International Partnership on Avian and Pandemic Influenza" in his remarks to the High-Level Plenary Meeting of the United Nations General Assembly. On September 15, 2005, Undersecretary of State for Democracy and Global Affairs, Dr. Paula Dobriansky was joined by the Director General of the WHO, Dr. Lee Jong-wook, Executive Director of UNICEF, Ann Veneman, and senior representatives from several participating countries to describe their goals of improving global readiness by elevating the issue on national agendas, coordinating efforts among donor and affected nations, mobilizing and leveraging resources, increasing transparency in disease reporting and surveillance, and building capacity to identify, contain and respond to a pandemic influenza (U.S. Department of Health and Human Services 2005e).

Currently, there is no completely effective treatment for H5N1 influenza. However, there are various drugs that were reported to inhibit the virus from spreading inside the body of infected individuals. Oseltamivir (marketed as Tamiflu by Roche AG), is the predominant player among these drugs. Tamiflu has become a focus for several governmental organizations trying to prepare for a pandemic (National Institutes of Health 2006). On April 20, 2006, Roche AG announced that a "stockpile of three million treatment courses of Tamiflu is waiting at the disposal of the World Health Organization to be used in case of a flu pandemic." Separately, Roche donated two million courses to the WHO for use in developing nations that may be affected by such a pandemic but lack the ability to purchase large quantities of the drug (Tamiflu 2006).

Animal and lab studies suggest that Relenza (Zanamivir), which is in the same class of drugs as Tamiflu, may also be effective against H5N1. In a study performed on mice in 2000, Zanamivir was shown to be "efficacious in treating avian influenza viruses H9N2, H6N1, and H5N1 transmissible to mammals" (Bernd 2006). While it is not known if Zanamivir will be useful or not on a possible pandemic strain of H5N1, it might be resourceful to stockpile Zanamivir as well as Oseltamivir in the event of an H5N1 influenza pandemic. Neither Oseltamivir nor Zanamivir can currently be manufactured in quantities that would be meaningful and efficient once human transmission starts. A recent experiment conducted at a London laboratory showed that an enzyme mixture, created by the Icelandic company Zymetech killed the H5N1 strain with a 99% success rate. The mixture kills the virus in less than 5 minutes without damaging healthy cells (Pagnamenta 2007).

There have been several talks about the development of a vaccine for the virus. However, in response to these increased demands, WHO expert Hassan al-Bushra has said:

> "Even now, we remain unsure about Tamiflu's real effectiveness. As for a vaccine, work cannot start on it until the emergence of a new virus, and we predict it would take six to

nine months to develop it. For the moment, we cannot by any means count on a potential vaccine to prevent the spread of a contagious influenza virus, whose various precedents in the past 90 years have been highly pathogenic" (Middle East 2006)

Although there are several vaccines for the H5N1 virus, the problem at hand is the continual mutation of the virus. This mutation renders the vaccines already produced ineffective. While vaccines can sometimes provide cross-protection against related flu strains, the best protection would be from a vaccine specifically produced for any future pandemic flu virus strain. Dr. Daniel Lucey, co-director of the Biohazardous Threats and Emerging Diseases graduate program at Georgetown University has made the argument that "there is no H5N1 pandemic so there can be no pandemic vaccine" (Schultz 2005). An important point to note, however, is that pre-pandemic vaccines are being created and tested in order to further both research and preparedness for a possible pandemic. These vaccines are also being developed in large volumes by countries for immediate use for a possible pandemic.

Sanofi Pasteur, a pharmaceutical company dedicated to manufacturing vaccines, has been at the forefront of vaccine development for the United States. The company has performed trials on adults testing the efficacy of a H5N1-derived vaccine, and has also been developing a cell-culture based influenza vaccine production in the United States. Aside from producing 30 million doses of the H5N1 vaccine in September 2005, Sanofi Pasteur has been involved in a wide variety of long-range pandemic planning projects in Europe with its parent company, Sanofi-Aventis Group (Matthews 2007). Recently, Korean scientists have been developing a needle-free vaccine that involves placing the medicine under the tongue, directly reaching the mucus membrane and promoting responses in both the mucus tissues throughout the body as well as the immune system itself; however, the vaccine is still being tested in mice (New Flu Vaccine 2008).

The avian influenza virus still poses a large threat upon birds, humans, and other animals. However, current research has been largely focused upon the eradication of this virus. The economic, social, and political impacts posed are vast. Improved influenza countermeasures require basic research on how viruses enter cells, replicate, mutate, evolve into new strains, and induce an immune response. Solutions to limitations in current prevention and preparatory methods are being researched, and are focused on the potential for a cure.

ACKNOWLEDGEMENTS

We wish to thank Ioana Marin for proofreading the manuscript.

LITERATURE CITED

Avian Flu Talk. (2006). Online Chat Forum: Bird Flu: Latest News: Pneumonia Vaccination for Flu Pandemic Severity Index. http://www.avianflutalk.com.

Bernd Sebastian Kamps and Christian Hoffmann. (2006). Zanamivir. Influenza Report. http://www.influenzareport.com/ir/drugs/zanami.htm.

Bragstad, K., Jorgensen, P. H., Handberg, K., Hammer, A. S., Kabell, S., Fomsgaard, A. (2007). First introduction of highly pathogenic H5N1 avian influenza A viruses in wild and domestic birds in Denmark, Northern Europe. *Journal of Virology*. 4:43.

Caution, not panic, is the guideword. (2008). *DNA India*, Mumbai, January 17, 2008, p. 11.

Chicken, well done: a caution by the National Egg Co-ordination Committee. (2008). *The Times of India*. Kolkata. January 25, 2008. p. 23.

Cohen, J. (2009). Swine flu outbreak—New details on viruses' promiscuous past. *Science*. 324: 1127.

Cooper, S., and D. Coxe. (2005). An Investor's Guide to Avian Flu. BMO Financial Group. http://www2.bmo.com/news/article/0,1257,contentCode-4922_divId-4_langId-1_navCode-112,00.html.

Democrats Work to Protect Americans From Avian Flu: America Can Do Better than No Action at All. (2005). Senate Democratic Communications Center. http://democrats.senate.gov/~dpc/press/05/2005b06424.html.

Fighting flu: caution is the key at state poultry farm. (2008). *The Times of India*, Kolkata, January 25, 2008, p. 5.

Gilbert, M., Xiao, X., Domenech, J., Lubroth, J., Martin, V., Slingenbergh, J. (2006). Anatidae migration in the western Palearctic and spread of highly pathogenic avian influenza H5N1 virus. *Emerging Infectious Diseases*. 12:1650–1656.

International Institute for Sustainable Development (IISD) (2006). Proceedings of Scientific Seminar on Avian Influenza, the Environment and Migratory Birds on 10–11 April, 2006.

Keawcharoen, J., Van Riel, D., Van Amerongen, G., Bestebroer, T., Beyer, W. E., Van Lavieren, R., Osterhaus, A., Fouchier, R., and Kuiken, T. Wild Ducks as Long-Distance Vectors of Highly Pathogenic Avian Influenza Virus (H5N1). (2008). *Emerging Infectious Diseases*. 14(4):600–607.

Kilpatrick, A. M., Chmura, A. A., Gibbons, D. W., Fleischer, R. C., Marra, P. P., Daszak, P. (2006). Predicting the global spread of H5N1 avian influenza. *Proceedings of the National Academy of Sciences*. 103:19368–19373.

Kolata, G. (1999). Flu: the Story of the Great Influenza Pandemic of 1918 and the Search for the Virus That Caused It. Simon & Schuster: New York, pp. 256.

Majumdar, Bappa. (2008). India isolates 26 people on bird flu fears. Reuters Alertnet foundation. http://www.alertnet.org/thenews/newsdesk/DEL46545.htm

Matthews, James T. (2007). Industry-related pandemic planning: working toward producing an adequate vaccine supply. *Journal of the Pennsylvania Academy of Science*, Vol. 80, Issue 2/3, p. 54–56.

Middle East: Interview with WHO experts Hassan al-Bushra and John Jabbour. (2006). Reuters Alertnet Foundation.

Morris, Shaun K. (2005). H5N1 Avian Influenza, Kampot Province, Cambodia. U.S. Department of Health and Human Services: Centers for Disease Control and Prevention. http://www.cdc.gov/ncidod/EID/vol12no01/05-0914.htm

Nagy, A., Machova, J., Hornickova, J., Tomci, M., Nagl, I., Horyna, B., et al. (2007). Highly pathogenic avian influenza virus subtype H5N1 in mute swans in the Czech Republic. *Veterinary Microbiology*. 120:9–16.

National Institutes of Health: Medline Plus (2006). Oseltamivir (Systemic). Retrieved on December 15, 2007.

New flu vaccine may no longer need needle. (2008). *The Times of India*, Kolkata, January 30, 2008, p. 19.

Olsen, B., Munster, V. J., Wallensten, A., Waldenstrom, J., Osterhaus, A. S., Fouchier, R. A. (2006). Global Patterns of influenza A virus in wild birds. *Proceedings of the National Academy of Sciences*. 103:19368–19373.

Pagnamenta, Robin. (2007). Cod enzyme kills avian flu. The Australian: Higher Education. http://www.theaustralian.news.com.au/story/0,20867,21070103-12332,00.html.

Poultry sector suffers despite absence of bird flu. (2007). Reuters. http://www.alertnet.org/thenews/newsdesk/IRIN/a13fd43bc74b6209dc90f6d849ffa45b.htm

Rosenthal, Elisabeth and Keith Bradsher. (2006). Is business ready for a flu pandemic? *The New York Times*.

Schultz, J. (2005). Bird flu vaccine won't precede pandemic. United Press International.

Tamiflu is Set Aside for WHO. (2006). *The Wall Street Journal*. April 20. page D6.

Teifke, J. P., Klopfleish, R., Globig, A., Starick, E., Hoffman, B., Wolf, P. U., et al. (2007). Pathology of natural infections by H5N1 highly pathogenic avian influenza virus in mute (*Cygnus olor*) and whooper (*Cygnus cygnus*) swans. Veterinary Pathology. 44:137–143.

Tiensin, T., Chaitaweesub, P., Songserm, T., Chaisingh, A., Hoonsuwan, W., Buranathai, C., Parakamawongsa, T., Premashthira, S., Amonsin, A., Gilbert, M., Nielen, M., Stegeman, A. (2006). Highly Pathogenic Avian Influenza H5N1, Thailand, 2004. U.S. Department of Health and Human Services: Centers for Disease Control and Prevention. http://www.cdc.gov/ncidod/EID/vol11no11/05-0608.htm.

U.S. Department of Health and Human Services: Centers for Disease Control and Prevention. (2005a). Reconstruction of the 1918 Flu Pandemic. http://www.cdc.gov/flu/about/qa/1918flupandemic.html.

U.S. Department of Health and Human Services: Centers for Disease Control and Prevention. (2005b). Influenza Viruses. http://www.cdc.gov/flu/avian/gen-info/flu-viruses.htm.

U.S. Department of Health and Human Services: Centers for Disease Control and Prevention. (2005c). Spread of Avian Influenza Viruses among Birds. http://www.cdc.gov/flu/avian/gen-info/spread.htm.

U.S. Department of Health and Human Services, Centers for Disease Control and Prevention. (2005d). Transmission of Influenza A Viruses Between Animals and People. http://www.cdc.gov/flu/avian/gen-info/transmission.htm.

U.S. Department of Human and Health Services: Centers for Disease Control and Prevention. (2005e). HHS Pandemic Influenza Plan. http://www.hhs.gov/pandemicflu/plan/appendixh.html .

U.S. Department of Health and Human Services, Centers for Disease Control and Prevention. (2006). Key Facts About Avian Influenza (Bird Flu) and Avian Influenza A (H5N1) Virus. http://www.cdc.gov/flu/avian/gen-info/facts.htm.

U.S. Department of Health and Human Services: Centers for Disease Control and Prevention (2007). Avian Influenza A Virus Infections of Humans. http://www.cdc.gov/flu/avian/gen-info/avian-flu-humans.htm .

United States Agency for International Development (2006). Avian Influenza Response: Key Actions to Date. Retrieved on January 04, 2008.

United States Department of Health and Human Services (2002). Pandemicflu.gov Monitoring outbreaks. Retrieved on January 12, 2008.

Webster, R. G., Bean, W. J., Gorman, O. T., Chambers, T. M., Kawaoka, Y. (1992). Evolution and ecology of influenza A viruses. Microbiology Review. 56:152–179.

Wijeratne, S. P., Majumdar, S. K. (2005). Re-Emergence of Prion and Certain Viral Diseases. In Wildlife diseases: landscape epidemiology, spatial distribution and utilization of remote sensing technology. Eds. S. K. Majumdar, J. E. Huffman, F. J. Brenner and A. I. Panah. Pennsylvania Academy of Science: Easton, Pennsylvania, pp. 7–19.

World Health Organization: H5N1 Avian Influenza: a Timeline of Major Events. (2007). http://www.who.int/csr/disease/avian_influenza/timeline_10_09_2007.pdf.

World Health Organization: Epidemic and Pandemic Alert and Response (EPR). (2008). Confirmed Human Cases of Avian Influenza A (H5N1). http://www.who.int/csr/disease/avian_influenza/country/en.

Avian Ecology and Conservation: A Pennsylvania Focus with National Implications. Edited by S. K. Majumdar, T. L. Master, M. C. Brittingham, R. M. Ross, R. S. Mulvihill and J. E. Huffman. © 2010. The Pennsylvania Academy of Science.

Chapter 26

Impacts of Environmental Contaminants on Bird Population Ecology

Nancy McCreary Waters

Department of Biology, Lafayette College, Easton, Pennsylvania 18042 USA,
watersn@lafayette.edu

INTRODUCTION

Organisms in nature typically all are governed by the same suite of environmental forces, no matter the species or its importance. Sources of natality and mortality, coupled with factors affecting immigration into and emigration out of defined populations, represent the sum total of dynamic change in abundance and distribution of population members over time. Such factors may be biotic or abiotic in origin; they may arise naturally or by virtue of human activity; they may elicit immediate change or do so indirectly. Yet no matter the source or proximity of these factors, they have potential to disrupt population patterns, and ultimately impact the larger ecosystem in which a given population functions.

The primary or ultimate factors contributing to wildlife depletion include human population growth coupled with rising use, as well as misuse, of natural resources as both capital and the services they provide (Miller and Spoolman 2008). From these basic underlying causes arise the array of secondary forces which we can see contributing to biodiversity decline—chief among them are habitat fragmentation, loss and degradation. While disturbance of moderate frequency and intensity may actually contribute to biodiversity by reducing interspecific competition and opening new niches for colonization (Huston 1979), the accelerated intensity of landscape disruption currently underway is thought to be a primary constituent of current biodiversity losses. Estimates are that extinctions currently range from 3–200 species lost, far exceeding background extinction rates of 1–5 species lost from a pool of 5 million per year (Miller and Spoolman 2008). The World Conservation Union (IUCN) maintains a database of global species in danger of extinction. This "Red List" is updated annually and analyzed in detail every 4 years (IUCN 2007).

Pollution and contamination of ecosystems by anthropogenic inputs pose an enormous challenge to all wildlife, but particularly to avian populations. Classically defined as rendering a resource unfit for use by addition of a substance, pollution of waterways, soils and the air arise by virtue of other secondary causes such as pest and predator control in conventional agricultural practice, as well as attempts to mitigate impacts of nonnative species. Such environmental stress acts on populations not only by direct changes in population size, but also by shifting age structure, loss of genetic diversity and adaptability, and increased sensitivity to pathogens. Furthermore, since among all larger animals, birds have the capacity to cross state, regional, national, even continental barriers, concerns about environmental contamination of avian fauna of necessity must consider the global landscape.

Nowhere is this better exemplified than the case in point of the Swainson's Hawk, a real frequent flyer, logging biannual trips of over 14,000 miles each way from Canadian/US summer breeding grounds to wintering areas in Buenos Aires and beyond (for review see Hooper et al. 2003). The population of these specialized feeding top-level predators crashed by nearly 5%—over 20,000 hawks—due to ingestion of the insecticide monocrotrophos, used to help control grasshopper pests by Argentinian landowners. These organochlorides kill by mimicking acetylcholine, binding with acetylcholinesterase, and disrupting neurotransmitters to generate lethal paralysis. Now an internationally protected species, the story of the Swainson's Hawk provides a chilling example of how state and regional avian conservation requires global perspective and coordination.

Rather than take primarily a local reductionist approach, this chapter sets the context by examining the global state of affairs in avian population trends. Given the wide array of vulnerable species, coupled with the myriad contaminants acting on them, this chapter could never do justice in providing a comprehensive review, nor even a representative one, of the toxins affecting bird populations. Instead, it presents a smorgasbord of sorts, with examples from specific studies of metal, organochloride, and pesticide toxicity which examine impacts on susceptible bird populations. With each, it highlights the implications not only for those species but also for the ecological systems in which they occur. Finally, it suggests some guidelines for assessing effective practices and policy changes, as well as increased coordination among ecologists and wildlife managers, to contend with dissemination of environmental contaminants that disrupt avian populations.

THE 'BIG' PICTURE—A GLOBAL OVERVIEW

One of the most authoritative assessments of global biodiversity status, the Red List system was established in 1963 and promulgated by the Species Survival Commission within the IUCN. Over the next 3 decades, the Commission evaluated conservation status, but not on a national or regional level, nor with attention to more objective metrics for determining vulnerability of populations. A four-year-long initiative among 800+ Commission members resulted in the 1994 adoption of the IUCN Red List Indices and criteria for determining categories of risk for wildlife. There are 8 specific categories in declining degree of peril—Extinct, Extinct in the Wild, Possibly Extinct, Critically Endangered, Endangered, Vulnerable, Near Threatened, Least Concern—as well as Data Deficient, Not Evaluated and Not Recognized. Furthermore, a special category of "Conservation Dependent" is subsumed within Near Threatened (Butchart et al. 2004). Generally usable categories are Vulnerable, Endangered and Critically Endangered; these differ, for example, by documented population size reductions over 3 generations of 50%, 70% or 90%, respectively.

Although every mammal species was not evaluated for placement on the Red List until 1996, the first definitive baseline assessment of 10,445 bird species occurred in 1988 wherein 115 bird species were categorized as extinct and an additional 1,664 species in some other perilous category. Over the intervening years, bird extinctions have risen 12% to include 129 species. More problematic though is the increased assignment of risk category to 1,990+ bird species, a rise of nearly 20% to place 1 in 8 known bird species at risk

(IUCN 2007). These data suggest that avian populations in particular exhibit continued deterioration in threat status, despite improvements for individual bird species and wider scale conservation efforts. Within the last decade, the IUCN Species Survival Commission has enhanced efforts at quantitative comprehensive global documentation by partnering with BirdLife International, NatureServe and the Center for Applied Biodiversity Science at Conservation International.

Butchart et al. (2004) have employed information from the Red List to examine rates of changes among bird species in particular, and offer use of a Red List Index (RLI) as a weighted means to track comprehensive changes in status of threatened birds. Assessing RLI values by biogeographic realm, ecosystem and habitat type does not alter the prevailing trend—biodiversity of bird species has deteriorated from an RLI of 100 to ~94 worldwide at similar rates and proportions in the Nearctic, Neotropical, Palearctic Afrotropical and Australasian/Oceanic realms, but more steeply (RLI=86) in the Indo/Malayan realm. Among marine, freshwater and terrestrial (segregating forest from shrubland/grasslands) ecosystems, declines among freshwater birds are the most severe from 100 to ~89. Among selected bird groups, albatrosses and petrels exhibit more recent declines, as do raptors, generally. The former are thought to be related to increased incidental mortality due to commercial longline fishing practices (Tuck et al. 2001), but the latter likely reflect enhanced bioamplification of toxins attributable to higher-order consumer status of raptors as predators. Where the RLI is particularly useful is in determining rates of relative extinction risk; the use of RLI in birds presents a template for application to other species of fauna and flora. But it cannot tease out the cause of changes, only document with confidence and robustness that they have occurred. Knowing why the status of a species changes is essential to understanding how to protect and ultimately prevent escalation in loss of avian populations.

SELECTED VARIETIES OF CONTAMINANTS—METALS

Among contaminants, metals enter the food web ubiquitously with routes of entry including ingestion, absorption and inhalation depending on the form of the metal. Once in the body, some metals may be excreted, but many are stored and accumulate in tissues of organisms that are subsequently consumed by higher-order predators. For some animals, a given metal may dissipate relatively quickly from the body—decades ago Clarkson (1972) demonstrated that poultry birds exhibited a 25 day half-life for retention of methyl mercury, but crabs retained the same compound an order of magnitude longer (a 400 day half-life) in their tissues. Heavy metals in particular elicit damaging effects on cells, and their proliferation in the environment is correlated to industrialization and urbanization (Fowler 1990). The United Nations Group of Experts on Scientific Aspects of Marine Pollution (GESAMP) suggests that mercury, lead and cadmium are among the most critical metal pollutants. Burger et al. (1992) examined these 3 metal concentrations in feathers of 5 species of seabirds, distributed among 4 distinct neotropical geographical locations. They hypothesized that birds consuming larger, older fish would exhibit higher metals contamination. Their study documented highly variable mercury concentrations of 360 to 2,460 ppb dry wt in sooty terns (*Sterna fuscata*), yet cadmium concentrations were as low as 30 to 253 ppb dry wt in the brown noddy (*Anous stolidus*). Clearly, species-specific differences in intake, accumulation and dissipation of metals require more investigation. Our laboratory (Caslake et al. 2006) has demonstrated that aquatic plants and invertebrates potentially can mitigate environmental methyl mercury contamination by associations with mercury-resistant bacteria ($Hg-R^+$). The highly variable range of metal concentrations in these birds provides an ideal system to investigate whether similar mechanisms might be useful, or indeed, employed by tolerant avian populations.

Closer to home, in the upper Mississippi River basin, concerns about mercury and selenium, as well as polychlorinated biphenyls and organochlorides, were examined in Great Blue Heron eggs (*Ardea herodias*) collected from 10 locations in the field, but exposed systematically in the laboratory to ecologically relevant concentrations of these toxicants (Custer et al. 1997). Egg volume and composition, as well as developing embryo organ and bone dimensions and brain asymmetry, were documented in response to toxicant exposures, but were lower than concentrations affecting reproduction in other freshwater birds such as mallards (*Anas platyrhynchos*; Heinz 1980). Yet, in particular, DDE concentrations were significantly inversely related to eggshell thickness. This kind of more subtle response has potential to impact normal population dynamics—perhaps reducing successful hatching and successive generational recruitment into the population—and thereby contribute to greater variation in bird abundance and susceptibility to unusual environmental stress.

On a more local scale, hydrocarbon and mercury concentrations in sediments were examined in correlation with egg and nestling development of two common passerines—the red-winged blackbird (*Agelaius phoeniceus*) and the tree swallow (*Tachycineta bicolor*) throughout the Laurentian Great Lakes, including Lake Erie (Bishop et al.1995). They found populations with as much as two orders of magnitude higher concentrations of contaminants in tissues than were recovered from sediments in the environment. The authors suggest that variable consumption of tainted macroinvertebrates contributed to observed patterns in contamination load. Yet, their data suggest that birds can accumulate these toxins and still tolerate these body burdens. The authors propose use of both common species as useful local indicators of persistent environmental contaminants. The advantages of using more common species in this way not only advances our understanding of how toxicants affect biota, but does so without sacrificing or exacerbating the population limitations for more rare species.

SELECTED VARIETIES OF CONTAMINANTS—ORGANOPHOSPHATES

Among chemical control employed in agricultural practices, organophosphorus pesticides (OP) are used to manage a wide array of pests. For example, the insecticide fenitrothion continues to be sprayed in northern spruce-fir forests since its introduction in the late 1960's as part of efforts to control spruce budworm (*Choristoneura fumiferana*). This lepidopteran larval pest defoliates conifers, yet spraying to attack the larval stage of the pest coincides with peak breeding seasons of many forest songbirds (Forsyth and Martin 1993). Used as well in the Midwest and Canada, OP applications to control grasshopper pests in cereal and cropland have cost as much as $12 million in the 1985/86 growing season (Johnson 1989). Similar to carbamates (Powell 1984), OP inhibits acetyl cholinesterase activity in the insect larva, impairing nervous system activity and ultimately causing death. Direct measurement of OP residues in tissues is methodologically difficult and often impractical, but assessment of brain or blood plasma cholinesterase (ChE) activity and inhibition is a useful and important tool for indicating exposure of birds to OP in the environment.

While some direct exposure is likely at application levels of 210 g insecticide per hectare, more troubling is the persistence and accumulation of OP in both target and non-target insects on which foraging birds rely (Martin et al. 1996, McInnes et al. 1996). Depressed ChE activity has been documented not only in directly exposed ring-necked pheasant chicks, but also was substantially in those unexposed chicks fed OP tainted food (Martin et al. 1996). White-throated sparrows exhibited degradation in a variety of behavioral and activity changes, ChE inhibition and ultimately death upon exposure through diet to 90 ppm fenitrothion; with 5 days post-exposure, mortality was 100% in 90 and 200 ppm diets, compared to 60% and 20% in 60 and 40 ppm diets, respectively (Forsyth and Martin 1993). These authors suggest that sparrows and other passerines in the wild easily encounter exposure levels in diet alone equivalent to 60–70 ppm. While larger birds may exhibit broader tolerance, such as common grackles (*Quiscalus quiscala*; Grue 1982), and northern bobwhite (*Colinus virginianus*; Hill et al. 1975), others such as zebra finches (*Poephila guttata*) exhibited ChE inhibition after low and dose-dependent exposure (Holmes and Boag 1990). Thus sensitivity to exposure, as well as route of entry of the toxicant, both contribute to a high range of variation in susceptibility among birds to a single compound.

Regulations are promulgated typically by individual responses of single species to an isolated compound. If we consider magnifying this single species sensitivity to an individual contaminant by the array of interactions evident in biological organization of ecosystems, added to the veritable 'pesticide cocktail' that occurs in runoff, the impacts can be devastating. For example, the groundbreaking work of Tyrone Hayes on atrazine and other agricultural contaminants has documented hormone mimicking effects on amphibians well below potable water regulations (Hayes et al. 2002, 2003, Hayes 2004). Endocrine disrupting contaminants have the potential to shape not only embryonic development of wildlife, but also exert artificial selective pressure on individual populations (Guilette et al. 1995). One ramification of our regulatory approach is that it simply does not accommodate adequately the complexity of nature. While we are beginning to investigate subtle impacts in amphibians and reptiles, similar investigations have yet to be undertaken on bird populations.

These studies demonstrate the intricate nature by which solely ecological mechanisms may contribute to converting non-lethal acute responses to pesticides into incapacitating chronic ones. Toxicity studies typically are short-term (only a few days to a few weeks), and use death as an acute endpoint response. Yet, sub-lethal concentrations may accumulate and elicit chronic responses; behavioral abnormalities that may occur at low-level exposure can contribute to territory loss, inability to attract a mate, and reproductive failure. And since exposure can occur by foraging on tainted foods, typical grazing and predatory interactions enhance the disruption waged by pesticides on birds.

SELECTED VARIETIES OF CONTAMINANTS—DELIVERY SYSTEMS

While additional literature continues to accumulate ranging from documentation of corticosterone impacts of pesticide-induced stress (Bortolotti et al. 2008) to neurochemical disruption by metals in common loons and Bald Eagles (Scheuhammer et al. 2008), from eggshell residues in grey herons and in black-crowned night herons (Ayas 2007) to blackbirds' impaired immunological response to botulism post-pesticide exposure (Goldberg et al. 2004), an unusual contaminant relationship has been documented based not on the specific chemical contaminant, but rather on the vehicle by which the pesticide is delivered!

Consider that agrochemicals are commonly formulated as water-soluble solutions, emulsifiable concentrates, and dusts or wettable powders (Knowles 2008); producers of pesticides are trying to develop safer formulations that enhance function of the active agrochemical but also minimize residues and negative risks of application. Granular formulations allow direct application of a pesticide and may include a carrier such as silica, kaolin, talc or even corn cob grits to increase absorptive capacity and control release rate of the active ingredient (Knowles 2008). Early studies have documented avian mortality associated with field application of granular pesticides (US EPA 1992, Best and Fischer 1992). One novel suggestion is that foraging birds approach granules as natural grit or food and intentionally target their consumption of them. In a study of the broadly distributed house sparrow (*Passer domesticus*), Best and Gionfriddo (1994) demonstrated that the sparrows clearly chose not only to visit trays of silica-based granules more than twice as often as other carrier particles, but they also pecked at those granules nearly six times as often as other carriers. Physical characteristics such as color and uniformity of shape influence the attractiveness of granular pesticides to birds (Best et al. 1996). More recently, retrospective analysis (Mineau et al. 2005) found bird abundance of American robin, horned lark, house sparrow, mourning dove, western meadowlark, black-billed magpie, European starling and killdeer all were negatively correlated with use of pesticide granules. These data suggest that use of granular pesticides may have long-term influences on population changes among a wide array of bird guilds.

CONCLUSIONS

By altering population abundance, either directly through increased mortality or indirectly through any of the aforementioned mechanisms, environmental contaminants act as factors of change in bird community dynamics; these responses are in addition to any acute or even chronic negative impacts. It is in the laboratory where molecules and cells and individual organisms are assessed for impacts of contaminants, yet proliferation in the environment is where regulatory efforts seem concentrated. There is a growing recognition of the need for better integration of toxicology with ecology, and for more studies on contaminant effects at higher levels of biological organization. As early as 1985, Kimball and Levin offered that among nearly 700 articles published over a two-year period, fewer than 12% reported effects on populations, communities or ecosystems. Yet over a decade later, a similar survey of the journal *Environmental Toxicology and Chemistry* reported only a 6% improvement in primary literature investigating higher-level biological organization (Clements and Kiffney 1994).

Many of the reasons variously cited for our collective resistance to integrating contaminant toxicology and ecology are demonstrated among the selected examples in this chapter—the need for regulatory decision-making and standardization, our preference for manageable scale reductionist approaches to experimental investigation, the challenge of quantifying measurable effects, the difficulties and costs of teasing out subtle indirect effects, and the variability inherent among bird species assemblages. Indeed, it has been suggested (Calow 1994) that we still simply do not know enough about community and ecosystem function to know what it *is* about them we *want* to protect and therefore need to measure! I would argue that our investigations into avian responses to environmental contaminants need to extend beyond the conventional regulatory framework. They need to incorporate the real, if challenging and frankly messy, characteristics of the natural environment when we execute and interpret our studies on compounds we introduce and allow to proliferate in the environment. The magnificence of a soaring harrier and the delicate call of the mourning dove deserve no less.

LITERATURE CITED

Ayas Z. 2007. Trace element residues in eggshells of grey heron (*Ardea cinerea*) and black-crowned night heron (*Nycticorax nycticorax*) from Nallihan Bird Paradise, Ankara-Turkey. Ecotoxicology 16:347–352.

Best L.B. and D.L. Fischer. 1992. Granular insecticides and birds: factors to be considered in understanding exposure and reducing risk. Environ. Toxicol. Chem. 11:1495–1508.

Best L.B. and Gionifriddo. 1994. House sparrow preferential consumption of carriers used for pesticide analysis. Environ. Toxicol. Chem. 13:919–925.

Best, L.B., T.R. Stafford and E.M Mihaich. 1996. House sparrow preferential consumption of pesticide granules with different surface coatings. Environ. Toxicol. Chem. 15:1763–1768.

Bishop, C.A., M.D. Koster, A.A. Chek, D.J.T. Hussell and K. Jock. 1995. Chlorinated hydrocarbons and mercury in sediments, red-winged blackbirds (*Agelaius phoeniceus*) and tree swallows (*Tachycineta bicolor*) from wetlands in the Great Lakes-St. Lawrence river basin. Environ. Toxicol. Chem. 14:491–501.

Bortolotti, G.R., T.A. Marchant, J. Blas, T. German. 2008. Corticosterone in feathers is a long-term integrated measure of avian stress physiology. Functional Ecology 22:494–500.

Burger, J. E.A.E. Schreiber, M. Cochfeld. 1992. Lead, cadmium, selenium and mercury in seabird feathers from the tropical mid-Pacific. Environ. Toxicol. Chem. 11:815–822.

Butchart, S.H.M., A.J. Stattersfiled, L.A. Bennun, S.M. Shutes, H.R. Akcakaya, J.E.M. Baillie, S.N. Stuart, C. Hilton-Taylor, G.M. Mace. 2004. Measuring global trends in the status of biodiversity: Red list indices for birds. PLoS Biol. 2(12); e383 doi:10.1371/journal.pbio.0020383.

Calow, P. 1994. Ecotoxicology: What are we trying to protect? Environ. Toxicol. Chem. 13:1549.

Caslake, L.F., S.S. Harris, C. Williams, N.M. Waters. 2006. Mercury-resistant bacteria associated with macrophytes from a polluted lake. Wat. Air Soil Poll. 174:93–104.

Clarkson, T.W. 1972. Recent advances in the toxicology of mercury with emphasis on the alkylmercurials. Crit. Rev. Toxicol. 1:203–234.

Clements W.H. and P.M. Kiffney. 1994. Assessing contaminant effects at higher levels of biological organization. Environ. Toxicol. Chem. 13:357–359.

Custer, T.W., R.K. Hines, M.J. Melancon, D.J. Hoffman, J.K. Wickliffe, J.W. Bickham, J.W. Martin, D.S. Henshel. 1997. Contaminant concentrations and biomarker response in Great Blue Heron eggs from 10 colonies on the upper Mississippi River, USA. Environ. Toxicol. Chem. 16:260–271.

Forsyth D.J and P.A. Martin. 1993. Effects of fenitrothion on survival, behavior and brain cholinesterase activity of white-throated sparrows (*Zonotrichia albicollis*). Environ. Toxicol. Chem. 12:91–103.

Fowler, S.W. 1990. Critical review of selected heavy metal and chlorinated hydrocarbon concentrations in the marine environment. Mar. Environ. Res. 29:1–64.

Goldberg. D.R., M.D. Samuel, T.E. Rocke, K.M. Johnson, G. Linz. 2004. Could blackbird mortality from avicide DRC-1339 contribute to avian botulism outbreaks in North Dakota? Wildlife Soc. Bull. 32:870–880.

Grue C.E. 1982. Response of common grackles to dietary concentrations of four organophosphate pesticides. Arch. Environ. Contam. Toxicol. 11:617–626.

Guillette, L.J. Jr., D.A. Crain, A.A. Rooney and D.B. Pickford. 1995. Organization versus activation: The role of endocrine-disrupting contaminants (EDCs) during embryonic development in wildlife. Environ. Health Perspect. 103:157–164.

Hayes, T.B. 2004. There is no denying this: Defusing the confusion about atrazine. BioScience. 54: 1138–1149

Hayes, T.B., A. Collins, M. Lee, M. Mendoza, N. Noriega, A.A. Stuart, and A. Vonk. 2002. Hermaphroditic, demasculinized frogs following exposure to the herbicide, atrazine, at ecologically relevant doses. Proc. Nat. Acad. Sciences (USA). 99: 5476–5480.

Hayes, T.B, K. Haston, M. Tsui, A. Hoang, C. Haeffele, and A. Vonk. 2003. Atrazine-induced hermaphroditism at 0.1 ppb in American leopard frogs: Evidence from the laboratory and the wild. Environ. Health. Perspect. 111: 1–8.

Heinz, G.H. 1980. Comparison of game-farm and wild-strain mallard ducks in accumulation of methylmercury. J. Environ. Path. Toxicol. 3:379–386.

Hill E.F., R.G. Heath, J.W. Spann, and J.D. Williams. 1975. Lethal dietary toxicities of environmental pollutants to birds. US Fish Wildl. Serv. Spec Sci. Rep. Wild. 191 p.

Holmes, S.B. and P.T. Boag. 1990. Inhibition of brain and plasma cholinesterase activity in zebra finches orally dosed with fenitrothion. Environ. Toxicol. Chem. 9:323–334.

Huston M.A. 1979. A general hypothesis of species diversity. Am. Nat. 113:81–101.

IUCN, World Conservation Union. 2007. Extinction crisis escalates; Red list shows apes, corals, vultures, dolphins all in danger. Accessed 19 Sept 2007. www.iu9cn.org/en/news/archive/2007/09/12_pr_redlist.htm#.

Hooper, M.J., P. Mineau, M.E. Zaccagnini, B. Woodbridge. 2002. Pesticides and international migratory bird conservation. Ch. 25, pages 737–754 IN: Handbook of Ecotoxicology, 2nd edition. D.J. Hoffman, B.A. Raffner, G.A. Burton, Jr., J. Cairns, Jr. Lewis Publishers, CRC Press LLC, Boca Raton, FL.

Johnson D.L. 1989. Spatial autocorrelation, spatial modeling and improvements in grasshopper survey methodology. Can. Entomol. 121:579–588.

Kimball K.D. and S.A. Levin. 1985. Limitations of laboratory bioassays: The need for ecosystem-level testing. BioScience 35:165–171.

Knowles A. 2008. Recent developments of safer formulations of agrochemicals. Environmentalist 28:35–44

Martin, P.A., D. L. Johnson, D.J. Forsyth. 1996. Effects of grasshopper-control insecticides on survival and brain acetylcholinesterase of pheasant (*Phasianus colchicus*) chicks. Environ. Toxicol. Chem. 15:518–524.

McInnes, P.F. D.E. Andersen, D.J. Hoff, M.J. Hooper, L.L. Kinkel. 1996. Monitoring exposure of nestling songbirds to agricultural application of an organophosphorus insecticide using cholinesterase activity. Environ. Toxicol. Chem. 15:544–552.

Miller, G.T. and S. Spoolman. 2008. Environmental Science: Problems, Concepts and Solutions, 12th ed. Brooks/Cole, Thomson Learning, Pacific Grove, CA.

Mineau, P. C.M. Downes, D.A. Kirk, E. Rayne and M. Csizy. 2005. Patterns of bird species abundance in relation to granular insecticide use in the Canadian prairies. Ecoscience 12:267–278.

Powell G.V.N. 1984. Reproduction by an altricial songbird, the red-winged blackbird, in fields treated with the organophosphate insecticide fenthion. J. Appl. Ecol. 21:83–95.

Scheuhammer, A.M., N. Basu, N.M. Burgess, J.E. Elliot, G.D. Campbell, M. Wayland, L. Champoux, J. Rodrigue. 2008. Relationships among mercury, selenium and neurochemical parameters in common loons (*Gavia immer*) and bald eagles (*Haliaeetus leucocephalus*). Ecotoxicology 17:93–101.

US Environmental Protection Agency. 1992. Comparative analysis of acute avian risk from granular pesticides. Office of Pesticide Programs, Washington, DC.

Tuck, G.N., T. Polacheck, J.P. Croxall, H. Weimerskirch. 2001. Modelling the impact of fishery by-catches on albatross populations. J. Anim. Ecol. 38:1182–1196.

Avian Ecology and Conservation: A Pennsylvania Focus with National Implications. Edited by S. K. Majumdar, T. L. Master, M. C. Brittingham, R. M. Ross, R. S. Mulvihill and J. E. Huffman. © 2010. The Pennsylvania Academy of Science.

Chapter 27

The Effects of Environmental Contaminants on Avian Populations

Jeffrey A. Stratford

Department of Biology and Health Sciences, Wilkes University, Wilkes-Barre PA 18766

jeffrey.stratford@wilkes.edu

INTRODUCTION

With few exceptions, the effects of environmental contaminants on avian populations are more subtle than habitat destruction. The exceptions are noteworthy, such as the immediate and persistent effects of the 1989 Exxon Valdez oil spill on marine birds (Irons et al. 2000). Popular media covering the spill was replete with images of petroleum-soaked bird carcasses. The more widespread effects of environmental contaminants involve less obvious effects such as reduced hatchability or reduced prey abundance. These cases may occur in areas that are contaminated but are seemingly natural to the human eye, such as rural lakes, beaches, and forests. Environmental contaminants were responsible for the drastic reductions in populations of brown pelican [*Pelecanus occidentalis*], bald eagle [*Haliaeetus leucocephalus*] and peregrine falcons [*Falco peregrinus*]. Before the ban, lead shot was responsible for the death of millions of waterfowl. Environment contaminants of all classes (e.g., heavy metals and pesticides) continue to present challenges to avian populations across the state (see Toschik et al. 2004) and continuous monitoring is necessary to assess emerging issues such as brominated flame retardants and pharmaceuticals (Koplin et al. 2002).

The sensitivity of birds to environmental contaminants has been known since the Industrial Revolution (Hoffman et al. 2003b). Spurred on by human population growth, technology, and agriculture, the diversity and quantity of threats has exploded since World War II. The 2006 U.S. Environmental Protection Agency Toxic Release Inventory includes 650 chemicals totaling approximately 4.25 billion pounds of potentially and known harmful contaminants (http://www.epa.gov/tri/tridata/tri06/pdr/key_findings_v12a.pdf). Contaminants may affect birds at every life history stage, every spatial scale and all levels of biological organization (e.g., individuals to populations to communities). Changes in avian populations are likely to affect ecological services such as seed dispersal, pest control, and ecosystem engineers (Sekercioglu 2006). Thus, understanding the ecological fate of contaminants and ecological functions of birds is essential to mitigating the potential negative effects of anthropogenic contaminants and maintaining populations.

The content of this review is restricted to contaminants that are likely to affect Pennsylvania birds that breed in the state or, at least, stop in the state during migration. Contaminants are divided into those that affect birds directly and those that have indirect effects. Direct effects of contaminants are those chemicals that are typically ingested and act to reduce survivorship and reproduction as well as skew sex ratios. Some contaminants, like oil, only need to make contact with the bird to have an effect, but this is exceptional. Contaminants may alter behaviors and make a bird more susceptible to predation or alter sexual behaviors. Contaminants may not kill a bird but alter development and affect sexual traits. Many of these effects are the result of contaminants that act as endocrine disruptors. Endocrine disruptors are chemicals that interfere with the normal functioning of the endocrine glands. It is difficult to scale the individual effects of contaminants to the population level but endocrine disruptors may alter sex ratios in a local population or decrease populations through increased mortality or decreased reproductive success (Ottinger et al. 2002). It is not necessary for contaminants to have direct effects to affect populations; loss of prey items or degradation of habitat can lead to drastic population declines. Loss of prey can be seen as a form of habitat loss that is as drastic as the removal of forests or the drainage of wetlands.

I do not attempt a comprehensive review of the properties and effects of contaminants, but I attempt to present recent studies that focus on field research. An excellent review of contaminants and other toxicological issues can be found in Hoffman and colleagues (2003a). My review emphasizes field studies, but I also include lab studies when data from natural populations are lacking. Unfortunately, most lab studies are taxonomically limited. The U.S. EPA requires the testing of the toxicity of pesticides for mallards [*Anas platyrhynchos*] and northern bobwhite [*Colinus virginianus*] and endocrine disruptors are primarily tested on Japanese Quail [*Coturnix japonica*] (Hoffman 2003). Consequently there are few studies conducted on the most diverse taxonomic group, the passerines.

DIRECT EFFECTS OF ENVIRONMENTAL CONTAMINANTS

Metals

Although naturally occurring, metals become pollutants when released by human activities at levels exceeding those in the environment. In Pennsylvania, the primary avenues that metals are released into the environment are smelting and mining. Both mines and smelters release several metals that are potentially toxic in addition to the target ore. Many of the metals released from mine drainages are eventually found in birds through consuming contaminated insects and fish (Wayland and Crosley 2006). At an intensively sampled site in Palmerton, Pennsylvania, a zinc smelter released toxic amounts of lead and cadmium as well as zinc (Beyer and Storm 1995). Many of the metals from this site have been found across a variety of verbrate taxa, including birds. For example, songbirds 2 km from the site had an average of 56 part per million (ppm) of lead in their carcasses compared to an average of 15 ppm from birds 12 km from the site (Beyer and Storm 1995). Nonpoint source, particularly runoff from urban streams, is another significant source of metals in aquatic systems (Paul and Meyer 2001).

The toxicity of metals is a consequence of their ability to bind with organic groups, which increases their lipophilic properties. Essential metals, those required in the diet (e.g., zinc), become toxic when ingested above a threshold level. Nonessential metals (e.g., lead and mercury) can compete and interfere with essential elements for binding sites on molecules such as enzymes.

Birds have several pathways available to detoxify and rid themselves of metals. The simplest is excretion through feces. Metals may also be excreted though feathers and eggs. Remarkably, birds may rid themselves of their entire mercury load through molting. Metals are integrated into feathers and eggs by binding to metallothioneins, specialized proteins that bind to metals. Mercury, for example, bonds to sulfhydryl groups in feather keratin (Burger 1993).

Lead

Mining, smelters, and shotgun pellets are the primary sources of lead in the environment (DeFrancisco et al. 2003). Fishing weights and runoff from urban areas can also be a smaller yet significant source of lead (Paul and Meyer 2001, DeFrancisco et al. 2003). Ingested lead accumulates in avian bone, several organs including the liver and kidney, and up to fifty percent of the lead burden can be found in feathers (Burger 1993).

Acute lead poisoning can lead to death within days of ingestion. For instance, American black ducks [*Anas rubripes*] can have acute lead poisoning and death with as little as six shotgun pellets (Pain 1992). Chronic exposure to lead can lead to death via starvation as digestive organs begin to malfunction. Before death, birds become weak and paralysis can spread to the head, wings and legs. In reproductive females, lead can mobilize to the eggs and decrease hatch rates. Chicks with toxic levels of lead have abnormal behaviors (DeFrancisco et al. 2003). One of the most intensely studied heavy-metal contaminated sites is a Finish smelter that emitted some of the same metals as the Palmerton smelter (e.g., zinc, lead). Recent research at this site by T. Eeva and colleagues have focused on pied flycatchers [*Ficedula hypoleuca*] and great tits [*Parus major*] and have revealed a wealth of information on the effect of heavy metals on wild birds. Some of results are predictable but some are surprising and contrary to expectation. For example, avian reproduction is diminished with increasing proximity to the site (Eeva and Lehikoinen 1995) but male survivorship increases closer to the studied smelter (Eeva et al. 2006). Lower reproduction at the Finish site may be related to smaller eggs, thinner eggshells, and low hatch rates (Eeva and Lehikoinen 1995). Heavy metals may also cause immunosuppression and decreased brain function. Gorissen and colleagues (2005) suggested heavy metals impaired brain function in a study showing a negative correlation between song repertoire and proximity to a smelter. Immune response by great tits near a European smelter was statistically less than the response of tits farther from the smelter (Snoeijs et al. 2004).

In the United States, a 1986 US Fish and Wildlife Service report (USFWS 1986) estimated that 1.5 to 3 million waterfowl die annually from lead poisoning. Soon afterwards, in 1991, lead shot was banned for waterfowl hunting in the United States. However, lead shot is highly persistent and is likely to still affect waterfowl in the state. Not only does lead accumulate and increase in concentration in birds such as waterfowl but contaminated and weak waterfowl become easy targets for peregrine falcons. Lead is currently affecting waterbirds in the Chesapeake Bay watershed (Rattner and McGowan 2007). In addition to waterfowl, Pennsylvanian birds likely to suffer from lead are top predators such as bald eagles and peregrine falcons and scavengers such as crows and ravens (Craighead and Bedrosian 2008). Urbanization and urban streams is another avenue of exposure of birds to lead. In a recent study, Roux and Marra (2007) found that adult gray catbirds [*Dumetella carolinensis*] in urban environments (Washington, DC) were in poorer condition due to lead toxicity compared to more rural catbirds. Large Pennsylvania cities that may also show the effects of increased lead concentrations include Philadelphia and Pittsburgh as well as rural areas near smelters.

Mercury

Sources of mercury include manufacturing, garbage incineration, mining, and coal-fired power plants. Sources of mercury in Pennsylvania do not need to be local. Gaseous mercury can be transported on a global scale (Weiner et al. 2003) and mercury deposited in Pennsylvania can come from sources across the continent. There are two relevant forms of mercury: inorganic mercury and methylmercury. In general, methylmercury is more toxic and is readily converted from inorganic mercury by anaerobic bacteria (Wolfe 1998). Inorganic and methylmercury have a suite of physiological effects. Acute and chronic levels of mercury affect digestive organs, particularly the kidneys, and the central nervous system. Contaminated birds will suffer ataxia and will often not feed, leading to starvation or making them more susceptible to predation. Reproductive effects of methylmercury toxicity include reduced egg production, smaller clutches and eggs (Albers 2007, see Wolfe 1998 and Scheuhammer et al. 2007 for reviews) and these effects occur at very low levels of mercury in the diet. Brasso and Cristol (2008) found tree swallows [*Tachycineta bicolor*] produced fewer fledgling at a contaminated site along a Shenandoah tributary in Virginia. Ninety percent of a bird's mercury load can be in the feathers (Burger 1993). Similar to lead, birds are able to reduce their load of mercury through excretion, including feather molt.

Mercury may still pose a threat for some Pennsylvania birds including those near mine drainages, urban centers, and near polluted river systems. Fortunately, levels of mercury in the Chesapeake Bay appear to be below toxic levels (Rattern and McGowan 2007). However, mercury may still affect terrestrial birds near polluted systems. Pennsylvania still has many river systems that have fish consumption advisories for mercury (http://www.depweb.state.pa.us/watersupply/lib/watersupply/fishadvisory08-tbl.doc). It is unlikely that fish-eating birds understand such warnings. Species most likely to be at risk are piscivorous birds such as mergansers [*Mergus* spp.] and bald eagles. Fish are not the only prey that are contaminated by mercury; Cristol and colleagues (2008) recently found mercury moved from a polluted stream into terrestrial birds via the spiders that fed on emergent insects.

The effects of mercury should be monitored in the state particularly near impacted waterways. In light of the call for increased power from coal-powered plants, the need for monitoring will likely become more essential.

Zinc, Cadmium and Selenium

The primary sources of zinc, cadmium and selenium in Pennsylvania are mining and smelting. Along with lead, these metals are often released together from smelters and bioaccumulate in insects and birds (Wayland and Crosley 2006). Compared to lead and mercury, we know much less about the toxic effects of zinc, cadmium and selenium in wild avian populations.

Zinc is an essential element necessary for enzyme activity and molt. In addition to mines and smelting, runoff from galvanized metals is a source of zinc. Zinc toxicity includes lesions in digestive organs, loss of motor function, immunosuppression, and death (Eisler 1993, Beyer et al. 2005). Compared to passerines, waterfowl appear to be less able to rid themselves of zinc and are more likely to suffer zinc toxicity (Beyer et al. 2005). Cadmium, like zinc, is a ubiquitous trace metal. Effects of cadmium on birds include decreased testes weight, reduced egg production, and egg shell thinning (Burger 1993), although specific thresholds have not been established (Rattner and McGowan 2007). Larison and colleagues (2000) showed bone loss in wild birds associated with increased cadmium exposure and suggested chronic cadmium toxicity is an under-recognized issue for avian populations.

Selenium is an essential trace element and the effects of selenium toxicity appear to be more variable than other metals and taxonomically-dependent (Albers 1996). Waterfowl appear to be more susceptible to selenium than passerines and birds of prey. American kestrels [*Falco sparverius*] fed organic forms of selenium only showed negative effects on reproduction at the highest levels (Santolo et al. 1999) and adult body fat decreased with increased selenium consumption (Yamamoto and Santolo 2000). Reproductive success in American robins [*Turdus migratorius*] and red-winged blackbirds [*Agelaius phoeniceus*] did not differ between a selenium-contaminated mine site and a reference site (Ratti et al. 2006). In a similar study, spotted sandpiper [*Actitis macularius*] and American dipper [*Cinclus mexicanus*] populations were not affected by selenium-laden runoff from coal mines. However, Fairbrother and colleagues (1994) found reduced immune response of American avocets [*Recurvirostra americana*] exposed to selenium and other metals. In wild common eiders [*Somateria mollissima*], selenium in the liver was negatively associated with mass, body fat and the heterophil-lymphocyte ratio, and indicator of stress (Wayland et al. 2002). Lethal effects of selenium were also found in controlled studies on mallards by Albers and colleagues (1996) and Heinz and colleagues (1989). Lethal effects of selenium were observed with as little as 80 ppm in mallards (Albers and colleagues 1996) and lesser amounts resulted in weight loss and reproductive failure.

The risk to Pennsylvania birds from zinc, cadmium and selenium, as well as other metals is similar to risks from lead and mercury. Birds near mine drainages and industrial discharges are at risk. Since these metals do not break down, proximity to smelters such as the Palmerton site, may also pose a relatively long-term risk (Beyer and Storm 1995). Levels of cadmium and selenium in the Chesapeake Bay appear to be below toxic levels (Rattner and McGowan 2007) suggesting levels in the Susquehanna River may also be below toxic levels.

Organic Compounds

Petroleum, Polyaromatic Hydrocarbons (PAHs) and Associated Pollutants

Petroleum, including refined and crude oils, contains a suite of potentially toxic substances including polyaromatic hydrocarbons and metals. Hydrocarbons comprise approximately fifty to seventy-five percent of petroleum (Albers 2002). Large oil spills along the Delaware River are the primary source of potentially toxic hydrocarbons in Pennsylvania. Since 1972, there have been four large (> 100,000 gallons) oil spills dumping over 1.4 million gallons of crude oil into the Delaware River (http://www.ocean.udel.edu/oilspill/). In the Chesapeake Bay watershed, two major oil spills had killed hundreds of birds and some 500 smaller oil spills occur annually (Rattner and McGowan 2007). Other significant sources of hydrocarbon pollutants include stormwater runoff, automobiles leaks, and illegal dumping of used motor oil. Consequently, urban streams are often highly contaminated with petroleum pollutants (Paul and Meyer 2001).

An immediate effect of oil spills is the soaking of birds in petroleum. Petroleum on feathers results in a breakdown of feather structure and feathers will lose buoyancy and thermoregulatory capabilities (Albers 2003). Exposed birds can die of hypothermia and drowning. The most susceptible birds are aquatic species and large oil spills during migration may result in the death of thousands of birds (Albers 2003).

When ingested, the primary toxic substances in petroleum are the polyaromatric hydrocarbons (PAHs), which affect the cell membrane functions and are carcinogenic (Albers 2006). PAHs make up to 7% of crude oil (Albers 2003). Other sources of PAHs include coal combustion, home heating, illegal dumping of used oil and garbage incineration. On eggs, even minute amounts (< 20 µl) of PAHs are toxic to developing embryos and result in death or abnormalities (Albers 2006). Other components of oil can lead to a variety of effects which include endocrine disruption, abnormal parental behaviors, immunosuppression, as well as dehydration and starvation (Albers 2002). Adult birds exposed to PAHs have reduced clutch size and increased nest abandonment (Albers 2006). PAHs may also act as endocrine disruptors; Peakall and colleagues (1981) found seabird chicks had elevated corticosterone and thyroxine levels after orally-administered petroleum and may have explained the slower growth rates of treated chicks. PAHs are metabolized by birds and do not bioaccumulate (Albers 2006).

Petroleum pollution via oil spills is likely to remain a significant, though episodic problem for Pennsylvania birds. Aquatic birds that nest or feed along Delaware Bay are particularly at risk. Populations of red knots [*Calidris canutus*] could be significantly impacted if an oil spill should occur during their migratory stopover in the Delaware Bay in April and May. This species forages on Delaware Bay beaches for horseshoe crab eggs and would be directly impacted by an oil spill. More persistent petroleum pollution will more likely come from urban runoff and the dumping of used motor oil into sewer systems.

Polychlorinated Biphenyls (PCB's), Polychlorinated Benzodioxins (PCDDs) and Dibenzofurans (PCDFs)

PCBs, PCDDs and PCDFs represent over 200 congeners, but share many structural and toxicological properties. These three chemical classes are polyhalogenated organic molecules that share two chlorinated phenyl rings. PCBs, PCDDs and PCDFs molecules are persistent in the environment, lipophilic and bioaccumulate in organisms. PCBs were, until banned, manufactured and PCDDs and PCDFs were produced as byproducts of PCB manufacturing.

PCB's were used in a variety of manufactured products as well as the manufacturing process. PCBs were primarily used in transformers and capacitors (Rice et al. 2003). Approximately 1.3 billion pounds of PCBs were produced until production was banned in 1979 (Rice et al. 2003). One particular source of PCDDs are pulp and paper mills and both PCDDs and PCDF are the products of garbage incineration and steel production plants. Consequently, PCBs are mainly transported through aquatic systems and PCDDs and PCDFs are transported through the atmosphere. Canadian studies have shown that emerging aquatic insects are able to mobilize PCBs from the sediment to terrestrial species (e.g., tree swallows (Papp et al. 2005).

PCBs, PCDFs and PCDDs are most likely to affect piscivorous birds in polluted river systems and raptors that feed on such species (Bustnes et al. 2008). Birds exposed to these molecules show many effects related to reproduction including reduced hatching success (Arenal and Halbrook 1997), smaller clutches (Fernie et al. 2001), and altered parental

behavior (Arenal and Halbrook 1997, Fisher 2006). However, the effects are highly dependent on the chemical species (Rice et al. 2003). PCBs are immunosuppressive (Smits et al.
2002) and are endocrine disruptors in birds (Bustnes et al. 2001, Ottinger et al. 2008). Fernie and colleagues (2001) demonstrated that adult American kestrels exposed to PCBs in
ovo manifest many of the same negative effects of adults exposed to PCBs as adults.

Like mercury, many Pennsylvania waterways have fish consumption advisories for PCBs
(http://www.depweb.state.pa.us/watersupply/lib/watersupply/fishadvisory08-tbl.doc).   One
river that deserves inquiry is the Susquehanna River. Ko and Baker (2004) identify the Susquehanna as being a major source of PCBs that flow in the Chesapeake Bay. There are local incidences of PCB contamination of waterbirds in the Chesapeake Bay (Rattner and McGowan
2007) but overall concentrations are declining slowly in the Chesapeake Bay area since the ban.
In the Delaware River and Bay, Toschik and colleagues (2004) found PCB's were detectable
and were associated with lower reproductive success in ospreys (*Pandion haliaetus*).

Polybrominated Diphenylethers (PBDE) and related flame-retardants

Polybrominated diphenylethers are structurally related to PCBs and related molecules.
PBDEs are primarily used as fire retardants and are found in a variety of common items
such as furniture and bedding. PBDEs are stable, unreactive and lipophilic. The amount of
PBDEs in the environment and concentrations in animals have increased exponentially or
doubled in the last few decades (Hites 2004). For example, PDBE concentrations from
herring gulls [*Larus argentatus*] from the Great Lakes have been doubling every couple of
years for over two decades (Norstrom et al. 2002). Peregrine falcons in Greenland have
some of the highest concentrations of flame retardants recorded in wildlife, demonstrating
the biomaginification ability of these chemicals.

The effects of flame retardants in birds are largely unknown but PDBEs may reduce
immune function. For example, experimental American kestrel nestlings that were exposed
to environmentally relevant concentrations of PBDE in the egg and later in the diet had
decreased immunity response with increasing concentrations of PBDE (Fernie et al. 2005).
More experimental research is needed but if flame retardants affect avian populations then
many Pennsylvania birds will be at risk, particularly birds of prey and piscivores.

Organochlorine Insecticides

Most organochlorine insecticides are neurotoxins and are highly toxic to insects. World
War Two marks a period where synthetic organic pesticides increased markedly in variety
and use (Blus 2003). Many organochlorine insecticides are highly persistent and all are
lipophilic. These two characteristics of organochlorines allow them to accumulate in non-
target species including birds and other vertebrates.

Large-scale use of organic pesticides is associated with agriculture and golf courses but
smaller-scale domestic use can also be an issue. Indeed, many pesticides have higher concentrations in urban streams compared to agricultural streams (Paul and Meyer 2001). This
is likely to be a consequence of lawn care products. However, Lepczyk et al. (2004) found
that pesticide use was more common at rural homes compared to more urbanized homes.
Consequently, birds found in relatively forested areas may still come into contact with
organic contaminants.

One organochlorine insecticide that deserves mention is DDT and its metabolite, DDE.
Large-scale commercial use of DDT began in the 1940's in Europe and North America and

other chlorinated hydrocarbons entered commercial use in the 1950's. As early as the 1960's, die-offs of North American songbirds had been attributed to the spraying of DDT to control Dutch elm disease (Blus 2003). At the same time, European birds of prey, including peregrine falcons, were found dead in large numbers (Walker et al. 2006). Soon after these studies a link between eggshell thickness and DDE was proposed (Ratcliffe 1967) and was supported by experiments and museum and field studies (see Blus 2003 for references). After a long court battle, DDT was banned in the United States in 1972. It remains however, unclear how DDE causes eggshell thinning. DDE does appear to interfere with calcium deposition in the eggshell gland (Lundholm 1992). Raptors and piscivores are the most vulnerable to eggshell thinning. In addition to peregrine falcons, other Pennsylvania species that were strongly affected by DDE were double-crested cormorant [*Phalacrocorax auritus*], osprey [*Pandion haliaetus*] and bald eagle.

Despite over two decades since the banning of DDT, this chemical still is persistent and pervasive enough to negatively affect birds in the United States and Canada. DDT is highly persistent, particularly in the soil (Loganathan and Kannan 1994). Studies by Harris and colleagues (2000) show that American robins in British Columbia were accumulating DDT twenty years after DDT was banned in Canada. Robins were exposed to DDT through ingesting earthworms in orchards where this pesticide was heavily used. In the United States, peregrine falcon eggs from the Chesapeake Bay area had DDE levels associated with eggshell thinning during the 1990s. In this same time period, over one-quarter of the falcons from the Chesapeake Bay area had eggshell thinning associated with population declines (Rattner and McGowan 2007). In a similar study (Rattner and McGowan 2007), black-crowned night-herons [*Nycticorax nycticorax*] in the Chesapeake Bay area also had DDE in the eggs but these were below levels associated with eggshell thinning. More recent studies however, suggest that levels of DDT are declining nationally and in the Chesapeake Bay area (Rattner and McGowan 2007).

In addition to eggshell thinning, DDE may reduce survivorship by reducing the ability of birds to respond to stress. For instance, eastern bluebirds [*Sialia sialis*] from DDE contaminated sites demonstrated reduced corticosterone response to acute stress compared to uncontaminated sites (Mayne et al. 2004). DDT may also act as an endocrine disruptor – an effect known since the 1950's (Zala et al. 2004).

Since DDT was banned several other organochlorine pesticides were developed but most of these were later banned. Today, only a few organochlorine pesticides are used in Pennsylvania. Data for pesticide use in Pennsylvania agriculture (see Tables 1–3) comes primarily from the U.S. Department of Agriculture Northeastern Integrated Pest Management Center farmer surveys (http://www.pested.psu.edu/infocenter/surveys.shtml hereafter "NeIPM survey"). The only organochlorine fungicide used in the NEIPM was chlorothalonil and presents a low risk to birds (http://extoxnet.orst.edu/pips/chloroth.htm). Organochlorine insecticides have been replaced by organophosphates, carbamates, pyrethroids, and a few other alternatives (Table 1).

Carbamates and Organophosphates

Carbamates and organophosphates are acetlycholinesterase inhibitor insecticides that are not stable in the environment and do not bioaccumulate. Carbamates and organophospates, are however, more acutely toxic. These pesticides inhibit neurotransmit-

Table 1. Summary of insecticide use in Pennsylvania reported by Northeastern Integrated Pest Management and available from http://www.pested.psu.edu/infocenter/surveys.shtml[1].

Pesticide	Chemical Class	Crop	Total Lbs x 1000[2]	Risk
Abamectin	avermectins	Apple	2	low(1)
Carbaryl	carbamate	Apple, Peaches, Cantaloupe, Grape, Pumpkin	35.1	moderate(1)
Carbofuran[3]	carbamate	Sweet Corn	0.8	high(1)
Methomyl	carbamate	Apple, Peaches, Cantaloupe, Sweet Corn, Pumpkin	7	high(1)
Oxamyl	carbamate	Potatoes, Apple	2.4	high(1)
Bifenazate	carbazate	Apple	0.4	low(2)–moderate(2)
Imidacloprid	chloro-nicotinyl	Potatoes, Apple, Peaches, Pumpkin	2.8	low(1)
Endosulfan	cyclodiene	Potatoes, Apple, Peaches, Cantaloupe, Sweet Corn, Pumpkin	9.2	moderate–high(1)
Petroleum Distillate	hydrocarbon	Apple, Peaches	222.54	inert, low(2)
Spinosad	microbial	Potatoes, Sweet Corn	4	low(2)
Acephate	organophosphate	Snap Bean	10	moderate(1)
Azinphos-methyl	organophosphate	Apple, Peaches, Cantaloupe, Grape	26.1	moderate(1)
Chlorpyrifos	organophosphate	Corn, Apple, Peaches, Sweet Corn	159.1	high(1)
Diazinon	organophosphate	Apple, Peaches	10.8	high(1)
Dimethoate	organophosphate	Potatoes, Soybean, Snap Bean	21.8	high(1)
Disulfoton	organophosphate	Snap Bean	1.5	high(1)
Methamidophos	organophosphate	Potatoes	3	high(1)
Methyl parathion	organophosphate	Grape, Sweet Corn	7.7	high(1)
Phosmet	organophosphate	Apple, Peaches, Grape	21.5	high(1)
Indoxacarb	oxadiazines	Apple	0.2	moderate(2)
Bifenthrin	pyrethroid	Snap Bean, Sweet Corn, Pumpkin	2.1	moderate(1)
Cyfluthrin	pyrethroid	Potatoes, Sweet Corn	4	low(1)
Esfenvalerate	pyrethroid	Apple, Peaches, Sweet Corn, Pumpkin	0.4	low(1)
Fenpropathrin	pyrethroid	Apple	0.8	low(2)
Lambda-cyhalothrin	pyrethroid	Apple, Sweet Corn, Pumpkin	2.2	low(1)
Tefluthrin	pyrethroid	Corn	21	unknown
Zeta-cypermethrin	pyrethroid	Snap Bean, Sweet Corn	0.4	low(1)
Permethrin	pyrethroids	Potatoes, Apple, Peaches, Sweet Corn, Pumpkin	3.5	low(1)
Pyridaben	pyridazinone	Apple	0.2	unknown
Clofentezine	tetrazine	Peaches	2	low(2)
Benzoic acid	organic acid	Apple	1.5	inert, low(1)

[1]Pesticide use data were originally compiled by the U.S.D.A. National Agricultural Statistical Service
[2]These surveys span the years 1997–2003. The amounts presented represent a single year use not the cumulative amount and may not reflect current use.
[3]Carbofuran and several other carbamates are currently banned for use in Pennsylvania.

ters and affect a suite of neuromuscular and central nervous system functions including senses, thermoregulation, and behavior. Birds metabolize these compounds quickly, but exposed birds may suffer from acute toxicity including death (Hill 1993). These incidences and others were primarily caused by the granular form of the carbamate, carbofuran. This granular carbfuran was banned in 1994 and, more recently, the organophospates diazinon and chlorpyrifos have been banned, as well as all forms of carbofuran.

Table 2. Summary of fungicide use in Pennsylvania reported by Northeastern Integrated Pest Management and available from http://www.pested.psu.edu/infocenter/surveys.shtml[1].

Pesticide	Chemical Class	Crop	Total Lbs x 1000[2]	Risk
Cymoxanil	acetimide	Potatoes	2	low(1, 2)
Oxytetracycline	antibiotic	Peaches	0.2	low(2)
Streptomycin	antibiotic	Apple	0.3	low(1)
Fenbuconazole	azole	Peaches	0.3	moderate(2)– high(2)
Myclobutanil	azole	Apple, Peaches, Grape, Pumpkin	5.3	low(2)
Tebuconazole	azole	Peaches, Grape	0.7	moderate(2)– high(2)
Triflumizole	azole	Apple	0.8	low(2)
Metalaxyl	benzenoid	Potatoes, Cantaloupe, Pumpkin	1.4	low(1)
Benomyl	benzimidazole	Apple, Cantaloupe, Pumpkin	0.5	moderate(1)
Thiophanate-methyl	benzimidazole	Apple, Peaches, Pumpkin	11.3	moderate(2)
Ferbam	carbamate	Peaches	0.6	low(2)– moderate(2)
Ziram	carbamate	Apple, Peaches, Grape	33.7	moderate (1)
Iprodione	dicarboximide	Grape	0.1	low(1)
Vinclozolin	dicarboximide	Snap Beans	7.5	low(1)
Thiram	dimethyl dithiocarbamate	Apple, Peaches	24.9	low(1)
Metiram	ethylene bisdithiocarbamate	Potatoes	9	low(1)
Mancozeb	ethylene bis-dithiocarbamate	Potatoes, Apple, Cantaloupe, Grape, Pumpkin	161.6	low(1)
Maneb	ethylene bis-dithiocarbamate	Apple, Grape	10.8	low(1)
Azoxystrobin	methoxyacrylate	Potatoes, Cantaloupe, Sweet Corn, Pumpkin	3	low(1)
Dimethomorph	morpholine	Pumpkin	0.1	low(1)
Chlorothalonil	organochloride	Potatoes, Peaches, Cantaloupe, Sweet Corn, Pumpkin	81.7	low(1)
Famoxadone	oxazolidinedione	Pumpkin	2	moderate(2)
Captan	phthalimide	Apple, Peaches, Grapes	87.8	low(1)
Cyprodinil	pyrimidine	Apple, Peaches	2.6	low(1)
Fenarimol	pyrimidine	Apple, Grape	0.8	low(2)
Kresoxim-methyl	strobin	Apple, Grape	1.5	low(2)
Pyraclostrobin	strobin	Pumpkin	0.3	low(2)
Trifloxystrobin	strobin	Apple, Pumpkin	2.2	low(2)
Propiconazole	triazole	Peaches, Sweet Corn	0.4	low(1)
Mefenoxam	xylylalanine	Potatoes, Pumpkin	1.3	moderate(2)
Copper hydroxide	metal	Potatoes, Apple, Peaches, Pumpkin	11.2	intert, low(1)
Copper oxychloride	metal	Peaches	0.5	intert, low(1)
Copper sulfate	metal	Apple, Peaches, Grape	4.1	intert, low(1)
Potassium bicarbonate	salt	Pumpkin	1	low(2)
Sulfur	elemental	Apple, Peaches	53.8	low(2)

[1]Pesticide use data were originally compiled by the U.S.D.A. National Agricultural Statistical Service
[2]These surveys span the years 1997–2003. The amounts presented represent a single year use not the cumulative amount and may not reflect current use.

Carbamates and organophosphates also reduce reproductive rates by reducing chick survivorship, egg survivorship and weight (Patnode and White 1991, Bishop et al. 2000). Eastern bluebirds and tree swallows studied by Bishop and colleagues (2000) suffered up to a 14% reduction in fecundity due to carbamates and organophosphate use in Canadian orchards. Reduced productivity was also detected by Patnode and White (1991) in Georgia pecan orchards but only when organophosphates and carbamates were used together. There were minimal effects on reproductive success when a single pesticide was used.

Birds in Pennsylvania that are going to be exposed to carbamates and organophosphates are associated with agriculture. Carbamates and organophosphates were commonly used in Pennsylvania agriculture although many of them have been banned including carbofuran that was primarily responsible for local avian die offs around the Chesapeake Bay (Rattner and McGowan 2007). The NeIPM surveys revealed Ferbam and ziram were two carbamate fungicides used for Pennsylvania fruit (Table 2). There were several carbamates and organophosphate insecticides used in the state including carbofuran, which has been banned for use in the United States. Other carbamates and organophosphates used as pesticides in birds were highly or moderately toxic to birds.

Miscellaneous Pesticides

Commonly used herbicides in Pennsylvania that present low risks to birds include acetochlor, metolachlor, glyphosate and pendimethalin (Table 3). Indeed, most herbicides used in the state pose a low risk to birds. Three herbicides, paraquat, linuron, and 2,4-D have some toxic effects and pose a moderate risk to birds (http://pmep.cce.cornell.edu/profiles/extoxnet/) and none are persistent in the environment.

Triazenes are widely used herbicides structurally based on a benezene ring where three carbons are substituted with three nitrogens. One of the widely used triazines is atrazine. Wilhelms and colleagues (2006) found no evidence of endocrine disruption of *in ovo* applied atrazine but Ottinger and colleagues (2008) found that male adult Japanese quail exposed to atrazine were sexually impaired. Over 3 million kg of atrazine was used in Pennsylvania (NeIPM survey), exclusively on corn (Table 3).

In general, the total amount of fungicides used in Pennsylvania is much less than herbicides and insecticides. There are two fungicides, fenbuconazole and tebuconazole, that are potentially toxic to birds but these are limited in use (~ 2000 kg total).

There is much less known about the effects of rodenticides, but the anticoagulants used, such as brodifacoum, are known to cause mortality in birds. Many anticoagulants are persistent in the body and repeated sublethal doses may eventually lead to internal hemorrhaging and death. Raptors are particularly at risk to anticoagulants but, to a lesser extent, waterbirds are also at risk (Stone et al. 2003, Lambert et al. 2007). Stone and colleagues (2003) detected anticoagulants in nearly half of the raptors examined and anticoagulants were responsible for at least 7% of the fatalities of birds found dead in the wild. Stone's study examined birds found in New York but cases have also been reported from New Jersey (*J. Huffman, pers. com.*). Given the extent of agricultural areas in Pennsylvania, more concern and study should be appropriated to surveys of anticoagulants in recovered birds.

Fluorinated Surfactants

Fluorinated surfactants are among the most common organic contaminants in industrial and domestic effluents (Kolpin et al. 2002, Sinclair and Kannan 2006) and include sever-

Table 3. Summary of herbicide use in Pennsylvania reported by Northeastern Integrated Pest Management and available from http://www.pested.psu.edu/infocenter/surveys.shtml[1].

Pesticide	Chemical Class	Crop	Total Lbs x 1000[2]	Risk
Acetochlor	acetamide	Corn, Sweet Corn	170.9	low(1)
Dimethenamid	amide	Sweet Corn	0.6	low(2)
Carfentrazone-ethyl	aryl triazolinone	Sweet Corn	2	low(1)
Dicamba	benzoic acid	Corn	30	low(1)
Paraquat	bipyridil	Corn, Apple, Peaches, Grape, Pumpkin	62.8	moderate(1)
Mesotrione	callistemone	Corn	14	low(2)
Metolachlor	chloracetanilide	Corn, Potatoes, Snap Bean, Pumpkin, Soybean, Sweet Corn	924.2	low(1)
2, 4 D	chlorinated phenoxy	Barley, Corn, Apple, Peaches, Sweet Corn	71.4	moderate(1)
Sethoxydim	cyclohexanone	Pumpkin	1	low(1)
Ethalfluralin	dinitroaniline	Pumpkin	1.6	low(2)
Pendimethalin	dinitroaniline	Corn, Potatoes, Soybean, Sweet Corn	629.4	low(1)
Trifluralin	dinitroaniline	Snap bean	0.2	low(1)
Fomesafen	diphenyl ether	Snap bean	1.2	low(2)
Imazaquin	imidazole	Soybean	1	low(1)
Imazethapyr	imidazole	Soybean	1	low(1)
Glyphosate	isopropylamine salt	Barley, Corn, Potatoes, Soybean, Apple, Peaches, Cantaloupe, Grape, Snap Bean, Sweet Corn, Pumpkin	620.6	low(1)
Isoxaflutole	isoxazole	Corn	1	low(2)
Clomazone	not available	Pumpkin	4.2	low(1)
Bensulide	organophosphate	Cantaloupe, Pumpkin	1.3	low(1)
Naptalam	phthalic acid	Cantaloupe	1.5	low(2)
Norflurazon	pyridazinone	Peaches, Grape	2.9	low(2)
Terbacil	substituted uracil	Apple, Peaches	0.5	low(1)
Diuron	substituted urea	Apple, Peaches, Grape	14.1	low(1)
Linuron	substituted urea	Soybean	2	moderate(1)
Primisulfuron	substituted urea	Corn	1	low(1)
Chlorimuron-ethyl	sulfonylurea	Soybean	1	low(2)
Halosulfuron	sulfonylurea	Snap bean, Pumpkin	2.1	low(2)
Nicosulfuron	sulfonylurea	Corn	3	low(1)
Rimsulfuron	sulfonylurea	Corn	2	low(2)
Thifensulfuron	sulfonylurea	Barley	2	unknown
Bentazon	thiadiazinol	Sweet Corn	1.6	low(1)
EPTC	thiocarbamate	Snap bean	27.8	low(1)
Atrazine	triazine	Corn, Sweet Corn	1383.7	low(1)
Metribuzin	triazine	Potatoes	7	moderate(1)
Simazine	triazine	Peaches, Grape	27.9	low(1)
Sulfentrazone	triazolone	Soybean	2	low(2)
Flumetsulam	triazolopyrimidine	Soybean	2	low(2)

[1]Pesticide use data were originally compiled by the U.S.D.A. National Agricultural Statistical Service
[2]These surveys span the years 1997-2003. The amounts presented represent a single year use not the cumulative amount and may not reflect current use.

al perfluoroalkyl surfactants (PASs) such as perfluorooctane sulfonate, perfluorodecane sulfonate, and perfluoroundecanoic acid. PASs have been used for industrial purposes for over 40 years and are highly persistent in the environment (Giesy and Kannan 2001, Sinclair and Kannan 2006). Fluorinated surfactants are highly mobile in aquatic systems and are found in wildlife globally, even in isolated islands (Giesy and Kannan 2001). Sinclair and colleagues (2006) surveyed lakes, fish, and birds around the state of New York and found PASs in all samples. Many PASs are no longer produced and have been replaced by perfluorobutane sulfonyl fluorides (PBSFs) (Newsted et al. 2008).

PASs and other related fluorinated organics bioaccumulate and some of the highest concentrations have been found in bald eagles (Giesy and Kannan 2001). The toxic effects of PASs and related fluorinated organics are not well known but seem to affect inter- and intracellular transport mechanisms (Giesy and Kannan 2001). PBSFs appear to be less toxic to birds and do not accumulate as rapidly as other PASs. In a laboratory study, adult northern bobwhite and mallards were not negatively affected by surfactants, however, chicks of these species gained weight at lower rates when fed perfluorobutane sulfonate, a degradation product of perfluorobutane sulfonyl fluoride, a common PBSF (Newsted et al. 2008). Rattner and McGowan (2007) identified surfactants as being potentially dangerous to waterbirds of the Chesapeake. Due to their ubiquity and possible negative effects, surfactants and detergents should be monitored in Pennsylvania's waterways. Like many other contaminants, the most vulnerable species are going to be species at higher trophic levels including piscivorous birds and raptors. Indeed, along with PCBs and several other contaminants, ospreys were accumulating perfluorinated compounds in the Delaware River and Bay (Toschik et al. 2004).

INDIRECT EFFECTS OF ENVIRONMENTAL CONTAMINANTS

Direct effects of contaminants primarily involve the ingestion of contaminants that interrupt physiological processes and consequently reduce survival and reproduction. If these effects are widespread enough they may reduce populations. Indirect effects may also reduce populations but the effects are not on the birds themselves but on their food supply or habitat. The effects of contaminants on birds, fish, and insects have been well studied for many contaminants but how changes the abundance of any of these organisms affects other organisms is not well known (Eeva et al. 2003).

Indirect effects of contaminants might simply be an increased efficiency in herbicides and insecticides action leaving fewer seeds and insects in agricultural settings or it might be reducing species that affect habitat. Pesticide applications to turf, including golf courses and lawns, may also reduce insect abundance for birds. These habitats are highly artificial and relatively isolated. A problem may arise in more natural habitats when pesticides mobilize to waterways and forests though runoff and wind.

Reduced invertebrate prey

For many songbirds, invertebrates are an essential element of diet and even species not considered to be insectivorous will feed invertebrates to their offspring during reproduction. The loss of invertebrate prey due to contaminants may then have a significant negative effect on avian fecundity and reduce populations.

Eeva and colleagues have been studying insect abundance as well as birds in forests near a Finish smelter. These studies revealed that caterpillars were less abundant and this had two effects on great tits (Eeva et al. 1997). One, plumage of chicks near smelters was duller closer to the smelter (Eeva et al. 1998). This was likely a consequence of not having a significant source of carotenoids found in the caterpillars. Two, fledging success was lower closer to the smelter (Eeva et al. 2005). Fledging success of pied flycatchers was also reduced along the pollution gradient, but this appears to be a direct effect of heavy metals rather than indirect effects on insect abundance (Eeva et al. 2005).

Although it seems straightforward that reducing a prey species would be to the detriment of the predator, alternative strategies for the predator may exist. Martin and colleagues (1998), for instance, found chestnut-collared longspurs [*Calcarius ornatus*] were able to switch to other prey when grasshopper densities were experimentally reduced by using a synthetic pyrethroid. Pesticides may influence predatory insects that affect the populations of other insects including those that are prey for birds (Pimentel 1994). It appears then, that predicting the effects of reducing insect abundance on birds is difficult and species specific.

Some cases are made even more difficult to predict because the insect and control of that insect have multiple effects. Pesticides may affect prey species that influence habitat. Gypsy moths [*Lymantria dispar*] are an exotic species in the United States that are able to defoliate canopy trees in a forest and increase growth of shrub and near ground vegetation (Thurber et al. 1994). Increased plant density in the understory increased nest success of birds that nest in these lower levels presumably by providing more concealment (Bell and Whitmore 1997). Moreover, Showalter and Whitmore (2002) show that cavity nesting species increase in abundance after gypsy moth outbreaks possibly as a result of increased snag abundance from trees that were killed or damaged by caterpillars. These studies, however, do not take into account mid-story and canopy species.

Control of gypsy moths includes aerial spraying of *Bacillus thuringiensis* (*Bt*) onto forests. The problem arises because *Bt* does reduce the abundance of other lepidopterans upon which many birds feed to young (Rastall et al. 2003). Norton and colleagues (2001) found that spruce grouse [*Dendragapus Canadensis*] chicks grew 30% less on sites treated with *Bt* and their stomachs contained half the food of control sites. Given the extent of damage that gypsy moths have on forests and the use of *Bt* in the state, the interaction between gypsy moth control and avian populations is worthy of further investigation.

Reduced vertebrate prey abundance

Vertebrates, such as small mammals and fish, are food for a variety of birds such as aquatic species and raptors but also smaller species such as shrikes. Similar to insectivorous birds, reduced prey populations may reduce fecundity and adult survivorship. Since predatory birds are positioned at higher trophic levels, they are more vulnerable to the changes in lower trophic levels including the invertebrates and plants upon which their prey feeds. There are suite of contaminants that do affect fish and, in general, the source of contaminants is runoff from agricultural (Schulz 2004) and urban systems (Paul and Meyer 2001), and mine drainage. Terrestrial vertebrates may not be as impacted by contaminants as aquatic species as a consequence of a lack of exposure.

The effects of heavy metals on fish are variable and vary with species, water pH and temperature. Like birds, organic forms of metals tend to be more toxic than elemental forms (Weiner et al. 2003). Fish are not very sensitive to petroleum (Albers 2003), however, fish are sensitive to a number of pesticides including atrazine (Gross et al. 2003). The effects of reduced fish abundance through pollution on birds are not well studied.

An obvious case where environmental contaminants negatively affect avian populations through habitat loss is the acres of bare rock around the Palmerton area. Though smelting operations were largely stopped in 1980 (Beyer and Storm 1995), large areas continue to be bare (*personal observation*). Such areas neither produced food nor offered nesting sites. A recent visit to this site in July 2008 revealed extensive grasslands on restored areas where there was once bare rock and several species of birds associated with grasslands including eastern bluebird and American kestrel.

BIRDS AS MONITORS OF ENVIRONMENTAL CONTAMINANTS

Several aspects of avian life histories make them ideal indicators of environmental contaminants. Despite historical interest in the effects of contaminants on avian populations, there is still a need for field and laboratory research. Rattner and McGowan (2007) point out that there have not been systematic studies of metals and other contaminants in the Chesapeake Bay watershed for fifteen years. Species can be selected to indicate the source of the contamination. For example, eastern phoebes [*Sayornis phoebe*] forage on emergent aquatic insects and a close relative, the eastern wood-pewee [*Contopus virens*], forages on terrestrial insects. Differences between these species may indicate that the source of pollution is terrestrial or aquatic. Species at higher trophic levels might be particularly useful to demonstrate the presence of contaminants in systems where they might be unsuspected. For example, organochlorine insecticides have been detected in polar sea birds (Furness 1993). When logistically feasible, several species at a site should be investigated. Even though both feed on invertebrates at the same site, tree swallows and eastern bluebirds experienced different reproductive effects from pesticides in Canadian apple orchards (Bishop et al. 2000).

Rigorous field studies are necessary to infer the effects of contaminants on wild birds. Lab studies are necessary and very useful; however, wild birds have stresses not found in laboratories that may increase susceptibility to contaminants and decrease survivorship or reduce fecundity. Such stresses include parasitism, migration, and reproduction. Since the effects of contaminants may not be immediate, long-term studies are necessary to infer effects on survival and require capture-recapture methods.

ACKNOWLEDGEMENTS

The author would like to thank Carol Stratford, Terry Masters, and Jane Huffman for thoughtful comments on the manuscript and Logan Stratford for his patience.

LITERATURE CITED

Albers, P.H. 2003. Petroleum and individual polycyclic aromatic hydrocarbons. In D.J. Hoffman, B.A. Rattner, G.A. Burton Jr., and J. Cairns Jr. (eds.) Handbook of Ecotoxicology, 2nd edition. CRC Press, Boca Raton.

Albers, P.H. 2006. Birds and polycyclic aromatic hydrocarbons. Avian and Poultry Biology Reviews 17:125–140.

Albers, P.H., D.E. Green, and C.J. Sanderson. 1996. Diagnostic criteria for selenium toxicosis in aquatic birds: dietary exposure, tissue concentrations, and macroscopic effects. Journal of Wildlife Diseases 32:468–485.

Albers, P.H., M.T. Koterba, R. Rossmann, W.A. Link, J.B. French, R.S. Bennett, and W.C. Bauer. 2007. Effects of methylmercury on reproduction in American Kestrels. Environmental Toxicology and Chemistry 26: 1856–1866.

Arenal, C.A. and R.S. Halbrook. 1997. PCB and heavy metal contamination and effects in European Starlings (*Sturnus vulgaris*) at a Superfund site. Bulletin of Environmental Contamination and Toxicology 58:254–262.

Bell, J.L. and R.C. Whitmore. 1997. Bird populations and habitat in *Bacillus thuringiensis* and Dimilin-treated and untreated areas of hardwood forest. American Midland Naturalist 137: 239–250.

Beyer, W.N., J. Dalgarn, S. Dudding, J.B. French, R. Mateo, J. Miesner, L. Sileo, and J. Spann. 2005. Zinc and lead poisoning in wild birds in the Tri-State Mining District (Oklahoma, Kansas, and Missouri). Archives of Environmental Contamination and Toxicology 48:108–117.

Beyer, W.N. and G. Storm. 1995. Ecotoxicological damage from zinc smelting at Palmerton, Pennsylvania. In Hoffman, D.J., B.A. Rattner, G.A. Burton Jr., and J. Cairney (eds.), Handbook of Ecotoxicology, 1st edition. Lewis Publishers, Boca Raton.

Bishop, C.A., B. Collins, P. Mineau, N.M. Burgess, W.F. Read, and C. Risley. 2000. Reproduction of cavity-nesting birds in pesticide-sprayed apple orchards in southern Ontario, Canada, 1988–1994. Environmental Toxicology and Chemistry 19:588–599.

Blus, L.J. 2003. Organochlorine pesticides. In D.J. Hoffman, B.A. Rattner, G.A. Burton Jr., and J. Cairns Jr. (eds.) Handbook of Ecotoxicology, 2nd edition. CRC Press, Boca Raton.

Brasso, R.L. and D.L. Cristol. 2008. Effects of mercury exposure on the reproductive success of tree swallows (Tachycineta bicolor). Ecotoxicology 17:133–141

Burger, J., I.C.T. Nisbet, and M. Gochfeld. 1992. Metal levels regrown in feathers: assessment of contamination on the wintering and breeding grounds in the same individuals. Journal of Toxicology and Environmental Health 37:363–374.

Burger, J. 1993. Metals in feathers: Bioindicators of environmental pollution. Reviews in Environmental Toxicology 5:203–311.

Bustnes, J.O., V. Bakken, and Erikstad, K. E. 2001. Patterns of incubation and nest-site attentiveness in relation to organochlorine (PCB) contamination in glaucous gulls. Journal of Applied Ecology 38: 791–801

Bustnes, J.O., K. Borgå, K.E. Erikstad, S.-H. Lorentsen, and D. Herze. 2008. Perfluorinated, brominated, and chlorinated contaminants in a population of Lesser Black-backed Gulls (*Larus fuscus*). Environmental Toxicology and Chemistry 27:1383–1392.

Craighead, D., and B. Bedrosian. 2008. Blood lead levels of Common Ravens with access to bird-game offal. Journal of Wildlife Management 72: 240–245.

Cristol, D.A., R.L. Brasso, A.M Condon, R.E. Fovargue, S.L. Friedman, K.K. Hallinger, A.P. Monroe, A.E. White. 2008. The movement of aquatic mercury through terrestrial food webs. Science 320:335.

DeFrancisco, N., J.D. Ruiz Troya, and E.I. Aguera. 2003. Lead and lead toxicity in domestic and free living birds. Avian Pathology 32:3–13.

Eeva, T., H. Hakkarainen, T. Laaksonen, and E. Lehikoinen. 2006. Environmental pollution has sex-dependent effects on local survival. Biology Letters 2:298–300.

_____, and E. Lehikoinen. 1995. Egg-Shell Quality, Clutch Size and Hatching Success of the Great Tit (Parus-Major) and the Pied Flycatcher (Ficedula-Hypoleuca) in an Air-Pollution Gradient. Oecologia 102: 312–323

_____, _____, and M. Nikinmaa. 2003. Pollution-induced nutritional stress in birds: an experimental study of direct and indirect effects. Ecological Applications 13:1242–1249.

_____, _____, and T. Pohjalainen. 1997. Pollution-related variation in food supply and breeding success in two hole-nesting passerines. Ecology 78:1120–1131.

_____, _____, and A.M. Ronk. 1998. Air pollution fades the plumage of the Great Tit. Functional Ecology 12:607–612.

_____, M. Ryoma, and J. Riihimaki. 2005. Pollution-related changes in diets of two insectivorous passerines. Oecologia 145: 629–639.

_____, S. Tanhuanpaa, C. Rabergh, S. Airaksinen, M. Nikinmaa, and E. Lehikoinen. 2000. Bio-markers and fluctuating asymmetry as indicators of pollution-induced stress in two hole-nesting passerines. Functional Ecology 14: 235–243.

Eisler, R. 1993. Zinc hazards to fish, wildlife, and invertebrates: a synoptic review. Biological Report 10, Contaminant Hazard Review Report 26. United States Fish and Wildlife Service, Laurel, Md.

Fairbrother, A., M. Fix., and T. O'Hara. 1994. Impairment of growth and immune function of avo-cet chicks from sites with elevated selenium, arsenic, and boron. Journal of Wildlife Diseases 30: 222–233.

Fernie, K. J., J.E. Smits, and G.R. Bortolotti. 2001. In ovo exposure to polychlorinated biphenyls: reproductive effects on second-generation American Kestrels. Archives of Environmental Conta-mination and Toxicology 40: 544–550.

_____, G. Mayne, J. Laird Shutt, C. Pekarik, K.A. Grasman, R. J. Letcher, and K. Drouillard. 2005. Evidence of immunomodulation in nestling American Kestrals (*Falco sparverius*) exposed to environmentally relevant PBDEs. Environmental Pollution 138:485–493.

Fisher, S.A., G.R. Bortolotti, K.J. Fernie, D.M. Bird, and J.E.Smits. 2006. Behavioral variation and its consequences during incubation for American kestrels exposed to polychlorinated biphenyls. Ecotoxicology and Environmental Safety 63: 226–235.

Furness, R.W. 1993. Birds as monitors of pollutants. In, Furness, R.W., J.D. Greenwood (eds.), Birds as Monitors of Environmental Change. Chapman and Hall, London.

Giesy, J.P. and K. Kannan. 2001. Global distribution of perfluorooctane sulfanate in wildlife. Envi-ronmental Science and Technology 35:1339–1342.

Gorissen, L., T. Snoeijs, E. Van Duyse, and M. Eens. 2005. Heavy metal pollution affects dawn singing behavior in a small passering bird. Oecologia 145:504–509.

Gross, T.S., B.S. Arnold, M.S. Sepulveda, and K. McDonald. 2003. Endocrine disrupting chemicals and endocrine active agents. In D.J. Hoffman, B.A. Rattner, G.A. Burton Jr., and J. Cairns Jr. (eds.) Handbook of Ecotoxicology, 2nd edition. CRC Press, Boca Raton.

Harris, M.L., L.K. Wilson, J.E. Elliot, C.A. Bishop, A.D. Tomlin, K.V. Henning. 2000. Transfer of DDT and metabolites from fruit orchard soils to American Robins (Turdus migratorius) twenty years after agricultural use of DDT in Canada. Archives of Environmental Contamination and Toxicology 39:205–220.

Heinz, G.H., D.J. Hoffman, and L.G. Gold. 1989. Impaired reproduction of mallards fed an organic form of selenium. Journal of Wildlife Management 53: 418–428.

Hill, E.F. 1993. Organophosphorus and carbamate pesticides. In Furness, R.W., and J.D. Greenwood (Eds.) Birds as Monitors of Environmental Change. Chapman and Hall, New York.

Hites, R.A. 2004. Polybrominated diphenyl ethers in the environment and people: a meta-analysis of the concentrations. Environmental Science and Techology 38:945–956.

Hoffman, D.J., 2003. Wildlife toxicity testing. In D.J. Hoffman, B.A. Rattner, G.A. Burton Jr., and J. Cairns Jr. (eds.) Handbook of Ecotoxicology, 2nd edition. CRC Press, Boca Raton.

_____, B.A. Rattner, G.A. Burton Jr., and J. Cairns Jr. 2003a. Handbook of Ecotoxicology, 2nd edition. CRC Press, Boca Raton.

_____, _____, G.A. Burton, Jr., J. Cairns, Jr. 2003b. Introduction. In D.J. Hoffman, B.A. Rat-tner, G.A. Burton Jr., and J. Cairns Jr. (eds.) Handbook of Ecotoxicology, 2nd edition. CRC Press, Boca Raton.

Irons, D.B., S.J. Kendall, W.P. Erickson, L.L. McDonald, and B.K. Lance. 2000. Nine years after the Exxon Valdez oil spill: effects on marine birds in Prince William Sound, Alaska. Condor 102:723–737.

Ko, F.-C. and J.E. Baker. 2004. Seasonal and annual loads of hydrophobic organic contaminants from the Susquehanna River basin to the Chesapeake Bay. Marine Pollution Bulletin 48:840–851.

Koplin, D.W., E.T. Furlong, M.T. Meyer, E.M. Thurman, S.D. Zaugg, L.B. Barber, and H.T. Buxton. 2002. Pharmaceuticals, hormones, and other organic wastewater contaminants in U.S. streams, 1999–2000: a national reconnaissance. Environmental Science and Technology 36:1202–1211.

Lambert, O., H. Pouliquen, C. Larhantec, C. Thorin, and M. L'Hostis. 2007. Exposure of raptors and waterbirds to anticoagulant rodenticides (difenacoum, bromadiolone, coumatetralyl, coumafen, brodifacoum): epidemiological survey in Loire Atlantique (France). Bulletin of Environmental Contamination and Toxicology 79:91–94.

Larison, J.R., G.E. Likens, J.W. Fitzpatrick, and J.G. Crock. 2000. Cadmium toxicity among wildlife in the Colorado Rocky Mountains. Nature 406:181–183.

Lepczyk, C.A., A.G. Mertig, and J. Liu. 2004. Assessing landowner activities related to birds across rural-to-urban landscapes. Environmental Management 33:110–125.

Loganathan, B.G. and K. Kannan. 1994. Global organochlorine contamination trends: an overview. Ambio 23:187–191.

Lundholm, C.E. 1992. DDE-induced eggshell thinning in birds: effects of p,p'-DDE on the calcium and prostaglandin metabolism of the eggshell gland. Comparative Biochemistry Physiology 118:113–128.

Martin, P.A., D.L. Johnson, D.J. Forsyth, and B.D. Hill. 1998. Indirect effects of the pyrethroid insecticide deltamethrin on reproductive success of chestnut-collared longspurs. Ecotoxicology 7:89–97.

Mayne, G.J., P.A. Martin, C.A. Bishop, and H.J. Boermans. 2004. Stress and immune responses of nestling tree swallows (*Tachycineta bicolor*) and Eastern Bluebirds (*Sialia sialis*) exposed to non-persistent pesticides and p,p'-dichlorodiphenyldichloroethylene in apple orchards of southern Ontario, Canada. Environmental Toxicology and Chemistry 23:2930–2940.

Newsted, J.L., S. A. Beach, S.P. Gallagher, and J.P. Giesy. 2008. Acute and chronic effects of per-fluorobutane sulfonate (PFBS) on the Mallard and Northern Bobwhite Quail. Archives of Environmental Contamination and Toxicology 54:535–545.

Norstrom, R.J., M. Simon, J. Moisey, B. Wakeford, and D.V.C. Weselow. 2002. Geographic distribution (2000) and temporal trends (1981–2000) of brominated diphenyl ethers in Great Lakes Herring Gull eggs. Environmental Science and Technology 36:4783–4789.

Norton, M.L., J.F. Bendell, L.I. Bendell-Young, and C.W. LeBlanc. 2001. Secondary effects of the pesticide Bacillus thuringiensis kurtstaki on chicks of Spruce Grouse (*Dendragapus canadensis*). Archives of Environmental Contamination and Toxicology 41:369–373.

Ottinger, M.A., Abdelnabi, M.A., Quinn, M., N. Golden, J. Wu., and N. Thompson. 2002. Reproductive consequences of EDC's in birds: What do laboratory effects mean in field species? Neurotoxicology and Teratology 24:17–29.

_____, E. Lavioe, N. Thompson, A. Barton, K. Whitehouse, M. Barton, M. Abdelanabi, M. Quinn, G. Panzica, and C. Viglietti-Panzica. 2008. Neuroendocrine and behavioral effects of embryonic exposure to endocrine disrupting chemicals in birds. Brain Research Reviews 57:376–385.

Papp, Z., G.R. Bortolotti, and J.E.G. Smits. 2005. Organochlorine contamination and physiological responses in nestling tree swallows in Point Pelee National Park, Canada. Archives of Environmental Contamination and Toxicology 49: 563–568.

Patnode, K.A. and D.H. White. 1991. Effects of pesticides on songbird productivity on songbird productivity in conjunction with pecan cultivation in southern Georgia: a multiple-exposure experimental design. Environmental Toxicology and Chemistry 10:1479–1486.

Paul, M.J. and Meyer, J.L. 2001. Streams in the urban landscape. Annual Review of Ecology and Systematics. 32:333–365.

Peakall, D.B., J. Tremblay, W.B. Kinter, and D.S. Miller. 1981. Endocrine dysfunction in seabirds caused by ingested oil. Environmental Research 24:6–14.

Pimentel, D. 1994. Insect population responses to environmental stress and pollutants. Environmental Reviews 2:1–15.

Rastall, K, C. Kondo, and J.S. Strazanac. 2003. Lethal effects of biological insecticide applications on nontarget lepidopterans in two Appalachian forests. Environmental Entomology 32: 1364–1369.

Rattner, B.A. and P.C. McGowan. 2007. Potential hazards of environmental contaminants to avifauna residing in the Chesapeake Bay Estuary. Waterbirds 30:63–81.

Ratti, J.T., A.M. Moser, and E.O. Garton. 2006. Selenium Levels in Bird Eggs and Effects on Avian Reproduction. Journal of Wildlife Management 70: 572–578.

Rice, C.P., P.W. O'Keefe, and T.J. Kubiak. 2003. Sources, pathways, and effects of PCBs, dioxins, and dibenzofurans. In D.J. Hoffman, B.A. Rattner, G.A. Burton Jr., and J. Cairns Jr. (eds.) Handbook of Ecotoxicology, 2nd edition. CRC Press, Boca Raton.

Roux, K.E. and P.B. Marra. 2007. The presence and impact of environmental lead in passerine birds along an urban to rural land use gradient. Archives of Environmental Contamination and Toxicology 53:261–268.

Santolo, G.M., J.T. Yamamoto, J.T., and J.M. Pisenti. 1999. Selenium accumulation and effects on reproduction in captive American kestrels fed selenomethionine. Journal of Wildlife Management 63: 502–511.

Scheuhammer, A.M., M.W. Meyer, and M.B. Sandheinrich. 2007. Effects of environmental methylmercury on the health of wild birds, mammals, and fish. Ambio 36:12–18.

Schulz, R. 2004. Field studies on exposure, effects, and risk mitigation of aquatic nonpoint-source insecticide pollution: a review. Journal of Environmental Quality 33:419–448.

Sekercioglu, C.H. 2006. Increasing awareness of avian ecological function. Trends in Ecology and Evolution. 21: 464–471.

Showalter, C.R. and R.C. Whitmore. 2002. The effect of gypsy moth defoliation on cavity-nesting bird communities. Forest Science 48:273–281.

Sinclair, E. and K. Kannan. 2006. Mass loading and fate of perfluoroalkyl surfactants in wastewater treatment plants. Environmental Science and Techology 40:1408–1414.

_____, D.T. Mayack, K.Roblee, N. Yamashita, K. Kannan. 2006. Occurrence of Perfluoroalkyl Surfactants in Water, Fish, and Birds from New York State. Archives of Environmental Contamination and Toxicology 50:398–410.

Smits, J. E., K. J. Fernie, and G.R. Bortolotti. 2002. Thyroid Hormone Suppression and Cell-Mediated Immunomodulation in American Kestrels (*Falco sparverius*) Exposed to PCBs. Archives of Environmental Contamination and Toxicology 43: 338–344.

Snoeijs, T., T. Dauwe, and R. Pinxten. 2004. Heavy metal exposure affects the humoral immune response in a free-living small songbird, the Great Tit (*Parus major*). Archives of Environmental Contamination and Toxicology 46:399–404.

Stone, W.B., J.C. Okoniewski, and J.R. Stedelin. 2003. Anticoagulant rodenticides and raptors: recent findings from New York, 1998–2001. Bulletin of Environmental Contamination and Toxicology 70: 34–40.

Thurber, D.K., W.R. McClain, and R.C. Whitmore. 1994. Indirect effects of gypsy moth defoliation on nest predation. Journal of Wildlife Management 58: 493–500.

Toschik, P.C., B.A. Rattner, P.C. McGowan, M.C. Christman, D.B. Carter, R.C. Hale, C.W. Matson, and M.A. Ottinger. 2004. Effects of contaminant exposure on reproductive success of osprey (Pandion haliaetus) nesting in Delaware River and Bay, USA. Environmental Toxicology and Chemistry 24:617–628.

U.S. Fish and Wildlife Service. 1986. Use of lead short for hunting migratory birds in the United States, Final Supplement Environmental Impact Statement, Department of Interior, Fish and Wildlife Service.

Walker, C.H., S.P. Hopkin, R.M. Sibly, and D.B. Peakall. 2006. Principles of Ecotoxicology, 3rd Edition. CRC Press, Boca Raton.

Wayland, M. and R. Crosley. 2006. Selenium and other trace elements in aquatic insects in coal-mine affected streams in the Rocky Mountains of Alberta, Canada. Archives of Environmental Contamination and Toxicology 50:511–522.

_____, H.G. Gilchrist, T. Marchant. 2002. Immune function, stress response, and body condition in arctic-breeding common eiders in relation to cadmium, mercury, and selenium concentrations. Environmental Research 90: 47–60.

Weiner, J.G., D. P. Krabbenhoft, G.H. Heinz, and A.M. Scheuhammer. 2003. Ecotoxicology of mercury. In Hoffman, D.J., B.A. Rattner, G.A. Burton, and J. Cairns Jr., (eds) Handbook of Ecotoxicology, 2nd edition. CRC Press, Boca Raton.

Wilhelms, K.W., K.F. Fitzpatrick, C.G. Scanes, and L.L. Anderson. 2006. *In ovo* exposure to a triazine herbicide: effects of atrazine on circulating reproductive hormones and gonadal histology in young Japanese Quail. Archives of Environmental Contamination and Toxicology 51:117–122.

Wolfe, M.F., S. Schwarzbach, S., and R.A. Sulaiman. 1998. Effects of mercury on wildlife: A comprehensive review. Environmental Toxicology and Chemistry 17: 146–160.

Yamamoto, J.T. and G.M. Santolo. 2000. Body condition effects in American Kestrals fed selenomethionine. Journal of Wildlife Diseases 36:646–652.

Zala, S.M. and D.J. Penn. 2004. Abnormal behaviors induced by chemical pollution: a review of the evidence and new challenges. Animal Behaviour 68: 649–664.

Subject Index

Critical habitat 194
Critically endangered birds 280
Crossbills 157-158
Cumulative loss 197

D

Dark-eyed junco (*Junco hyemalis*) 17
DDT 97, 346-347
Deciduous forest 65, 67-69
  deciduous habitat 67
  deciduous shade trees 69
  deciduous vegetation 68
  upland deciduous forests 65
Deer 97
Deforestation 210
Degradation 192, 197-199
  environmental 192
  habitat 199
  insular habitat 197
  species specific habitat 198
Delaware river 12, 67
Delaware water gap 114, 240
Delaware Water Gap National Recreation Area
  (DEWA) 65
Dibenzofurans (PCDF) 345
Dichloro-Diphenyl-Trichloroethane (DDT) 105-106
Directed dispersal 32, 38
Dispersal 34, 82-83, 175-187
  of invasive species 34
Distributional shifts 217
Disturbance dependent species 77-78 , 83
Diurnal 138, 140, 143, 300
  flying animals 300
  raptors 138, 140, 143
Diversity 63, 66-68
  alpha 63
  beta 63
  gamma 63
Dogwood (*Cornus* spp.) 79-80
Dominant nuclear markers 177
  arbitrary fragment length polymorphisms
    (AFLP) 177-178
  randomly amplified polymorphic DNA (RAPD)
    177-178
Double crested cormorant (*Phalacrocorax auritus*)
  69, 259, 261-263, 265, 267-270
Douglas-fir (*Pseudotsuga menziesii*) 143
Dragonflies 294
Drainage basins 63
  Allegheny 63
  Delaware 63
  Genesee 63
  Monongahela 63
  Ohio 63

Potomac 63
Susquehanna 63
Droughts 292
Dutch elm disease (*Ophiostoma spp.*) 15

E

Eastern bluebirds (*Sialia sialis*) 33, 36, 150, 310
Eastern chipmunk (*Tamias striatus*) 305
Eastern deciduous forests 28, 34
Eastern equine encephalitis virus 309
Eastern golden eagles 111-118, 120-123
Eastern hemlock (*Tsuga canadensis*)
  14-15, 144, 168, 232-245
  decline 232-245
Eastern meadowlark (*Sturnella magna*) 86, 151
Eastern milk snake (*Lampropeltis triangulum*) 91
Eastern red cedar (*Juniperus virginiana*) 143
Eastern screech owls 320
Eastern towhee (*Pipilo erythrophthalmus*) 67, 78
Eastern wood pewee (*Contopus virens*) 17
Ecological communities 45
Ecological function 214
Ecology 97-98, 175-177
Ecosystems 44-45, 47, 188-189, 276
Ecotones 63-65, 67, 70
  forested riparian ecotones 63
  lateral ecotones 70
  lateral riparian ecotones 65
  riparian ecotones 64
Edge habitats 36
Elevation gradient 297
Emerald ash borer (*Agrilus planipennis*) 169
Endangered 192, 195
Endangered species 281, 333
Endangered Species Act (ESA) 192, 277, 286
Endemic species 297
Endozoochory 29-32
Environment 188
  Chesapeake bay 342, 344, 347, 350, 352
  Delaware river 344, 352
  Susquehanna river 344, 346
Environmental 192, 198, 291, 332-339, 340-356
  contaminants 291, 332-339, 340-356
  contamination 192
  direct effects 341
  indirect effects 341, 352
  organic compounds 344
Environmental Protection Agency (EPA) 63
Environmental Quality Incentives Program (EQIP)
  226, 228
Enzootic cycle 304, 306
Enzyme Linked ImmunoSorbent Assay (ELISA)
  316-318
Epizootic cycle 304, 323